MW00846473

Absolute Value

$|x| < b$ means that $-b < x < b$. $|x| > b$ means that $x < -b$ or $x > b$.

The Quadratic Formula

The roots of the quadratic equation $ax^2 + bx + c = 0$ are given by $x = \dfrac{-b \pm \sqrt{b^2 - 4ac}}{2a}$.

Sequences

Arithmetic sequences: $a_n = a_1 + (n - 1)d$ $S_n = \frac{1}{2}n(a_1 + a_n)$

Geometric sequences: $a_n = a_1 r^{n-1}$ $S_n = a_1 \dfrac{1 - r^n}{1 - r}$

Permutations and Combinations

Permutations of n objects taken k at a time: $P_{n,k} = \dfrac{n!}{(n-k)!}$

Combinations of n objects taken k at a time: $C_{n,k} = \dfrac{n!}{(n-k)!k!}$

Laws of Logarithms (where $\log_b x = y$ means $x = b^y$)

$\log_b (M \cdot N) = \log_b M + \log_b N$ $\log_b \left(\dfrac{M}{N}\right) = \log_b M - \log_b N$

$\log_b (M^x) = x \cdot \log_b M$ $\log_b b = 1$ $\log_b 1 = 0$

$\log_{10} x = \log x$ $\log_e x = \ln x$ $\ln x = \dfrac{\log x}{\log e}$

College Algebra
with Applications

FOURTH EDITION

College Algebra
with Applications

FOURTH EDITION

Bernard J. Rice
Jerry D. Strange
University of Dayton

Brooks/Cole Publishing Company
Pacific Grove, California

Brooks/Cole Publishing Company
A Division of Wadsworth, Inc.

Printed in the United States of America
10 9 8 7 6 5 4 3 2 1

Library of Congress Cataloging-in-Publication Data
Rice, Bernard J.
College algebra : with applications / Bernard J. Rice, Jerry D. Strange.—4th ed.
p. cm.
Includes index.
ISBN 0-534-10206-9
1. Algebra. I. Strange, Jerry D. II. Title.
QA154.2.R53 1989
512.9—dc 19 88-29305
CIP

Sponsoring Editors: Sue Ewing, Jeremy Hayhurst
Editorial Assistants: Heidi Wieland, Virge Kelmser
Production Editor: Phyllis Larimore
Production Assistant: Dorothy Bell
Manuscript Editor: Lieselotte Hoffman
Interior and Cover Design: Flora Pomeroy
Cover Photo: D. Forer/The Image Bank West
Art Coordinator: Lisa Torri
Interior Illustration: ANCO/Boston, Carl Brown
Typesetting: Polyglot Compositors, Ltd.
Cover Printing: The Lehigh Press, Inc.
Printing and Binding: Arcata Graphics, Fairfield

Preface

In this fourth edition of *College Algebra* we have brought the topical material in line with recent trends in college-level algebra courses. We follow current pedagogy in continuing to make the functional concept the central theme, with special emphasis on graphing. As in the previous editions, we stress the many utilitarian aspects of mathematics by including a variety of problems stated in the jargon of business, science, social science, and engineering.

We have streamlined the discussions wherever possible by eliminating some topics and combining others. Our aim has been to cover the essential topics more efficiently. The major changes in this edition include the following:

- Chapters 1 and 2 have been combined and reorganized to reduce from 14 to 7 the number of sections devoted to reviewing basic high school algebra skills.
- The chapter on elementary functions (Chapter 4) has been reorganized to make the coverage more concise.
- A new chapter on vectors and complex numbers (Chapter 7) has been added. For those who wish to cover Chapter 7, an introduction to (or review of) some basic trigonometry is given in Appendix B and should provide students with the necessary background.
- Sequences, counting, probability, and mathematical induction have been combined in Chapter 10.
- Compound interest has been moved to the chapter on exponential and logarithmic functions (Chapter 5) as a lead-in to the discussion of the value of e.
- A section on polar coordinates and equations has been added to the chapter on conic sections (Chapter 10).
- Calculator readouts have been included where appropriate, with subsequent comments on rounding off numbers.

More topics are included than can be adequately covered in a one-semester course, so instructors can use their experience and judgment to choose those topics deemed most important. The first two chapters may be treated as a review of basic algebra skills, and Chapter 7, as we have noted, requires some basic trigonometry as a prerequisite. The essential material occurs in Chapters 3–6 and 9–10.

The presentation of material in this book presupposes some ability in algebra. However, important topics such as special products, factoring, and exponents are reviewed. Comments and expository remarks highlighting the use of calculators are included throughout the text.

The answers to the odd-numbered exercises are given in the back of the book. A calculator was used to find the numerical answers. Because decimal approximations to certain irrational numbers such as e and π will vary depending on the calculator used, students' answers may differ slightly from those at the back of the book. The effect of truncated values on answers to the exercises can be disconcerting, but at this time we know of no easy solution to the problem.

This edition of *College Algebra with Applications* has benefited from critical reviews and comments. Our thanks go to the reviewers of all four editions:

Richard Armstrong, *Florissant Valley Community College;* Thomas E. Armstrong, *University of Minnesota;* Soo Bong Chae, *New College of USF;* Phyllis G. Cox, *Shelby State Community College;* Richard J. Easton, *Indiana State University, Terre Haute;* Douglas Hall, *Michigan State University;* James Hall, *University of Wisconsin, Madison;* T. Ray Hamlett, *East Central University;* George A. Huff, *Kansas State University;* Kendell Hyde, *Weber State College;* Ki Woong Kim, *Morgan State University;* Helen Kriegsman, *Pittsburg State University;* Richard W. Marshall, *Eastern Michigan University;* Ann Martin, *Oklahoma City Community College;* Janet Milles, *James Madison University;* Jane Morrison, *Thornton Community College;* Lynda Morton, *University of Missouri, Columbia;* Glenda Owen, *Central State University;* Anthony A. Patricelli, *Northeastern Illinois University;* Kenneth A. Rager, *Metropolitan State College;* David J. Shannon, *University of Kentucky;* W. Richard Slinkman, *Bemidji State University;* LeRoy V. Stoldt, *College of DuPage;* Mary Swarthout, *Baylor University;* John Vasak, *University of Wisconsin, Milwaukee;* Paul J. Vesce, *University of Missouri, Kansas City;* Albert W. Zechmann, *University of Nebraska, Lincoln;* and Charles Ziegenfus, *James Madison University.*

We would particularly like to thank Caroll Schleppi for preparing a solutions manual, helping us improve the exercise sets, and correcting errors in the answers.

It is also a pleasure to acknowledge the fine cooperation of the staff of Brooks/Cole, particularly our editors Jeremy Hayhurst and Sue Ewing, production editor Phyllis Larimore, art coordinator Lisa Torri, and designer Flora Pomeroy.

Bernard J. Rice
Jerry D. Strange

Contents

College Algebra
with Applications

FOURTH EDITION

1 Basic Algebra

Algebra is the branch of mathematics that uses numbers and symbols to express and analyze relationships between known and unknown quantities. In its most elementary form, algebra is an extension of arithmetic.

The word **algebra** comes from the Arabic word **al-jabr,** which was included in the title of a ninth-century work by Mohammed ibn Mûsâ al-Khowârizmî, *Hisâb al-jabr w'al-muquâbalah.* This text first explained some of the basic concepts used in working with known and unknown numbers. Latin translations later introduced European mathematicians to its contents, and in the process made the word *algebra* synonymous with the science of solving equations. Today, algebra means much more than equation solving, but it is always concerned with numbers.

1.1 Real Numbers

Numbers are the central theme of algebra. Consequently, you must be familiar with the terminology of numbers. We begin with a discussion of the real number system: three important subsets of the real numbers are integer numbers, rational numbers, and irrational numbers.

The most familiar subset of the real numbers is the set of counting numbers 1, 2, 3, 4, 5, . . . , also called the **positive integers** or the natural numbers and denoted by N. The **negative integers** $-1, -2, -3, -4, -5, \ldots$, together with the positive integers and the number 0, make up the set of **integers** I.

A real number is said to be **rational** if it can be represented as a quotient a/b, where a is any integer and b is any nonzero integer. Numbers such as $-\frac{3}{2}, \frac{2}{7}, 3$, and $\frac{17}{11}$ are examples of rational numbers. The set of all rational numbers is denoted by Q. Since each integer, n, can be written as $n/1$, I is a proper subset of Q, as shown graphically in Figure 1.1.

Rational numbers can also be written in *decimal form,* as:

1. **Terminating decimals;** for example,

$$\frac{1}{2} = 0.5, \quad \frac{25}{4} = 6.25, \quad \frac{19}{8} = 2.375, \quad \text{or}$$

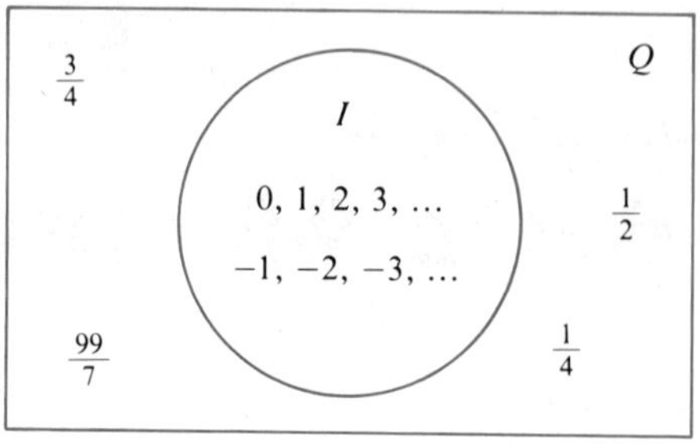

Figure 1.1

2. **Infinite repeating decimals,** where infinitely many decimal places are necessary, but a block of digits continually repeats itself; for example,

$$\frac{1}{6} = 0.166666\ldots \qquad \frac{11}{7} = 1.571428571428\ldots$$

Instead of the three dots, a bar, called a **vinculum,** is often placed over the repeating block so that $\frac{1}{6} = 0.1\overline{6}$ and $\frac{11}{7} = 1.\overline{571428}$.

Some real numbers are not rational. For example, there is no rational number whose square is 2. (The real number whose square is 2 is denoted by $\sqrt{2}$, read "radical two.") Real numbers that cannot be expressed as the ratio of two integers are called **irrational.** Well-known examples are $\sqrt{2}$ and π.

Irrational numbers have nonterminating, nonrepeating decimal representations. (When we write $\sqrt{2} = 1.4142\ldots$ or $\pi = 3.14159\ldots$, it is understood that the decimal is nonterminating and that no block of digits repeats itself.) Thus, irrational numbers may be thought of either as

1. Numbers that *cannot* be expressed as the ratio of two integers, or
2. Numbers whose decimal representation is *not* terminating and *not* infinite repeating; for example, 0.1001000100001 . . . .

The rational and irrational numbers together make up the real numbers. Rational numbers and irrational numbers are mutually exclusive; that is, no rational number is irrational and, conversely, no irrational number is rational. Figure 1.2 graphically displays the hierarchy of real numbers.

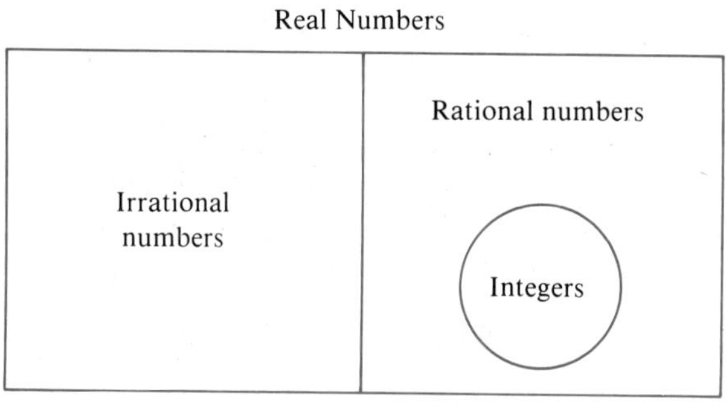

Figure 1.2

You should know the various kinds of real numbers and how they fit in the hierarchy of the real number system. For instance, 3 is a natural number, an integer, a rational number, and a real number; $\frac{1}{2}$ is *both* rational and real, but not an integer or an irrational number; and π is *both* irrational and real, but not an integer or a rational number.

Computers and calculators use ***truncated*** *numbers; that is, numbers rounded off after several decimal places. The number of digits and the method of representing truncated numbers vary with the particular computer or calculator; some calculators truncating to seven decimal places will display* $\frac{2}{3}$ *as* 0.6666667, *some as* 0.6666666. *In* 0.6666667, *the number is said to be* ***rounded up.*** *Most calculators round up if the truncated digit is* 5 *or greater.*

Throughout the text you will find special exercise problems to be solved using a calculator. Of course, a calculator can be used for any arithmetic operation, and we advise you to do so. However, a calculator will not reason for you. You must supply the mathematical reasoning and precise thinking.

In this text we do not tell you how to use a calculator, except in the most general terms, but you should become increasingly more skilled at using your calculator as you progress through the text and increase your mathematical knowledge. Since calculators differ in their method of operation, consult the operations manual of your calculator for its peculiarities.

Symbols of Grouping and Order of Operation

Parentheses, brackets, and braces are used to group numbers and indicate the precise order in which arithmetic operations are to be performed. For instance, $5 + (2 \cdot 3)$ indicates that the multiplication $2 \cdot 3$ is performed first and then added to 5 to give 11, while $(5 + 2) \cdot 3$ means that 5 is added to 2 before multiplying by 3 to give 21. Often the multiplication sign is omitted next to a grouping symbol. Thus, the expressions $4 \cdot (3 + 8)$ and $4(3 + 8)$ mean the same thing.

Confusion can arise if grouping symbols are omitted or if multiple grouping symbols are used. Therefore, we adopt the following conventions for sequences of arithmetic operations.* These conventions are also used in most computers.

1. Perform all operations within any grouping symbol before performing other operations. If grouping symbols are contained within one another, begin with the innermost pair.

   Example: a. $(7 \cdot 4) + (8 - 5) - (16 - 4) + (42 \div 6)$
   $= 28 + 3 - 12 + 7 = 26$

   b. $3 + \{6 + (2 + [7 - 2])\}$
   $= 3 + \{6 + (2 + 5)\}$
   $= 3 + \{6 + 7\}$
   $= 3 + 13 = 16$

2. In a sequence of multiplications and divisions, perform the operations in the order in which they occur from left to right.

   Example: a. $3 \cdot 18 \div 9 = 54 \div 9 = 6$

   b. $24 \div 8 \cdot 5 \div 15 = 3 \cdot 5 \div 15 = 15 \div 15 = 1$

* Note the distinction between a "law" and a "convention" governing mathematical operations. A law is a direct consequence of the nature of the operation. A convention is merely a convenient widespread usage of the operation.

3. In a sequence of additions, subtractions, multiplications, and divisions, perform the multiplications and divisions first and then perform the additions and subtractions. Multiplication and division are said to be **higher-priority** operations than addition and subtraction.
   Example: $5 \cdot 6 - 3 \cdot 7 + 24 \div 8 = 30 - 21 + 3 = 12$

Most scientific calculators can group operations together by a [(] *key and a* [)] *key. Keystrokes performed after pushing the* [(] *key and before pushing the* [)] *key are separated from the sequence of operations outside the grouping symbol. For example,* $3 \cdot (6 + 4) + 7$ *is evaluated by the following sequence:*

3 [×] [(] 6 [+] 4 [)] [+] 7 [=] **37**

If the grouping keystrokes are not included, the display will show 29 since $3 \cdot 6$ *is performed first.*

Fundamental Laws

Five basic laws govern the operations of addition and multiplication. Although you may not be aware of their specific nature, you already use these laws every day. For instance, we know that the sum of two numbers is independent of the order of the numbers. Thus, $2 + 7 = 7 + 2$. This property, which is called the **commutative law of addition,** is valid for all real numbers. Another addition law, called the **associative law of addition,** states that the sum of three or more numbers is the same regardless of how they are grouped for addition; that is, $2 + (9 + 1) = (2 + 9) + 1$. We use x, y, and z to represent real numbers and to state the laws that govern addition and multiplication for your reference.

- **Commutative Law of Addition:** $x + y = y + x$
  For example, $5 + 2 = 2 + 5$.
- **Commutative Law of Multiplication:** $x \cdot y = y \cdot x$
  For example, $2 \cdot 7 = 7 \cdot 2$.
- **Associative Law of Addition:** $(x + y) + z = x + (y + z)$
  For example, $(7 + 3) + 5 = 7 + (3 + 5)$.
- **Associative Law of Multiplication:** $x \cdot (y \cdot z) = (x \cdot y) \cdot z$
  For example, $2 \cdot (7 \cdot \pi) = (2 \cdot 7) \cdot \pi$.
- **Distributive Law of Multiplication over Addition:** $x \cdot (y + z) = x \cdot y + x \cdot z$
  For example, $2 \cdot (\pi + 7) = 2 \cdot \pi + 2 \cdot 7$.

The distributive law tells us that the grouping symbols can be removed from an expression of the form $x \cdot (y + z)$ by simply multiplying each of the numbers within the parentheses by x.

EXAMPLE 1

a. $x(2 + \sqrt{3}) = 2x + x\sqrt{3}$
b. $5(x + y + z) = 5x + 5y + 5z$
c. $-2(3 - a) = -6 + 2a$

■

Warning: There is a commutative law and an associative law of multiplication but not of subtraction or division. For example, since $8 \div 4 = 2$ and $4 \div 8 = \frac{1}{2}$, it is clear that division is not commutative. Likewise, the fact that $8 \div (4 \div 2) = 4$ and $(8 \div 4) \div 2 = 1$ shows that division is not associative.

The Real Number Line

The real numbers can be represented geometrically by associating each number with a point on a straight line, called the **real number line,** or simply the number line. The number line helps in visualizing the number system.

Begin by choosing an arbitrary point 0 on the line l and calling it the **origin** (see Figure 1.3). With the point 0 we associate the real number 0. Any other point to the right of 0 can be associated with the real number 1. The line segment determined by the origin and the point corresponding to 1 is called a **unit distance.** Proceeding from 0, we lay off 1 unit, 2 units, 3 units, and so on, associated with the numbers 1, 2, 3, respectively. In this way the entire set of natural numbers is associated with equispaced points on the line. Similarly, equispaced points to the left are associated with the negative integers.

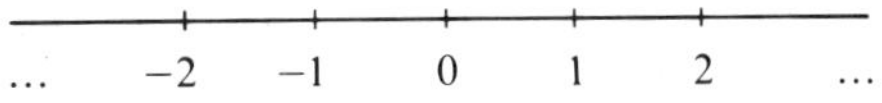

Figure 1.3

Rational numbers such as $\frac{1}{2}$ and $-\frac{7}{3}$ can be located on the real number line by dividing the unit distance into an appropriate number of equal parts. Irrational numbers such as $\sqrt{2}$ and π can also be represented on the real number line, and it can be shown that every point on the number line that is not associated with a rational number corresponds to an irrational number. The rational and irrational numbers just mentioned are shown in Figure 1.4.

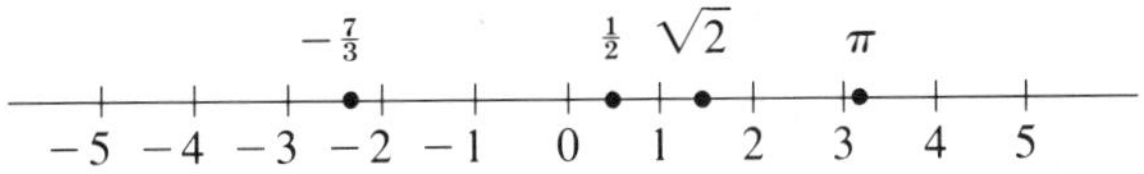

Figure 1.4

When a point on the number line is associated with a real number, the number is called the **coordinate** of the point. The point is called the **graph** of the number. In other words, the point represents the real number. The two concepts are often used interchangeably; that is, we say "the point 2" instead of "the point whose coordinate is 2."

If a and b are real numbers, we use the notation $a > b$ to indicate the fact that a is greater than b. We observe that $a > b$ if $a - b$ is positive. If $a - b$ is negative, we say that a is less than b and denote this by $a < b$. The symbols $>$ and $<$ are called **inequality symbols.** The notation $a \geq b$ includes the possibility that $a = b$ as well as that $a > b$. Similarly, $a \leq b$ includes the possibilities that either $a < b$ or $a = b$.

EXAMPLE 2

a. $9 > 5$, since $9 - 5 = 4$ is positive. The relation $9 > 5$ can also be written $5 < 9$.
b. $0 > -2$, since $0 - (-2) = 2$ is positive. The relation $0 > -2$ can also be written $-2 < 0$.
c. $-1 > -8$, since $(-1) - (-8) = (-1) + 8 = 7$ is positive. The relation $-1 > -8$ can also be written $-8 < -1$.
d. Every positive number is greater than every negative number. Thus, $-1000 < 0.0001$. ■

Comment: The number line gives an easy geometric interpretation of order. If a and b are real numbers, $a < b$ means that point a is to the left of point b (a to the *left* of b means that a is *less* than b). See Figure 1.5.

EXAMPLE 3 Several inequalities are shown graphically in Figure 1.5.

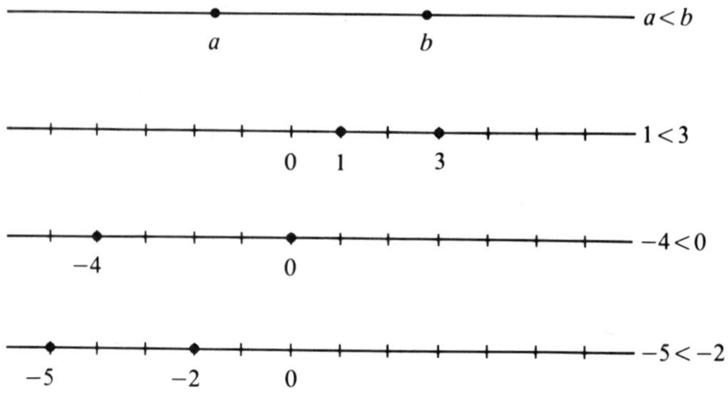

Figure 1.5 ■

As we noted earlier, a real number is the coordinate of some point on the number line. The nonnegative distance between the point whose coordinate is a and the origin is denoted by $|a|$ and is called the **absolute value** of a. Referring to Figure 1.6, we see that -2 and 2 are both 2 units from the origin. Thus, $|-2| = 2$ and $|2| = 2$. To motivate an algebraic definition of the absolute value of a real number, we note that

$$|-2| = -(-2) = 2 \quad \text{and} \quad |2| = 2$$

That is, if the number a is negative, we change its sign to find $|a|$; and if a is positive, $|a|$ is equal to a. This procedure is the basis of the following definition.

Definition

$$|a| = \begin{cases} a & \text{if } a \geq 0 \\ -a & \text{if } a < 0 \end{cases}$$

It follows that the absolute value of every nonzero real number is positive because if $a > 0$, $|a| = a$, which is positive, and if $a < 0$, $|a| = -a$, which is also positive.

EXAMPLE 4 Evaluate a. $|19|$ b. $|-2|$ c. $|3 - \pi|$

Solution

a. Since $19 > 0$, it follows that $|19| = 19$.
b. Since $-2 < 0$, it follows that $|-2| = -(-2) = 2$.
c. Since $3 - \pi < 0$, it follows that $|3 - \pi| = -(3 - \pi) = \pi - 3$. ■

Graphically, the absolute value of $a - b$ corresponds to the distance between two points on the coordinate line. Thus, $|a - b|$ represents the number of units between the numbers a and b on the coordinate line. Denoting the distance between a and b by $d(a, b)$, we define $d(a, b)$ by

$$d(a, b) = |a - b|$$

From the definition of absolute value, it follows that $d(a, b) = d(b, a)$.

EXAMPLE 5 Find the distance between the indicated points in Figure 1.6.

Solution $d(-3, 2) = |-3 - 2| = |-5| = 5$

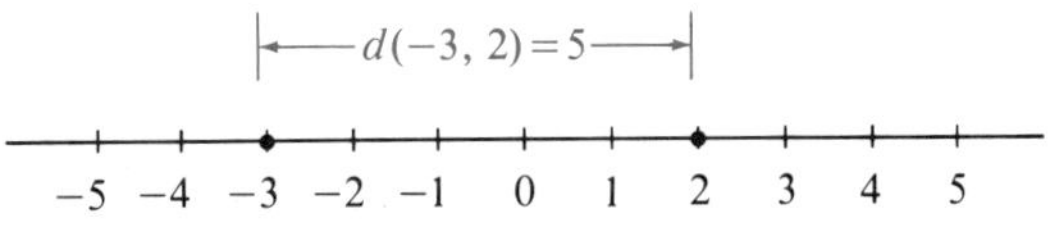

Figure 1.6

■

Exercises Section 1.1

In Exercises 1–10, answer True or False.

1. An integer is also a rational number.
2. A real number is either positive or negative.
3. An irrational number is the ratio of two rational numbers.
4. If a is to the left of b on the number line, then $a < b$.
5. If a and b are real numbers, then $a + b = b + a$.
6. The real number $-a$ is always negative.
7. A number may be rational and irrational.
8. Every rational number is real.
9. The absolute value of $\sqrt{3}$ is $-\sqrt{3}$.
10. The absolute value of $-a$ is a.

In Exercises 11–20, find the decimal representation of the given rational number and indicate whether it is terminating or nonterminating.

11. $1/7$ **12.** $29/3$ **13.** $3/8$
14. $6/11$ **15.** $11/9$ **16.** $9/8$
17. $11/6$ **18.** $12/6$ **19.** $6/13$
20. $7/13$

In Exercises 21–28, write each statement as a single number. For some a calculator will be handy.

21. $-2 - (7 - 10)(5)$ **22.** $-(-3)(5)$
23. $-[2 + 3(6 - 8)][4 - (5 + 2)]$
24. $[3 - (6 + 1)][-2 - (-5)]$
25. $[-(-2) - (4 - 6)][3 + (7 - 3)]$
26. $[3 - 7(5 - 6)][-3(-2 - 5(-4))][-6 + (5 - 7)]$
27. $-2[7.1 + (1.2 - 2.8) - 6(2.5 - 3.2)]$
28. $16.3(3.1 - (6.2 - (7.8(4.3 + 2.1) + 8.2)))$

In Exercises 29–38, locate the indicated number on the number line.

29. 2.3 **30.** -3.5 **31.** 1.67
32. 4.16 **33.** 3.14 **34.** $3/8$
35. $11/8$ **36.** $-9/4$ **37.** -0.017
38. 1.414

In Exercises 39–48, indicate the correct inequality symbol for the two given numbers.

39. 25 17 **40.** 0.01 0.009
41. $-7/6$ $9/7$ **42.** -10 -2
43. -0.1 0.002 **44.** 100 -200
45. $99/12$ $-99/7$ **46.** $-1/9$ $-1/7$
47. $\sqrt{2}$ π **48.** $-\sqrt{5}$ $-\sqrt{7}$

In Exercises 49–58, evaluate the given expression.

49. $|7|$ **50.** $|-3|$ **51.** $|6 - 9|$
52. $|3 - 1|$ **53.** $5 + |-9|$ **54.** $3 + |-2|$
55. $3 + |-3|$ **56.** $6 - |9|$ **57.** $1 - |3|$
58. $|5 + (-9)|$

In Exercises 59–68, find the distance between the indicated points on the number line.

59. $-3, 1$ **60.** $5, 9$

61. $-5, -1$ **62.** $-2, 7$

63. $-0.1, 7$ **64.** $-0.5, -0.3$

65. $-6, 0$ **66.** $-8, -1$

67. $-0.125, 0.176$ **68.** $-0.385, 4.671$

69. By an example, show that $|a + b| \neq |a| + |b|$. When does $|a + b| = |a| + |b|$?

1.2 Integral Exponents

In Section 1.1 we indicated that the product of two real numbers, x and y, is written $x \cdot y$ or simply xy. A special notation, called **exponential notation,** is used for repeated multiplications of the *same* number. Ordinarily, the product $x \cdot x$ is written x^2 (read "x squared" or "x to the second power"). The product $x \cdot x \cdot x$ is written x^3 (read "x cubed" or "x to the third power"). In general, if n is a positive integer, x^n (read "x to the nth power") is defined by

$$\mathbf{x^n = \overbrace{x \cdot x \cdot x \cdot \cdots \cdot x}^{n \text{ times}}}$$

The letter x is called the **base,** and n the **exponent** of x. The quantity x^n is called the **nth power** of x.

EXAMPLE 1
a. $2 \cdot 2 \cdot 2 \cdot 2 \cdot 2 \cdot 2 = 2^6 = 64$ (2 is the base, 6 is the exponent)
b. $(\frac{1}{3})(\frac{1}{3})(\frac{1}{3})(\frac{1}{3}) = (\frac{1}{3})^4$
c. $(-\pi)(-\pi)(-\pi) = (-\pi)^3$
d. $(5x + 4)(5x + 4)(5x + 4) = (5x + 4)^3$ ■

You can find squares of numbers with a calculator by using the [x^2] *key. You can calculate higher powers by using the* [y^x] *key. Thus, calculate* $(3.1)^9$ *by using the following keystrokes.*

3.1 [y^x] 9 [=] 26439.62216

We note that a term of the form $3x^5$, where 3 is the coefficient of x^5, is not the same as $(3x)^5$. To illustrate the difference in $3x^5$ and $(3x)^5$, consider the case where $x = 2$. Then

$$3 \cdot 2^5 = 3 \cdot 32 = 96 \quad \text{and} \quad (3 \cdot 2)^5 = 6^5 = 7776$$

Similarly, you must be careful to distinguish between $-x^4$ and $(-x)^4$. In the former we mean $(-1)x^4$. Thus, $-2^4 = -16$ and $(-2)^4 = 16$.

Multiplication and division of terms with exponents are frequently performed operations in algebra. Observe that if we take the product of $a^m \cdot a^n$, we get

$$a^m \cdot a^n = \overbrace{(a \cdot a \cdot a \cdot \cdots \cdot a)}^{m \text{ factors}}\overbrace{(a \cdot a \cdot \cdots \cdot a)}^{n \text{ factors}}$$

Since there is a total of $m + n$ factors on the right-hand side, we conclude that

$$\mathbf{a^m \cdot a^n = a^{m+n}}$$

We have derived Rule 1 of the following rules of exponents.

Rule 1	$a^m \cdot a^n = a^{m+n}$
Rule 2	$(a^m)^n = a^{mn}$
Rule 3	$(ab)^n = a^n b^n$
Rule 4	$\left(\dfrac{a}{b}\right)^n = \dfrac{a^n}{b^n}, \quad b \neq 0$
Rule 5	$\dfrac{a^m}{a^n} = a^{m-n}, \quad m > n \quad \text{and} \quad a \neq 0$
	$= \dfrac{1}{a^{n-m}}, \quad m < n \quad \text{and} \quad a \neq 0$

EXAMPLE 2 a. $x^4 \cdot x = x^{4+1} = x^5$
b. $y^3 y^5 = y^8$
c. $a^4(a^2 - 3b^3) = a^4(a^2) - a^4(3b^3) = a^6 - 3a^4b^3$ ■

To verify Rule 2, we note that

$$(a^m)^n = \overbrace{a^m \cdot a^m \cdot \cdots \cdot a^m}^{n \text{ factors}}$$

Since a^m means that a occurs m times, the total number of times that a occurs is mn.

EXAMPLE 3 a. $(x^3)^4 = x^{12}$ b. $(2^3)^2 = 2^6 = 64$ ■

We can verify Rule 3 by the same procedure.

$$(a \cdot b)^n = \overbrace{(a \cdot b)(a \cdot b)(a \cdot b) \cdots (a \cdot b)}^{n \text{ factors}}$$

Grouping all the a factors together and all the b factors together, we can write

$$(a \cdot b)^n = \overbrace{(a \cdot a \cdot a \cdot \cdots \cdot a)}^{n \text{ factors}} \cdot \overbrace{(b \cdot b \cdot b \cdot \cdots \cdot b)}^{n \text{ factors}}$$

Therefore, for positive integer exponents we have

$$(ab)^m = a^m b^m$$

EXAMPLE 4 a. $(2x)^3 = 2^3x^3 = 8x^3$ b. $(5xy)^2 = 5^2x^2y^2 = 25x^2y^2$ c. $64a^3 = 4^3a^3 = (4a)^3$ ■

Rules 4 and 5 are established in a similar manner. The next two examples show how these rules are applied.

EXAMPLE 5 a. $\left(\frac{3x}{y}\right)^2 = \frac{3^2x^2}{y^2} = \frac{9x^2}{y^2}$ b. $\left(\frac{2}{3}\right)^4 = \frac{2^4}{3^4} = \frac{16}{81}$ ■

EXAMPLE 6 a. $\frac{a^5}{a^3} = a^{5-3} = a^2$ b. $\frac{r^7}{r^{11}} = \frac{1}{r^{11-7}} = \frac{1}{r^4}$ ■

In passing we note the difference between $(a^m)^n$ and $(a)^{m^n}$. The first of these is equal to a^{mn} (by Rule 2), but the value of the second quantity is obtained by first taking the power of the exponent and then taking a to this power. Thus,

$$(2^3)^2 = 2^6 = 64 \quad \text{but} \quad (2)^{3^2} = 2^9 = 512$$

Exponential notation may be extended to include zero and negative integers. To give meaning to zero as an exponent, observe that $a^2 = a^{2+0}$. If Rule 1 is to continue to hold, $a^{2+0} = a^2 \cdot a^0$. Thus, in order for a^2 to be equal to $a^2 \cdot a^0$, we make the following definition:

Rule 6

$$\boldsymbol{a^0 = 1, \qquad a \neq 0}$$

To define negative integer exponents, note that

$$1 = a^0 = a^{n-n}$$

Under the assumption that Rule 1 can be extended to hold, we have

$$a^{n-n} = a^n \cdot a^{-n} = 1$$

or

Rule 7

$$\boldsymbol{a^{-n} = \frac{1}{a^n}, \qquad a \neq 0}$$

The last two rules follow from the others.

Rule 8

$$\boldsymbol{a^n = \frac{1}{a^{-n}}}$$

Rule 9

$$\boldsymbol{\left(\frac{a}{b}\right)^{-n} = \left(\frac{b}{a}\right)^n}$$

EXAMPLE 7 Simplify $\frac{xy^{-2}}{3xb^{-3}}$.

Solution Eliminating the negative exponents first, we get

$$\frac{xy^{-2}}{3xb^{-3}} = \frac{x \cdot \frac{1}{y^2}}{3x\frac{1}{b^3}} = \frac{\frac{1}{y^2}}{\frac{3}{b^3}} = \frac{1}{y^2} \cdot \frac{b^3}{3} = \frac{b^3}{3y^2}$$

■

EXAMPLE 8 Simplify $\frac{x^0 + y^0}{(x + y)^0}$.

Solution $\frac{x^0 + y^0}{(x + y)^0} = \frac{1 + 1}{1} = \frac{2}{1} = 2$ ■

Scientific Notation

Scientists often express positive real numbers in an abbreviated manner called **scientific notation.** The real number is written as the product of a number between 1 and 10 and a power of 10. If x is a positive real number, then

$$x = m \cdot 10^c$$

where m is a number between 1 and 10 and c is an integer equal to the number of places the decimal point must be moved to produce a number between 1 and 10. The exponent c is positive if the given number x is greater than 1 and negative if x is less than 1.

EXAMPLE 9 Write the following numbers in scientific notation: a. 37,910,000 b. 0.000172

Solution

a. The given number is greater than 1 and the decimal point must be moved seven digits to the left to produce a number between 1 and 10, so we write

$$37{,}910{,}000 = 3.791 \times 10^7$$

b. The given number is less than 1 and the decimal point must be moved four digits to the right to produce a number between 1 and 10, so we write

$$0.000172 = 1.72 \times 10^{-4}$$

■

EXAMPLE 10 Write the following numbers without scientific notation:
a. 4.76×10^4 b. 9.93×10^{-2}

Solution

a. The exponent c is positive, so we move the decimal point four digits to the right to get a number greater than 1.

$$4.76 \times 10^4 = 47{,}600$$

b. The exponent c is negative, so we move the decimal point two digits to the left to produce a number less than 1.

$$9.93 \times 10^{-2} = 0.0993$$

■

Scientific notation is especially valuable for either very large or very small numbers. For example, 0.000000000000000000000053 represents the weight of an oxygen molecule. In scientific notation this is 5.3×10^{-23} since the decimal point is moved to the right by 23 places to obtain the number 5.3, which is between 1 and 10.

Most scientific calculators have a button that you can push to display the numbers in scientific notation. The number between 1 and 10 occurs with the usual 8-to-10-digit accuracy. To the right appears a two-digit number for the exponent. Such a calculator can handle any number between 10^{-99} *and* 10^{99}.

Your calculator displays the number 3.6513×10^5 *as* 3.6513 05 . *Similarly, the number* 2.0715×10^{-4} *is displayed as* 2.0715 -04 .

Exercises Section 1.2

In Exercises 1–40, simplify the given expression. (Expand and write each expression without zero or negative exponents.)

1. 3^5
2. 4^3
3. $(-2)^4$
4. $(-10)^3$
5. x^6x^8
6. b^3b^{10}
7. $(2x^3)(3x^5)$
8. $(\frac{1}{2}a^8)(6a^2)$
9. $(c^{12})^4$
10. $(y^4)^7$
11. $(3^2)^3$
12. $(2^4)^2$
13. $(xy)^5$
14. $(3z)^4$
15. $(2x^3y^7)^3$
16. $(-4a^2b^5)^3$
17. $5(99^0)$
18. $3(25x^3y)^0$
19. $(\frac{2}{7})^2$
20. $(-\frac{3}{4})^3$
21. $\dfrac{7x^2y^5}{27xy}$
22. $\dfrac{a^5b^8}{a^0b^{11}}$
23. $\left(\dfrac{x^2}{y^5}\right)^6$
24. $\left(\dfrac{2c^3}{d^6}\right)^3$
25. $(8)^{-1}$
26. $(3)^{-4}$
27. $5x^{-2}$
28. $3z^{-3}$
29. $(x^{-2}y^5)^4$
30. $(r^5s^{-1})^6$
31. $\left(\dfrac{2x}{y}\right)^{-3}$
32. $\left(\dfrac{6}{5}\right)^{-1}$
33. $\left(\dfrac{a^{-3}b^7}{a^2b^4}\right)^{-2}$
34. $\left(\dfrac{xy^9}{x^{-4}y^{-1}}\right)^{-1}$
35. $\left(\dfrac{x^3y^{-6}}{x^7y^{-4}}\right)^{-2}$
36. $\left(\dfrac{m^{-2}n^{-4}}{m^{-6}n^{-9}}\right)^0$
37. $(x+y)^{-1}$
38. $(x+y)^0$
39. $x^0 + (2y)^0$
40. $((2xyz)^7)^0$

Write Exercises 41–46 in scientific notation.

41. 8,234,400,000
42. 93,002
43. 0.000000000052
44. .00786
45. 46 followed by 38 zeros
46. 53 followed by 13 zeros

Write Exercises 47–52 without scientific notation.

47. 3.4852×10^9
48. 1.423×10^{19}
49. 9.385×10^{-7}
50. 8.99×10^{-11}
51. 2.222×10^{-2}
52. 7.003×10^{-20}
53. The speed of light is approximately 30 billion cm/sec. Write this number in scientific notation.
54. A television rating service estimates that 28 million people watch a particular program. Write this number in scientific notation.
55. An economist estimates that 1.5×10^6 people will be unemployed next year. Write this number without scientific notation.

Determine whether the stated equalities in Exercises 56–59 are true or false. Give reasons.

56. $\dfrac{a^2}{b^2} = \left(\dfrac{a}{b}\right)^2$
57. $(x+y)^{-1} = x^{-1} + y^{-1}$
58. $(2x)^3 = 8x^3$
59. For any nonzero x, $(x^2)^3 = x^{2^3}$.

1.3 Radicals and Fractional Exponents

Radicals

The statement $5^2 = 25$ means that 25 is the square of 5 or, equivalently, that 5 is the square root of 25. Similarly, in the expression $(-2)^3 = -8$, we call -2 the cube root of -8; in the expression $3^4 = 81$, we call 3 the fourth root of 81; and in the expression $4^5 = 1024$, we call 4 the fifth root of 1024.

Definition

> If r is a real number and n is a positive integer such that $r^n = a$, then r is an ***n*th root of *a*.**

The *n*th root of a number is not unique. For example, both 5 and -5 are square roots of 25. To avoid confusion, when taking roots, we use one root, called the **principal root.** The principal nth root of a number a is denoted by $\sqrt[n]{a}$ where $\sqrt{}$ is called a **radical sign,** n the **index** of the radical, and the quantity inside the radical the **radicand.** The meaning attached to $\sqrt[n]{a}$ depends upon the values of a and n and is governed by the definition of the principal nth root.

Definition

> The principal nth root of a number a is denoted by $\sqrt[n]{a}$ and defined as follows:
>
> - If n is even and $a > 0$, then $\sqrt[n]{a}$ is the positive nth root.
> - If n is odd and a is any real number, then $\sqrt[n]{a}$ is the real nth root.
> - $\sqrt[n]{0} = 0$ for all n.

Comment: If n is even and $a < 0$, the principal nth root is not a real number. We shall treat the special case of the principal square root of a negative number in the next chapter.

The radical sign without an index is understood to be the principal square root. This operation is included on most calculators and is simply a matter of entering the number and then pushing the [√] *key.*

The [√] *key can be used in small programmable calculators to obtain the absolute value of a number. For any number in a register, the keystrokes* [x^2] [$\sqrt{x}$] *give* $|x|$.

EXAMPLE 1 Find the principal root of a. $\sqrt[4]{81}$ b. $\sqrt[5]{-32}$ c. $\sqrt{25}$ d. $\sqrt{6.783}$

Solution a. $\sqrt[4]{81} = 3$, not ± 3 b. $\sqrt[5]{-32} = -2$ c. $\sqrt{25} = 5$

d. (From your calculator) $\sqrt{6.783} =$ 2.604419321 ■

The principal nth root of a^n is denoted $\sqrt[n]{a^n}$. If n is even, then $\sqrt[n]{a^n} = |a|$. The absolute value is necessary because the principal nth root is a positive number when n is even. If n is odd, no absolute value signs are necessary. Thus, $\sqrt[4]{(-2)^4} = |-2| = 2$, but $\sqrt[3]{(-2)^3} = -2$. To avoid considering these cases separately we shall assume that all variables are nonnegative real numbers.

The following rules are useful in working with radical expressions.

Rule 1	$\sqrt[n]{a}\,\sqrt[n]{b} = \sqrt[n]{ab}$	$a \geq 0,\ b \geq 0$
Rule 2	$\dfrac{\sqrt[n]{a}}{\sqrt[n]{b}} = \sqrt[n]{\dfrac{a}{b}}$	$a \geq 0,\ b > 0$

Comment: Rules 1 and 2 tell how to multiply or divide numbers taken to the same root. **No corresponding rule exists for combining radicals by addition.**

EXAMPLE 2 Simplify $\sqrt{16x^3y^6}$; that is, remove any perfect square roots. Assume $x \geq 0$ and $y \geq 0$.

Solution $\sqrt{16x^3y^6} = \sqrt{16}\,\sqrt{x^3}\,\sqrt{y^6} = 4xy^3\sqrt{x}$

An alternate approach is

$$\begin{aligned}\sqrt{16x^3y^6} &= \sqrt{16x^2 \cdot x \cdot y^6}\\ &= \sqrt{x} \cdot \sqrt{16x^2y^6}\\ &= 4xy^3\sqrt{x}\end{aligned}$$

■

EXAMPLE 3 Simplify $\sqrt[3]{-16x^5}$.

Solution $\sqrt[3]{-16x^5} = \sqrt[3]{(-8x^3)(2x^2)} = \sqrt[3]{-8x^3}\,\sqrt[3]{2x^2} = -2x\sqrt[3]{2x^2}$ ■

Writing a fraction without radicals in the denominator is called **rationalizing the denominator.** Thus, the rationalized form of $\sqrt{7/9}$ is $\sqrt{7}/3$. When a perfect square root does not appear in the denominator, we multiply both denominator and numerator by a radical that will make the denominator rational. For example, to rationalize $\sqrt{3/5}$, we write

$$\sqrt{\frac{3}{5}} = \frac{\sqrt{3}}{\sqrt{5}} = \frac{\sqrt{3}}{\sqrt{5}} \cdot \frac{\sqrt{5}}{\sqrt{5}} = \sqrt{\frac{3 \cdot 5}{5 \cdot 5}} = \frac{\sqrt{15}}{5}$$

EXAMPLE 4

a. $\dfrac{2}{\sqrt{3}} = \dfrac{2}{\sqrt{3}} \cdot \dfrac{\sqrt{3}}{\sqrt{3}} = \dfrac{2\sqrt{3}}{3}$

b. $\dfrac{x}{\sqrt[4]{x+y}} = \dfrac{x}{\sqrt[4]{x+y}} \cdot \dfrac{\sqrt[4]{(x+y)^3}}{\sqrt[4]{(x+y)^3}} = \dfrac{x\sqrt[4]{(x+y)^3}}{\sqrt[4]{(x+y)^4}} = \dfrac{x\sqrt[4]{(x+y)^3}}{x+y}; \quad x+y>0$

c. $\dfrac{1}{\sqrt[3]{2}} = \dfrac{1}{\sqrt[3]{2}} \cdot \dfrac{\sqrt[3]{4}}{\sqrt[3]{4}} = \dfrac{\sqrt[3]{4}}{\sqrt[3]{8}} = \dfrac{\sqrt[3]{4}}{2}$ ■

Fractional Exponents

The definition of exponential notation can be extended to include fractional exponents. We assume that the laws of exponents will continue to hold. Thus,

$$(3^{1/2})^2 = 3^{2/2} = 3^1 = 3$$
$$(5^{1/3})^3 = 5^{3/3} = 5^1 = 5$$
$$((-7)^{1/3})^3 = (-7)^{3/3} = (-7)^1 = -7$$

Consequently, we interpret $3^{1/2}$ as a square root of 3, $5^{1/3}$ as a cube root of 5, and $(-7)^{1/3}$ as a cube root of -7. In general, since $(a^{1/n})^n = a^{n/n} = a^1 = a$, we defined $a^{1/n}$ to be the principal nth root of a, assuming $\sqrt[n]{a}$ exists. It follows that

$$\boldsymbol{a^{1/n} = \sqrt[n]{a}}$$

Similarly, if the fraction p/q, where p and q are integers, is in lowest terms, $a^{p/q}$ is interpreted as

$$a^{p/q} = (a^{1/q})^p = (a^p)^{1/q}$$

and hence $a^{p/q}$ is defined as

$$\boldsymbol{a^{p/q} = \sqrt[q]{a^p} = (\sqrt[q]{a})^p}$$

This means that the numerator of a fractional exponent corresponds to the power to which the number is raised and the denominator corresponds to the order of the root to be taken. Note that the sequence in which the root is taken is immaterial. Thus, $\sqrt[3]{x^2} = (\sqrt[3]{x})^2$.

EXAMPLE 5
a. $\sqrt[5]{y^2} = (y^2)^{1/5} = y^{2/5}$
b. $(x-1)^{3/4} = \sqrt[4]{(x-1)^3}$
c. $2^{5/3} = \sqrt[3]{2^5} = \sqrt[3]{2^3 \cdot 2^2} = 2\sqrt[3]{4}$ ■

EXAMPLE 6 Evaluate $(27)^{4/3}$.

Solution We can write either $\sqrt[3]{(27)^4}$ or $(\sqrt[3]{27})^4$, as both will yield the correct answer. However, the second form is simpler. If we use the first form, we get

$$\sqrt[3]{(27)^4} = \sqrt[3]{531{,}441} = 81$$

By the second form,

$$(\sqrt[3]{27})^4 = (3)^4 = 81$$

Since the rules of exponents apply here, we can also write

$$(3^3)^{4/3} = 3^4 = 81$$ ■

EXAMPLE 7 Simplify $(-8)^{2/3}(9)^{-3/2}$.

Solution $(-8)^{2/3}(9)^{-3/2} = [(-8)^{1/3}]^2[(9^{1/2})]^{-3} = (-2)^2(3)^{-3} = \dfrac{(-2)^2}{3^3} = \dfrac{4}{27}$ ■

EXAMPLE 8 Simplify $\left[\dfrac{3x^{2/3}}{y^{5/2}}\right]^3\left[\dfrac{7y^{1/6}}{5x^{5/6}}\right]^{-1}$.

Solution $\left[\dfrac{3x^{2/3}}{y^{5/2}}\right]^3\left[\dfrac{7y^{1/6}}{5x^{5/6}}\right]^{-1} = \dfrac{27x^2}{y^{15/2}} \cdot \dfrac{5x^{5/6}}{7y^{1/6}} = \dfrac{135x^{17/6}}{7y^{23/3}}$ ■

EXAMPLE 9 a. $\sqrt[8]{81} = (3^4)^{1/8} = 3^{1/2} = \sqrt{3}$

b. $\sqrt[3]{x}\sqrt{x} = x^{1/3}x^{1/2} = x^{5/6} = \sqrt[6]{x^5}$ ■

EXAMPLE 10 Simplify a. $\sqrt[3]{\sqrt{8}}$ b. $\sqrt{x\sqrt{x}}$

Solution a. $\sqrt[3]{\sqrt{8}} = (8^{1/2})^{1/3} = ((2^3)^{1/2})^{1/3} = (2^{3/2})^{1/3} = 2^{1/2} = \sqrt{2}$

b. $\sqrt{x\sqrt{x}} = (x \cdot x^{1/2})^{1/2} = (x^{3/2})^{1/2} = x^{3/4} = \sqrt[4]{x^3}$ ■

EXAMPLE 11 Write $\sqrt{x}\sqrt[3]{y}$ as a single radical.

Solution The key here is to express the given radicals in exponent form. Thus,

$$\sqrt{x}\sqrt[3]{y} = x^{1/2}y^{1/3}$$

Since the exponents $\frac{1}{2}$ and $\frac{1}{3}$ can be written as $\frac{3}{6}$ and $\frac{2}{6}$, respectively, we can write the given product as a sixth-order radical:

$$\sqrt{x}\sqrt[3]{y} = x^{1/2}y^{1/3} = x^{3/6}y^{2/6} = \sqrt[6]{x^3}\sqrt[6]{y^2} = \sqrt[6]{x^3y^2}$$ ■

Comment: The exponent concept can be further extended to include irrational numbers so that the rules of exponents hold for all real numbers. The proof of this extension is beyond the scope of this text, but we shall use the result when necessary.

A scientific calculator with a [y^x] *button can be used to give rational approximations to any real positive number taken to any real exponent.*

Example: *Use a calculator to evaluate* *a.* $\sqrt[4]{3.7}$ *b.* $2^{-\sqrt{3}}$

Solution: *a.* $\sqrt[4]{3.7}$ *is computed by noting that*

$$\sqrt[4]{3.7} = (3.7)^{1/4} = (3.7)^{0.25}$$

Thus, $\sqrt[4]{3.7}$ *is evaluated by the following keystroke sequences:*

3.7 [y^x] 0.25 [=] 1.386916871

Since $\sqrt[4]{3.7} = \sqrt{\sqrt{3.7}}$, *the same result follows from*

3.7 [$\sqrt{\ }$] [$\sqrt{\ }$] = 1.386916871

b. To compute $2^{-\sqrt{3}}$, *use the following keystroke sequence:*

2 [y^x] 3 [$\sqrt{\ }$] [+/−] [=] 0.301023744

Exercises Section 1.3

Simplify the expressions in Exercises 1–28. Rationalize all denominators. Assume variables are positive.

1. $\sqrt{49}$ **2.** $\sqrt{225}$ **3.** $\sqrt[3]{125}$

4. $\sqrt[3]{-64}$ **5.** $\sqrt[5]{-32}$ **6.** $\sqrt[4]{x^8}$

7. $\sqrt[7]{5^{14}}$ **8.** $2\sqrt{72}$ **9.** $5\sqrt{243}$

10. $\sqrt{4x^2}$ **11.** $\sqrt{a^4b^2}$ **12.** $\sqrt{8z^6}$

13. $\sqrt{63a^5b^8}$ **14.** $\sqrt[5]{8x^4y^5}$ **15.** $\sqrt[4]{2x^3z^{12}}$

16. $3x\sqrt{8x^3y^4}$ **17.** $2m\sqrt{m^5n^3}$ **18.** $\sqrt[3]{\dfrac{32}{27}}$

19. $\sqrt{\dfrac{x^7}{y^4}}$ **20.** $\sqrt[3]{\dfrac{c^{12}}{d^9}}$ **21.** $\dfrac{2}{\sqrt{5}}$

22. $\dfrac{1}{\sqrt{7}}$ **23.** $\dfrac{1}{\sqrt{a}}$ **24.** $\dfrac{3}{\sqrt{y}}$

25. $\sqrt{5}\sqrt{20}$ **26.** $\sqrt{3}\sqrt{12}$ **27.** $\sqrt[3]{2a}\sqrt[3]{4a^2}$

28. $\sqrt{5xy^2}\sqrt{10x^3y^4}$

Write Exercises 29–36 in fractional exponent form.

29. $\sqrt[3]{x}$ **30.** $\sqrt{a}$ **31.** $\sqrt[4]{x/y}$

32. $\sqrt{x\sqrt{x\sqrt{x}}}$ **33.** $\sqrt[3]{x^2}$ **34.** $\sqrt{x} + \sqrt{y}$

35. $\sqrt{x\sqrt{x\sqrt[3]{x}}}$ **36.** $\sqrt{5x\sqrt[3]{x}}$

Write Exercises 37–42 in radical form.

37. $x^{3/5}$ **38.** $x^{3/4}$ **39.** $(a^{3/2})^{1/4}$

40. $\dfrac{1}{x^{-1/2}}$ **41.** $(a + b)^{1/3}$ **42.** $x + y^{1/2}$

Simplify the expressions in Exercises 43–56. Write all answers using positive exponents when exponents are required.

43. $(64)^{1/2}$ **44.** $(64)^{2/3}$ **45.** $(81)^{3/4}$

46. $8^{-5/3}$ **47.** $(32)^{-3/5}$ **48.** $(-125)^{1/3}$

49. $x^{1/2}x^{2/3}$ **50.** $a^{1/4}a^{1/3}$ **51.** $y^{4/3}y^{-1/2}$

52. $x^{3/8}x^{1/4}$ **53.** $(125a^3b^9)^{1/3}$

54. $(9x^4y^{10})^{1/2}$ **55.** $(9x^{2/3})^{1/2}$

56. $(16a^{-8/9}b^{4/3})^{3/4}$

Write the expressions in Exercises 57–63 using a single radical.

57. $\sqrt[4]{y}\sqrt[3]{y}$ **58.** $\sqrt[3]{2}\sqrt{7}$ **59.** $\sqrt[3]{5}\sqrt[4]{4}$

60. $\sqrt[5]{x^2}\sqrt{y}$ **61.** $\sqrt{x}\sqrt[3]{(x + y)}$

62. $\sqrt{\sqrt[3]{a^8}}$ **63.** $\sqrt{\sqrt[5]{x^4}}$

Write each of the following as a square root.

64. $\sqrt[4]{25}$ **65.** $\sqrt[6]{27}$ **66.** $\sqrt[4]{(x - 3)^2}$

67. $\sqrt[4]{(a + 1)^2}$ **68.** $\sqrt[6]{(x + 1)^3}$ **69.** $\sqrt[6]{(y + 2)^3}$

Using a calculator, approximate the numbers in Exercises 70–78.

70. $2^{\sqrt{3}}$ **71.** $8^{-\sqrt{8}}$ **72.** $\pi^{\sqrt{2}}$

73. π^{π} **74.** $(\sqrt{2})^{\pi}$ **75.** $3^{0.78}$

76. $(102.67)^{3/8}$ **77.** $(226.4)^{-1.25}$

78. $\sqrt[3]{29.38} + 41.6\sqrt[3]{29.38}$

79. In the theory of ballistics, the *ballistic limit* of a material in m/sec is given approximately by

$$v = kT^{1.2}$$

where T is the thickness in meters of a sheet of the material and k is a constant that is dependent on the material being used. Compute the ballistic limit given that $k = 2.3 \times 10^4$ and $T = 13$ cm.

80. In the study of traffic flow on a particular freeway, the expression

$$225(2.7)^{-0.12t}$$

is used to predict the number of gaps in the traffic pattern greater than some time, t, in seconds. How many gaps are there on this freeway greater than 1.3 sec?

81. In minimizing the distance traveled by a charged particle in a magnetic field, the following two quantities must be evaluated for various values of a and b:

$$(a^{2/3} + b^{2/3})^{3/2} \quad \text{and} \quad (\sqrt{a} + \sqrt{b})^2$$

Compute these two quantities for $a = 1.3$ and $b = 2.5$.

1.4 Multiplication of Algebraic Expressions

Any grouping of numbers and symbols generated by the elementary arithmetic operations or by taking powers or extracting roots is called an **algebraic expression.** Symbols that represent arbitrary elements of a set are usually called **variables** and, unless stated otherwise, are real numbers. The set of all values of a variable for which the expression itself is a real number is called the **domain** of the expression. For instance, the domain of $1/x$ includes all values of x except $x = 0$ since division by 0 is not permitted. The domain is also called the set of **permissible values.**

Terms are groupings of symbols within an algebraic expression that are separated from other groupings by a plus or minus sign. Thus, x^3, $5x^2y^2$, $2(x - 3y)$, and 8 are terms of the expression

$$x^3 + 5x^2y^2 - 2(x - 3y) + 8$$

Likewise, x and $3y$ are terms of the expression $x - 3y$.

When a term is composed of a product of numbers and symbols, each number and symbol is called a **factor** of the term. For example, 5, x^2, and y^2 are factors of the term $5x^2y^2$. Similarly, 2 and $(x - 3y)$ are factors of the term $2(x - 3y)$.

Algebraic expressions are frequently classified according to their number of terms. An expression with one term is called a **monomial,** with two terms a **binomial,** and with three terms a **trinomial.** When an expression has more than three terms, it is called a **multinomial.** A **polynomial** is any expression involving only constant terms or terms in which the variables have positive integer exponents. Each expression in the next example is a polynomial.

EXAMPLE 1

a. Monomials: $2x$, $5x^2y^2$, $3(x + y)(x - y)$
b. Binomials: $3x + 2y$, $9(a + b) + 4(a + b + c)$
c. Trinomials: $5 + x - w$, $r + 2s - 3(r + s)$ ■

An algebraic expression written as a product of other algebraic expressions is said to be in a **factored form.** The individual expressions are called the **factors.** An algebraic expression written as a sum of terms is said to be in **expanded form.**

EXAMPLE 2

a. The algebraic expression $x^3 - yx^2 - xy^2 + y^3$ is in expanded form. One of its factored forms is $(x - y)(x^2 - y^2)$. Another of its factored forms is $(x - y)^2(x + y)$.
b. The expression $3x(x + 2y - 4z)$ is in a factored form, whereas the expanded form of the same expression is $3x^2 + 6xy - 12xz$. ■

In mathematics, you must know how to express algebraic expressions in either their factored form or their equivalent expanded form. The following examples show how to expand a product using the distributive law; that is, $x(y + z) = xy + xz$.

EXAMPLE 3 Expand $3x(x + 2x^2 - 4x^3)$.

Solution

$$\begin{aligned} 3x(x + 2x^2 - 4x^3) &= 3x(x) + 3x(2x^2) - 3x(4x^3) && \text{Distributive law} \\ &= 3x^2 + 6x^3 - 12x^4 && \text{Using } x^m x^n = x^{m+n} \end{aligned}$$ ■

EXAMPLE 4 Expand $(x^2 + 5x - 3)(x^3 - x^2 - 7)$.

Solution a. The distributive law is the key to expanding products.

$$\begin{aligned} &(x^2 + 5x - 3)(x^3 - x^2 - 7) \\ &\quad = (x^2 + 5x - 3)x^3 + (x^2 + 5x - 3)(-x^2) && \text{Distributive law} \\ &\quad\quad + (x^2 + 5x - 3)(-7) \\ &\quad = x^5 + 5x^4 - 3x^3 - x^4 - 5x^3 + 3x^2 - 7x^2 && \text{Distributive law again} \\ &\quad\quad - 35x + 21 \\ &\quad = x^5 + 4x^4 - 8x^3 - 4x^2 - 35x + 21 && \text{Collecting like terms} \end{aligned}$$

b. The given product can also be expanded as follows:

$$
\begin{array}{rrrrrrl}
x^2 & +5x & -3 & & & & \\
x^3 & -x^2 & -7 & & & & \\
\hline
x^5 & +5x^4 & -3x^3 & & & & \quad x^3(x^2+5x-3) \\
 & -x^4 & -5x^3 & +3x^2 & & & \quad -x^2(x^2+5x-3) \\
 & & & -7x^2 & -35x & +21 & \quad -7(x^2+5x-3) \\
\hline
x^5 & +4x^4 & -8x^3 & -4x^2 & -35x & +21 & \quad \text{Combining like terms}
\end{array}
$$

■

Special Products

An algebraic expression involving the sum or difference of two terms is called a **binomial.** The product of two binomials $(ax + by)(cx + dy)$ can be expanded as shown.

$$
\begin{aligned}
(ax + by)(cx + dy) &= ax(cx + dy) + by(cx + dy) \\
&= acx^2 + adxy + bcxy + bdy^2
\end{aligned}
$$

$$\boldsymbol{(ax + by)(cx + dy) = acx^2 + (ad + bc)xy + bdy^2}$$

This result can be applied to the product of *any* two binomials. The final form of the expansion has the following structure:

- The first term is the product of the first terms of the given binomials.
- The middle term is the sum of the products obtained by multiplying the first term in each binomial by the second term in the other.
- The third term is the product of the second terms of the given binomials.

EXAMPLE 5 Expand $(2x + 3)(5x - 4)$.

Solution

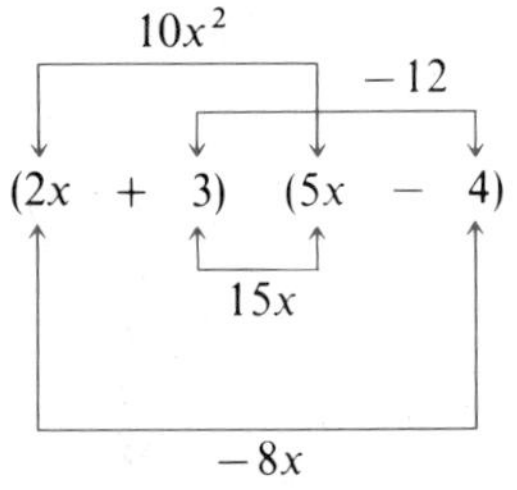

Referring to the diagram, we see that

$$(2x + 3)(5x - 4) = 10x^2 + 15x - 8x - 12 = 10x^2 + 7x - 12$$

■

EXAMPLE 6 Expand $(a - 4b)(8a - 3b)$.

Solution

$$
\begin{aligned}
(a - 4b)(8a - 3b) &= (1)(8)a^2 + [(1)(-3) + (-4)(8)]ab + (-4)(-3)b^2 \\
&= 8a^2 - 35ab + 12b^2
\end{aligned}
$$

■

EXAMPLE 7 Perform the indicated multiplication: $(\sqrt{x} + 3)(\sqrt{x} + 5)$.

Solution $(\sqrt{x} + 3)(\sqrt{x} + 5) = \sqrt{x}\sqrt{x} + 5\sqrt{x} + 3\sqrt{x} + 15 = x + 8\sqrt{x} + 15$ ■

Special Products

Certain special products occur so frequently in algebraic expressions that we memorize their expansions. The following list contains some of these in factored and expanded form.

1. $(x + y)^2 = x^2 + 2xy + y^2$
2. $(x - y)^2 = x^2 - 2xy + y^2$
3. $(x + y)(x - y) = x^2 - y^2$
4. $(ax + b)(cx + d) = acx^2 + (ad + bc)x + bd$
5. $(x + y)^3 = x^3 + 3x^2y + 3xy^2 + y^3$
6. $(x - y)^3 = x^3 - 3x^2y + 3xy^2 - y^3$
7. $(x + y)(x^2 - xy + y^2) = x^3 + y^3$
8. $(x - y)(x^2 + xy + y^2) = x^3 - y^3$

EXAMPLE 8 Expand $(x - 7)(x + 7)$.

Solution Using Formula 3 from the list of special products, where $7 = y$, we have

$$(x - 7)(x + 7) = x^2 - 7^2 = x^2 - 49$$ ■

EXAMPLE 9 Expand $(3z + 5)^2$.

Solution Letting $x = 3z$ and $y = 5$ in Formula 1 yields

$$\begin{aligned}(3z + 5)^2 &= (3z)^2 + 2(3z)(5) + (5)^2 \\ &= 9z^2 + 30z + 25\end{aligned}$$ ■

EXAMPLE 10 Expand $(2x - 3y)^3$.

Solution Using Formula 6, where x is replaced by $2x$ and y is replaced by $3y$, we get

$$\begin{aligned}(2x - 3y)^3 &= (2x)^3 - 3(2x)^2(3y) + 3(2x)(3y)^2 - (3y)^3 \\ &= 8x^3 - 36x^2y + 54xy^2 - 27y^3\end{aligned}$$ ■

EXAMPLE 11 Expand $(a + 5b)(a^2 - 5ab + 25b^2)$.

Solution Using Formula 7 with $x = a$ and $y = 5b$, we have

$$(a + 5b)(a^2 - 5ab + 25b^2) = a^3 + (5b)^3 = a^3 + 125b^3$$ ■

Exercises Section 1.4

Use the distributive law to expand the products in Exercises 1–20.

1. $x^2(x^3 + 2)$
2. $(x^2 + 3x - 5)x^3$
3. $x^3(x^2 - 5x)$
4. $x^9(x^3 + x^5)$
5. $(x + 2y)(x - 2y)$
6. $(x - 1)(x^2 - 1)$
7. $(x^2 - 1)(x^2 + 1)$
8. $(x + 3)(x^2 - 2x + 5)$
9. $\sqrt{x}(\sqrt{x} + \sqrt{y})$
10. $\sqrt{2}(\sqrt{3} + \sqrt{7})$
11. $(xy + 1)(xy - 1)$
12. $(x^2 + 1)(x^2 - 2)$
13. $(x + y^2)^3$
14. $(2x + 4)^2(3x - 2)$
15. $(x + y)(x - y)(x^2 - y)$
16. $(x^2 - y)(x - y^2)$

17. $(x + y + z)^2$

18. $(x + y)^2(x^2 - y^2)$

19. $(3x + 4y - z)(2x - 3y)$

20. $(x^2 + 2x - 3)^2(x + 3)$

Use the table of special products to help you expand the products in Exercises 21–44.

21. $(x + 4)^2$

22. $(x - 2)^2$

23. $(x + 15)^2$

24. $(a - 9)^2$

25. $(b + 12)(b - 12)$

26. $(y + \sqrt{7})(y - \sqrt{7})$

27. $(2x + 5)^2$

28. $(3a + 2)^2$

29. $(\sqrt{a} - \sqrt{b})^2$

30. $(2x + 3)(2x - 3)$

31. $(4x + 5)(4x - 5)$

32. $(\sqrt{x} + 9)(\sqrt{x} - 9)$

33. $(x + 2)^3$

34. $(x - 4)^3$

35. $(5a + b)^3$

36. $(4x + 3)^3$

37. $(2x - 5)^3$

38. $(a + 3b)^3$

39. $(x + 2)(x^2 - 2x + 4)$

40. $(x^2 - 5x + 25)(x + 5)$

41. $(x - 3)(x^2 + 3x + 9)$

42. $(x + 1)(x^2 - x + 1)$

43. $(\sqrt{C} + \sqrt{D})(C - \sqrt{CD} + D)$

44. $(3x - 2)(9x^2 + 6x + 4)$

Use the general rule for expanding the product of two binomials in Exercises 45–54.

45. $(x + 5)(x + 9)$

46. $(y + 3)(y + 7)$

47. $(2x - 8)(3x + 5)$

48. $(x - 4)(3x + 9)$

49. $(2y + 5)(y + 2)$

50. $(8x - 3)(3x - 2)$

51. $(2x - 3y)(x + 4y)$

52. $(6m + 1)(7m - 3)$

53. $(12x - 5)(3x - 8)$

54. $(x + 2y)(5x - 4y)$

55. Simplify the expression $\dfrac{(2 + h)^3 - 8}{h}$.

56. Simplify the expression $\dfrac{(h - 1)^2 - 1}{h}$.

57. The product $(5t - 3)(2t - 1)$ is encountered in finding the displacement of a certain particle. Write this in expanded form.

58. An expression encountered in the study of thermodynamics is $v^2(v - c)^2$. Expand this product.

59. In the calculation of the area of a metal plate being heated in a furnace, the expression $4(2T + 3)(3T + 1)$ arises. Write this in expanded form.

60. In the calculation of the temperature variation of a certain oven, the expression $(3T^4 + 4)(T^2 - 5)$ occurs. Write this expression in expanded form.

1.5 Factoring

Expanding a product is a straightforward application of the distributive property. Factoring, on the other hand, requires more ingenuity. We can often use "factoring formulas," the reverse of the product formulas of Section 1.4, to help us in this process.

Factoring Formulas

1. $x^2 + 2xy + y^2 = (x + y)^2$
2. $x^2 - 2xy + y^2 = (x - y)^2$
3. $x^2 - y^2 = (x + y)(x - y)$
4. $acx^2 + (ad + bc)x + bd = (ax + b)(cx + d)$
5. $x^3 + 3x^2y + 3xy^2 + y^3 = (x + y)^3$
6. $x^3 - 3x^2y + 3xy^2 - y^3 = (x - y)^3$
7. $x^3 + y^3 = (x + y)(x^2 - xy + y^2)$
8. $x^3 - y^3 = (x - y)(x^2 + xy + y^2)$

Comment: Sometimes factoring is simply a matter of recognizing common factors, as in Example 1.

EXAMPLE 1 Factor $6x^5 + 12x^2 - 2x$.

Solution Each term contains $2x$ as a factor; therefore, by applying the distributive law we obtain

$$6x^5 + 12x^2 - 2x = 2x \cdot 3x^4 + 2x \cdot 6x - 2x \cdot 1 = 2x(3x^4 + 6x - 1)$$ ■

EXAMPLE 2 Factor $9x^2 + 24x + 16$.

Solution Observe that $9x^2 = (3x)^2$ and $16 = 4^2$. Since $24x = 2(3x)(4)$, we can use Formula 1 with x replaced by $3x$ and y replaced by 4 to give

$$9x^2 + 24x + 16 = (3x)^2 + 2(3x)(4) + 4^2 = (3x + 4)^2$$ ■

EXAMPLE 3 Factor a. $9x^2 - 25y^2$ b. $w^2 - 5$

Solution Since each expression is the difference of two squares, we can use Formula 3.
a. $9x^2 - 25y^2 = (3x)^2 - (5y)^2 = (3x - 5y)(3x + 5y)$
b. $w^2 - 5 = w^2 - (\sqrt{5})^2 = (w - \sqrt{5})(w + \sqrt{5})$ ■

EXAMPLE 4 Factor $2x^2 - x - 1$.

Solution If this expression can be factored, it will be of the form $(ax + b)(cx + d)$. To see if it fits Formula 4, we let $ac = 2$ and $bd = -1$. Now the signs of b and d must be opposite for their product to be negative. Hence, the only possibilities are

$$(2x - 1)(x + 1) \quad \text{and} \quad (2x + 1)(x - 1)$$

Which is correct? The clue is the coefficient of the x term. Which of these possibilities, when expanded, gives a middle term of $-x$? The second one is correct since

$$2x(-1) + (x)(1) = -2x + x = -x$$

The correct factorization is therefore

$$2x^2 - x - 1 = (2x + 1)(x - 1)$$ ■

EXAMPLE 5 Factor $5x^2 + 13x - 6$.

Solution As in the previous example, if the expression $5x^2 + 13x - 6$ can be factored, it will be of the form $(ax + b)(cx + d)$. Here $ac = 5$ and $bd = -6$. The factors of 5 are $+5, -5, +1, -1$, and the factors of 6 are $+6, -6, +1, -1, +2, -2, +3, -3$. Since the sign of bd is negative, we know that b and d must have opposite signs. We can also investigate the x term. In its general form the coefficient of x is given by

$$(ad + bc)$$

Here the x term coefficient is $+13$. This means that any possible factorizations must yield a middle term of $+13x$ when expanded. The following are possible factors and their expanded forms. We can ignore factors having $-5x$ and $-x$ as the first terms in the two factors (why can we do this?).

$$(5x + 6)(x - 1) \rightarrow 5x^2 + x - 6$$
$$(5x - 6)(x + 1) \rightarrow 5x^2 - x - 6$$
$$(5x + 1)(x - 6) \rightarrow 5x^2 - 29x - 6$$
$$(5x - 1)(x + 6) \rightarrow 5x^2 + 29x - 6$$

$$(5x+2)(x-3) \to 5x^2 - 13x - 6$$
$$(5x-2)(x+3) \to 5x^2 + 13x - 6 \qquad \text{Correct}$$
$$(5x+3)(x-2) \to 5x^2 - 7x - 6$$
$$(5x-3)(x+2) \to 5x^2 + 7x - 6$$

Thus, $(5x-2)(x+3)$ is the correct factorization. ■

EXAMPLE 6 Factor a. $2x^2 + 7x + 3$ b. $3a^2 - 13a + 12$ c. $15x^2 - 8xy - 12y^2$

Solution a. In factoring this expression we note that the factors of $2x^2$ are $2x$ and x and the factors of 3 are 3 and 1. Therefore, possible binomial factors of $2x^2 + 7x + 3$ are $2x + 3$, $x + 3$, $2x + 1$, and $x + 1$. To get the correct middle term, $7x$, we choose $2x + 1$ and $x + 3$. The desired factored form is

$$2x^2 + 7x + 3 = (2x+1)(x+3)$$

b. The factors of $3a^2$ are $3a$ and a. The factors of 12 are $\pm 12, \pm 6, \pm 4, \pm 3, \pm 2, \pm 1$. In order to get the middle term, $-13a$, we choose $3a - 4$ and $a - 3$. The factorization is

$$3a^2 - 13a + 12 = (3a-4)(a-3)$$

Other combinations of the factors of $3a^2$ and 12 can be shown to give improper middle terms.

c. The factors that yield the correct middle term are

$$15x^2 - 8xy - 12y^2 = (3x+2y)(5x-6y)$$

You can find this factorization by trying combinations of factors of $15x^2$ and $12y^2$ until you obtain the correct middle term, $-8xy$. ■

EXAMPLE 7 Factor $x^3 + 27$.

Solution From Formula 7, $x^3 + y^3 = (x+y)(x^2 - xy + y^2)$; and since $x^3 + 27 = x^3 + 3^3$, we can write

$$x^3 + 27 = (x+3)(x^2 - 3x + 9)$$ ■

EXAMPLE 8 Factor $27r^3 - 54r^2s + 36rs^2 - 8s^3$.

Solution $27r^3 = (3r)^3$ and $8s^3 = (2s)^3$, so the expression can be written

$$(3r)^3 - 3(3r)^2(2s) + 3(3r)(2s)^2 - (2s)^3$$

This looks like Formula 6 if we let $x = 3r$ and $y = 2s$. Therefore,

$$27r^3 - 54r^2s + 36rs^2 - 8s^3 = (3r - 2s)^3$$ ■

EXAMPLE 9 Write $\sqrt{4 + 2\sqrt{3}}$ as an expression with a single radical.

Solution

$$\begin{aligned} \sqrt{4+2\sqrt{3}} &= \sqrt{3 + 2\sqrt{3} + 1} && \text{Write 4 as } 3+1 \\ &= \sqrt{(\sqrt{3})^2 + 2\sqrt{3} + 1} && \text{Write 3 as } (\sqrt{3})^2 \\ &= \sqrt{(\sqrt{3}+1)^2} && \text{Factor } a^2 + 2ab + b^2 \\ &= \sqrt{3} + 1 \end{aligned}$$ ■

Factoring by Grouping

Sometimes algebraic expressions can be factored by making an appropriate grouping of terms. The next example illustrates the technique.

EXAMPLE 10 Factor $a + 2ab - 3c - 6cb$.

Solution Inspection shows that the factor a is common to the first two terms and that $-3c$ is common to the last two. Therefore, we write

$$a + 2ab - 3c - 6cb = a(1 + 2b) - 3c(1 + 2b)$$

However, we can now see that $(1 + 2b)$ is a common factor. Thus,

$$a + 2ab - 3c - 6cb = (1 + 2b)(a - 3c)$$

■

Completing the Square

The expression $x^2 + 6x + 9$ is said to be a **perfect square** since it factors into $(x + 3)^2$. Likewise, $x^2 - 3x + \frac{9}{4}$ is a perfect square since it equals $(x - \frac{3}{2})^2$. From the preceding examples, can you guess what value of c will make $3x^2 - 7x + c$ a perfect square? For expressions that cannot be factored easily, we use a method called **completing the square.** The process is based on the rule*

$$(x + k)^2 = x^2 + (2k)x + (k)^2$$

The constant term k^2 in the expression on the right side of this equation is exactly the square of one-half the coefficient of x, when the coefficient of x^2 is 1. Thus, the expression $x^2 + 8x + c$ is a perfect square if $c = [\frac{1}{2}(8)]^2 = 16$. The method of completing the square is explained in the next two examples.

EXAMPLE 11 Factor $x^2 + 6x + 4$ by completing the square.

Solution We can make $x^2 + 6x$ a perfect square by adding $[\frac{1}{2}(6)]^2 = 9$. Therefore, we add and subtract 9 in the given quadratic to get

$$\begin{aligned} x^2 + 6x + 4 &= x^2 + 6x + 9 - 9 + 4 \\ &= x^2 + 6x + 9 - 5 && -9 + 4 = -5 \\ &= (x + 3)^2 - (\sqrt{5})^2 && x^2 + 6x + 9 = (x + 3)^2 \\ &= (x + 3 - \sqrt{5})(x + 3 + \sqrt{5}) && a^2 - b^2 = (a - b)(a + b) \end{aligned}$$

■

* Imagine a square of side $x + k$ units on a side as shown in the accompanying figure. Then $x^2 + 2kx$ is represented by the shaded area. To complete the area of the square, we need to add the area k^2 to the area $x^2 + 2kx$.

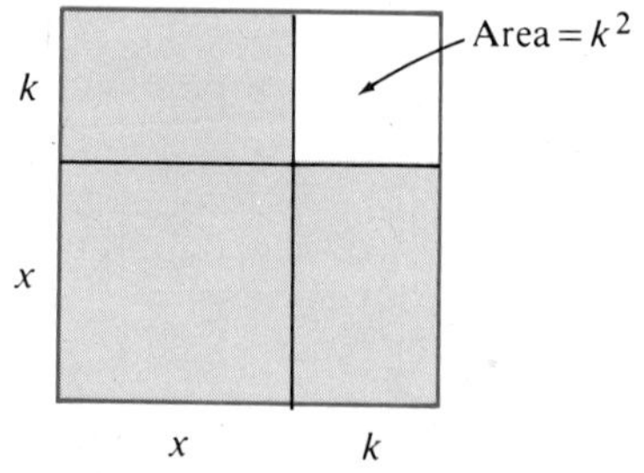

EXAMPLE 12 Factor $4x^2 - 12x - 1$ by completing the square.

Solution We first factor 4 from the terms $4x^2 - 12x$. Thus,

$$4x^2 - 12x - 1 = 4(x^2 - 3x \qquad) - 1$$

Now we complete the square inside the parentheses by adding $(\frac{3}{2})^2 = \frac{9}{4}$ to $x^2 - 3x$. Adding $\frac{9}{4}$ inside the parentheses is equivalent to adding 9 to the given expression; consequently, we must also subtract 9. The factorization is written

$$\begin{aligned}
4x^2 - 12x - 1 &= 4(x^2 - 3x + \tfrac{9}{4}) - 1 - 9 \\
&= 4(x - \tfrac{3}{2})^2 - 10 && \text{Factoring} \\
&= [2(x - \tfrac{3}{2})]^2 - (\sqrt{10})^2 && \text{Using } a^2b^2 = (ab)^2 \\
&= [2(x - \tfrac{3}{2}) - \sqrt{10}][2(x - \tfrac{3}{2}) + \sqrt{10}] && \text{Factoring} \\
&= [2x - 3 - \sqrt{10}][2x - 3 + \sqrt{10}] && \text{Removing parentheses}
\end{aligned}$$

■

Summary of Factoring Approaches

1. Look for common factors in all terms of the expression.
2. Look for special factors (for example, the difference of two squares).
3. See if you can factor by grouping.
4. Try factoring by completing the square.
5. If all these approaches fail, ask a friend for help.

Exercises Section 1.5

Factor the expressions in Exercises 1–56.

1. $3x^3 - 5x^2 + 15x$
2. $x^{10} + 16x^5$
3. $13y^7 - 27y^3$
4. $y^2 + 14y + 49$
5. $z^2 - 24z + 144$
6. $x^2 + 50x + 625$
7. $9x^2 + 6x + 1$
8. $25x^2 - 10x + 1$
9. $\frac{1}{4}x^2 + x + 1$
10. $x^2 - 25$
11. $x^2 - 169$
12. $x^2 - 400$
13. $4m^2 - 64$
14. $9y^2 - 25$
15. $x^2 - 7$
16. $16x^2 - 13$
17. $\frac{1}{4}x^2 - \frac{1}{9}$
18. $\frac{4}{9}x^2 - \frac{1}{25}$
19. $9x^2 + 12x + 4$
20. $25x^2 - 30x + 9$
21. $\frac{1}{9}x^2 + \frac{2}{9}x + \frac{1}{9}$
22. $x^2 - x - 6$
23. $x^2 - x - 12$
24. $a^2 - a - 2$
25. $y^2 + 13y + 42$
26. $m^2 + m - 42$
27. $x^2 - 3x - 54$
28. $b^2 - 4b - 21$
29. $2x^2 + 7x + 3$
30. $2x^2 + 5x + 3$
31. $5x^2 - 28x + 15$
32. $5y^2 - 3y - 2$
33. $6(a + b)^2 - 11(a + b) + 5$
34. $6(h + k)^2 + 29(h + k) - 5$
35. $3x^2 + 4xy - 15y^2$
36. $x^2 - xy - 12y^2$
37. $3x^2 - 4xy - 4y^2$
38. $12a^2 + 13ab - 35b^2$
39. $8x^2 - 20xy + 8y^2$
40. $x^3 - 27$
41. $x^3 + 64$
42. $y^3 - 125$
43. $8x^3 + 1$
44. $27y^3 - 8$
45. $a^3 + \frac{1}{8}$
46. $x^3 + 6x^2 + 12x + 8$
47. $y^3 - 9y^2 + 27y - 27$
48. $a^3 - 6a^2b + 12ab^2 - 8b^3$
49. $8x^3 + 12x^2 + 6x + 1$
50. $8x^3 - 24x^2 + 24x - 8$
51. $a^2 + a^3b + ab^3 + b^2$
52. $x^2 + y - y^2 - x$
53. $z^2 - w^2 - 3z + 3w$
54. $r^5 + 4r^3 + 3r^2 + 12$
55. $a^2 - c^2 + 2cd - d^2$
56. $9 - x^2 - 4xy - 4y^2$

In Exercises 57–66, complete the square to factor the expressions.

57. $x^2 + 4x + 1$
58. $y^2 - 6y - 2$
59. $a^2 - 8a - 5$
60. $x^2 + 12x + 21$
61. $x^2 + 3x + \frac{3}{4}$
62. $w^2 - 2w + \frac{1}{2}$
63. $4y^2 - 8y - 8$
64. $3x^2 + 12x - 7$
65. $2b^2 + 6b - 3$
66. $4z^2 - 4z - 1$

67. The expression $x^2 + Lx - 2L^2$ occurs in the process of designing a bridge. Write this expression in factored form.

68. The path of a certain projectile is described by the expression $12 - 4t - 16t^2$. Write this expression in factored form.

69. The resistance of a certain circuit is found to be given by $5R - 5r + r(R - r)$, where R and r represent different resistances. Write the expression in factored form.

Using the technique of Example 9, simplify the radicals in Exercises 70–78.

70. $\sqrt{6 - 2\sqrt{5}}$
71. $\sqrt{5 + 2\sqrt{6}}$
72. $\sqrt{37 + 20\sqrt{3}}$
73. $\sqrt{71 - 16\sqrt{7}}$
74. $\sqrt{8 + 2\sqrt{15}}$
75. $\sqrt{16 + 6\sqrt{7}}$
76. $\sqrt{19 - 8\sqrt{3}}$
77. $\sqrt[3]{7 + 5\sqrt{2}}$

(*Hint for 77:* $7 = 6 + 1 = 3(\sqrt{2})^2 + 1$)

78. $\sqrt[3]{26 - 15\sqrt{3}}$

1.6 Fractional Expressions

The division of two numbers x and y $(y \neq 0)$ is written x/y and is called the **quotient** of the two numbers. The process of simplifying fractions rests on the fact that if both numerator and denominator are the same nonzero number, the value of the fraction is 1. Thus, each of the following expressions is equal to 1.

$$\frac{x+2}{x+2} = 1 \quad \text{for } x \neq -2$$

$$\frac{2xy}{2xy} = 1 \quad \text{for } x \neq 0,\ y \neq 0$$

$$\frac{3-4x}{3-4x} = 1 \quad \text{for } x \neq \tfrac{3}{4}$$

An important application of this principle is contained in the cancellation law. The name of this law comes from the fact that replacing a fraction with the same numerator and denominator with 1 gives the appearance of canceling the expressions.

Cancellation Law

If $b \neq 0$ and $c \neq 0$, then

$$\frac{ac}{bc} = \frac{a}{b}$$

Comment: The cancellation law allows us to simplify a fraction by "removing" a factor that is equal to 1.

EXAMPLE 1 Reduce $(x^2 + 3x + 2)/(x^2 - 1)$ to its simplest form.

Solution

$$\frac{x^2 + 3x + 2}{x^2 - 1} = \frac{(x + 2)(x + 1)}{(x - 1)(x + 1)} \quad \text{Factoring numerator and denominator}$$

$$= \frac{x + 2}{x - 1} \quad \text{Cancellation law}$$

Note that this form is valid only if $x \neq \pm 1$. ■

Warning: Only *common factors* may be removed by the cancellation law. The law does not apply to common terms in a fraction. Thus,

$$\frac{x + 2}{x + 3} \text{ IS NOT EQUAL TO } \frac{2}{3}$$

Division of a multinomial by a monomial is accomplished by dividing the monomial into each term of the multinomial. Thus,

$$\frac{a + b}{c} = \frac{a}{c} + \frac{b}{c} \tag{1.1}$$

EXAMPLE 2

a. $\dfrac{x^3 + y}{x} = \dfrac{x^3}{x} + \dfrac{y}{x} = x^2 + \dfrac{y}{x}$

b. $\dfrac{4x^2y^3 - 3x^3y^4 + x^4}{2xy^2} = \dfrac{4x^2y^3}{2xy^2} - \dfrac{3x^3y^4}{2xy^2} + \dfrac{x^4}{2xy^2}$

$$= 2xy - \frac{3}{2}x^2y^2 + \frac{x^3}{2y^2}$$ ■

Warning: $\dfrac{a}{b + c}$ IS NOT EQUAL TO $\dfrac{a}{b} + \dfrac{a}{c}$.

Multiplication of Fractions

The product of two fractions is the product of the two numerators divided by the product of the two denominators. Thus, if a/b and c/d are the given fractions,

$$\frac{a}{b} \cdot \frac{c}{d} = \frac{a \cdot c}{b \cdot d} = \frac{ac}{bd} \tag{1.2}$$

Any common factors in the numerator and the denominator of the product should then be "removed" using the cancellation law.

EXAMPLE 3 Simplify $\dfrac{3(x^2 - y^2)}{x^2 + x - 6} \cdot \dfrac{x^2 + 3x}{x + y}$.

Solution

$$\frac{3(x^2 - y^2)}{x^2 + x - 6} \cdot \frac{x^2 + 3x}{x + y} = \frac{3\cancel{(x + y)}(x - y)}{(x - 2)\cancel{(x + 3)}} \cdot \frac{x\cancel{(x + 3)}}{\cancel{x + y}} = \frac{3x(x - y)}{x - 2}$$ ■

EXAMPLE 4 Rationalize the expression $\dfrac{2}{\sqrt{3}-\sqrt{8}}$.

Solution To rationalize this fraction, use the fact that $(\sqrt{x})^2 = x$ and the special product $(a+b)(a-b) = a^2 - b^2$ to write

$$\frac{2}{\sqrt{3}-\sqrt{8}} = \frac{2}{\sqrt{3}-\sqrt{8}} \cdot \frac{\sqrt{3}+\sqrt{8}}{\sqrt{3}+\sqrt{8}} = \frac{2(\sqrt{3}+\sqrt{8})}{(\sqrt{3})^2-(\sqrt{8})^2} = \frac{2(\sqrt{3}+\sqrt{8})}{3-8} = -\frac{2(\sqrt{3}+\sqrt{8})}{5}$$ ■

Division of Fractions

For each nonzero number n, there is a unique number called the **reciprocal** of n, denoted by $1/n$, for which $n(1/n) = 1$. For example, the reciprocal of 2 is $1/2$ and the reciprocal of $3/4$ is $4/3$.

Recall that in arithmetic the rule for dividing one fraction by another is to invert the divisor and multiply. The same rule is used to divide two algebraic fractions, but we state it in terms of the concept of a reciprocal. To divide one fraction by another, multiply by the reciprocal of the divisor. Thus, if a/b and c/d are the given fractions, then

$$\frac{a}{b} \div \frac{c}{d} = \frac{a}{b} \cdot \frac{d}{c} = \frac{ad}{bc} \qquad (1.3)$$

EXAMPLE 5 Simplify $\dfrac{x^2-3x-4}{x^2-1} \div \dfrac{x^2-16}{x-1}$.

Solution

$$\frac{x^2-3x-4}{x^2-1} \div \frac{x^2-16}{x-1} = \frac{x^2-3x-4}{x^2-1} \cdot \frac{x-1}{x^2-16}$$ Multiplying by the reciprocal of the divisor

$$= \frac{\cancel{(x-4)}\cancel{(x+1)}}{\cancel{(x+1)}\cancel{(x-1)}} \cdot \frac{\cancel{x-1}}{(x+4)\cancel{(x-4)}}$$ Factoring numerator and denominator

$$= \frac{1}{x+4}$$ Cancellation law ■

Addition and Subtraction of Fractions

Summing algebraic fractions is analogous to summing arithmetic fractions. The general procedure is:

1. Factor the numerator and the denominator of each fraction.
2. Reduce the fractions to lowest terms.
3. Find the lowest common denominator (LCD).*

* The LCD of two or more fractions is the simplest expression that is exactly divisible by each of the given denominators.

4. Multiply the numerator and the denominator of each fraction by the quotient obtained by dividing the specific denominator into the LCD.
5. Add the numerators of the fractions and place over the LCD to obtain

$$\frac{a}{b} + \frac{c}{d} = \frac{ad}{bd} + \frac{bc}{bd} = \frac{ad + bc}{bd}$$

6. Reduce the resulting fraction to lowest terms.

EXAMPLE 6 Simplify $\dfrac{x}{x+1} - \dfrac{x}{x-2}$.

Solution The LCD is $(x + 1)(x - 2)$. Thus,

$$\frac{x}{x+1} - \frac{x}{x-2} = \frac{x(x-2)}{(x+1)(x-2)} - \frac{x(x+1)}{(x-2)(x+1)}$$ Obtaining the same denominator for each fraction

$$= \frac{x(x-2) - x(x+1)}{(x+1)(x-2)}$$ Adding numerators over the LCD

$$= \frac{x^2 - 2x - x^2 - x}{(x+1)(x-2)}$$ Expanding the numerator

$$= \frac{-3x}{(x+1)(x-2)}$$ Collecting like terms ■

EXAMPLE 7 Simplify $\dfrac{2a}{3b^2c^2} - \dfrac{3b}{5a^2c^5} - \dfrac{c}{2ab^3}$.

Solution The LCD is $30a^2b^3c^5$; therefore, multiply the numerator and the denominator of the first fraction by $10a^2bc^3$, of the second by $6b^3$, and of the third by $15ac^5$.

$$\frac{2a}{3b^2c^2} - \frac{3b}{5a^2c^5} - \frac{c}{2ab^3} = \frac{2a}{3b^2c^2}\cdot\frac{10a^2bc^3}{10a^2bc^3} - \frac{3b}{5a^2c^5}\cdot\frac{6b^3}{6b^3} - \frac{c}{2ab^3}\cdot\frac{15ac^5}{15ac^5}$$

$$= \frac{20a^3bc^3}{30a^2b^3c^5} - \frac{18b^4}{30a^2b^3c^5} - \frac{15ac^6}{30a^2b^3c^5}$$

$$= \frac{20a^3bc^3 - 18b^4 - 15ac^6}{30a^2b^3c^5}$$ ■

EXAMPLE 8 Simplify $\dfrac{a-4}{a^2-7a+12} + \dfrac{5}{a^2-9} - \dfrac{3a-6}{a^2+a-6}$.

Solution Factor the denominators before finding the LCD. The given fractions can be rewritten as

$$\frac{\cancel{a-4}}{(a-3)\cancel{(a-4)}} + \frac{5}{(a+3)(a-3)} - \frac{3\cancel{(a-2)}}{\cancel{(a-2)}(a+3)} = \frac{1}{a-3} + \frac{5}{(a+3)(a-3)} - \frac{3}{a+3}$$

From this we see that $a^2 - 9 = (a + 3)(a - 3)$ is the LCD. Therefore, the original expression is equal to

$$\begin{aligned}\frac{1}{a-3}\cdot\frac{a+3}{a+3} + \frac{5}{(a+3)(a-3)} - \frac{3}{a+3}\cdot\frac{a-3}{a-3} &= \frac{a+3}{a^2-9} + \frac{5}{a^2-9} - \frac{3a-9}{a^2-9}\\ &= \frac{(a+3)+5-(3a-9)}{a^2-9}\\ &= \frac{a+3+5-3a+9}{a^2-9} = \frac{-2a+17}{a^2-9}\end{aligned}$$

■

Complex Fractions

A fraction that contains fractions in its numerator or denominator is called a **complex fraction.** Some examples of complex fractions are

$$\frac{\dfrac{2}{x}+1}{\dfrac{1}{x}-x^2} \quad \text{and} \quad \frac{\dfrac{a}{a+b}-\dfrac{b}{a-b}}{\dfrac{a}{a+b}}$$

Complex fractions may be reduced to a simple fraction by combining the fractions in the numerator and denominator into simple fractions and then following the rule for dividing one fraction by another.

EXAMPLE 9 Simplify $\dfrac{x^{-1}-y^{-1}}{1-xy^{-1}}$.

Solution Expressing x^{-1} and y^{-1} as fractions, we have

$$\frac{x^{-1}-y^{-1}}{1-xy^{-1}} = \frac{\dfrac{1}{x}-\dfrac{1}{y}}{1-\dfrac{x}{y}}$$

We then combine fractions as follows.

$$\frac{\dfrac{1}{x}-\dfrac{1}{y}}{1-\dfrac{x}{y}} = \frac{\dfrac{y}{xy}-\dfrac{x}{xy}}{\dfrac{y}{y}-\dfrac{x}{y}}$$ Obtaining least common denominators for the fractions

$$= \frac{\dfrac{y-x}{xy}}{\dfrac{y-x}{y}}$$ Adding the fractions in the numerator and the denominator

$$= \frac{y-x}{xy}\cdot\frac{y}{y-x}$$ Multiplying by the reciprocal of the denominator

$$= \frac{1}{x}$$ Reducing the fraction to lowest terms by the cancellation law

■

EXAMPLE 10 Simplify the following fraction:

$$\frac{3 - \dfrac{x+3y}{x+y}}{1 + \dfrac{y}{x-y}}$$

Solution

$$\frac{3 - \dfrac{x+3y}{x+y}}{1 + \dfrac{y}{x-y}} = \frac{\dfrac{3(x+y)}{x+y} - \dfrac{x+3y}{x+y}}{\dfrac{x-y}{x-y} + \dfrac{y}{x-y}}$$

Obtaining LCDs for fractions in the numerator and the denominator

$$= \frac{\dfrac{3(x+y) - (x+3y)}{x+y}}{\dfrac{x-y+y}{x-y}}$$

Adding fractions in the numerator and the denominator

$$= \frac{\dfrac{2x}{x+y}}{\dfrac{x}{x-y}}$$

Combining like terms

$$= \frac{2x}{x+y} \cdot \frac{x-y}{x}$$

Multiplying by the reciprocal of the denominator

$$= \frac{2(x-y)}{x+y}$$

Cancellation law ■

Exercises Section 1.6

Perform the indicated multiplications and divisions in Exercises 1–24.

1. $\dfrac{b}{3a} \cdot \dfrac{5c}{4ab^3}$

2. $\dfrac{x^2y}{5xy^2} \cdot \dfrac{3xy^2}{x^3y^5}$

3. $\dfrac{3x}{4y^3} \div \dfrac{9x^4}{2y}$

4. $\dfrac{xyz}{5x^2y^3z} \div \dfrac{4}{25x^3y^2z^2}$

5. $\dfrac{9b^2}{4c^3} \cdot \dfrac{24ac^2}{18b^5} \div \dfrac{c}{2a^3b}$

6. $\dfrac{3x+6}{x+3} \cdot \dfrac{x^2+3x}{5x+10}$

7. $\dfrac{x^2+x-6}{x^2-9} \cdot \dfrac{x^2-6x+9}{2x-4}$

8. $\dfrac{2x^2+11x+15}{x^2+2x-3} \cdot \dfrac{x^2-x}{4x^2+20x+25}$

9. $\dfrac{4xy^2}{4x^2-9} \div \dfrac{10x^2y}{6x+9}$

10. $\dfrac{15ab^2}{a^2+a-12} \div \dfrac{25a^2b}{a-3}$

11. $\dfrac{x^2-xy}{y(x+y)} \cdot \dfrac{x^2+xy}{y(x-y)} \div \dfrac{x^2-x}{xy-2y}$

12. $\dfrac{xy^2+xy}{x^2-4} \cdot \dfrac{x^2-2x}{y^2+y} \div \dfrac{x}{y(x+2)}$

13. $\dfrac{2y^2+11y+5}{2y^2+7y+6} \div \dfrac{y^2+4y-5}{2y^2+y-3}$

14. $\dfrac{6m^2+m-1}{2m^2+5m+2} \div \dfrac{3m^2-7m+2}{m^2-m-6}$

15. $\dfrac{2x^2+x-3}{3x^2+10x-8} \cdot \dfrac{3x^2-2x}{x^2-1} \div \dfrac{x+6}{x^2+5x+4}$

16. $\dfrac{2x^2+3x-9}{6x^2-7x+2} \cdot \dfrac{3x-2}{4x^2-8x+3} \div \dfrac{x^2+3x}{2x^2+13x-7}$

17. $\dfrac{(s-2)s-3}{s-2} \div \dfrac{s^2-9}{(s+1)(s-2)}$

18. $\dfrac{x(x+3)+2}{x+5} \cdot \dfrac{x(x+3)+5(x+3)}{x^2+5x+6}$

19. $\dfrac{ax+ay+bx+by}{ax-ay+bx-by} \div \dfrac{x+y}{x-y}$

20. $\dfrac{x(x-2)-3(x-2)}{x^2-4} \cdot \dfrac{x+2}{x(x-3)+(x-3)}$

21. $\dfrac{2y^2 - 5y - 3}{y - 4} \div \left[\dfrac{(y-3)^2}{y^2 - 16} \cdot \dfrac{1}{3 - y}\right]$

22. $\dfrac{x^5 + x^4 - x - 1}{x - 1} \div \dfrac{x + 1}{2x}$

23. $\dfrac{a^2 + 300a + 20{,}000}{1600 - a^2} \cdot \dfrac{a^2 + 360a - 16{,}000}{2a + 400}$

24. $\dfrac{(2x + 3)x + 1}{(2x + 3)(x - 1)} \cdot \dfrac{(x + 1)x - 2}{x(x + 1) + 2(x + 1)}$

Perform the indicated additions and subtractions in Exercises 25–48.

25. $\dfrac{2}{b} + \dfrac{1}{c} - \dfrac{3}{a}$

26. $\dfrac{a}{bc} - \dfrac{b}{ac}$

27. $\dfrac{2}{3s} - \dfrac{1}{t} + \dfrac{4}{12st}$

28. $\dfrac{1}{x^2} - \dfrac{1}{y^2}$

29. $\dfrac{3}{xy^2} + \dfrac{2}{x} - \dfrac{3}{y}$

30. $\dfrac{s + 1}{s} + \dfrac{s}{2} - \dfrac{1}{s}$

31. $\dfrac{3}{x + 1} + \dfrac{2}{x - 3}$

32. $5(x + 3)^{-1} - 3(x - 2)^{-1}$

33. $x(x - 5)^{-1} + 2(x + 3)^{-1}$

34. $\dfrac{3x}{2x + 3} + \dfrac{x}{x - 2}$

35. $\dfrac{3}{x} - \dfrac{2}{x + 2} - \dfrac{1}{x(x + 2)}$

36. $\dfrac{x - y}{x} + \dfrac{y}{x + y} + \dfrac{y^2}{x^2 + xy}$

37. $\dfrac{2}{a} + \dfrac{3}{2a + 3} - \dfrac{2}{a(2a + 3)}$

38. $\dfrac{5}{2x - 1} + \dfrac{x}{4x^2 - 1} - \dfrac{7}{2x + 1}$

39. $4 - (9x - 16)(3x + 4)^{-1}$

40. $x + (4 - x^2)(x - 3)^{-1}$

41. $\dfrac{2}{p} + \dfrac{2}{p^2 + 2p + 1} - \dfrac{1}{p + 1}$

42. $\dfrac{xy}{x - y} + \dfrac{x^2}{y - x} + x$

43. $\dfrac{1}{(x + 3)(x - 2)} + \dfrac{1}{(x + 1)(x + 3)} - \dfrac{1}{(x + 1)(x - 2)}$

44. $\dfrac{3}{x(x + 2)} - \dfrac{1}{(x + 2)(x - 1)} + \dfrac{4}{x(x - 1)}$

45. $\dfrac{5x + 6}{x^2 + x - 6} + \dfrac{x + 1}{x^2 - 4x + 4} - \dfrac{x^2}{x^3 - 2x^2}$

46. $\dfrac{2 - k}{k^2 + k - 6} + \dfrac{5}{k^2 - 9} - \dfrac{4 - k}{k^2 - 5k + 6}$

47. $(x + 3)(x - 2)^{-1/2} + (x - 2)^{1/2}$

48. $(x - 1)(x + 1)^{-1/2} + 2(x + 1)^{1/2}$

Write the expressions in Exercises 49–52 with rational denominators.

49. $\dfrac{\sqrt{5} + 3}{\sqrt{3} + \sqrt{5}}$

50. $\dfrac{2\sqrt{2}}{\sqrt{2} - \sqrt{7}}$

51. $\dfrac{\sqrt{x} - \sqrt{y}}{\sqrt{x} + \sqrt{y}}$

52. $\dfrac{\sqrt{a} + \sqrt{b}}{\sqrt{a} - \sqrt{b}}$

In Exercises 53–66, simplify the complex fraction.

53. $\dfrac{x - \dfrac{1}{x}}{1 - \dfrac{1}{x}}$

54. $\dfrac{1 - \dfrac{3}{x} + \dfrac{2}{x^2}}{\dfrac{1}{x} - \dfrac{2}{x^2}}$

55. $\dfrac{\dfrac{a}{b} - \dfrac{b}{a}}{1 + \dfrac{b}{a}}$

56. $\dfrac{x + 2}{x - \dfrac{4}{x}}$

57. $\dfrac{1 - x^{-2}}{x^{-1} - 1}$

58. $\dfrac{a + ba^{-1}}{a^{-1}}$

59. $\dfrac{\dfrac{c}{d} + \dfrac{d}{c}}{\dfrac{1}{c} + \dfrac{1}{d}}$

60. $\dfrac{x - 1 - \dfrac{6}{x}}{2 - \dfrac{6}{x}}$

61. $\dfrac{2(x - 1)^{-1} - x - 2}{1 - x + 2(x + 2)^{-1}}$

62. $\dfrac{\dfrac{1}{x} + \dfrac{2}{x + 1} - x}{1 - \dfrac{1}{x^2 + 2x + 1}}$

63. $\dfrac{\dfrac{x}{x - 4} + \dfrac{1}{x - 1}}{\dfrac{x}{x - 1} + \dfrac{2}{x - 3}}$

64. $\dfrac{x^2 - 4y^2}{1 - \dfrac{2x + y}{x - y}}$

65. $\dfrac{1 + \dfrac{y}{x - y}}{x - \dfrac{y}{1 - \dfrac{x}{x + y}}}$

66. $\dfrac{\dfrac{a - 1}{a} + 1}{\dfrac{1}{1 - \dfrac{1}{a + 1}}}$

67. An exothermal process is one that releases heat. To calculate how much heat is released by a new process, a chemist uses the expression

$$\frac{1}{3} + \frac{2}{4t} - \frac{5}{2t^3}$$

Combine the terms and simplify.

68. In calculating the center of gravity of a certain concrete beam, the difference

$$\frac{1}{x} - \frac{1}{x(2x + 1)}$$

is encountered. Simplify this expression.

69. A marketing student uses the expression

$$\frac{3}{s^2 + s} + \frac{2}{s^2 + 4s + 3}$$

while analyzing past trends in the sales of a certain product. Simplify this expression.

1.7 Common Errors

We have reviewed many of those algebraic skills necessary for the remainder of this book. In addition to learning the concepts, you must also develop manipulative skills. These skills require knowing the appropriate algebraic rule and developing such traits as precision, carefulness, and experience in "knowing what to do next."

Everyone has made careless errors; for example, writing a number illegibly, omitting signs, leaving out necessary parentheses, or writing the exponent of a number as a coefficient. Such "trivial" mistakes can be disastrous. Computer programmers soon find out how a computer responds to the omission of a right parenthesis. The computer will unhesitatingly reject the entire program for such a "trivial" error. Likewise, failure to distinguish between $(3x)^2$ and $3x^2$ or to change the sign of every term when removing parentheses from expressions such as $-(x^2 - 4xy + y^2)$ might cause your bridge to collapse if you are a civil engineer. Perhaps these examples are extreme, but carelessness and imprecision *can* be costly. You must know the laws of real numbers and be very careful when applying them. The following exercise set shows some of the "trivial" errors that have occurred on exam papers. See if you can spot them.

Exercises Section 1.7

Each of the statements in Exercises 1–21 is false. Correct the right-hand side of each statement to make it true.

1. $(2x)^2 = 2x^2$

2. $(3x)^2 = 3x^2$

3. $-(2x - 1) = -2x - 1$

4. $-(x^2 - 5x - 6) = -x^2 - 5x - 6$

5. $\frac{1}{2} + \frac{3}{4} = \frac{4}{6}$

6. $\frac{2}{6} - \frac{1}{2} = \frac{1}{4}$

7. $\dfrac{x+2}{x} = x + \dfrac{2}{x}$

8. $(x + y)^2 = x^2 + y^2$

9. $(x^{-1} + y^{-1})^{-1} = x + y$

10. $\sqrt{x + y} = \sqrt{x} + \sqrt{y}$

11. $(x^3 + x^2) = x^2(x + x^2)$

12. $(\sqrt{x} + \sqrt{y})^2 = x + y$

13. $\dfrac{1}{x + y} = \dfrac{1}{x} + \dfrac{1}{y}$

14. $\sqrt{2x} = \sqrt{2}x$

15. $(-x)^2 = -x^2$

16. $\dfrac{2}{x^2 + 2x + 1} = \dfrac{1}{x^2 + x + 1}$

17. $(x^2)^3 = x^5$

18. $x^2 \cdot x^6 = x^{12}$

19. $x + x = x^2$

20. $4^{1/2} = \frac{1}{2}$

21. $\dfrac{3(5x + 2)}{x^2 + 5x + 2} = \dfrac{3}{x^2}$

Review Exercises Chapter 1

In Exercises 1–5, answer True or False.

1. If a number has a terminating decimal expansion, it is rational.
2. The exact value of $\sqrt{2}$ is 1.414.
3. Every real number is rational or irrational.
4. An integer is rational.
5. The absolute value of $-x$ is x.

In Exercises 6–8, find the decimal representation of the given rational number.

6. 2/7 **7.** 17/8 **8.** 9/5

In Exercises 9–14, indicate the correct inequality symbol for each pair of numbers.

9. 24 17 **10.** -3 5
11. -21 -8 **12.** -35 1
13. 145 -2007 **14.** -0.05 -1.68

In Exercises 15–20, evaluate the expression.

15. $|5-9|$ **16.** $|-4-(-7)|$
17. $|-10-(-4)|$ **18.** $72-|-35|$
19. $-22-|-39|$
20. $-16-|28-|-14||$

Find the distance between the given points on the number line in Exercises 21–26.

21. 14, 5 **22.** -4, 6 **23.** -2, 0
24. -5, -3 **25.** -7, -10 **26.** 0.9, 0.2

In Exercises 27–30, remove the symbols of grouping and simplify.

27. $a-(2a+b-c)$
28. $-(2x+7y)-(15x-9y)$
29. $5x-6[2x-(3x+7y)-y]$
30. $[r+3s-4(3s-5r)]+12r$

Perform the indicated multiplications in Exercises 31–42.

31. $a^3(5-ab^2)$ **32.** $y^7(y^4+3y-7)$
33. $(x-2y)(3x+7y)$ **34.** $(a^2+x^2)(a-x)$
35. $(2y+3)(x-3y+5)$
36. $(a+3)(a^2+3a+2)$
37. $(x^2+5x+25)(x-5)$
38. $(a+4)(a^2-4a+16)$
39. $(2+3y)^3$ **40.** $(2x-3)^3$
41. $(x+\sqrt{2})(x-\sqrt{2})$ **42.** $(\sqrt{x}+\sqrt{y})^2$

In Exercises 43–60, factor each of the expressions.

43. $5x-15xy+5x^2$ **44.** $ax^2+abx^3-ax^3$
45. $x^2-50x+625$ **46.** $y^2+20y+100$
47. $4b^2-169$ **48.** $25z^4-1$
49. $8-125x^3$ **50.** $27h^3+r^3$
51. $y^3+15y^2+75y+125$
52. $-8+12(rs)-6(rs)^2+(rs)^3$
53. $15x^2+14x-8$ **54.** $14a^2-23a+3$
55. $-2x^2+7x-3$ **56.** $6x^2-x-35$
57. $2a^2+ab-6b^2$ **58.** $ay^2-ay-6a$
59. $ab-ax-3b+3x$
60. $x^2-xy-mx+my$

Perform the indicated multiplications and divisions in Exercises 61–66.

61. $\dfrac{2x}{3xy}\cdot\dfrac{5x^2y^3}{4xy^4}\div\dfrac{15x^4y}{3x^3y^2}$

62. $\dfrac{a^2-2ax+x^2}{a^2-x^2}\div\dfrac{a^2+x^2}{a+x}$

63. $\dfrac{a^2+6a+9}{a^2-b^2}\cdot\dfrac{a^2+ab}{ab+3b}$

64. $\dfrac{y^2-25}{y^2-9}\div\dfrac{5y+25}{y^2-3y}$

65. $\dfrac{r^2-4r+4}{r^2-9}\div\dfrac{r^2-4}{r^2-2r-3}\cdot\dfrac{r^2+3r}{r-2}$

66. $\dfrac{3x^2-2xy-y^2}{9x^2-y^2}\div\dfrac{x+y}{27x^3-y^3}\cdot\dfrac{5}{x-y}$

In Exercises 67–74, perform the indicated additions and subtractions.

67. $\dfrac{2}{a}-\dfrac{3}{b}+\dfrac{1}{ab}$ **68.** $\dfrac{a}{x^2}+\dfrac{b}{x^2y}+\dfrac{c}{2y}$

69. $2+\dfrac{3}{x+3}-\dfrac{1}{x}$

70. $(x-1)^{-1}+(x+1)^{-1}$

71. $a(a-2)^{-1}-(a-5)^{-2}$

72. $\dfrac{2b+3}{2b^2-b-3}-\dfrac{3b-1}{2b^2-7b+6}$

73. $\dfrac{\dfrac{1}{x+y}-\dfrac{1}{x-y}}{\dfrac{1}{x+y}+\dfrac{1}{x-y}}$

74. $1-\dfrac{1}{1+\dfrac{a}{1-a}}$

Express each of Exercises 75–85 without negative exponents. Simplify.

75. $(a^{-2}b^{-5})^0$

76. $[x^{-1}+y-(2^{-1}+y^{-1})^{-1}]^0$

77. $(xy^{-2}+1)^{-1}$

78. $[(xy)^{-2}+1]^{-1}$

79. $\dfrac{x+y^{-1}}{3+x^{-2}+y^{-2}}$

80. $[(2xy)^{-1}]^{-3}$

81. $\left(\dfrac{x^3y^{-7}}{2x^5y^{-2}}\right)^{-3}$

82. $\dfrac{x^{-2}-4^{-2}}{x^{-1}-4^{-1}}$

83. $\dfrac{x^{-1}+x^{-2}}{x^{-1}-x^{-2}}$

84. $(3x^{-1}+2x^{-2})^{-1}$

85. $\dfrac{a^{-2}}{1-a^{-1}}-\dfrac{a^{-1}}{1-a^{-2}}$

Simplify each of Exercises 86–100. Express in simplest radical form. Variables are positive.

86. $\sqrt{8}$

87. $\sqrt{32}-\sqrt{18}$

88. $\sqrt{27}+5\sqrt{12}$

89. $\sqrt{48}+5\sqrt{49}-3\sqrt{3}$

90. $\sqrt{125}+3\sqrt{45}-2\sqrt{20}$

91. $\dfrac{\sqrt{2}}{5+\sqrt{2}}$

92. $\dfrac{\sqrt{3}}{1-\sqrt{3}}$

93. $\sqrt[5]{\sqrt{\sqrt[3]{9}}}$

94. $\sqrt[3]{2x\sqrt{y}}$

95. $\sqrt{2c^{-1}+d^{-2}}$

96. $(\sqrt{x}+3)(\sqrt[3]{x}-7)$

97. $\dfrac{\sqrt{x}-\sqrt{y}}{\sqrt{x}+\sqrt{y}}$

98. $\sqrt[3]{128x^4y^{12}}$

99. $\sqrt[3]{a^4(bc^3)^{-1}}$

100. $\sqrt[4]{x^{-10}}+\sqrt[4]{x^{-18}}$

Expand and simplify the expressions in Exercises 101–110. Variables are positive.

101. $(a^{1/3}+b^{1/2})(a^{1/2}+b)$

102. $x^{1/2}(x^{1/2}-x^{-1/2})$

103. $(x^{1/2}-x^{-1/2})^{-1}$

104. $(x^{1/3}-x^{1/2})^3$

105. $(2x^{-1/2})^2$

106. $[(2x)^{-1/2}]^2$

107. $(a^{-1/3}-2b^{1/3})^2$

108. $(a^{1/3}+b^{1/6})^3$

109. $(ax^{1/2}+bx^{1/4}+c)^2$

110. $\dfrac{x^{-1}+y^{-1/2}}{y^{-1}+x^{-1/2}}$

111. A machine design problem involves the expression

$$3+\frac{5}{x+1}-\frac{x}{x^2-2x-3}$$

Write this expression as a single fraction.

112. In order to calculate the time required to clear a certain intersection of cars, a traffic engineer must simplify the expression

$$(t^{-1}+1)(t^{-1}-1)$$

Show that this expression is equivalent to $t^{-2}(1-t^2)$.

113. The force causing an object to accelerate is given by $F=m\cdot a$. Write the formula for force if $m=25-2t$ and $a=(25+23t-2t^2)^{-1}$.

114. In studying Fermat's principle in optics concerning the minimum time path, one meets the expression

$$t=c_1^{-1}(a^2+x^2)^{1/2}+c_2^{-1}[b^2+(d-x)^2]^{1/2}$$

where c_1 and c_2 are the velocities of light in two media. Compute t for $c_1=3\times10^8$, $c_2=2.9\times10^8$, $a=1$, $x=1.5$, $b=1$, and $d=2$.

Test 1 Chapter 1

Answer True or False to Exercises 1–10.

1. An exponent of -2 means to take the square root.

2. $(\sqrt{x+y})^2=x+y$ for real numbers x and y.

3. $(2^3)^2=2^{(3^2)}$

4. $(x+4)^3=x^3+4^3$

5. $\dfrac{x+y}{x}=1+\dfrac{y}{x}$

6. $\dfrac{x^2-y^2}{x^2+y^2}=\dfrac{1-\dfrac{x^2}{y^2}}{1+\dfrac{y^2}{x^2}}$

7. $a\div(b+c)=(a\div b)+(a\div c)$

8. $\sqrt{4}=\pm2$

9. $-4x^2=16x^2$

10. $\dfrac{x/y}{z}=\dfrac{x}{y/z}$

11. Eliminate negative exponents and simplify:

$$(x^{-1}+y^{-1})(x^{-1}-y^{-1})$$

12. Simplify

a. $\sqrt[3]{4x^2}\sqrt[3]{16x^4}$ b. $\dfrac{c}{c^{1/2} + d^{1/2}}$

13. Multiply $x^3 + x^2 - 5x + 2$ by $x^2 - 3x - 3$.

14. Factor

a. $r^2 - 9r + 14$ b. $8a^3 - 27b^3$

15. a. Write in scientific notation: 762,500.

b. Write without scientific notation:

4.23×10^{-5}

16. Simplify

a. $\dfrac{1 - \dfrac{6}{x} + \dfrac{5}{x^2}}{\dfrac{1}{x} - \dfrac{5}{x^2}}$

b. $\dfrac{2}{x^2 - 2x - 3} - \dfrac{5}{x^2 + 3x + 2} + \dfrac{4}{x^2 - x - 6}$

Test 2 Chapter 1

1. Express in scientific notation:

a. 5,375,000 b. 0.000139

2. Simplify

a. $\sqrt[3]{128x^4y^{12}}$ b. $x^{2/3}x^{-1/2}$

c. $a^{-2} + ab^{-2}$

3. Rationalize

a. $\dfrac{x + 5}{\sqrt{x - 3}}$ b. $\dfrac{\sqrt{2}}{\sqrt{2} - \sqrt{3}}$

c. $\dfrac{t}{\sqrt[3]{s + 2t}}$

4. Write $(x + 2y)(x^3 - 5y^2 + 2)$ in expanded form.

5. Write $x^2 - 6x + 9$ in factored form.

6. Write $6x^2 + 7x - 3$ in factored form.

Perform the indicated operations in Exercises 7–10, and write in simplest form.

7. $\dfrac{x^2 - 3x + 2}{3x - x^2} \div \dfrac{x^2 + 2x - 8}{x - 3}$

8. $\dfrac{2}{ab} + \dfrac{3}{ac^2} - \dfrac{5}{b^3c}$

9. $3 + \dfrac{5}{x + 1} - \dfrac{x}{x^2 - 2x - 3}$

10. $\dfrac{(xy)^{-2}}{x^{-2} - y^{-2}} + x^{-2}$

2

Equations and Inequalities

2.1 Linear Equations

In this chapter we introduce equations and inequalities. We begin by discussing some of the terminology used in the study of equations. Much of the same terminology is used for inequalities.

An **equation** is a statement that two expressions are equal. However, an equation might do more than state the equality; it often raises a question. For instance, the equation $x + 3 = 7$ states that the expressions $x + 3$ and 7 are equal, but it also prompts us to ask, "What number x must be added to 3 to equal 7?" Since $4 + 3 = 7$, we conclude that $x = 4$ makes the equation a true statement and we say that $x = 4$ *satisfies* the equation. In general, a **solution** or a **root** of an equation is any real number in the domain of the variable of the equation that makes the equation a true statement. The set of all solutions of an equation is called the **solution set.** For the equation $x + 3 = 7$, the solution set consists of the one element 4. The equation $x^2 = 4$ has both -2 and 2 in its solution set since $(-2)^2 = (2)^2 = 4$. "To solve the equation" means to find the solution set.

Equations such as $x + 3 = 7$ and $x^2 = 4$, which are true for some but not all of the permissible values of the variable, are called **conditional** equations.* If the statement is never true, the solution set of the equation is the empty set; that is, it contains no elements. For instance, $x^2 = -1$ is considered to be a conditional equation even though there is no real number that, when squared, is equal to -1. In some cases all permissible values of the variable make the statement true. Equations of this kind are called **identities.** The equation $x + 3x = 4x$ is an example of an identity.

An equation that can be arranged in the form

$$ax + b = 0$$

where a and b are constants and $a \neq 0$ is called a **linear** equation in the variable x. The solution set of the linear equation $ax + b = 0$ consists of one number, $-b/a$.

* The "permissible values" of the variable are real numbers unless otherwise stated. In Section 2.3 we will note how a different set of permissible values will allow a different solution set.

Two equations are said to be **equivalent** if they have exactly the same solution set. Thus, the equations $x + 3 = 7$ and $x + 2 = 6$ are equivalent since each has the one and only solution 4. The equations $x = 2$ and $x^2 = 4$ are *not* equivalent since the solution set for the first is 2 and for the second is 2, -2. The idea in solving an equation is to perform manipulations that change it into an equivalent equation in which the solution is more or less obvious. Usually, the aim is to isolate the variable on one side of the equation. After a series of steps, the solution becomes obvious.

We say that a manipulation is **allowable** if it transforms an equation into an equivalent one. Two allowable manipulations are

1. Adding the same quantity to or subtracting the same quantity from both sides of a conditional equation.
2. Multiplying or dividing both sides by any nonzero quantity.

EXAMPLE 1 Solve $3x + 12 = 48$.

Solution

$$3x + 12 = 48$$

$$3x = 36 \qquad \text{Subtracting 12 from both sides}$$

$$x = 12 \qquad \text{Dividing both sides by 3}$$

To check this value, let $x = 12$ in the original equation. We see that

$$3(12) + 12 = 48$$

is a true statement. The solution is $x = 12$. ■

EXAMPLE 2 Solve $2(x + 3) = 7x$.

Solution

$$2(x + 3) = 7x$$

$$2x + 6 = 7x \qquad \text{Expanding the left side}$$

$$6 = 5x \qquad \text{Subtracting } 2x \text{ from both sides}$$

$$x = \frac{6}{5} \qquad \text{Dividing both sides by 5}$$

Check by substituting into the original equation.

$$2\left(\frac{6}{5} + 3\right) = 7\left(\frac{6}{5}\right)$$

$$2\left(\frac{21}{5}\right) = \frac{42}{5}$$

This shows that $x = \frac{6}{5}$ is the solution. ■

Some equations in which the variable occurs in the denominator of one or more terms can be solved by the previous methods, after multiplying each term in the equation by the lowest common denominator to eliminate the fractions. If the resulting equation is linear (that is, of the form $ax + b = 0$), it can be solved accordingly.

Warning: **Any value of the variable that produces a zero denominator cannot be a solution.** Therefore, you must check all apparent solutions for validity.

EXAMPLE 3 Solve $\dfrac{1}{x} + \dfrac{3}{2x} = \dfrac{3}{x-5}$.

Solution Multiply each member of the equation by $2x(x - 5)$, the LCD of the fractional terms.

$$\frac{1}{x}\cdot 2x(x-5) + \frac{3}{2x}\cdot 2x(x-5) = \frac{3}{x-5}\cdot 2x(x-5)$$

$$\begin{aligned} 2(x-5) + 3(x-5) &= 3(2x) && \text{Cancellation law} \\ 2x - 10 + 3x - 15 &= 6x && \text{Expanding} \\ -x &= 25 && \text{Collecting like terms} \\ x &= -25 && \text{Multiplying by } -1 \end{aligned}$$

Check: Since none of the denominators is zero for $x = -25$, it is a valid solution. ■

EXAMPLE 4 Solve $\dfrac{2}{x+1} - \dfrac{4x}{(x+1)(x-1)} = \dfrac{3}{x-1}$.

Solution In this case, multiply each term by $(x + 1)(x - 1)$ to get

$$\begin{aligned} 2(x-1) - 4x &= 3(x+1) \\ 2x - 2 - 4x &= 3x + 3 && \text{Expanding} \\ -5x &= 5 && \text{Collecting like terms} \\ x &= -1 && \text{Dividing by } -5 \end{aligned}$$

Check: Observe that $x = -1$ makes the denominators of the first and second terms equal to zero. Therefore, $x = -1$ is not a permissible solution. The value $x = -1$ is called an **extraneous solution** since it appears to be a solution, but is not. Therefore, this equation has no solution. ■

We can also use the methods discussed here to solve equations that involve absolute values. Notice that the absolute-value expressions cause the equation to take on different forms.

EXAMPLE 5 Solve the equation $|x - 1| + 3x = 6$.

Solution Since

$$|x-1| = \begin{cases} x - 1, & \text{if } x \geq 1 \\ -(x-1), & \text{if } x < 1 \end{cases}$$

we must solve two equations; namely,

$$(x-1) + 3x = 6 \quad \text{and} \quad -(x-1) + 3x = 6$$

The first equation is valid for $x \geq 1$. Solving for x, we get

$$\begin{aligned} x - 1 + 3x &= 6 \\ x + 3x &= 7 && \text{Adding 1 to both sides} \\ 4x &= 7 && \text{Combining like terms} \\ x &= 7/4 && \text{Dividing by 4} \end{aligned}$$

Since $7/4 > 1$, it is in the domain of the equation and, hence, is a valid solution. The second equation is valid for $x < 1$. Solving for x, we get

$$-(x-1)+3x=6$$
$$-x+1+3x=6 \quad \text{Expanding}$$
$$-x+3x=5 \quad \text{Subtracting 1 from both sides}$$
$$2x=5 \quad \text{Collecting like terms}$$
$$x=5/2 \quad \text{Dividing by 2}$$

However, 5/2 is not a solution since it is not in the domain of the second equation. Consequently, the only solution is 7/4. ■

Exercises Section 2.1

In Exercises 1–25, find the solution set. Check for extraneous solutions when fractional expressions occur.

1. $2x+5=2$

2. $6x-1=-x-3$

3. $3(2x-1)-x=4-(x+3)$

4. $3(x-2)+7(2x+4)=-x-1$

5. $3x+5=4(x-2)$

6. $3y+7(4-y)=3(5-2y)$

7. $\frac{4a}{3}-5a+2=\frac{a}{2}-1$

8. $\frac{3x}{5}+4=\frac{x}{2}+5$

9. $\frac{2x+1}{3}+16=3x$

10. $\frac{x+1}{3}+\frac{x+2}{7}=5$

11. $\frac{2}{c}+\frac{3}{c}=10$

12. $\frac{4}{y}-3=\frac{5}{2y}$

13. $\frac{3x}{x+5}-4=0$

14. $\frac{4}{x+2}+4=0$

15. $\frac{3}{6y+2}=\frac{4}{7y+3}$

16. $\frac{2}{x+3}=\frac{5}{2x-1}$

17. $\frac{2}{x-2}-\frac{3}{x+5}=\frac{10}{(x-2)(x+5)}$

18. $\frac{1}{2x+3}+\frac{1}{x-1}=\frac{1}{(2x+3)(x-1)}$

19. $\frac{5}{5m-11}=\frac{3}{m-5}-\frac{4}{2m-3}$

20. $\frac{2}{x+3}+\frac{3}{x-4}=\frac{5}{x+6}$

21. $(x+7)(x-1)=(x+9)^2$

22. $(x-3)(x+4)=x^2-1$

23. $2x^2+1=(2x-1)(x+3)$

24. $3x(x-1)=(3x-7)(x+1)$

25. $x(x^2+3)=5+x^3$

26. Solve for x: $\frac{1}{x-a}+\frac{1}{x+a}=\frac{2}{x-1}$

27. Solve for x: $\frac{p+q}{x+1}=\frac{p-q}{x-1}$

Solve the equations in Exercises 28–37 by considering the different forms of the equation.

28. $|x|+x=3$

29. $|x|+2=-2$

30. $2x-|x|=-3$

31. $3x-1=|x|$

32. $|x+3|=5$

33. $|2x-3|=-1$

34. $|x-2|+x=3x-4$

35. $|x+5|-2x=1+x$

36. $|2x+7|-3(x+5)=0$

37. $|5x-1|+2=3(x+13)$

2.2 Formulas and Applications of Linear Equations

Frequently, formulas involving two or more variables must be solved explicitly for one of the variables in terms of the other variables in the formula. The procedure used to solve a formula for a specific variable is similar to the one we have used to solve equations; that is, we generate an equivalent formula when we add the same quantity to both sides or multiply both sides of the formula by the same quantity. The next two examples show this procedure.

EXAMPLE 1 The distance s traveled by a projectile in time t is given by

$$s = v_0 t + \tfrac{1}{2}gt^2$$

where v_0 is the initial velocity of the projectile and g is the acceleration due to the force of gravity. Solve this formula for v_0 in terms of the remaining variables.

Solution

$s = v_0 t + \tfrac{1}{2}gt^2$

$s - \tfrac{1}{2}gt^2 = v_0 t$ Adding $-\tfrac{1}{2}gt^2$ to both sides

$\dfrac{s - \tfrac{1}{2}gt^2}{t} = v_0$ Multiplying both sides by $1/t$

Writing v_0 on the left, we have

$$v_0 = \frac{s - \tfrac{1}{2}gt^2}{t}$$

■

EXAMPLE 2 The expression $S = \dfrac{a - rL}{1 - r}$ occurs in the study of geometric progressions. Solve for r.

Solution Multiplying both sides of the equation by $1 - r$, we get

$S(1 - r) = a - rL$

$S - Sr = a - rL$ Expanding the left side

$rL - Sr = a - S$ Isolating terms involving r

$r(L - S) = a - S$ Factoring

$r = \dfrac{a - S}{L - S}$ Dividing by $L - S$

■

In the remainder of this section we show how to formulate physical problems in terms of algebraic language, using symbols to represent unknown quantities. We let symbols, such as letters of the alphabet, stand for the unknowns and then try to express the desired relationship in terms of these symbols.

EXAMPLE 3

1. If we let w represent the width of a rectangle, l its length, and A its area, then the fact that "the area of the rectangle is the product of the length and the width" is written as $A = l \cdot w$.
2. If you have to pay 8% tax on the cost of a car, then by letting x represent the cost of the car, the tax you pay is written $.08x$.
3. The distance traveled in miles, d, is equal to the product of the speed in miles per hour, v, and the time in hours, t. Symbolically, we have $d = vt$.
4. The sum of two numbers is 12. If x is one of the numbers, $12 - x$ is the other.
5. By letting x be the units digit of a number and y the tens digit, we can write the value of the number as $10y + x$.
6. If x represents a number, then $x + 4$ represents the number that is 4 greater than x; $5x$ represents the number 5 times x; and $5x + 4$ represents the number 4 greater than 5 times x.
7. If it takes t hr to do a job, then $1/t$ is the fraction of the job that can be done in 1 hr.

■

Example 3 shows how algebraic language can be used to represent an English expression in an abstract, symbolic form, which can be studied independently of the sentence itself. In the abstract setting, seemingly dissimilar problems often turn out to be mathematically identical.

There are no set "rules" to follow in setting up equations, but the following guidelines give you a systematic approach.

1. **Read the problem.** Read the given problem carefully to determine precisely what is known and what you are trying to find. If at all possible, draw a picture of the problem. Drawing a picture frequently helps you to get a clear idea of the situation.
2. **Identify the variable and constant quantities.** Assign letters to the quantities that you want to find, thereby denoting them as variables. In each problem your solution should begin with "Let $x =$" or "Let $n =$."
3. **Form an equation.** The problem itself should tell you how the variables are related. Use the given data to establish an equation involving the unknown variables.* You will need to know certain elementary relations such as those mentioned in Example 3.
4. **Solve the equation.** Solving the equation is a mathematical process independent of the physical conditions of the given problem.
5. **Check your solution.** Solutions should always be checked to be sure that the answer is at least feasible. For instance, -2 would not be a realistic answer for one dimension of a rectangle.

EXAMPLE 4 A student pays \$278 for a calculator and a typewriter. If the calculator costs \$64 less than the typewriter, how much does each cost?

Solution Here we let $x =$ the cost of the typewriter. Then $x - 64 =$ the cost of the calculator. Since the total cost of the two items is \$278, we have

[Cost of the typewriter] + [Cost of the calculator] = [Total cost]

Substituting the variable expressions for the cost of the typewriter and the cost of the calculator, the desired equation is

$$x + (x - 64) = 278$$

$$2x = 278 + 64 \qquad \text{Collecting like terms}$$

$$x = \frac{342}{2} = 171 \qquad \text{Dividing both sides by 2}$$

Hence, the typewriter costs \$171 and the calculator costs \$107. ■

EXAMPLE 5 A plane leaves New York City for Los Angeles at 10:00 P.M. cruising at 400 mph. A second plane leaves New York at 11:30 P.M. for the same destination cruising at 550 mph. (See Figure 2.1.) How long will it take the second plane to overtake the first?

* An equation that represents a set of physical conditions is sometimes called a **mathematical model** of those conditions.

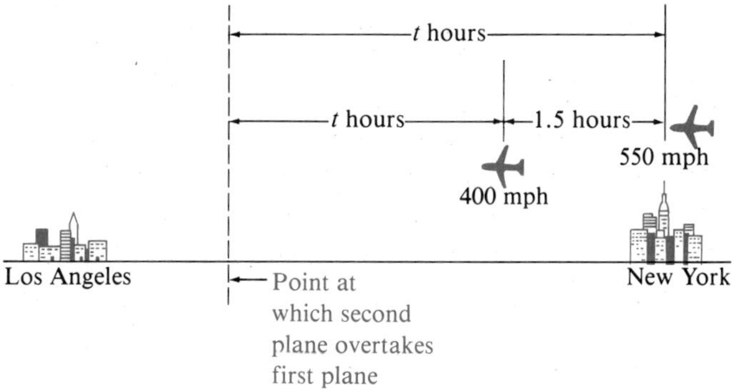

Figure 2.1

Solution Let t equal the time required for the second plane to overtake the first. At the time of rendezvous, the first plane will have been in the air $t + 1.5$ hr (from 10:00 P.M. to 11:30 P.M.). Using the formula $d = vt$ (Example 3), we write

$$400(t + 1.5) = \text{distance traveled by first plane}$$
$$550t = \text{distance traveled by second plane}$$

Since the distance traveled by each plane is equal when the second plane overtakes the first, we have

Distance traveled by first plane	=	Distance traveled by second plane

Consequently, the equation is

$$400(t + 1.5) = 550t$$
$$150t = 600 \qquad \text{Collecting like terms}$$
$$t = 4 \text{ hr} \qquad \text{Dividing by 150}$$

It takes 4 hr for the second plane to overtake the first. ■

EXAMPLE 6 A man has two types of solder. One is 55% tin and the other is 15% tin. How much of each must he mix to yield 75 lb of solder containing 40% tin?

Solution Let n be the number of pounds of solder with 55% tin in the final mixture. Since the final mixture is to weigh 75 lb, then $75 - n$ is the number of pounds of solder with 15% tin. The amount of tin in the two types of solder is then $0.55n$ and $0.15(75 - n)$. The total amount of tin in the 40% mixture is $0.40(75)$. Hence,

Amount of tin from 55% mix	+	Amount of tin from 15% mix	=	Amount of tin in 40% mix

$$0.55n + 0.15(75 - n) = 0.40(75)$$
$$0.55n + 11.25 - 0.15n = 30.00 \qquad \text{Expanding}$$

$$0.40n = 18.75 \qquad \text{Collecting like terms}$$
$$n = 46.9 \text{ lb of solder with } 55\% \text{ tin}$$
$$75 - n = 75 - 46.9 = 28.1 \text{ lb of solder with } 15\% \text{ tin}$$

Note the implicit physical limitations on this solution. For example, if the man had only 40 lb of the solder with the 55% tin available, then there would be no solution. ■

The following example shows two typical methods of "marking up" the price of an item in determining the retail price to the consumer.

EXAMPLE 7 A pair of shoes costs a retailer \$22. Determine the retail price if the markup is
a. 40% of the wholesale price
b. 40% of the retail price

Solution In both cases, let x be the retail price.
a. Here x is just the sum of the wholesale price and 40% of that price. That is,

$$x = 22 + 0.4(22) = \$30.80$$

b. In this case the markup is $0.4x$. Thus,

$$x = 22 + 0.4x$$

from which

$$0.6x = 22$$
$$x = \$36.67$$
■

EXAMPLE 8 Fresh water is added to seawater to reduce the salt content to make it usable for irrigation. What percentage of seawater (3.8% salt) and fresh water (0.5% salt) should be combined to get irrigation water of 1% salt?

Solution Consider a 100-gal mixture. Let $x =$ the number of gallons of seawater in the mixture. Thus $100 - x$ is the number of gallons of fresh water. The amount of salt contributed from the seawater is $0.038x$, and from the fresh water is $0.005(100 - x)$. The total amount of salt in the mixture is $0.01(100)$. Hence,

Amount of salt from seawater	+	Amount of salt from fresh water	=	Amount of salt in irrigation water

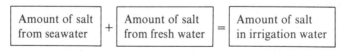

Substituting the appropriate algebraic expressions yields

$$0.038x + 0.005(100 - x) = 0.01(100)$$
$$38x + 5(100 - x) = 10(100) \qquad \text{Multiplying by 1000 to clear the decimals}$$
$$38x + 500 - 5x = 1000 \qquad \text{Expanding}$$
$$33x = 500 \qquad \text{Collecting like terms}$$
$$x = 15.15 \text{ gal} \qquad \text{Dividing by 33}$$

Hence, there should be about 15% seawater and 85% fresh water in the mixture. ■

EXAMPLE 9 An engineer needs to fill a filtration pool in 8 hr. She knows that the built-in water line will take 12 hr to fill the pool. What should be the minimum rate of an auxiliary hose, in "hours to fill a pool," to fill the pool on time if both the main line and the auxiliary hose are used?

Solution Let x = minimum rate of the auxiliary hose. Then

$$\frac{1}{12} = \text{part of the pool filled by main line in 1 hr}$$

$$\frac{1}{x} = \text{part of the pool filled by auxiliary hose in 1 hr}$$

$$\frac{1}{8} = \text{part of the pool that must be filled in 1 hr by both hoses}$$

Since the part of the pool that can be filled in 1 hr is the sum of the capacities of the main and auxiliary lines, we have

Amount filled by main line in 1 hr	+	Amount filled by auxiliary hose in 1 hr	=	Amount filled by both in 1 hr

$$\frac{1}{12} + \frac{1}{x} = \frac{1}{8}$$

$2x + 24 = 3x$ Multiplying by $24x$ to eliminate denominators

$x = 24$ Collecting like terms

Hence, the auxiliary hose must be able to fill the pool (when operating alone) in 24 hr. ■

Exercises Section 2.2

Express the sentences or phrases in Exercises 1–20 in algebraic symbols.

1. The area of a triangle is equal to one half the product of the base times the height.
2. The area of a circle is equal to the product of π times the square of the radius.
3. The perimeter of a square is four times the side length.
4. The perimeter of a triangle is the sum of the length of the sides.
5. Acceleration of an object is equal to its velocity divided by the time.
6. Voltage across a resistive circuit is equal to the current in the circuit times the resistance of the circuit.
7. A number that is 8 less than another number.
8. A number three times the square of another number.
9. A number five times the sum of another number plus 3.
10. A number 3 more than five times another number.
11. Twenty percent of the amount by which a number exceeds 12,000.
12. The sum of two numbers divided by 2.
13. The average of three numbers.
14. The portion of a job done in one day if it takes x days to do the entire job.
15. Interest paid in one year equals principal times interest rate.
16. The product of the sum and difference of two numbers.
17. Twice the sum of two numbers.

18. The area of a triangle whose base is twice the height.

19. The surface area of a cube.

20. The volume of a rectangular box.

21. The expression for linear velocity v has the form $v = at + b$. Solve for t.

22. The simple interest formula is given by $A = P(1 + i \cdot n)$. Solve for n.

23. The area of a trapezoid with bases a and b and height h is given by the formula $A = \frac{1}{2}h(a + b)$. Solve for b.

24. The velocity of an object may be written $v^2 = v_0^2 + 2as$, where a is the acceleration and s is the displacement. Solve for a.

25. The length of a metal rod whose temperature changes from T_0 to T_1 is given by

$$L = L_0[1 + \alpha(T_1 - T_0)]$$

Solve for T_1.

26. The equivalent resistance of a certain electric circuit is given by

$$R = \frac{r}{1 + r}$$

Solve for r.

27. A formula from the mechanics of gears is

$$D = \frac{nd}{n + 2}$$

Solve for n.

28. The expression $l = a + (n - 1)d$ appears in the discussion of arithmetic progressions. Solve for d.

29. The formula

$$\frac{1}{R} = \frac{1}{R_1} + \frac{1}{R_2}$$

occurs in electric circuit analysis. Solve for R.

30. Degrees Fahrenheit (F) and degrees Celsius (C) are related by the formula $F = \frac{9}{5}C + 32$. Solve for C.

31. Two wires in parallel carry a total current of 20 amperes (A). What is the current in each wire if one wire carries 2 A more than the other?

32. Two gears together weigh 17 lb. If one gear weighs 3 lb more than the other, what is the weight of each?

33. Find three consecutive even integers whose sum is 312.

34. The total monetary value of 73 nickels and dimes is \$5.75. How many nickels are there?

35. A jogger who can run a 7-min mile starts one-tenth mile ahead of a jogger who can run a 6-min mile. How far does the faster jogger have to run to catch the slower jogger?

36. The average of the salaries of Jane, Jim, and Nancy is \$15,000 per year. If Jane earns \$3000 more than Nancy, and Jim earns one half as much as Jane, how much does each earn?

37. A car that averages 22 mi/gal of gasoline for city driving and 28 mi/gal for highway driving uses 20 gal of gasoline in 500 mi of driving. How much of the driving was in the city?

38. A woman wishes to winterize her car and finds that her 10-qt radiator is 30% antifreeze. How much of the fluid should she drain and replace by pure antifreeze to double the strength of the mixture?

39. The wholesale price of a bicycle is \$100. What should the retail price be for each of the two methods of markup described in Example 7? Assume a markup of 75%.

40. A camera costs a wholesaler \$150. The wholesaler marks up the price by 20% of the wholesale price, and the retailer's markup is 25% of the retail selling price. What is the retail selling price?

41. An airplane flew with the wind for 1 hr and returned the same distance against the wind in 2 hr. If the cruising (air) speed of the plane is 400 mph, find the velocity of the wind.

42. In driving, suppose that you average 70 mph outside the city limits and 30 mph within the city limits. If you take 5 hr to make a 270-mi trip, how much of the time did you spend inside and outside the limits of cities?

43. The distance around the Indianapolis speedway track is 2.5 mi. If one driver averages 170 mph and another averages 165 mph, in how much time will the first driver "lap" the second?

44. If you and a man can build in 20 days a house that he would take 30 days to build alone, how long would it take you alone to build the house, assuming you know how?

45. In football a team scored 44 points by scoring equal numbers of touchdowns (6 points), extra points (1 point), and field goals (3 points) and half as many safeties (2 points). How many of each scoring play did the team make?

46. An oil tanker is being filled by two pipelines that can separately fill it in 12 hr and 16 hr, respectively. How long will it take to fill the tanker?

47. A girl weighing 100 lb sits on one end of a 20-ft teeterboard and a boy weighing 150 lb sits on the other. Where must the fulcrum be placed for the two to be balanced?

48. A man has a 20-lb mixture that is one-quarter cement and three-quarters sand. How much of a mixture that is one-half cement and one-half sand must be added to the 20-lb mixture to produce a mixture that is one-third cement?

49. A car leaves Cincinnati for Toledo at 55 mph. Thirty minutes later a truck leaves Toledo for Cincinnati at 45 mph. If the two cities are 206 mi apart, how many hours must the truck travel before it meets the car? Assume that both vehicles are using Interstate 75.

50. Jane can overhaul an engine in 20 hr and Fred can do the same job in 30 hr. If they both work together for a time and then Jane finishes the job by herself in 5 hr, how many hours did they work together?

2.3 Quadratic Equations

Suppose we wish to construct a rectangle that has an area of 36 sq in. and whose length is 5 in. greater than its width. We can write these conditions in equation form by letting x equal the width of the rectangle. The length is then given by $x + 5$. (See Figure 2.2.) Since the area of a rectangle is equal to the length times the width, we write

$$x(x + 5) = 36$$

Expanding the left-hand side gives

$$x^2 + 5x = 36$$

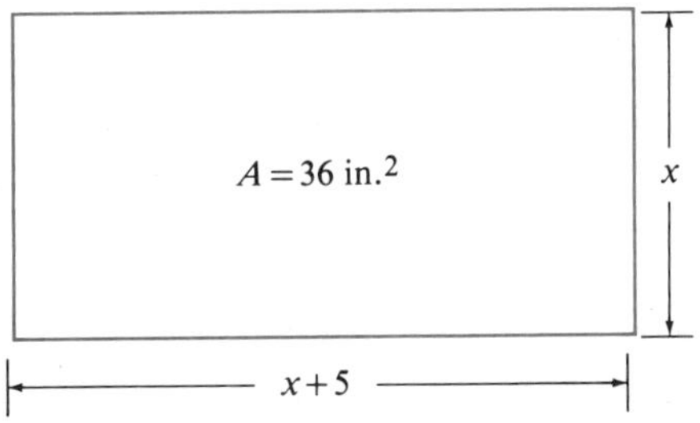

Figure 2.2

This equation, which is not a linear equation because of the x^2 term, is typical of a whole class of equations called quadratic equations.

Equations that can be put into the form

$$\boldsymbol{ax^2 + bx + c = 0}$$

where a, b, and c are constants and $a \neq 0$, are **quadratic equations.** These equations must contain a square term and may (depending upon the values of b and c) contain a linear term and a constant term. Each of the following equations is a quadratic equation.

$$3t^2 - 5t - 9 = 0$$

$$t^2 = t + 2$$

$$x^2 + 3x = 0$$

$$3u^2 - 7 = 0$$

$$(y + 2)(y - 1) = 0$$

The last of these equations is quadratic since $(y + 2)(y - 1) = y^2 + y - 2$.

There are two basic approaches to finding the solution set of a quadratic equation:

a. Factoring the quadratic expression.
b. Completing the square, which generalizes to a formula in which the roots, or solutions, of the equation are given in terms of the coefficients a, b, and c. This formula is known as the **quadratic formula.**

Solution by Factoring

If a quadratic equation can be factored into a product of linear factors, it is said to be a **factorable** equation. The roots of a factorable equation can be found by taking advantage of the following fundamental property of real numbers.

If u and v are any two real numbe and

$$u \cdot v = 0$$

then $u = 0$ or $v = 0$.

Thus, the roots of a factorable equation can be found by setting each factor equal to zero and solving the resulting linear equation. The procedure is summarized as follows:

1. Arrange the given equation in the form $ax^2 + bx + c = 0$.
2. Factor the quadratic expression into linear factors.
3. Determine the value of x for which each factor will equal zero. These are the roots of the equation.

EXAMPLE 1 Solve the quadratic equation $x^2 + 5x = 36$.

Solution First, we write the equation in the form

$$x^2 + 5x - 36 = 0$$

This quadratic expression factors into $(x + 9)(x - 4)$, so

$$(x + 9)(x - 4) = 0$$

Since $x = -9$ will make the first factor equal zero and $x = 4$ will make the second factor zero, we conclude that the roots are -9 and 4. ■

EXAMPLE 2 Solve the equation $t^2 = 3t$.

Solution When we subtract $3t$ from both sides, the given equation becomes

$$t^2 - 3t = 0$$

Or, factoring t out of each term, we get

$$t(t - 3) = 0$$

Since the first factor is zero for $t = 0$, and the second is zero for $t = 3$, the roots are 0 and 3. ■

EXAMPLE 3 Solve the equation $3m^2 + 14m - 5 = 0$.

Solution Factoring, we get

$$(3m - 1)(m + 5) = 0$$

The factor $3m - 1$ will equal zero for $m = \frac{1}{3}$ and the factor $m + 5$ will equal zero for $m = -5$. Hence, the roots of the equation are $\frac{1}{3}$ and -5. ■

Solution by the Quadratic Formula

The roots of $3x^2 + 9x + 4 = 0$ are difficult to obtain by factoring. To find the roots of equations like this, we use the quadratic formula, which is obtained from the general equation $ax^2 + bx + c = 0$ by applying the method of completing the square.*

To complete the square on $ax^2 + bx + c = 0$, we first subtract c from both sides of the equation and then divide by a,

$$x^2 + \frac{b}{a}x = -\frac{c}{a}$$

Completing the square on the left-hand side by adding $(b/2a)^2$ to both sides yields

$$x^2 + \frac{b}{a}x + \frac{b^2}{4a^2} = -\frac{c}{a} + \frac{b^2}{4a^2}$$

Factoring the expression on the left side and adding the fractions on the right side, we get

$$\left(x + \frac{b}{2a}\right)^2 = \frac{b^2 - 4ac}{4a^2}$$

Taking the square root of both sides yields

$$x + \frac{b}{2a} = \pm\sqrt{\frac{b^2 - 4ac}{4a^2}} = \pm\frac{\sqrt{b^2 - 4ac}}{2a}$$

Subtracting $\frac{b}{2a}$ from both sides, we get

$$x = \frac{-b}{2a} \pm \frac{\sqrt{b^2 - 4ac}}{2a}$$

Combining the terms on the right yields the desired formula.

The Quadratic Formula

The roots of the quadratic equation $ax^2 + bx + c = 0$ are given by

$$x = \frac{-b \pm \sqrt{b^2 - 4ac}}{2a} \qquad (2.1)$$

* The method of completing the square was discussed in Section 1.5.

To use Formula 2.1, match the coefficient of x^2 with a, the coefficient of x with b, and the constant term with c in the standard form of the quadratic equation, $ax^2 + bx + c = 0$. From Formula 2.1 we can see that $ax^2 + bx + c = 0$ has two roots:

$$x = \frac{-b + \sqrt{b^2 - 4ac}}{2a} \quad \text{and} \quad x = \frac{-b - \sqrt{b^2 - 4ac}}{2a}$$

Warning: When using the quadratic formula do not forget to include the sign of each coefficient. For instance, if $3x^2 - 2x + 5 = 0$, then $a = 3$, $b = -2$, and $c = 5$.

EXAMPLE 4 Use the quadratic formula to solve $3x^2 = 2x + 5$.

Solution To use the quadratic formula, write the given equation in the form $ax^2 + bx + c = 0$. Subtracting $2x + 5$ from both sides of the given equation, we get

$$3x^2 - 2x - 5 = 0$$

From this you can see that $a = 3$, $b = -2$, and $c = -5$. Substituting these values in the quadratic formula, we have

$$\begin{aligned} x &= \frac{-(-2) \pm \sqrt{(-2)^2 - 4(3)(-5)}}{2(3)} \\ &= \frac{2 \pm \sqrt{4 + 60}}{6} = \frac{2 \pm \sqrt{64}}{6} \\ &= \frac{2 \pm 8}{6} \end{aligned}$$

Therefore, the equation $3x^2 - 2x - 5 = 0$ has the roots

$$x = \frac{2 + 8}{6} = \frac{10}{6} = \frac{5}{3} \quad \text{and} \quad x = \frac{2 - 8}{6} = \frac{-6}{6} = -1$$

■

With a calculator, the same effort is involved in solving a quadratic equation with integer coefficients or "messy" irrational coefficients. Begin by computing the quantity $b^2 - 4ac$ inside the radical. Solve a few equations using the quadratic formula and a calculator. Notice any peculiarities of your particular calculator. For example, what kind of error message do you get if $b^2 - 4ac$ is negative?

EXAMPLE 5 Solve the quadratic equation $\sqrt{2}x^2 - 3x - \pi = 0$.

Solution Using the quadratic formula with $a = \sqrt{2}$, $b = -3$, and $c = -\pi$, we have

$$x = \frac{-(-3) \pm \sqrt{(-3)^2 - 4(\sqrt{2})(-\pi)}}{2\sqrt{2}}$$

Using a calculator to approximate these values, we get

$$x = 2.89 \quad \text{and} \quad -0.769$$

■

EXAMPLE 6 Solve the quadratic equation $x^2 + 2x + 3 = 0$.

Solution In this case $a = 1, b = 2$, and $c = 3$. Thus,

$$x = \frac{-2 \pm \sqrt{4 - 12}}{2} = \frac{-2 \pm \sqrt{-8}}{2}$$

Since the quantity inside the radical is negative, the radical does not represent a real number; so we conclude that there are no real roots. ■

Complex Roots

The preceding example shows that quadratic equations do not always have real roots. Another example is $x^2 + 4 = 0$, where it is clear that there is no real number whose square is -4. To represent solutions to equations that do not have real roots, we are naturally led to the **imaginary number** i, with the property that $i^2 = -1$. To avoid ambiguity, the number i is defined by

$$i = \sqrt{-1}$$

Any number of the form bi, where b is a real number, is called an imaginary number. Since $-4 = 4i^2 = (2i)^2$, the nonreal roots to the quadratic equation $x^2 + 4 = 0$ may be written as $x = \pm 2i$.

To consider nonreal solutions to more general equations, we extend the concept of imaginary numbers. Adding a real number to an imaginary number gives a number called a **complex number.** Complex numbers are numbers of the form $a + bi$, where a and b are real numbers.

EXAMPLE 7 a. Imaginary numbers: $2i, 7i, \pi i, \sqrt{3}i$

b. Complex numbers: $2 + 3i, -1 + i, 5 - 8i$ ■

Complex numbers differing only in the sign of their imaginary part are said to be **conjugate pairs.** Thus, $2 + 5i$ and $2 - 5i$ are a conjugate pair. The general form of conjugate pairs is $a \pm bi$.

Except for our immediate use of complex numbers to represent nonreal roots of a quadratic equation,* we defer the discussion of the algebra of complex numbers until Chapter 7. At this point we need to know only that complex numbers are manipulated like real numbers, with the understanding that $i^2 = -1$.

EXAMPLE 8 Solve the quadratic equation $m^2 + 2m + 2 = 0$.

Solution Using the quadratic formula with $a = 1, b = 2$, and $c = 2$, we have

$$m = \frac{-2 \pm \sqrt{2^2 - 4(1)(2)}}{2(1)} = \frac{-2 \pm \sqrt{-4}}{2} = \frac{-2 \pm 2i}{2} = -1 \pm i$$

This is typical of nonreal roots of quadratic equations with real coefficients; that is, **complex roots occur in conjugate pairs.** ■

* We note that such a representation of nonreal roots has effectively enlarged the permissible values of the variable to include the set of complex numbers. However, aside from representing nonreal roots of a quadratic, we will continue to restrict the permissible values to the real numbers.

The Discriminant

The previous examples show that the nature of the roots of a quadratic equation depends on the expression $b^2 - 4ac$ inside the radical.

The **discriminant** D of the quadratic equation $ax^2 + bx + c = 0$ is given by

$$D = b^2 - 4ac$$

Using this notation, we may express the roots of the quadratic in the form

$$x = \frac{-b \pm \sqrt{D}}{2a}$$

If the coefficients of the quadratic are real, we can use the discriminant to determine the nature of the roots.

- If $D > 0$, there are two distinct real roots of the form $(-b \pm \sqrt{D})/2a$.
- If $D = 0$, there is one root of the form $-b/2a$. (*Note:* We sometimes say there are two equal real roots, or a **double** root.)
- If $D < 0$, there are two complex roots of the form $(-b \pm i\sqrt{|D|})/2a$.

EXAMPLE 9 Determine k so that $kx^2 + 3kx + 2k + 1 = 0$ has equal roots.

Solution In this case $a = k$, $b = 3k$, and $c = 2k + 1$. Since for equal roots the discriminant must be 0,

$$b^2 - 4ac = (3k)^2 - 4k(2k + 1) = 0$$

Simplifying gives

$$9k^2 - 8k^2 - 4k = 0$$
$$k(k - 4) = 0$$

Hence, $k = 4$. Why is $k = 0$ not a valid solution? ■

The two roots to a quadratic equation may be written separately as

$$x_1 = \frac{-b + \sqrt{b^2 - 4ac}}{2a} \qquad x_2 = \frac{-b - \sqrt{b^2 - 4ac}}{2a}$$

From this it is easy to show that

$$x_1 + x_2 = -b/a$$

and that

$$x_1 x_2 = c/a$$

That is, the sum and the product of the roots of a quadratic equation can be expressed in terms of the coefficients a, b, and c.

For example, consider the equation $2x^2 + 3x - 1 = 0$. Without actually finding the roots, we know that their sum is $-b/a = -3/2$ and that their product is $c/a = -1/2$. Since the roots can be found directly from the quadratic formula to be $(-3 \pm \sqrt{17})/4$, this conclusion may be verified directly.

Using the sum and product of roots formulas, the coefficients can be found *after* specifying the roots.

EXAMPLE 10 Determine the values of b and c so that $2x^2 + bx + c = 0$ has roots of 5 and -4.

Solution Here we have $x_1 = 5$, $x_2 = -4$, and $a = 2$. Therefore,

$$x_1 + x_2 = 5 - 4 = \frac{-b}{2} \quad \text{or} \quad b = -2$$

Likewise,

$$x_1 \cdot x_2 = 5(-4) = \frac{c}{2} \quad \text{or} \quad c = -40$$

■

Exercises Section 2.3

Solve the equations in Exercises 1–18 by factoring.

1. $x^2 - 2x = 0$
2. $3x^2 + 5x = 0$
3. $x^2 - x - 2 = 0$
4. $x^2 - x = 12$
5. $x^2 = x + 6$
6. $x^2 + 7x + 12 = 0$
7. $z^2 + 3z - 10 = 0$
8. $x^2 + 10x = 0$
9. $2x^2 + 5x - 12 = 0$
10. $2x^2 = x + 6$
11. $3w^2 - 5w - 2 = 0$
12. $4x^2 + 2 = 9x$
13. $10v^2 - 2v = 0$
14. $6x^2 - x - 12 = 0$
15. $-t^2 + 3t + 10 = 0$
16. $6y^2 + 7y = 3$
17. $35x^2 + 2x - 24 = 0$
18. $60y^2 + y - 10 = 0$

Solve Exercises 19–39 by using the quadratic formula. Express all nonreal roots in the form $a + bi$.

19. $3x^2 + 4x - 4 = 0$
20. $2x^2 + 4x - 5 = 0$
21. $5x^2 + 2x - 3 = 0$
22. $8x^2 + 3x - 5 = 0$
23. $2x^2 - x - 2 = 0$
24. $3x^2 + x + 9 = 0$
25. $x(2x - 1) = 4$
26. $x(x + 1) = 3$
27. $x^2 - 5x + 5 = 0$
28. $12x^2 + x - 1 = 0$
29. $5x^2 + 12x + 6 = 0$
30. $2x^2 - x + 5 = 0$
31. $3x^2 - 2x + 2 = 0$
32. $6x(x - 1) + 1 = 0$
33. $2x^2 - 2x + 5 = 0$
34. $\sqrt{3}x^2 - 2x - \pi = 0$
35. $3x^2 - \pi x + 2 = 0$
36. $2x^2 + 4x - \sqrt{5} = 0$
37. $\sqrt{6}x(x + 1) = 2.7$
38. $0.4x^2 - 1.3x + 2.3 = 0$
39. $1.1x^2 - 0.2x + 0.8 = 0$

Determine the value of k for which the roots of the equations in Exercises 40–49 satisfy the indicated condition.

40. $x^2 + 2x + k = 0$; the product of the roots is -1.
41. $kx^2 - 3x + 1 = 0$; the sum of the roots is π.
42. $2x^2 - kx + 7 = 0$; the sum of the roots is 10.
43. $kx^2 + x + 8 = 0$; both roots are real.
44. $x^2 + 4x + k = 0$; both roots are nonreal.
45. $x^2 - kx - 5 = 0$; give two values of k for which the roots are rational.
46. $x^2 + x - (k + 3) = 0$; one of the roots is zero.
47. $x^2 - kx + k - 1 = 0$; the two roots are equal.
48. $2x^2 + x = -k$; one root is the reciprocal of the other.
49. $kx^2 - 2kx + 5 = 0$; one root exceeds the other by 3.
50. Show that the sum of the two roots of a quadratic equation is $-b/a$.
51. Show that the product of the two roots of a quadratic equation is c/a.

2.4 Applied Problems That Lead to Quadratic Equations

Quadratic equations arise in applied problems.

EXAMPLE 1 Find the dimensions of a rectangle whose area is 36 cm^2 and whose length exceeds its width by 5 cm.

Solution Let x equal the length of the rectangle; then $x - 5$ is its width. The area of a rectangle is the product of its length and its width, so

$$x(x - 5) = 36$$

or

$$x^2 - 5x - 36 = 0$$
$$(x - 9)(x + 4) = 0$$

Therefore, the two roots are $x = 9$ and $x = -4$. Obviously, only $x = 9$ has meaning since a negative length is impossible. The width of the rectangle is $9 - 5$, or 4, and the desired dimensions are 9 by 4. ■

EXAMPLE 2 The height, h, in feet, of a projectile t sec after it is fired from a gun is given by

$$h = kt - \frac{1}{2}gt^2$$

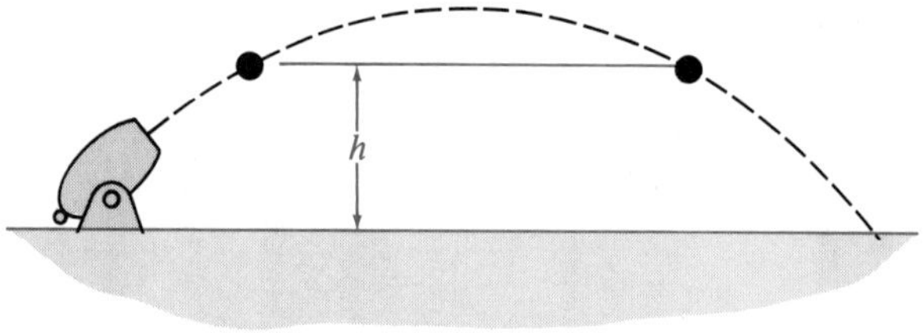

where g is the constant acceleration of gravity and k is a constant that depends upon the angle of elevation of the gun and the initial velocity of the projectile. Assuming that $k = 100$ and $g = 32$, when is the projectile at a height of 50 ft ($h = 50$)?

Solution Substituting these values into the equation, we have

$$50 = 100t - \frac{1}{2}(32)t^2 \quad \text{or} \quad -16t^2 + 100t - 50 = 0$$

Since this is a quadratic equation in the variable t, use the quadratic formula to write

$$t = \frac{-100 \pm \sqrt{100^2 - 4(-16)(-50)}}{2(-16)}$$
$$= \frac{-100 \pm \sqrt{6800}}{-32}$$
$$= \frac{-100 \pm 82.5}{-32}$$
$$= \frac{-17.5}{-32} \quad \text{and} \quad \frac{-182.5}{-32}$$
$$= 0.55 \quad \text{and} \quad 5.7 \text{ sec}$$

(These two times correspond to the projectile going up and then coming down.) ■

EXAMPLE 3 A physics student finds that the power, p, in watts, that is being consumed by an electrical circuit varies with elapsed time, t, in seconds, according to the equation

$$p = 8t + 2t^2$$

How long will it take the power consumption to reach 42 w (watts)?

Solution Letting $p = 42$ in the given equation, we get

$$42 = 8t + 2t^2$$

$$2t^2 + 8t - 42 = 0 \quad \text{Subtracting 42 from both sides}$$

$$t^2 + 4t - 21 = 0 \quad \text{Dividing both sides by 2}$$

$$(t + 7)(t - 3) = 0 \quad \text{Factoring}$$

The roots are then $t = -7$ and $t = 3$. Since a negative time does not make sense in the problem, we conclude that the power will equal 42 w when $t = 3$ sec. ■

EXAMPLE 4 Working together, Jack and Jim can complete a job in six days. Working alone, Jack can do it in five days less than the time required by Jim. In how much time does each do the job alone?

Solution The desired equation has the form

[Work done by Jack in 1 day] + [Work done by Jim in 1 day] = [Work done by both in 1 day]

Let x be the time in days required by Jack to complete the job. Then Jim takes $x + 5$ days. The fraction of the job done by Jack in one day is $1/x$; the fraction of the job done by Jim in one day is $1/(x + 5)$. Since the work done by both in one day is $1/6$, we have

$$\frac{1}{x} + \frac{1}{x+5} = \frac{1}{6}$$

$$6(x + 5) + 6x = x(x + 5) \quad \text{Multiplying both sides of the equation by } 6x(x+5)$$

$$6x + 30 + 6x = x^2 + 5x \quad \text{Expanding}$$

$$x^2 - 7x - 30 = 0 \quad \text{Collecting like terms}$$

$$(x - 10)(x + 3) = 0 \quad \text{Factoring}$$

$$x = 10, -3 \quad \text{Solving for } x$$

The root $x = -3$ obviously has no meaning in the context of this problem. Hence, Jack could do the job in 10 days and Jim in 15 days. ■

Exercises Section 2.4

1. In analyzing the motion of a certain spring-mass-damper system, the equation $d^2 + 6d + 7 = 0$ must be solved. What values of d satisfy the equation?

2. The equation $R^2 - 3R + 1 = 0$ arises in calculating the equivalent resistance of two electric circuits. What values of R satisfy this equation?

3. The bending moment of a certain simple beam is given by $M = 20x - x^2$, where x is the distance in feet from one end. For what values of x is $M = 60$?

4. The specific heat of a substance varies with temperature in accordance to $c = 5.1T^2 + 0.3T$. For what values of T is $c = 6.0$?

5. The ionization constant of an acid is $K = x^2/[5(1 - x)]$. For what value of x is $K = 3$?

6. The amount of propellant remaining in a certain rocket decreases with time according to $w = 20 - t - t^2$ lb where t is measured in seconds. How long after ignition will the amount of propellant remaining equal 8 lb?

7. A biologist finds that the number of water mites in a sample of river water depends upon the temperature in degrees Fahrenheit. If $N = 100T - T^2$ describes this relation, at what temperature is $N = 1100$?

8. The surface area of a right circular cylinder is given by $A = 2\pi r^2 + 2\pi rh$, where r is the radius and h is the height. Find the radius of the cylinder in the following figure if the cylinder has a surface area of 50 in.^{2} and a height of 4 in.

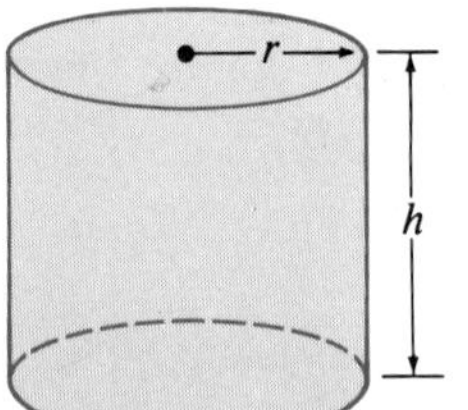

9. If the area of the L-shaped field shown in the accompanying figure is 10 km^2, what is the dimension x?

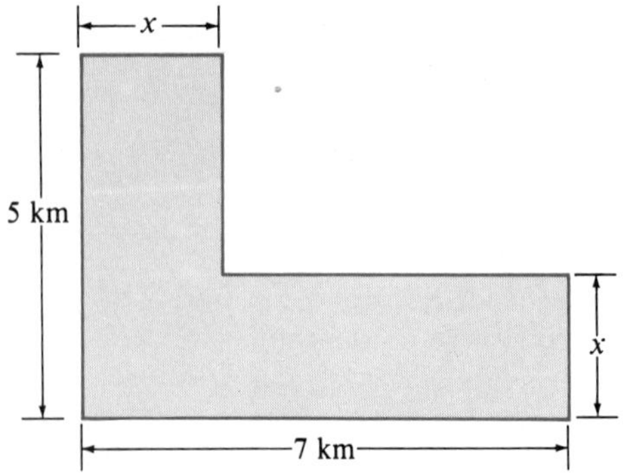

10. The area of a triangle is 14 ft^2. Find the base and altitude of the triangle if the altitude exceeds the base by 3 ft.

11. The hypotenuse of a right triangle is 13 m long. Find the lengths of the sides of the triangle in the following figure if one side is 7 m longer than the other.

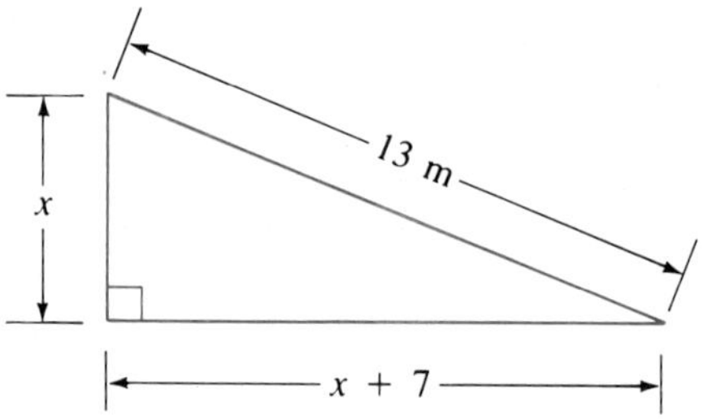

12. Mary can audit a set of books in 7 hr less than Jane, and together they can do the work in 9 hr less than Mary alone. Find the time they take when they work together.

13. A rectangular piece of glass has an area of 1875 cm^2. If the length of the rectangle is 50 cm greater than the width, what are the dimensions of the piece of glass?

14. A man finds that a trip of 70 mi driven at his normal speed can be decreased by 15 min if he travels 5 mph faster. What is his normal speed?

15. A boy mows a strip 7 ft wide around a rectangular yard that he determines to be 50% of the yard. Find the dimensions if the width of the yard is three quarters its length.

16. A rectangular field 250 ft long and 180 ft wide has a concrete walkway of uniform width on its border. If there are 2616 ft^2 of concrete in the walkway, what is the width of the walkway?

17. A man can row 20 mi downstream and back in 7.5 hr. If his rate of rowing in still water is 6 mph, find the rate of the stream.

18. The percent markup on the cost price of a pair of shoes is the same as the cost price in dollars. If the shoes sold for $24, what was the cost price of the shoes?

19. A new labor contract provides for an increase of $1 per hour and a reduction of 5 hr in the work week. A worker who receives $240 per week would receive $5 more per week under the new contract. How long was the work week before the new contract?

20. Joan and Jim working together can mow and manicure a lawn in 3 hr less than Joan alone. Jim alone takes 1 hr more than Joan. Find the approximate time they take when they work together.

21. Find three consecutive integers the sum of whose squares equals 434.

22. A 2-in. square is cut from each corner of a rectangular piece of cardboard whose length exceeds the width by 4 in. The sides are then turned up and a box is formed. Find the three dimensions of the box if the volume is 64 cu in.

23. The area of a triangular plate is 20 ft^2. Find its base and height if the base is 6 ft longer than the height. Area $= \frac{1}{2}$(base)(height).

24. A rectangular piece of metal is 10 cm long and 4 cm wide. Strips of equal width are to be added to one end and one side. Find the width of the strip necessary to double the area of the original rectangle.

25. Two fuel lines of different diameter can fill a tank in 5 hr. If the larger pipe will fill the tank in 4 hr less than the smaller one, what time is required for the larger pipe to fill the tank?

26. A couple bought some steaks for their freezer for a total of \$120. If each steak had cost \$1 more, they would have obtained six fewer steaks for their \$120. How many steaks did they receive?

27. The tens digit of a two-digit number is five less than the units digit. Twice the number is one more than the sum of the squares of the digits. What is the number?

28. The sum of the areas of the two inner circles in the following figure is 0.8 of the area of the outer circle. What is the radius of the smallest circle?

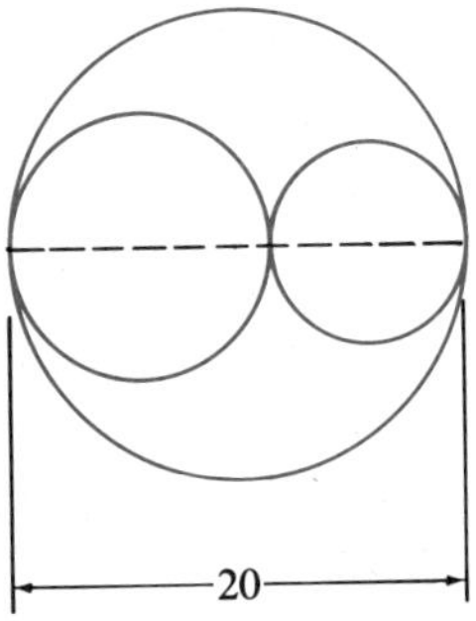

2.5 Equations in Quadratic Form

Some equations that are not strictly quadratic can be solved by the methods of the previous sections if an appropriate substitution is made first. For instance, by letting $z = \sqrt{x}$, we can transform the equation

$$3x - 2\sqrt{x} - 5 = 0$$

into the quadratic equation

$$3z^2 - 2z - 5 = 0$$

Similarly, by letting $z = x^{1/3}$, we can write

$$2x^{2/3} + 3x^{1/3} - 2 = 0$$

as

$$2z^2 + 3z - 2 = 0$$

EXAMPLE 1 Find the real roots of $x^4 + x^2 - 12 = 0$.

Solution The solution of this equation is obtained by letting $z = x^2$ and writing

$$z^2 + z - 12 = 0$$

which can be factored into

$$(z + 4)(z - 3) = 0$$

From this we get $z = -4$ and $z = 3$. In order to find the roots of $x^4 + x^2 - 12 = 0$, we note that $z = x^2$ and, therefore,

$$x^2 = -4 \quad \text{and} \quad x^2 = 3$$

Since only $x^2 = 3$ has real roots, the real roots of the equation are

$$\sqrt{3}, -\sqrt{3}$$

■

EXAMPLE 2 Solve $6/x^2 + (1/x) = 1$.

Solution We can convert $(6/x^2) + (1/x) = 1$ into a quadratic equation by making the transformation $z = 1/x$. Making this substitution, we get

$$6z^2 + z = 1$$

$$6z^2 + z - 1 = 0 \qquad \text{Adding } -1 \text{ to both sides}$$

$$(3z - 1)(2z + 1) = 0 \qquad \text{Factoring}$$

from which $z = \frac{1}{3}$ and $z = -\frac{1}{2}$. Thus, $1/x = \frac{1}{3}$ and $1/x = -\frac{1}{2}$. Solving for x in both cases gives

$$x = -2 \quad \text{and} \quad x = 3$$

Since neither value produces a zero denominator in the original equation, both are valid solutions.

■

EXAMPLE 3 Solve the equation $\dfrac{1}{x-2} + \dfrac{2}{x+3} = 5$.

Solution The given equation can be simplified by multiplying through on both sides by $(x - 2)(x + 3)$ to give

$$x + 3 + 2(x - 2) = 5(x - 2)(x + 3)$$

$$3x - 1 = 5x^2 + 5x - 30 \qquad \text{Expanding and collecting like terms}$$

$$5x^2 + 2x - 29 = 0 \qquad \text{Adding } -3x + 1 \text{ to both sides}$$

From the quadratic formula, we have

$$x = \frac{-2 \pm \sqrt{4 + 580}}{10} = \frac{-2 \pm \sqrt{584}}{10}$$

$$\approx -2.62, 2.22 \qquad (\approx \text{ means approximately equal})$$

Check: Since neither value produces a zero denominator in the original equation, we conclude that both are valid solutions.

■

Equations that contain a square root term frequently are solved by squaring both sides to eliminate the radical. However, since squaring is not one of the allowable operations, it is necessary to test the validity of each root by substituting it into the given equation. Any root that does not satisfy the original equation is extraneous and must be rejected.

EXAMPLE 4 Solve the equation $\sqrt{5x - 1} = x - 3$.

Solution Squaring both sides, we get

$$5x - 1 = x^2 - 6x + 9 \qquad (\sqrt{5x-1})^2 = (x-3)^2$$

$$x^2 - 11x + 10 = 0 \qquad \text{Collecting like terms}$$

$$(x-1)(x-10) = 0 \qquad \text{Factoring}$$

$$x = 1 \quad \text{and} \quad x = 10 \qquad \text{Solving for } x$$

The root $x = 10$ satisfies the original equation since $\sqrt{50 - 1} = 10 - 3$. However, $x = 1$ is not a solution since $\sqrt{5 - 1} \neq 1 - 3$. Thus, the only solution is $x = 10$. ■

EXAMPLE 5 Solve the equation $\sqrt{3x+1} - \sqrt{x-1} = 2$.

Solution Equations involving two radical terms are usually solved by putting one radical on each side of the equation. Thus, we write the given equation as

$$\sqrt{3x+1} = \sqrt{x-1} + 2$$

Now, squaring both sides, we get

$$3x + 1 = (x-1) + 4\sqrt{x-1} + 4 \qquad (\sqrt{3x+1})^2 = (\sqrt{x-1} + 2)^2$$

$$2x - 2 = 4\sqrt{x-1} \qquad \text{Isolating the radical term}$$

$$4x^2 - 8x + 4 = 16x - 16 \qquad \text{Squaring both sides}$$

$$4x^2 - 24x + 20 = 0 \qquad \text{Collecting like terms}$$

$$4(x-1)(x-5) = 0 \qquad \text{Factoring}$$

Thus, the possible roots of the equation are $x = 1$ and $x = 5$. Both values are valid roots since $\sqrt{3+1} - \sqrt{1-1} = 2$ and $\sqrt{15+1} - \sqrt{5-1} = 2$. ■

Exercises Section 2.5

Solve the equations in Exercises 1–18. (Find all real solutions.)

1. $x^4 - x^2 - 12 = 0$
2. $4x^2 - x^4 = 0$
3. $x^4 - 6x^2 - 16 = 0$
4. $3x^4 = 2x^2 + 1$
5. $x^4 + 9x^2 + 8 = 0$
6. $x^{-2} + x^{-1} - 6 = 0$
7. $2x^{-2} - 5x^{-1} - 3 = 0$
8. $x^{-4} - 9x^{-2} + 14 = 0$
9. $3x^{-2} = 4(x^{-1} + 1)$
10. $(x-3)^2 + 5(x-3) + 6 = 0$
11. $(x+2)^2 - 2(x+2) - 8 = 0$
12. $(x^2 + x)^2 - 18(x^2 + x) + 72 = 0$
13. $(x^2 + 2)^2 + 12(x^2 + 2) + 11 = 0$
14. $(x+3)^4 = 4 - 3(x+3)^2$
15. $(x-2)^{-2} + 35 = 12(x-2)^{-1}$
16. $(x^2 - 1)^2 - 3(x^2 - 1) + 2 = 0$
17. $4(x^2 + 1)^2 - 7(x^2 + 1) - 2 = 0$
18. $(x^2 + 3)^2 - 7(x^2 + 3) - 8 = 0$

Find the real solutions for the equations in Exercises 19–28.

19. $\dfrac{3}{x-1} - \dfrac{2}{x+3} = \dfrac{1}{2}$
20. $\dfrac{x}{x-4} = 6 - \dfrac{x}{x+4}$
21. $\dfrac{1}{2} - \dfrac{1}{x-1} = \dfrac{6}{x^2-1}$
22. $\dfrac{x}{x-2} + \dfrac{x-1}{2} = x - 1$
23. $\dfrac{2}{x-1} + \dfrac{5}{x-7} = \dfrac{4}{3x-1}$
24. $\dfrac{1}{x} + \dfrac{3}{x-1} - \dfrac{2}{x+1} = 0$
25. $\dfrac{x}{x^2-4} + \dfrac{1}{x-2} = \dfrac{x+5}{x^2-3x+2}$
26. $\dfrac{2x+7}{x^2-5x+4} - \dfrac{x-8}{x^2-4x+3} = \dfrac{x}{x^2-7x+12}$
27. $\dfrac{x^2-7}{x^2+4} + \dfrac{3}{x^2-1} = \dfrac{x^2+3}{x^2}$

28. $\dfrac{2x^2+5}{x^2-9}+\dfrac{x^2-5}{3x^2-1}=3$

Find the real solutions for the radical equations in Exercises 29–46.

29. $5\sqrt{x-6}=x$
30. $\sqrt{x+2}=x$
31. $\sqrt{2y+3}=y$
32. $2\sqrt{3z-5}=z$
33. $\sqrt{x^2-16}=3$
34. $\sqrt{y^2-11}=5$
35. $\sqrt{z^2+5z+2}=4$
36. $2=\sqrt{x^2-3x}$
37. $y+1=\sqrt{3y+7}$
38. $z-2=\sqrt{z-2}$
39. $2x-1=\sqrt{2x+5}$
40. $\sqrt{1+9p}=p+1$
41. $\sqrt{x+5}=\sqrt{x}-1$
42. $2\sqrt{x}=x-3$
43. $\sqrt{3y-5}-\sqrt{y+7}=2$
44. $\sqrt{2x+3}-\sqrt{x+1}=1$
45. $\sqrt{5z+4}-\sqrt{z}=2$
46. $\sqrt{5x+6}-\sqrt{3x+7}=1$

47. One side of a right triangle is 12 in. long. If the other side is lengthened by 4 in., the hypotenuse is lengthened by 2 in. Find the perimeter of the original triangle.

48. Find the dimensions of a rectangle whose area is 192 in.^{2} and whose diagonal is 20 in.

49. The surface area of a right circular cone is given by the formula

$$S=\pi r\sqrt{r^2+h^2}$$

Solve this equation for h.

50. A company estimates that the cost of a labor contract will be given approximately by

$$C(t)=2t-\sqrt{2t+5}$$

where C is in millions of dollars and t is in years. When will the cost reach a million dollars?

51. If the pressure (in pounds) in a waste disposal tank varies with time according to $P=3+\sqrt{t+2}$, at what time will $P=5$?

2.6 Linear Inequalities; Intervals

In addition to mathematical statements involving the equality of algebraic expressions, there are corresponding statements involving inequalities. The set of values for which an inequality is true is called its **solution set** and we say we have *solved* the inequality when we find its solution set. Two inequalities are **equivalent** if they have the same solution set.

Solving linear inequalities is similar to solving linear equations. We use manipulations that give a chain of equivalent inequalities to isolate the variable on one side of the inequality. The *allowable* manipulations look much like the allowable manipulations with equalities.

1. Adding the same quantity to both sides of an inequality or subtracting therefrom results in an equivalent inequality; for example, if $x<y$, then $x+3<y+3$.
2. Multiplying or dividing both sides of an inequality by the same positive quantity results in an equivalent inequality; for example, if $x>y$, then $2x>2y$.
3. Multiplying or dividing both sides of an inequality by the same negative quantity results in an equivalent inequality **if the sense of the inequality is reversed;** for example, if $x<y$, then $-5x>-5y$.

EXAMPLE 1 Solve the inequality $x-2<3$.

Solution Adding 2 to each side of the inequality, we have

$$x-2+2<3+2 \quad \text{or} \quad x<5$$

Thus, the solution set consists of all real numbers less than 5. ■

EXAMPLE 2 Solve the inequality $x + 1 < 3x - 2$.

Solution To get the terms involving x on one side and the constants on the other, add $-3x$ and -1 to both sides to get the equivalent inequality.

$$-2x < -3$$

Multiplying this result by $-\frac{1}{2}$ yields

$$x > \frac{3}{2}$$

Notice that the sense of the inequality changed when we multiplied by $-\frac{1}{2}$. The solution set is the set of all real numbers greater than $\frac{3}{2}$. ■

Solutions to inequalities can also be written in interval notation. An **interval** is the set of all real numbers between two given real numbers. Special notation is used to indicate intervals. The set of real numbers greater than a and less than b, called an **open interval,** is denoted by (a, b) and defined by

$$(a, b) = \{x \mid a < x < b\}$$

The notation $\{x \mid a < x < b\}$ is read "the set of all x such that x is greater than a and less than b." The notation (a, b) presumes that $a < b$. The set of real numbers greater than or equal to a and less than or equal to b, called a **closed interval,** is denoted by $[a, b]$ and defined by

$$[a, b] = \{x \mid a \leq x \leq b\}$$

The points corresponding to a and b are called **endpoints** of the interval. Thus, the difference between an open and a closed interval is the exclusion or inclusion of the endpoints. Graphically, an endpoint to be included in the interval is represented by a closed dot. Otherwise an open dot is used. See Figure 2.3.

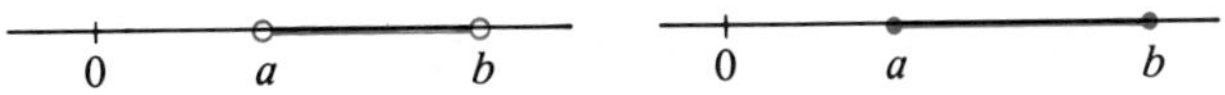

Open interval (a, b) Closed interval $[a, b]$

Figure 2.3

If only one of the endpoints is included in an interval, the interval is said to be **half-open.** The half-open intervals $(a, b]$ and $[a, b)$ are depicted in Figure 2.4.

$(a, b]$ $[a, b)$

Figure 2.4

Finally, the set of all real numbers greater than a is represented in interval notation by (a, ∞). The symbol ∞ (infinity) means that there is no finite upper bound for the interval and it should not be thought of as a number. The symbol $-\infty$ is used to indicate that there is no lower bound for an interval and, therefore, $(-\infty, a)$

denotes all real numbers less than a. Similarly, $(-\infty, a]$ is an interval that corresponds to $x \leq a$, and $[a, \infty)$ an interval that corresponds to $x \geq a$. These intervals are shown in Figure 2.5.

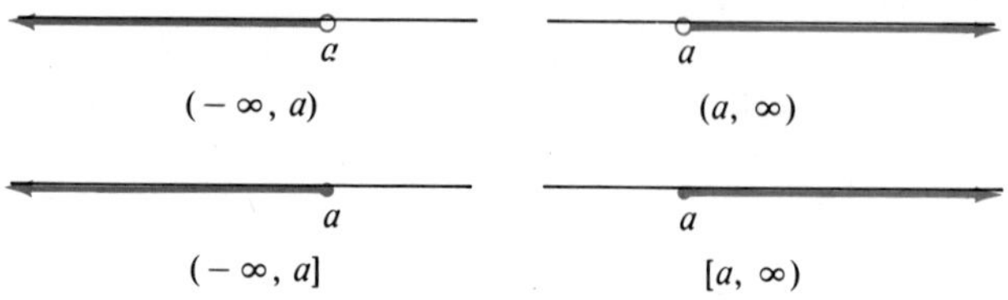

Figure 2.5

EXAMPLE 3 Solve the inequality $x^2 - 5x + 3 \geq (x - 2)^2$. Write the solution using interval notation and sketch its graph.

Solution Expanding the binomial on the right side of the given inequality, we have

$$x^2 - 5x + 3 \geq x^2 - 4x + 4$$

Adding $-x^2 + 4x - 3$ to both sides, we get

$$-x \geq 1$$
$$x \leq -1$$

Notice that the sense of the inequality changed when both sides of the inequality were multiplied by -1. The desired solutions are given by $(-\infty, -1]$ and represented in Figure 2.6.

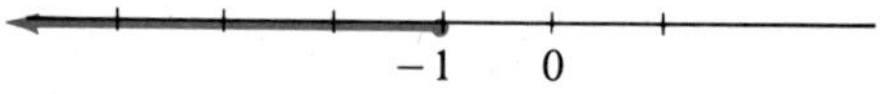

Figure 2.6 ■

The solution set to an inequality of the form $q < p < r$ consists of all real numbers that are solutions to both of the inequalities $q < p$ and $p < r$.

EXAMPLE 4 Solve the inequality $x - 20 < 3x - 8 \leq 4$ and graph the solution interval.

Solution Any solution to the inequality $x - 20 < 3x - 8 \leq 4$ must be a solution to both $x - 20 < 3x - 8$ and $3x - 8 \leq 4$. Solving these two inequalities separately, we get the following results.

$x - 20 < 3x - 8$	$3x - 8 \leq 4$
$x - 12 < 3x$	$3x \leq 12$
$-12 < 2x$	$x \leq 4$
$-6 < x$	

Since the solution of the given inequality must satisfy both $-6 < x$ and $x \leq 4$, we conclude that the solution is

$$-6 < x \leq 4$$

The solution is all numbers in the half-open interval $(-6, 4]$. The graph of this interval is shown in Figure 2.7.

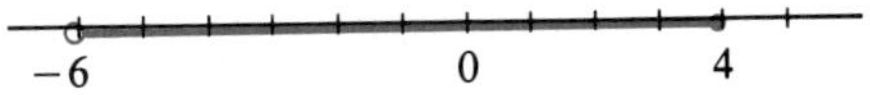

Figure 2.7

The points common to both $(-\infty, 4]$ and $(-6, \infty)$ are denoted by $(-\infty, 4] \cap (-6, \infty)$, called the **intersection** of the intervals. Thus, the solution to this problem can be written

$$(-\infty, 4] \cap (-6, \infty) = (-6, 4]$$ ■

The absolute inequalities $|x| < b$ and $|x| > b$ both describe sets of real numbers that can be represented by intervals on the real line. From the discussion of absolute value in Section 1.1, it follows that $|x| < b$ and $|x| > b$ have the following interpretations.

$$\begin{aligned} &\boldsymbol{|x| < b} \quad \textbf{means that } \boldsymbol{-b < x < b} \\ &\boldsymbol{|x| > b} \quad \textbf{means } \boldsymbol{x < -b} \quad \textbf{or} \quad \boldsymbol{x > b} \end{aligned} \tag{2.2}$$

Equivalently, $|x| < b$ represents the open interval $(-b, b)$ and $|x| > b$ represents the union of $(-\infty, -b)$ and (b, ∞). The **union** of the intervals means that x can be either in $(-\infty, -b)$ or in (b, ∞) and is denoted by $(-\infty, -b) \cup (b, \infty)$. Figure 2.8 pictures these two intervals.

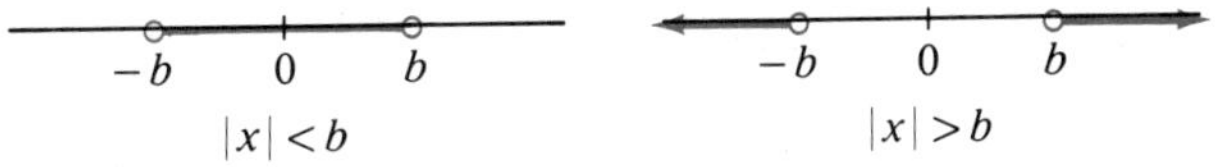

Figure 2.8

We can extend the use of Equation 2.2 to solving inequalities that involve the absolute value of linear expressions. For example, we can use Equation 2.2 to solve $|t - 3| < 5$ by letting $x = t - 3$ and $b = 5$.

EXAMPLE 5 Solve the inequality $|t - 3| < 5$.

Solution Using Equation 2.2 as a guide with $x = t - 3$ and $b = 5$, we have the double inequality $-5 < x < 5$ or, equivalently,

$$-5 < t - 3 < 5$$

By adding 3 to each member of this inequality, we get

$$-2 < t < 8$$

as the solution set. This is written in interval notation as $(-2, 8)$ and is illustrated in Figure 2.9.

Figure 2.9 ■

EXAMPLE 6 Solve the inequality $|2x + 5| < 7$.

Solution The given absolute value inequality can be represented by the double inequality

$$-7 < 2x + 5 < 7$$

Subtracting -5 from all three terms gives

$$-12 < 2x < 2$$

Dividing through by 2, we have the solution

$$-6 < x < 1$$

The graph of this solution set is shown in Figure 2.10.

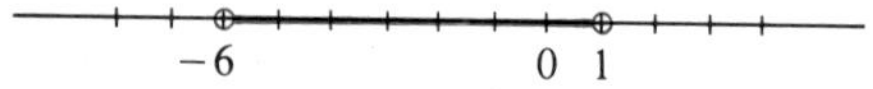

Figure 2.10 ■

EXAMPLE 7 Solve the inequality $|3x - 1| \geq 8$.

Solution Using Equation 2.2, we see that the inequality $|3x - 1| \geq 8$ is equivalent to the two inequalities

$$3x - 1 \leq -8 \quad \text{or} \quad 3x - 1 \geq 8$$

These two are independently solved to obtain

$$x \leq -7/3 \quad \text{or} \quad x \geq 3$$

The solution is written in interval notation as $(-\infty, -7/3] \cup [3, \infty)$. The graph is sketched in Figure 2.11.

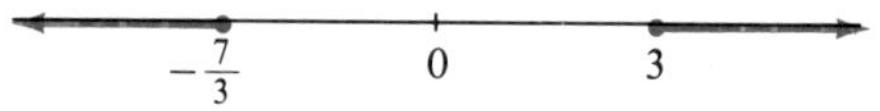

Figure 2.11 ■

In the previous examples we have used interval notation to represent solutions to linear inequalities involving absolute values. Another important use of inequalities with absolute values is as an alternate method of describing intervals on the real line. Recall from Section 1.1 that the distance between two points a and b on the real line is given by

$$d(a, b) = |a - b|$$

Thus, $|x - 2|$ denotes the distance from x to 2 and, therefore, the inequality $|x - 2| < 3$ represents the set of all points whose distance from 2 is less than 3. A sketch of this inequality is shown in Figure 2.12. From the figure it is clear that all values of x less than three units from 2 are represented by the interval $(-1, 5)$. Therefore, $(-1, 5)$ and $|x - 2| < 3$ describe the same interval.

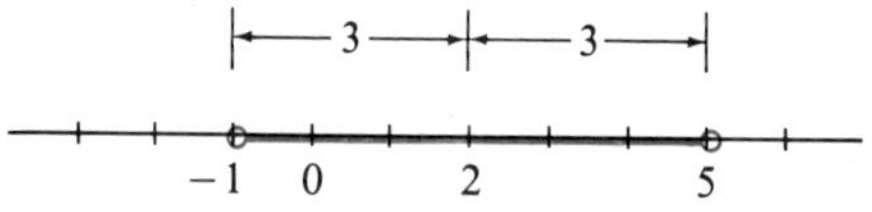

Figure 2.12

In general, $|x - p| < b$ represents all values of x less than b units from p, and $|x - p| > b$ represents all values of x more than b units from p. The point p is the **midpoint** of the interval, and the endpoints of the interval are $p - b$ and $p + b$. See Figure 2.13.

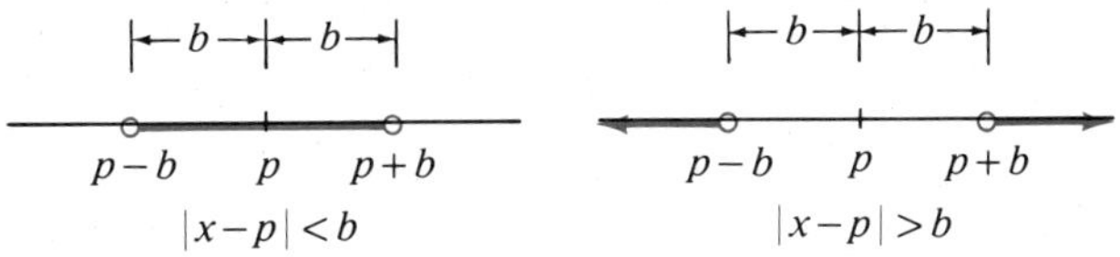

Figure 2.13

EXAMPLE 8 Using interval notation, write the interval on the real line that describes the inequality $|x - 2| < 5$. Also display it graphically.

Solution The point $x = 2$ is the midpoint of the interval that has a total length of 10. The given inequality can be written as

$$-5 < x - 2 < 5 \quad \text{or} \quad -3 < x < 7$$

or, in terms of interval notation, $(-3, 7)$. Figure 2.14 displays the interval.

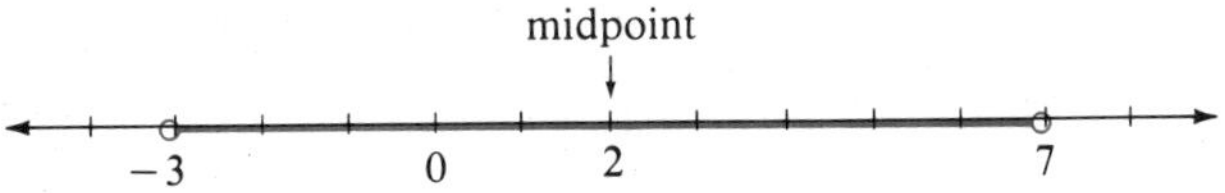

Figure 2.14

■

Sometimes we wish to describe a given interval (a, b) using an absolute value with an inequality. To do this, compute the midpoint and half the length of the interval. The midpoint of (a, b) is given by

$$\textbf{midpoint} = \frac{a + b}{2} \tag{2.3}$$

and half the length of the interval is given by

$$\textbf{half-length} = \frac{|a - b|}{2} \tag{2.4}$$

Then, the inequality

$$|x - \textbf{midpoint}| < \textbf{half-length of interval} \tag{2.5}$$

is another representation of (a, b). A similar analysis describes the union of the two intervals $(-\infty, a)$ and (b, ∞) with an absolute value inequality.

EXAMPLE 9 Describe the interval $(-4, 10)$ in terms of an absolute value inequality.

Solution The midpoint and half-length of $(-4, 10)$ are given by

$$\text{midpoint} = \frac{-4 + 10}{2} = \frac{6}{2} = 3$$

and

$$\text{half-length} = \frac{|-4 - 10|}{2} = \frac{14}{2} = 7$$

Hence, the interval may be represented by $|x - 3| < 7$. The interval is shown in Figure 2.15.

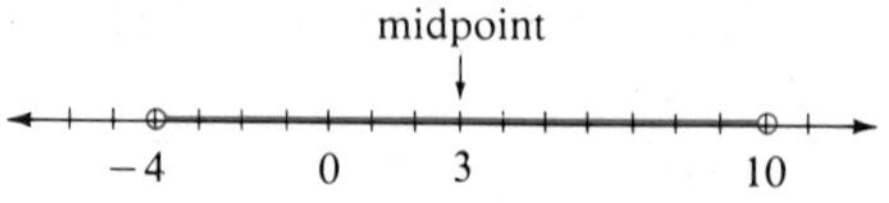

Figure 2.15

EXAMPLE 10 Describe the union of the two intervals $(-\infty, -8) \cup (0, \infty)$ in terms of one absolute value inequality. The intervals are shown in Figure 2.16.

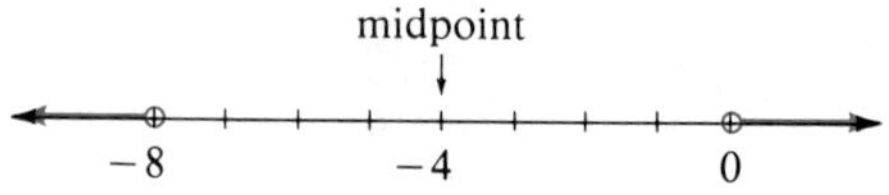

Figure 2.16

Solution In this case, the midpoint of -8 and 0 is -4 and the half-length of the interval that we wish to exclude is 4. Hence, the notation

$$|x - (-4)| > 4 \quad \text{or} \quad |x + 4| > 4$$

describes the given interval.

Exercises Section 2.6

Sketch the graph of the intervals in Exercises 1–16.

1. $(-2, 3)$ **2.** $[-2, 3]$ **3.** $(-\infty, 0]$
4. $[1, \infty)$ **5.** $(-\infty, \infty)$ **6.** $(-3, 3]$
7. $[2, 3]$ **8.** $[\frac{1}{4}, \frac{1}{2})$ **9.** $(-1, 3)$
10. $[-3, -1]$ **11.** $[-5, 0)$
12. $(0, 1) \cup (\frac{1}{2}, 1)$ **13.** $(2, 3) \cap (3, \infty)$
14. $(-\infty, -3) \cup (3, \infty)$ **15.** $(-3, 5) \cap [4, 7)$
16. $(2, \infty) \cap (3, \infty)$

Solve the inequalities in Exercises 17–35 and sketch the graph of each solution set on the number line.

17. $3x + 1 > x - 4$ **18.** $2 - 5x > -x$
19. $x + 1 \geq \sqrt{2} - x\sqrt{3}$ **20.** $x \leq x + 1$
21. $\frac{2}{3}x + 5 < \frac{7}{5}x + \frac{1}{3}$
22. $3(2x - 1) + 4(x - 2) > 0$
23. $(x - 3)(x + 4) > (x - 5)(x + 5)$
24. $x^2 - 9 \leq (x - 3)(x + 2)$
25. $x^2 - 1 \geq (x + 3)^2$
26. $2x + x(x - 2) < (x - 3)(3 + x)$
27. $x(x - 1) > x(x - 3)$
28. $(2x - 1)^2 > (2x + 3)^2$
29. $x^2 - 5x + 4 < x(x - 2)$
30. $x(x^2 - 4) > x(x^2 - 9) + 5$
31. $x + 2 < 2x + 5 \leq 6x + 7$
32. $x - 1 \leq 3x + 5 < 2x + 7$
33. $x < 2x + 3 < 3x - 5$
34. $x^2 - 2x < x^2 + 2x - 3 < (x - 3)(x - 2)$
35. $x^2 + 1 < (x - 3)(x - 4) \leq (x + 3)(x + 5)$

In Exercises 36–50, describe the given absolute value inequality by an interval or a union of intervals.

36. $|x| \leq 6$ **37.** $|x| < 1.5$
38. $|x| > 7$ **39.** $|x| \geq 4$
40. $|x| < -1$ **41.** $|x - 2| < 3$
42. $|3x + 6| > 9$ **43.** $|x + 2| < 5$
44. $|2x + 7| < 5$ **45.** $|x - 5| > 1$
46. $|x + 3| > 0$ **47.** $|\frac{1}{2}x - 3| \leq 5$
48. $|3x| \geq 6$ **49.** $|2x - 3| \leq 2$
50. $|x + 1| \leq 1$

Describe the intervals in Exercises 51–62 using absolute value notation.

51. $(-5, 5)$ **52.** $(-10, 10)$

53. $(-\infty, -3) \cup (3, \infty)$ **54.** $(-\infty, -1] \cup [1, \infty)$

55. $(2, 6)$ **56.** $(-\infty, -2) \cup (0, \infty)$

57. $(-10, 16)$ **58.** $(-\infty, 4) \cup (12, \infty)$

59. $(-\infty, -2) \cup (2, \infty)$ **60.** $(-\infty, 2] \cup [6, \infty)$

61. $[2, 7]$ **62.** $(-12, -3)$

63. What is wrong with the notation $-2 > x > 2$?

64. The strength, s, of a sheet of material sufficient to hold a certain weight is given by the inequality $s + 3 \leq 2s + 1$, where s is in pounds per square inch (psi). Find the range of s required to hold this weight.

65. The measurement, M, of a machined part for a vacuum cleaner must satisfy the inequality $|M - 10| < 0.01$, where M is in centimeters (cm). Express this as a double inequality.

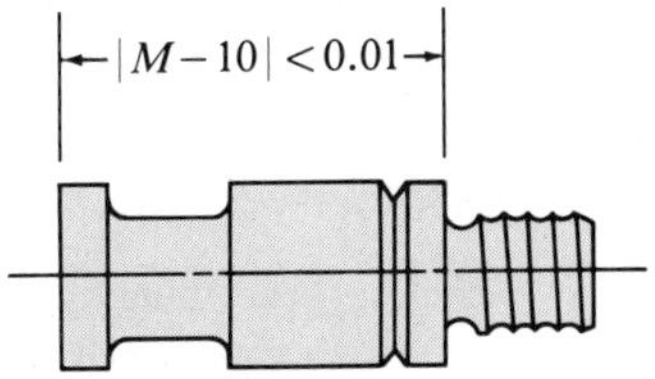

66. The in-flight time in minutes of a certain projectile is given by $|3t - 7| < 7$. Find the interval of time that the projectile is in flight.

2.7 Quadratic Inequalities

An inequality containing a quadratic expression is called a **quadratic inequality.** As a basic rule for solving nonlinear inequalities, begin by gathering all terms to one side of the inequality. If the resulting expression is quadratic, factor it, and determine where the signs of the individual factors become positive and negative. We usually accompany this method with a diagram showing the signs of the linear factors. Hence the method is often called the method of sign diagrams.

EXAMPLE 1 Solve the inequality $4x^2 + 2x + 4 < 2x^2 + 13x + 25$.

Solution Gathering all the terms to the left side of the inequality and simplifying, we get

$$2x^2 - 11x - 21 < 0$$

Factoring the quadratic expression gives

$$(2x + 3)(x - 7) < 0$$

The linear factor $2x + 3$ is positive for $x > -\frac{3}{2}$ and negative otherwise. The factor $x - 7$ is positive for $x > 7$. To display these facts, construct a sign diagram for the linear factors as shown in Figure 2.17. An algebraic product of like signs gives a positive number, while a product of unlike signs gives a negative number. The sign of the product of the two linear factors is shown in Figure 2.17. Since we wish those values of x for which the product is negative, the diagram tells us immediately that the solution is $-\frac{3}{2} < x < 7$.

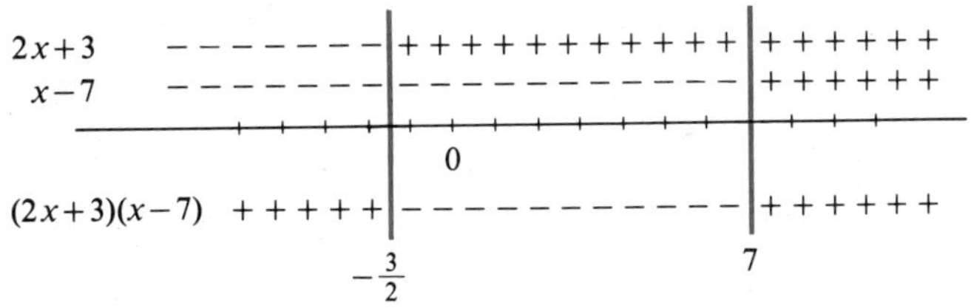

Figure 2.17

Beginners often make the mistake of considering $(2x + 3) \cdot (x - 7) < 0$ to be equivalent to the two linear inequalities $2x + 3 < 0$ and $x - 7 < 0$. However, the solutions to the two latter inequalities are $x < -3/2$ and $x < 7$ and their union is $x < 7$, which is clearly not the solution set to the given quadratic inequality. For example, the quadratic expression is positive when $x = -2$. ■

EXAMPLE 2 Solve the inequality $x^2 < x + 1$.

Solution Bringing everything to the left-hand side of the inequality gives $x^2 - x - 1 < 0$. The quadratic expression $x^2 - x - 1$ cannot be factored by inspection, but the factors can be determined if the two roots r_1, r_2 of $x^2 - x - 1 = 0$ are known. The factors are $(x - r_1)$ and $(x - r_2)$. From the quadratic formula, the two roots are

$$\frac{1 \pm \sqrt{1+4}}{2} = \frac{1 \pm \sqrt{5}}{2}$$

Hence, we have the following sign diagram (see Figure 2.18), where

$$r_1 = \frac{1+\sqrt{5}}{2} \quad \text{and} \quad r_2 = \frac{1-\sqrt{5}}{2}$$

Therefore, since we want to know those numbers for which the product is negative, the solution is

$$\frac{1-\sqrt{5}}{2} < x < \frac{1+\sqrt{5}}{2}$$

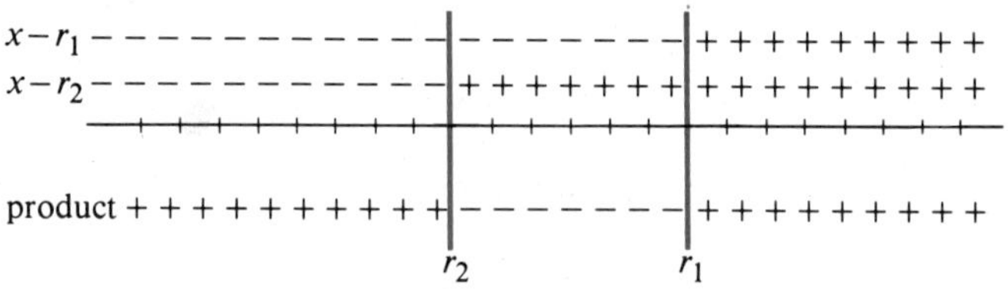

Figure 2.18 ■

EXAMPLE 3 Solve the inequality $x^2 < 2x - 5$.

Solution The given inequality is equivalent to

$$x^2 - 2x + 5 < 0$$

The roots of $x^2 - 2x + 5$ are both nonreal because the discriminant D is equal to $(-2)^2 - 4 \cdot 5 = -16$. Hence the quadratic expression $x^2 - 2x + 5$ never changes sign. Since for $x = 0$, $x^2 - 2x + 5$ is $+5$, the expression is *always* positive and the solution to the given inequality is the empty set. (We could also say that there is "no solution.") ■

Comment: The use of sign diagrams is not restricted to solving quadratic inequalities; in fact, any time you can factor an inequality into linear factors or irreducible quadratic factors the sign diagram method is useful. Remember to **bring all nonzero terms to one side of the inequality before simplifying and factoring.**

EXAMPLE 4 Solve the inequality $\dfrac{2x+1}{x-2} \geq 1$.

Solution First, bring all nonzero terms to one side and then solve the resulting inequality. Thus, if we subtract 1 from both sides of the given inequality, we have

$$\frac{2x+1}{x-2} - 1 \geq 0$$

Simplifying, we get

$$\frac{2x+1-x+2}{x-2} \geq 0$$

$$\frac{x+3}{x-2} \geq 0$$

The sign diagram in Figure 2.19 associated with this quotient shows the signs of the individual factors $x + 3$ and $x - 2$ for any real number, and the last line shows the sign of the quotient. From the quotient sign line we can read off the solution set as $(-\infty, -3] \cup (2, \infty)$. It would be wrong to write $[2, \infty)$ since the denominator is zero for $x = 2$.

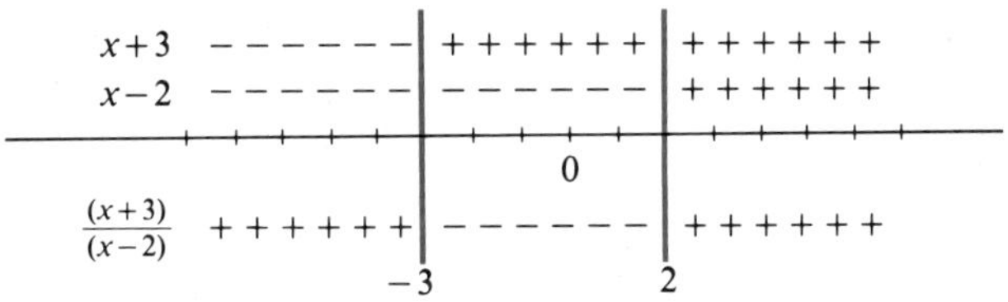

Figure 2.19 ■

EXAMPLE 5 Solve the inequality $\dfrac{x^2(3-x)(x+1)}{(x+10)(x-1)} \geq 0$.

Solution Figure 2.20 shows the associated sign diagram. The factor x^2 is always nonnegative, so it affects the solution set only when it is equal to zero. From the sign diagram we are able to determine the sign of the entire expression for all values of x. The solution set is $(-10, -1] \cup \{0\} \cup (1, 3]$. The values of x for which the numerator is zero (that is, $-1, 0, 3$) are

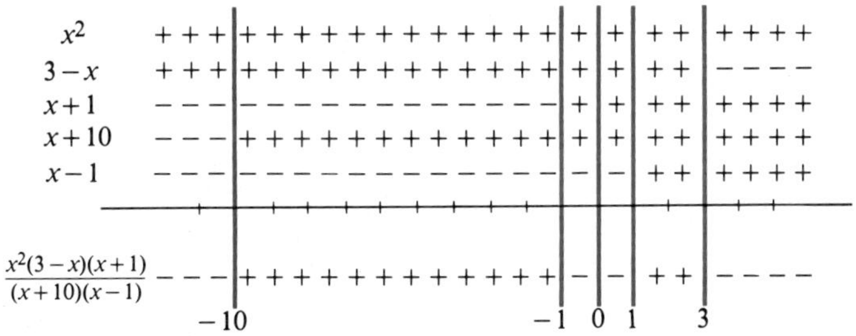

Figure 2.20

included here because the given problem allows for equality also. The values of x for which the denominator is zero (that is, -10 and 1) are never included since the given expression is meaningless for those values. ■

Exercises Section 2.7

Use sign diagrams to solve the quadratic inequalities in Exercises 1–10.

1. $x^2 + 2x \geq 3$
2. $x^2 < x + 2$
3. $5x < 3x^2 - 2$
4. $(x + 1)(x - 3) > 4x^2 - 10x + 2$
5. $x(6 - x) \geq 3x^2 + 2x - 15$
6. $x^2 + 3x + 2 < 11x^2 + 6x - 16$
7. $x - 1 < x^2 + 1$
8. $3x^2 - 4 < (x - 4)^2$
9. $x + 4 < x^2 - 4$
10. $(x - 3)^2 > (2x + 1)^2$

Solve the inequalities in Exercises 11–22 using sign diagrams. Be sure to bring all nonzero terms to one side of the inequality before proceeding.

11. $\dfrac{(x + 4)(x + 5)}{x + 1} < 0$
12. $\dfrac{x + 1}{x + 2} < 1$
13. $\dfrac{x + 1}{2x + 3} \leq 1$
14. $\dfrac{(x + 5)(x + 2)(x - 1)}{x^2 - 4} \leq 0$
15. $\dfrac{(x^2 - 1)(x^2 + 1)}{x^2 - 4} \leq 0$
16. $\dfrac{(x + 5)(x - 3)(2 - x)}{x^2 - 4} \geq 0$
17. $\dfrac{x^2 + 1}{x^2 + 4} \leq 1$
18. $\dfrac{x^2 + x + 1}{x + 1} \geq 0$
19. $\dfrac{x - 2}{x^2 + x - 1} \geq 0$
20. $\dfrac{x^2}{(x^2 + 4)(x - 3)} \geq 0$
21. $\dfrac{x + 2}{x^2 - 3} \leq 1$
22. $\dfrac{(x + 1)(x^2 - 1)}{(x^2 - 9)(x + 5)} \leq 0$
23. Determine the values of k such that both the roots of the equation $4x^2 - kx + 3 = 0$ are real.
24. Determine the values of k such that the expression $2kx^2 + 7x + 2k$ is always positive.
25. Suppose that the profit in a business varies in an 8-hr day according to the formula $P = 15t - 3t^2$, where t is the time in hours. For what values of t is $P > 0$? (Assume that $t \geq 0$.)
26. The height of a certain projectile above ground level is given by $h = 32t - 16t^2$, where t is the time in seconds. For what values of t ($t > 0$) is $h > 4$ ft?
27. The tensile strength of a new plastic varies with temperature according to $S = 500 + 600T - 20T^2$ psi. For what temperature range is $S > 4500$?

Review Exercises Chapter 2

In Exercises 1–18, solve the indicated equation.

1. $2x - 3(x - 5) = 12$
2. $7 + 3(2x - 4) - 2x = 5x$
3. $\dfrac{3x}{2} + 2(3x - 5) = \dfrac{x}{3}$
4. $5x - \dfrac{x + 6}{2} = \dfrac{2x - 9}{5}$
5. $x - 3a(6 - 7x) = 19ax$
6. $a(bx + d) - 3x = c$
7. $\dfrac{2}{x} + \dfrac{3}{2x} = 5$
8. $1 + \dfrac{x}{x + 3} = \dfrac{2(x - 3)}{x}$
9. $\dfrac{2}{2y - 3} = \dfrac{5}{y + 4}$
10. $\dfrac{4}{x + 2} = \dfrac{1}{x - 1} + \dfrac{3}{x^2 + x - 2}$
11. $4(t - 5)^{-1} + 3 - 3t(t + 4)^{-1} = 0$
12. $y(y - 3)^{-1} = 2 + 3(y - 3)^{-1}$
13. $|x| + 3 = 7$
14. $x + |x| = 5$
15. $|x - 4| = 10$
16. $|3 + t| = 3$
17. $2y + |y - 7| = 5$
18. $1 + (1 - x) = |x + 2|$

In Exercises 19–26, solve each of the equations by factoring.

19. $3x^2 - 7x = 0$

20. $4x + 5x^2 = 0$

21. $y^2 - 10 = 0$

22. $14y^2 - 23y + 3 = 0$

23. $7a = 2a^2 + 3$

24. $2x^2 + x = 6$

25. $z^2 + 6z + 5 = 0$

26. $2x^2 = 3 + x$

In Exercises 27–36, use the quadratic formula to solve the equations.

27. $4y^2 - 4y - 11 = 0$

28. $a^2 - 5a + 5 = 0$

29. $2x^2 - 12x - 15 = 0$

30. $2r^2 = r + 3$

31. $15y^2 + 14y = 8$

32. $t^2 - t - 13 = 0$

33. $t^2 - 4t + 8 = 0$

34. $2x^2 + 3x + 5 = 0$

35. $3x^2 + 7x - 2 = 0$

36. $42b^2 - 7b - 245 = 0$

In Exercises 37–46, solve the equations by an appropriate method. (Find all real solutions.)

37. $h^4 - 7h^2 + 12 = 0$

38. $2x^4 + 7x^2 = 4$

39. $3(x - 1)^2 - 10(x - 1) - 8 = 0$

40. $x^{-2} + 15x^{-1} + 56 = 0$

41. $\dfrac{1}{t+1} + \dfrac{1}{t} = \dfrac{9}{20}$

42. $\dfrac{5}{y+1} = \dfrac{2}{3y-1} + 1$

43. $\sqrt{x + 12} - \sqrt{x} = 3$

44. $x + 3 = \sqrt{x + 4}$

45. $\sqrt{7t + 23} - \sqrt{3t + 7} = 2$

46. $\sqrt{2x - 3} = \sqrt{x + 7} - 2$

Solve each of the inequalities in Exercises 47–58 and graph each solution set on the real line.

47. $x - 4 > 2x + 3$

48. $4x \le 8 + 3x$

49. $3x + 5 \le 2 - 3x$

50. $3(4x - 1) \ge 15x$

51. $x(x - 5) < (x + 1)(x - 2)$

52. $(x + 5)^2 > x^2 + 5$

53. $3 \le 2x - 5 < 8$

54. $-1 < x + 3 < 0$

55. $x - 1 < 2x < 3x + 5$

56. $x \le 2x - 3 \le 7x - 8$

57. $|x + 3| > 1$

58. $|x + 2| \ge 6$

In Exercises 59–62, describe the given interval by using absolute value notation.

59. $(-2, 5)$

60. $(3, 11)$

61. $(-\infty, -1] \cup [3, \infty)$

62. $(-\infty, 0] \cup [4, \infty)$

Solve the inequalities in Exercises 63–68.

63. $x^2 + 5x - 6 \le 0$

64. $2t^2 - 3t > 2$

65. $x + 2 > x^2 + 2x$

66. $(x - 3)(x + 3) < 3x^2 + 2x - 12$

67. $\dfrac{x - 5}{x^2 - 8x + 15} \ge 0$

68. $\dfrac{x(x + 2)}{(x - 1)(x + 4)} \ge 0$

69. The formula $P_1 - P_2 = \frac{1}{2}\rho(v_2^2 - v_1^2)$ occurs in the study of the mechanics of fluids. Solve this formula for ρ.

70. In the study of the underlying principles of jet engines and rockets, the formula $F(t_2 - t_1) = mv$ is encountered. Solve for t_1.

71. The kinetic energy of a charged particle is given by $E = c^2(m - m_0)$. Solve for m_0.

72. A person's salary is equal to \$300 plus the square root of the salary. What is the salary?

73. Two recliner chairs are offered as a set at a price of \$787. If the price of one of the chairs is three times that of the other, what is the price of each chair?

74. A car moving 50 mph passes a point. Two minutes later a second car moving in the same direction as the first passes the point at 55 mph. How long will it take the second car to overtake the first?

75. A 6% acid solution and a 2% acid solution are to be mixed together to yield 10 liters of a 5% acid solution. How much of each must be used?

76. An industrial engineer determines that 200 parts from a punch press are needed for each 8-hr shift to keep the assembly line running. The punch press doing the job takes 15 hr to make 200 parts so a second press is to be added to the line. What should be the minimum rating of the new press in "hours to make 200 parts" to supply the specified assembly line?

77. If the velocity in feet per second of a falling object is given by $v = 5t - 16t^2$, where t is the elapsed time in seconds, how long will it take the object to reach a velocity of 100 fps? (*Hint:* Velocity is considered negative for a falling object.)

78. The length of a rectangular room is 6 ft more than its width. What are the dimensions of the room if its area is 216 ft^2?

79. The following equation is encountered in the design of a thin refraction lens:

$$\frac{1}{p} + \frac{1}{p - 3} = \frac{1}{3}$$

Solve for p.

80. In calculating the escape velocity of a rocket, the

following equation must be solved for R:

$$\frac{1}{2} = \frac{1}{R} - \frac{1}{60R}$$

Show that $R = \frac{59}{30}$.

81. According to Einstein's special theory of relativity, the mass of a particle depends upon its speed according to the equation

$$m = m_0\left(1 - \frac{v^2}{c^2}\right)^{-1/2}$$

where m_0 is the "rest mass" and c is the velocity of light. Solve for v.

Test 1 Chapter 2

Answer True or False to Exercises 1–10.

1. The equation $x + (1/x) = 0$ is a linear equation.

2. The interval described by $|x - 2| < 2$ is 2 units long.

3. $|x - 1| > 2$ represents the same set as $2 < x < -2$.

4. If a, b, and c are real numbers in the equation $ax^2 + bx + c = 0$, $a \neq 0$, then both roots are real.

5. If a quadratic equation has real roots, then it can be factored into real linear factors.

6. The equation $1 - x^2 = 0$ is a quadratic equation.

7. $x = 5$ is a root of the equation $\sqrt{x + 4} = 2 - x$.

8. The quadratic formula can be used to solve the equation $ax^3 + bx^2 + c = 0$.

9. A linear equation can have two roots.

10. If the discriminant of $ax^2 + bx + c = 0$ is greater than zero, the equation has nonreal roots.

11. Solve the equation $3x + 5 = x - 10$.

12. Represent the interval $(-10, 2)$ with an absolute value inequality.

13. Solve the equation $x^2 + 5x + 2 = 0$.

14. Solve $\sqrt{x} + 2 = \sqrt{x + 8}$.

15. Solve the inequality $x^2 \leq 11x - 28$.

16. Solve the inequality $x(x - 1) < 2(x + 2)(x + 1)$.

17. Ben has a gallon mixture of orange concentrate and water that contains 20% of the orange concentrate. How much of the orange concentrate must he add to make a 30% mixture? (Express your answer in gallons.)

Test 2 Chapter 2

1. Solve $3(x + 2) - 5x = 7$.

2. Solve $\dfrac{3}{x + 2} - \dfrac{1}{x - 2} = \dfrac{10}{x^2 - 4}$.

3. Solve $3 + 2x < 5(x - 2)$.

4. Solve $|x + 4| \geq 8$ and graph the solution set.

5. Solve $2x(x + 5) = 12$ by factoring.

6. Solve $x^2 - 6x + 2 = 0$ by using the quadratic formula.

7. Find two values of x such that

$$x^{2/3} - 3x^{1/3} - 4 = 0$$

8. Solve $\sqrt{5 - y} = y + 1$.

9. A girl paid \$35 for a tennis racket and a pair of shoes. If the racket cost \$7 more than the shoes, how much did each cost?

10. Two water lines can fill a swimming pool in 6 hr. The larger of the lines will fill the pool in 2 hr less than the smaller. What time is required for the larger water line alone to fill the pool?

11. The formula for the area of a right circular cylinder is $A = 2\pi r^2 + 2\pi rh$, where r is the radius and h is its height. If the height of a cylindrical can is 6 in., what must the radius be to give an area of 14π in.^{2}?

12. Solve the inequality $\dfrac{2x - 1}{x + 1} \leq 1$.

3

The Idea of a Function

3.1 The Cartesian Coordinate System

In Section 1.1 you learned that each point on a line is associated with a real number, called the coordinate of the point. In this section we will show how to establish a correspondence between points in a plane and ordered pairs of real numbers.

A pair of numbers a and b is said to be an **ordered pair** if the order in which the elements are written is significant. An ordered pair for which a is identified as the "first" element and b as the "second" is denoted by (a, b). Two ordered pairs are equal if they have the same first element and the same second element; otherwise, they are not equal. For example, the ordered pair (3, 2) is not equal to the ordered pair (2, 3).

Notice that the notation for ordered pairs is the same as that for an open interval on the real line. Whenever there is possible confusion, we will specify whether (a, b) refers to an open interval or an ordered pair. In this chapter, the notation will always indicate an ordered pair.

Just as we form a correspondence between real numbers and points on a line, we associate ordered pairs of numbers with points in a plane. Several approaches accomplish this association, but the most common is called the **rectangular coordinate system** or the **Cartesian* coordinate system.** To construct such a system, first draw a pair of perpendicular number lines that intersect at the zero point of each line, as shown in Figure 3.1.

Normally the horizontal line is called the ***x*-axis,** the vertical line the ***y*-axis,** and their intersection the **origin.** Considered together, the two axes are called the coordinate axes. As you can see, the coordinate axes divide the plane into four zones, or **quadrants.** The upper right quadrant is called the first quadrant and the others are numbered consecutively counterclockwise as in Figure 3.1. The coordinate axes are not considered to be in any quadrant.

To locate points in the plane, use the origin as a reference point. The displacement of a point in the plane to the right or left of the y-axis is called the ***x*-coordinate,** or **abscissa,** of the point, and is denoted by x. Values of x measured to the right of the y-axis are *positive* and to the left, *negative.* The displacement of a point in

* Named in honor of René Descartes (1596–1650), the first person to systematically use ordered pairs of numbers.

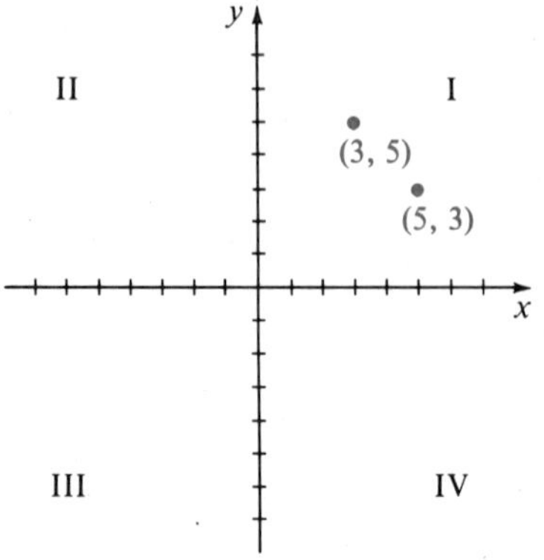

Figure 3.1

the plane above or below the x-axis is called the **y-coordinate,** or **ordinate,** of the point, and is denoted by y. Values of y above the x-axis are *positive* and below the x-axis, *negative*. Together, the abscissa and the ordinate of a point are called the **coordinates** of the point, conventionally written in parentheses, with the abscissa written first and separated from the ordinate by a comma; that is, (x, y).

We see that a point (x, y) lies

- In quadrant I if both coordinates are positive,
- In quadrant II if the x-coordinate is negative and the y-coordinate is positive,
- In quadrant III if both coordinates are negative,
- In quadrant IV if the x-coordinate is positive and the y-coordinate is negative.

Since the first number represents the horizontal displacement and the second the vertical displacement, we see the significance of order. For example, the ordered pair (3, 5) represents a point three units to the right of the origin and five units up, while (5, 3) represents a point that is five units to the right and three units up.

To be precise, we should distinguish between the point and the ordered pair; however, the distinction is usually blurred and we say "the point (x, y)" instead of "the point whose coordinates are (x, y)."

Use of the rectangular coordinate system establishes a one-to-one correspondence between the points in a plane and all possible ordered pairs of real numbers (x, y); that is, each point in the plane can be described by a unique ordered pair of numbers (x, y) and each ordered pair of numbers (x, y) can be represented by a unique point in the plane called the **graph** of the ordered pair.

EXAMPLE 1 Locate the points $P(-1, 2)$, $Q(2, 3)$, $R(-3, -4)$, $S(3, -5)$, and $T(\pi, 0)$ in the plane.

Solution $P(-1, 2)$ is in quadrant II because the x-coordinate is negative and the y-coordinate is positive.

$Q(2, 3)$ is in quadrant I because both coordinates are positive.

$R(-3, -4)$ is in quadrant III because both coordinates are negative.

$S(3, -5)$ is in quadrant IV because the x-coordinate is positive and the y-coordinate is negative.

$T(\pi, 0)$ is not in any quadrant, but lies on the positive x-axis.

The points are plotted in Figure 3.2.

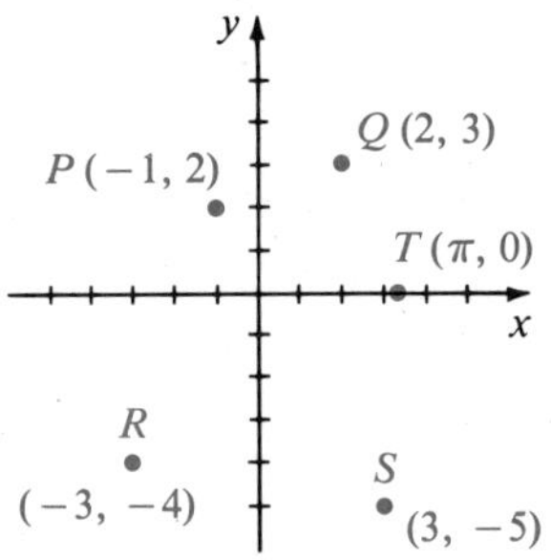

Figure 3.2 ■

In plotting an entire *set* of ordered pairs, the corresponding set of points in the plane is called the **graph** of the set. Sometimes the points in the graph form a recognizable pattern, such as a straight line or a circle.

EXAMPLE 2 Graph the set $\{(-4, -2), (-2, -1), (0, 0), (2, 1), (4, 2)\}$ and indicate the pattern of the points in the graph.

Solution The graph is shown in Figure 3.3. The points in the graph fall in a straight line.

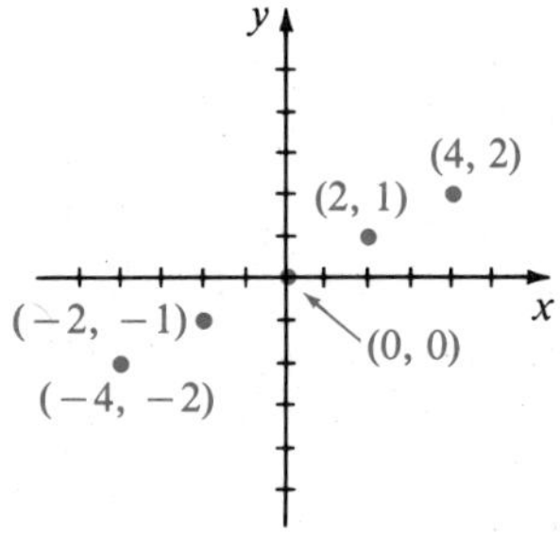

Figure 3.3 ■

EXAMPLE 3 Graph the set of points in the plane whose ordinate, y, is 3.

Solution This is the set defined by the equation $y = 3$. The graph is shown in Figure 3.4.

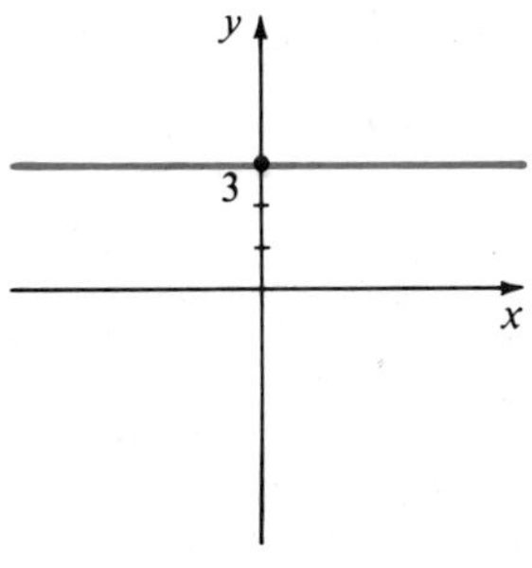

Figure 3.4 ■

EXAMPLE 4 Graph the set of points whose abscissas are greater than -1 and whose ordinates are less than or equal to 4.

Solution This set is described by the pair of inequalities $x > -1$, $y \leq 4$. The shaded region in Figure 3.5 is the graph of the set. The solid line is part of the region, whereas the broken line is not.

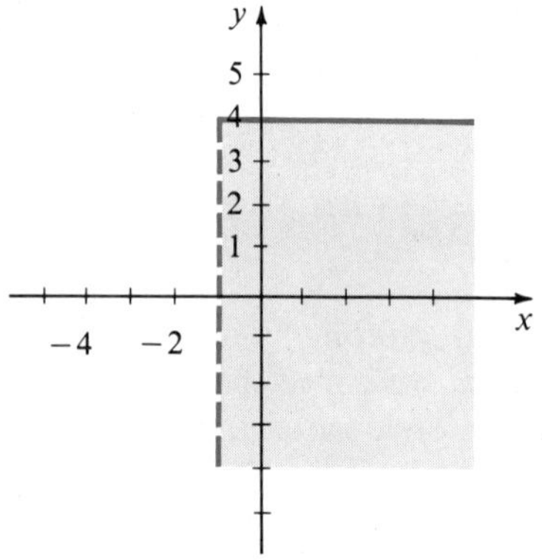

Figure 3.5

The Distance Between Two Points

Consider two points P_1 and P_2 on the x-axis as shown in Figure 3.6. The distance between these two points can be found by counting the units between them, or algebraically, by subtracting their coordinates. To ensure that the distance will be positive, we define it in terms of an absolute value.

$$d(P_1, P_2) = |P_2 - P_1|$$

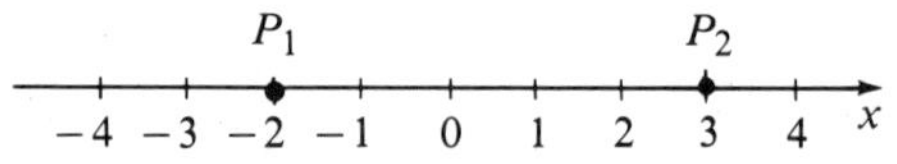

Figure 3.6

Computing the distance in Figure 3.6, we have

$$d(-2, 3) = |3 - (-2)| = |5| = 5$$

A similar scheme is followed if the points lie on the y-axis.

Now consider two points $P_1(x_1, y_1)$ and $P_2(x_2, y_2)$ that determine a slanted line segment, as shown in Figure 3.7. Draw a line through P_1 parallel to the x-axis and a line through P_2 parallel to the y-axis. These two lines intersect at the point $M(x_2, y_1)$. Hence, by the Pythagorean theorem,

$$[d(P_1, P_2)]^2 = [d(P_1, M)]^2 + [d(M, P_2)]^2 \tag{3.1}$$

We see from Figure 3.7 that $d(P_1, M)$ is the horizontal distance between P_1 and P_2. Therefore, the distance $d(P_1, M)$ is given by

$$d(P_1, M) = |x_2 - x_1|$$

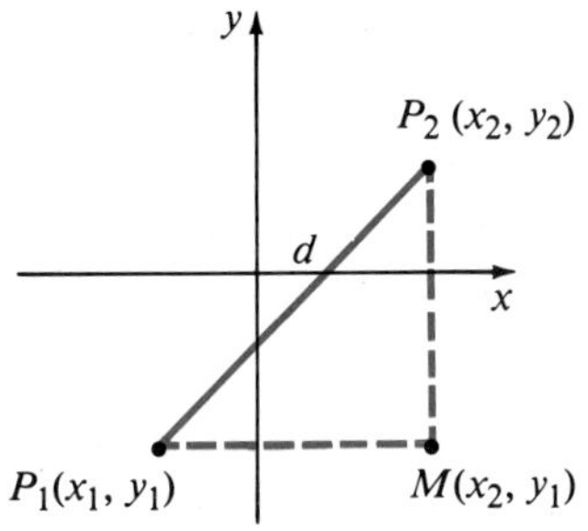

Figure 3.7

Likewise, the vertical distance $d(M, P_2)$ is given by

$$d(M, P_2) = |y_2 - y_1|$$

Making these substitutions into Equation 3.1 and denoting $d(P_1, P_2)$ by d, we get

$$d^2 = (x_2 - x_1)^2 + (y_2 - y_1)^2$$

Taking the square root yields the distance formula.

The Distance Formula

The length of the line segment from $P_1(x_1, y_1)$ to $P_2(x_2, y_2)$ is

$$d = \sqrt{(x_2 - x_1)^2 + (y_2 - y_1)^2} \qquad (3.2)$$

Formula 3.2 is used to find the distance between two points in the plane directly from their coordinates. The order in which the two points are labeled is immaterial since

$$(x_2 - x_1)^2 = (x_1 - x_2)^2 \quad \text{and} \quad (y_2 - y_1)^2 = (y_1 - y_2)^2$$

Warning: When you substitute values in the distance formula, remember to include the signs of the coordinates.

EXAMPLE 5 Find the distance between $(-3, -6)$ and $(5, -2)$. (See Figure 3.8.)

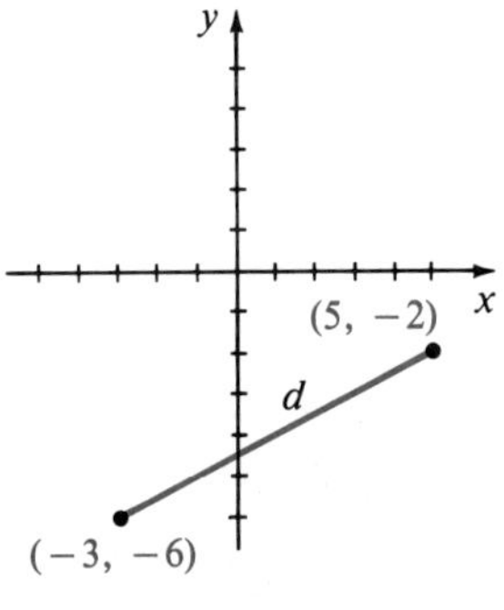

Figure 3.8

Solution Let $(x_1, y_1) = (-3, -6)$ and $(x_2, y_2) = (5, -2)$. Substituting these values into the distance formula, we get

$$\begin{aligned} d &= \sqrt{(x_2 - x_1)^2 + (y_2 - y_1)^2} \\ &= \sqrt{[5 - (-3)]^2 + [-2 - (-6)]^2} \\ &= \sqrt{64 + 16} = \sqrt{80} = 4\sqrt{5} \approx 8.9 \end{aligned}$$

■

EXAMPLE 6 Find the distance between (2, 5) and (2, −1).

Solution In this case the two given points lie on a vertical line since they have the same abscissa. (See Figure 3.9.) The distance between the two points, therefore, can be found directly.

$$d = |5 - (-1)| = |5 + 1| = 6 \text{ units}$$

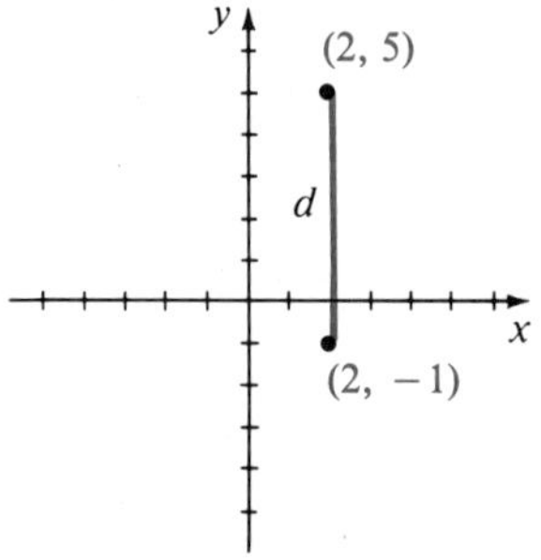

Figure 3.9

The distance can also be found from the distance formula. Letting $(x_1, y_1) = (2, 5)$ and $(x_2, y_2) = (2, -1)$, we have

$$d = \sqrt{(2-2)^2 + (-1-5)^2} = \sqrt{36} = 6 \text{ units}$$

■

The Midpoint Formula

The midpoint of the line segment connecting $P_1(x_1, y_1)$ and $P_2(x_2, y_2)$ is indicated by M in Figure 3.10. To obtain the coordinates of M draw lines through the three points P_1, M, and P_2 parallel to the y-axis so that they intersect the x-axis at Q_1, N,

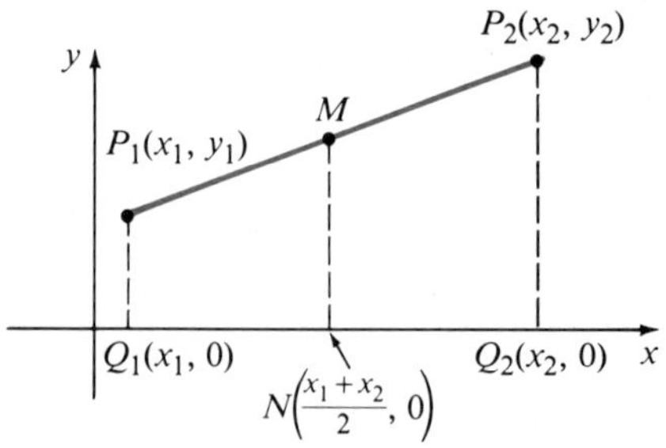

Figure 3.10

and Q_2. We know from geometry that if M is a midpoint of the line segment from P_1 to P_2, then N must be the midpoint of the line segment from Q_1 to Q_2. The midpoint of the line segment from Q_1 to Q_2, which corresponds to the abscissa of M, is given by $(x_1 + x_2)/2$. A similar analysis shows that the ordinate of M is given by $(y_1 + y_2)/2$.

The Midpoint Formula

The midpoint of the line segment from $P_1(x_1, y_1)$ to $P_2(x_2, y_2)$ is located at

$$\left(\frac{x_1 + x_2}{2}, \frac{y_1 + y_2}{2}\right) \tag{3.3}$$

EXAMPLE 7 Find the midpoint of the line segment from $(2, -3)$ to $(-1, -5)$.

Solution By Formula 3.3, the coordinates of the midpoint are

$$\left(\frac{2 + (-1)}{2}, \frac{-3 + (-5)}{2}\right)$$

This simplifies to $(\frac{1}{2}, -4)$. Check this result by drawing the indicated line segment to scale and locating the midpoint. ■

Exercises Section 3.1

Plot the ordered pairs in Exercises 1–6.

1. $(3, 2)$ **2.** $(4, 6)$ **3.** $(-2, \frac{1}{2})$

4. $(-6, -5)$ **5.** $(\frac{1}{4}, \frac{1}{2})$ **6.** $(-2.5, 1.7)$

7. In which two quadrants do the points have positive abscissas?

8. In which two quadrants do the points have negative ordinates?

9. In which quadrant are both the abscissa and ordinate negative?

10. In which quadrants is the ratio y/x negative?

11. What is the ordinate of a point on the x-axis?

In Exercises 12–20, graph the given set.

12. $\{(0, 0), (1, 1), (2, 2), (3, 3)\}$

13. $\{(0, 5), (1, 4), (2, 3), (3, 2), (4, 1), (5, 0)\}$

14. $\{(-2, 7), (0, 7), (3, 7), (7, 7)\}$

15. $\{(\sqrt{2}, 5), (\sqrt{2}, 2), (\sqrt{2}, 0), (\sqrt{2}, -\sqrt{3})\}$

16. $\{(-2, -1), (-1, -1), (0, -1), (1, \frac{1}{2}), (2, 1), (3, \frac{3}{2})\}$

17. $\{(0, 0), (1, 1), (2, 2), (3, 2), (4, 2), (5, 2)\}$

18. $\{(-5, 0), (-4, 3), (-3, 4), (0, 5), (3, 4), (4, 3), (5, 0)\}$

19. $\{(0, 4), (1, \sqrt{15}), (2, \sqrt{12}), (3, \sqrt{7}), (4, 0)\}$

20. $\{(1, 1), (3, 1), (1, 3), (3, 3)\}$

Graph the set of points defined by the given equations or inequalities in Exercises 21–31.

21. $y \geq 0$ **22.** $x = 0$ **23.** $x = -2$

24. $x \geq 0$ **25.** $y = 2$ **26.** $y = -1$

27. $x > -1$ and $y \geq 0$

28. $y = x$ **29.** $y = -x$

30. The points common to $x \geq 0$, $y \geq 0$ and $x < 1$, $y < 1$

31. The points common to $x > -1$, $y < -1$, and $x \leq -1$, $y \geq -1$

Plot the pairs of points in Exercises 32–39. Find the distance between the points and locate the midpoint of each line segment.

32. $(1, 2), (5, 4)$ **33.** $(0, 4), (-1, 3)$

34. $(-1, 5), (-1, -6)$ **35.** $(\frac{1}{2}, \frac{1}{2}), (\frac{1}{2}, -\frac{3}{4})$

36. $(-5, 3), (2, -1)$ **37.** $(0.5, 1.6), (6.2, 7.5)$

38. $(-3, 4), (0, 4)$ **39.** $(2, -6), (-\sqrt{3}, -3)$

40. The point $(x, 3)$ is 4 units from $(5, 1)$. Find x.

41. Find the distance between the points $(\sqrt{x}, \sqrt{y})$ and $(-\sqrt{x}, -\sqrt{y})$.

42. Find the distance between the points (x, y) and $(-x, y)$.

43. Find the distance between the points (x, y) and $(x, -y)$.

44. Find the point on the x-axis that is equidistant from $(0, -1)$ and $(3, 2)$.

45. Find the point on the y-axis that is equidistant from $(-4, -1)$ and $(-1, 2)$.

3.2 Variation

Most mathematical applications deal with the relationship of one quantity to another; for example, how acceleration of an object is related to the force causing the acceleration, or how a company's profit is related to its workforce. This section shows how mathematics is used to describe such relationships.

The relationship between two or more physical quantities can often be expressed by a mathematical formula. For instance, the area A of a circle is related to its radius r by the formula $A = \pi r^2$, where π is an irrational number approximated by 3.14159. Since the radius can be any positive real number, we call r the **independent variable.** The area A is called the **dependent variable** since it depends upon the value of r.

EXAMPLE 1 The formula $C = \pi d$ is used to calculate the circumference of a circle whose diameter is d. Here d is the independent variable and C the dependent variable. ■

The ratio of a to b is the number obtained by dividing a by b; that is, a/b. For example, the ratio of 3 to 5 is $\frac{3}{5}$ and the ratio of 12 to 4 is $\frac{12}{4} = 3$. If the ratio of two variables is always a constant, then the two variables are said to exhibit **direct variation.**

Definition

> The variable y is said to vary directly as x if $y = kx$, where k is the *constant of direct proportionality*.

Given that two variables vary directly, knowing the value of the variables in only one case will give the general formula of y in terms of x for all cases.

EXAMPLE 2 Newton's second law of motion states that the acceleration a of an object varies directly as the force F applied to it. Suppose that an object is accelerated 10 m/sec^2 by a force of 5 newtons. What acceleration will the same object experience if a force of 20 newtons is applied?

Solution Symbolically, Newton's law is written $a = k \cdot F$ where k is a constant. Since $a = 10$ when $F = 5$, we see that $10 = k \cdot 5$, or $k = 2$. Hence, the general formula is $a = 2F$. In particular, if $F = 20$, then $a = 2 \cdot 20 = 40$ m/sec^2. ■

Inverse variation occurs when the *product* of the variables is a constant.

Definition

> The variable y is said to vary inversely as x if $y = k/x$, where k is the *constant of inverse proportionality*.

In direct variation the two variables increase (or decrease) together. But in inverse variation an increase in one variable means a decrease in the other.

EXAMPLE 3 Boyle's law states: *If the temperature of a gas is constant, then the product of the volume V and pressure P is constant.* Suppose that the volume of a gas is 100 cu in. when the pressure is 20 psi. What is the volume when the pressure is 14.7 psi, assuming the temperature remains constant? (psi = pounds per square inch)

Solution Boyle's law states that $VP = k$, which can be expressed as $V = k(1/P)$. Hence, if $V = 100$ when $P = 20$, we have

$$100 = k\left(\frac{1}{20}\right)$$

or

$$k = 20(100) = 2000$$

Boyle's law for this gas is then

$$V = (2000)\frac{1}{P}$$

Substituting $P = 14.7$ psi into this formula yields

$$V = \frac{2000}{14.7} = 136.1 \text{ cu in.}$$

■

Comment: Variation that involves the product or quotient of two or more variables, such that $z = kxy$ and $z = k(x/y)$, is called **joint variation.** The words *directly* and *inversely* are still used to describe joint variation. Thus, in the joint variation $z = k(x/y)$, z is said to vary directly as x and inversely as y.

EXAMPLE 4 The ACE Light Bulb Company finds that the price P of each light bulb it produces varies directly as the cost C of material and inversely as the square root of the number produced, n. If materials cost \$2000 to produce 40,000 light bulbs priced at \$0.30 each, how much should the company charge for a new bulb if \$1500 of materials will make 10,000 bulbs?

Solution The joint variation among P, C, and n may be written

$$P = k\frac{C}{\sqrt{n}}$$

The condition $P = 0.30$, $C = 2000$, and $n = 40{,}000$ yields

$$0.30 = k\frac{2000}{\sqrt{40{,}000}} = \frac{2000k}{200} = 10k$$

Solving for k, we have

$$k = 0.03$$

Thus, the price is given by

$$P = \frac{0.03C}{\sqrt{n}}$$

Substituting $C = 1500$ and $n = 10{,}000$,

$$P = \frac{0.03(1500)}{\sqrt{10{,}000}} = 0.45$$

Hence, the company should charge \$0.45 for each of the new bulbs. ■

Exercises Section 3.2

In Exercises 1–10, write the indicated variation in equation form.

1. v varies directly as t.
2. a varies directly as k.
3. r varies inversely as $\sqrt{p}$.
4. q varies inversely as $(t - 2)$.
5. m varies directly as the square of x and the cube of y.
6. z varies directly as t and inversely as the square of v.
7. y varies directly as the fourth power of h and inversely as the square of g.
8. x varies directly as the square root of t and inversely as the cube of c.
9. n varies inversely as the product of r times t.
10. w varies inversely as the product of p times q times t.

In the remaining exercises, solve the indicated problem.

11. A road map uses a scale of 1 in. = 20 mi. How far is Cincinnati from Cleveland if the map distance measures 12.6 in.?
12. In a blueprint scale, 1 in. = 5 ft. What are the dimensions of a room that measures 9 in. by 7 in. on the blueprint?
13. The ratio of sodium to chlorine in common table salt is approximately $\frac{5}{3}$. Find the approximate amount of each element in a salt compound weighing 100 lb.
14. A quality-control sample revealed that on a certain day, for every 1000 baseballs manufactured, 20 were defective. If 15,250 were manufactured on that day, how many were defective?
15. A piece of wire 8 ft long is to be cut so that the parts are in the ratio of 5 to 4. How long should each part be?
16. A saloon keeper advertises 18-oz steins of beer for \$0.40, while the neighborhood grocer advertises a case of twenty-four 12-oz cans for \$6.10. Which is the better buy and why?
17. An automobile has a list price of \$8266. If the ratio of list price to dealer cost is 1.18, how much does the dealer pay for the car?
18. The ratio of water weight to actual weight for most humans is approximately 0.68. If Susan weighs 92 lb, how much of her weight is water?
19. The *slope* of an inclined plane is the ratio of the vertical rise to the corresponding horizontal run. What is the slope of an incline having a vertical rise of 15 ft for a horizontal run of 100 ft?

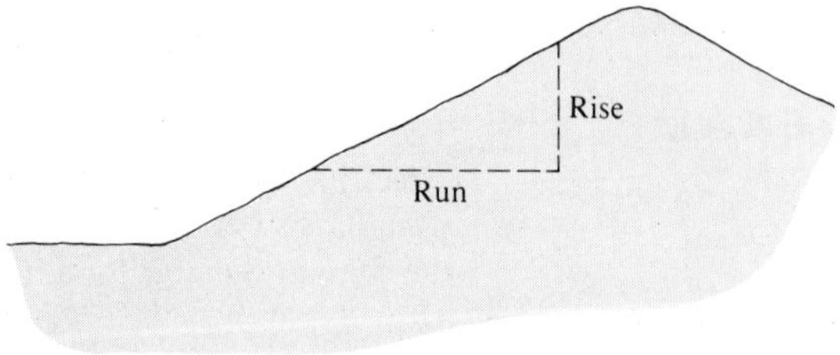

20. The *density* of an object is the ratio of the object's weight to its volume. What is the density of an object having a volume of 25 cu in. and a weight of 75 lb?
21. If y varies directly as x and if $y = 5$ when $x = 10$, find the value of y when $x = 12$.

22. If r varies directly as the square of t and if $r = 3$ when $t = 4$, find the value of r when $t = 5$.

23. If z varies inversely as t and if $z = 4$ when $t = \frac{1}{2}$, find the value of z when $t = 2$.

24. If y varies inversely as the square root of x and if $y = 2$ when $x = 9$, find the value of y when $x = 4$.

25. When an object falls from rest, its velocity varies directly as the time of fall. Find the velocity of an object 2 sec after release if it has a velocity of 96 ft/sec at the end of 3 sec.

26. Hooke's law states that the force required to stretch a spring is directly proportional to the elongation of the spring. If a 5-lb force stretches the spring 1.5 in., how much force is required to stretch it 2.0 in.?

27. The unit cost of producing a monthly magazine varies inversely as the square root of the circulation. If it costs \$0.40 per unit when the circulation is 200,000, what will it cost if the circulation jumps to 400,000?

28. The distance an object falls from rest varies directly as the square of the elapsed time. If an object fell 64 ft in 2 sec, how far had it fallen at the end of $\frac{1}{2}$ sec?

29. The intensity of light varies inversely as the square of the distance from the source. If the intensity 5 ft from a light is 4 foot-candles, what is the intensity 10 ft from the light?

30. The law of gravitational attraction states that the gravitational force between two objects varies inversely as the square of the distance between them. If the gravitational force between two objects is 150 lb when they are 200 mi apart, what is the gravitational force between them when they are 50 mi apart?

31. The power in a resistive circuit varies directly as the resistance and the square of the current. If the power in a 50-ohm resistor is 50 watts when the current is 0.5 amp, what is the power when the current is 1.0 amp?

32. The cost of labor varies directly as the number of workers and the number of days they work. If three men work five days for \$1500, how many days must five men work to earn \$1500?

33. Ohm's law states that the electric current in a circuit varies directly as the voltage and inversely as the resistance. Given that the current in a 20-ohm resistor is 0.5 amp when a voltage of 10 volts is applied, what is the current in the resistor when the applied voltage is 12 volts?

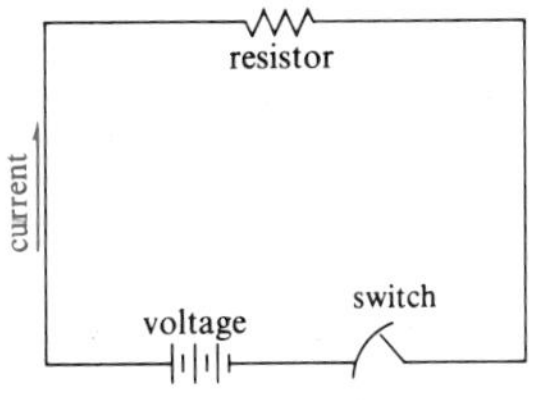

34. The volume of a gas varies directly as the temperature and inversely as the pressure. Find a formula relating volume, temperature, and pressure. Suppose that the volume is 100 cu in. when $T = 200°$ C and the pressure is 50 lb/sq in. Find the volume when the temperature is 300° C and the pressure is 100 lb/sq in.

35. The cost of publishing a pamphlet is \$2000 plus an amount varying directly with the number of copies published. If 1000 copies of the pamphlet cost \$2200, how much will it cost to publish 1500 copies?

36. The number of gallons of gasoline used by an automobile traveling at a constant speed is directly proportional to the number of miles traveled, while the number of miles traveled is in turn directly proportional to the number of hours spent driving. Can you conclude that the number of gallons used is directly proportional to the time driven?

37. If y is directly proportional to t and if x is directly proportional to t, what can you say about the following?

a. xy **b.** $\frac{x}{y}$ **c.** $x + y$

38. Kepler's third law states that the time in which a planet revolves about the sun varies directly as the square root of the cube of the maximum radius of its orbit. Using 93 million miles as the maximum radius of the Earth's orbit and 142 million miles as the maximum radius of Mars' orbit, in how many days will Mars make one revolution about the sun?

3.3 Functions

A very important idea in mathematics is that of pairing a number x with a number y by some specified rule called a **rule of correspondence.** The rule of correspondence indicates how a value of x is used to obtain a value of y. We used this idea in the study of direct variation when we paired each number x with a number y by the rule of correspondence $y = kx$. Direct variation is an example of a more general idea called **functional pairing.** The pairings in the following table were generated using $y = 3x^2$ as the rule of correspondence.

x	-2	-1	0	1	2	3
y	12	3	0	3	12	27

If we let X represent the set of values that we can assign to x and Y the corresponding set of values obtained by the rule $y = 3x^2$, then Figure 3.11 represents the general pairing. The figure emphasizes the idea that the pairings are **ordered;** that is, the value of y is obtained *from* the value of x. The figure is also intended to show that the functional pairing is **unique;** that is, only one value of y is paired with each value of x.

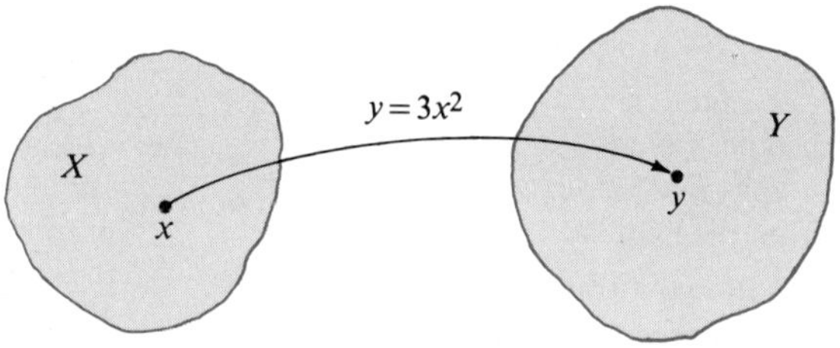

Figure 3.11

Rules of correspondence that assign a unique value of y in Y to each x in X are of particular interest in mathematics and we make the following definition.

Definition

> A correspondence f that assigns to each x in X exactly one element y in Y is called a **function.** The set X is called the **domain** of the function and the set of ys is called the **range** of the function. We say that "y is the image of x" or that "y is a function of x."

Functions are frequently expressed by a formula such as $y = 3x^2$, but other means may be used. For instance, a set of ordered pairs $\{(x, y)\}$ is a function if no two distinct pairs have the same first element. This follows from the fact that a function assigns to each x in X a unique y in Y. The following remarks should clarify the important points of the definition of a function.

- A formula such as $y = \pm\sqrt{x}$ does *not* define y as a function of x since it assigns two values to each positive value of x. For example, ± 2 are both images of $x = 4$. However, we note that each of the formulas $y = \sqrt{x}$ and $y = -\sqrt{x}$ taken separately does define a function.
- The expression $y = 8$ defines a function since y has the value 8 for every value of x. The definition does not require that y have a different value for each x, but only that it be unique.
- The expression $x = 5$ is not a function because many values of y correspond to $x = 5$. For example, $(5, -1)$, $(5, 0)$, $(5, 3)$ are some of the ordered pairs that satisfy the expression $x = 5$.
- The set $\{(2, 3), (-1, 4), (0, -5), (3, 4)\}$ is a function since each first element is paired with a unique second element.
- The set $\{(-3, 4), (2, 5), (2, -6), (9, 7)\}$ is not a function because the distinct pairs $(2, 5)$ and $(2, -6)$ have the same first element. Therefore, two different values of y are assigned to the same x.

Comment: Rules of correspondence that permit more than one value of y to be paired with a value of x are called **relations.** Hence $y = \pm\sqrt{x}$, $x = 5$, and $\{(-3, 4), (2, 5), (2, -6), (9, 7)\}$ are relations. Note that every function is a relation but a relation is not necessarily a function.

The domain of a function can be quite arbitrary. For example, we could limit the domain of $y = 3x^2$ to $x = 0, 1, 2$. In this case, the range elements are 0, 3, 12 and the functional pairings are $\{(0, 0), (1, 3), (2, 12)\}$. **If the domain is not specified, we assume that it consists of all real numbers for which the rule of correspondence will yield a real number.** Examples 2 and 3 show functions with restricted domains.

EXAMPLE 1 The equation $y = x^2 + 5$ defines a function since each value of x determines only one value of y. The domain consists of all real numbers and the range consists only of those real numbers greater than or equal to 5 (since the smallest possible value of x^2 is 0). ■

EXAMPLE 2 Find the domain and range of the function $y = \sqrt{x}$.

Solution If we substitute a negative real number for x in $y = \sqrt{x}$, we do not get a real number for y. However, each nonnegative real number substituted for x yields a nonnegative real number for y. Therefore, both the domain and range of this function consist of all nonnegative real numbers. ■

EXAMPLE 3 Find the domain and range of the function $y = \dfrac{4}{x - 3}$.

Solution Since division by zero is not allowed, we must exclude 3 as a domain element; we conclude that the domain consists of all real numbers except 3.

To find the range of this function we solve for x and note any restrictions on y. Thus,

$$y = \frac{4}{x - 3}$$

$$xy - 3y = 4 \qquad \text{Multiplying both sides by } x - 3$$

$$xy = 3y + 4 \qquad \text{Adding } 3y \text{ to both sides}$$

$$x = \frac{3y + 4}{y} \qquad \text{Dividing both sides by } y$$

The only limitation on y is that it cannot equal 0. Therefore, the range consists of all real numbers except 0. ■

Functional rules are not restricted to formulas or mathematical expressions. The next two examples show functions that are described by diagrams and tables.

EXAMPLE 4 Let A denote the set $\{a, b, c, d\}$ and B denote the set $\{5, 2, 4, \sqrt{6}, 12\}$. Figure 3.12 diagrams a function in which 5 is the image of a, $\sqrt{6}$ is the image of b, and 4 is the image of d. Notice that no number is paired with c. We say that the function is **undefined** for the element c. The domain of this function is the set $\{a, b, d\}$ and the range is the set $\{5, 4, \sqrt{6}\}$. We note that the function defined in Figure 3.12 may also be written as the set of ordered pairs $\{(a, 5), (b, \sqrt{6}), (d, 4)\}$.

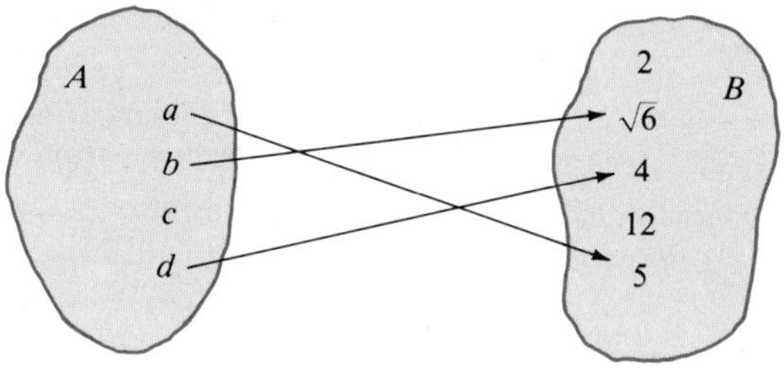

Figure 3.12 ■

EXAMPLE 5 A table is a listing of ordered pairs. The following table defines a function.

x	-3	-2	-1	0	1	2	3
y	4	0	1	2	0	5	-4

In this case, the domain consists of the numbers $-3, -2, -1, 0, 1, 2, 3$. The range consists of the numbers $-4, 0, 1, 2, 4, 5$. The table is the rule of correspondence for this function. ■

Although a functional relation can be given in a variety of forms, it must never assign more than one range element to the same domain element. Figure 3.13 does not describe a function, since c is assigned to the two different elements 5 and 6.

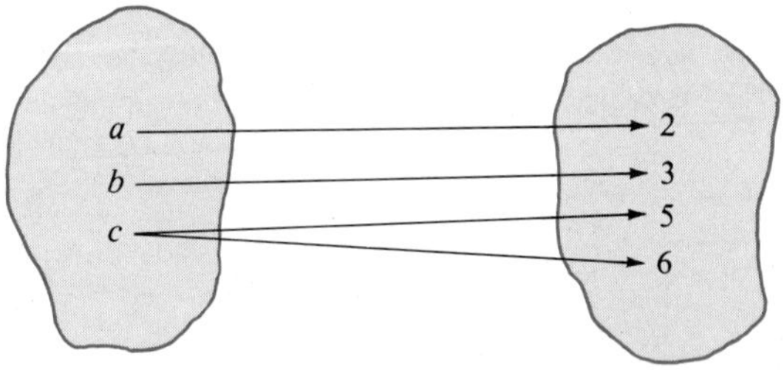

Figure 3.13

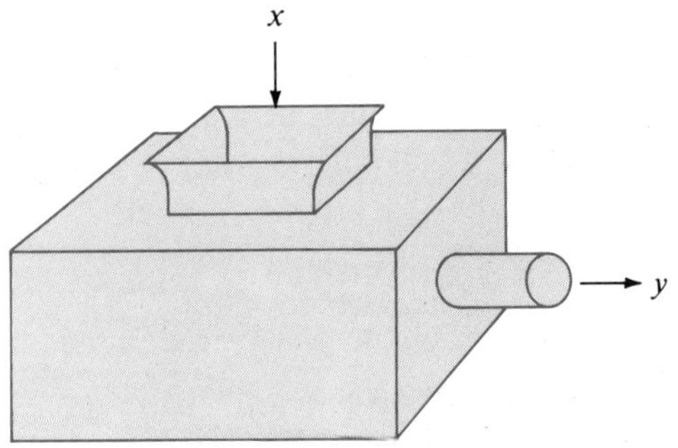

Figure 3.14

In a useful analogy, we can compare a function to a machine that has an input and an output. (See Figure 3.14.) When an element x enters the machine, it is transformed by the machine (function) into a new element, y. The set of elements that can be put into the machine represents the domain of the function and the output represents the elements of the range.

EXAMPLE 6 An ice-vending machine dispenses a 5-lb bag of ice for \$1, a 10-lb bag for \$2, and a 15-lb bag for \$3. This machine represents a function in which the money is input and the corresponding output is 5 lb of ice, 10 lb of ice, or 15 lb of ice. If we ignore the units of measurement (dollars and pounds), the function can be represented by the ordered pairs $\{(1, 5), (2, 10), (3, 5)\}$.

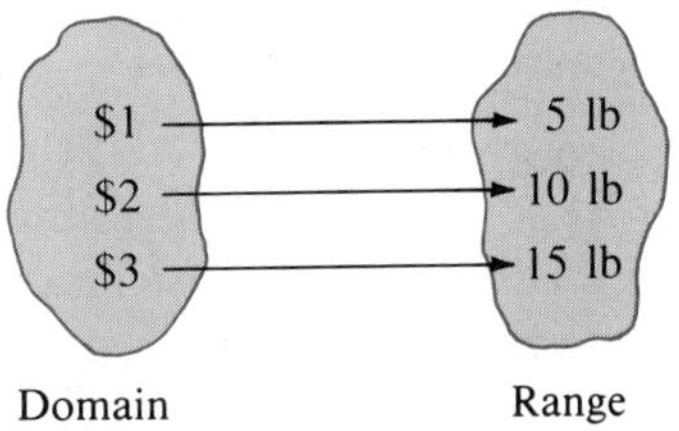

Figure 3.15

■

Functional Notation

Single letters or symbols customarily denote functions; for instance f, F, G, g, h, or H. If x is an element of the domain of a function f, then the corresponding value in the range is denoted by $f(x)$, which is read "f of x," or the "function evaluated at x." Referring back to Figure 3.12, we note that $f(a) = 5$, $f(b) = \sqrt{6}$, $f(c)$ is undefined, and $f(d) = 4$. The domain element x is sometimes called the **argument** of f.

Warning: The symbol $f(x)$ does NOT mean the product of f times x.

The function f may or may not have a definite mathematical expression describing the rule of correspondence. If, however, such a specific expression is available, functional notation offers a convenient way of indicating numbers in the range. To find a number in the range that is associated with any number in the domain, merely replace the letter x wherever it appears in the expression for $f(x)$ by the number from the domain.

It is sometimes helpful to think of x as representing a blank so that the functional notation tells us what to put in the blank. For example, if $f(x) = x^2 + 3x$, we may think:

$$f(\ ) = (\ )^2 + 3(\ )$$

Then, anything may be placed in the blank. For example,

$$f(a^2) = (a^2)^2 + 3(a^2) = a^4 + 3a^2$$

Calculators take the drudgery out of evaluating complex functions for specified values of the domain. Thus, with a calculator, it is just as easy to evaluate $f(x) = \pi x^3 + \sqrt{x+2}$ *for* $x = 3.105$ *as for* $x = 2$.

EXAMPLE 7 Let $f(x) = x^2 + 3x$.
a. Find $f(2)$. b. Find $f(a - 4)$.

Solution a. Substitute 2 for x, so that

$$f(2) = 2^2 + 3 \cdot 2 = 10$$

b. Substitute $a - 4$ for x, so that

$$f(a - 4) = (a - 4)^2 + 3(a - 4) = a^2 - 8a + 16 + 3a - 12 = a^2 - 5a + 4$$ ■

Warning: Do not confuse functional notation with the distributive law. Thus, $f(a - 4) \neq f(a) - f(4)$.

Although functional notation does not follow the distributive law, we can combine the values of two functions by the operations of addition, subtraction, multiplication, and division. For example, if $f(x) = 2x$ and $g(x) = x + 3$, we can form

$$f(x) + g(x) = 2x + x + 3 = 3x + 3$$
$$f(x) - g(x) = 2x - (x + 3) = x - 3$$
$$f(x) \cdot g(x) = 2x(x + 3) = 2x^2 + 6x$$
$$\frac{f(x)}{g(x)} = \frac{2x}{x + 3}$$

In combining two functions to form a new function, the domain of the new function need not be the same as either of the original functions. Thus, the function formed above by $f(x)/g(x)$ is not defined at $x = -3$, but the original functions $f(x) = 2x$ and $g(x) = x + 3$ are both defined at $x = -3$.

EXAMPLE 8 If $f(x) = 2x + 3$, find and expand the product $f(x + 1) \cdot f(5x)$.

Solution Note that $f(x + 1) = 2(x + 1) + 3 = 2x + 5$ and $f(5x) = 2(5x) + 3 = 10x + 3$. Therefore,

$$\begin{aligned} f(x + 1) \cdot f(5x) &= (2x + 5)(10x + 3) \\ &= 20x^2 + 56x + 15 \end{aligned}$$ ■

The function $f(x) = x^2$ has the property that $f(2) = 2^2 = 4$ and $f(-2) = (-2)^2 = 4$, so $f(-2) = f(2)$. We say that $f(x) = x^2$ is an even function. The function $g(x) = x^3$ has the property that $g(2) = 2^3 = 8$ and $g(-2) = (-2)^3 = -8$, so $g(-2) = -g(2)$. We say that this function is an odd function. In general, we define even and odd functions as follows.

Definition

- A function f is **even** if

$$f(-x) = f(x)$$

for every x in the domain of f.

- A function f is **odd** if

$$f(-x) = -f(x)$$

for every x in the domain of f.

EXAMPLE 9 a. Show that $f(x) = 5 - x^4$ is an even function.
b. Show that $g(x) = 2x^3 + x$ is an odd function.
c. Show that $h(x) = x^2 - 3x$ is neither even nor odd.

Solution a. To show that f is an even function we must show that $f(-x) = f(x)$ for any real number x.

$$f(-x) = 5 - (-x)^4 = 5 - x^4 = f(x)$$

This shows that f is an even function.

b. For any real number x, we have

$$g(-x) = 2(-x)^3 + (-x) = -2x^3 - x = -(2x^3 + x) = -g(x)$$

This shows that g is an odd function.

c. For any real number x, we have

$$h(-x) = (-x)^2 - 3(-x) = x^2 + 3x$$

Since $x^2 + 3x$ is not $h(x)$ or $-h(x)$, we conclude that h is neither even nor odd. ■

The Difference Quotient

If f is a function, a is a given constant, and h is any nonzero number, then the following expression is called the **difference quotient** of the function f.

$$\frac{f(a+h) - f(a)}{h}$$

The difference quotient is encountered frequently in the study of calculus.

EXAMPLE 10 Given the constant a, find the difference quotient for $f(x) = 3x + 2$.

Solution Here, $f(a + h) = 3(a + h) + 2 = 3a + 3h + 2$ and $f(a) = 3a + 2$. Therefore, the difference quotient is

$$\frac{f(a+h) - f(a)}{h} = \frac{(3a + 3h + 2) - (3a + 2)}{h} = \frac{3h}{h} = 3$$ ■

EXAMPLE 11 Given the constant a, find the difference quotient for $f(x) = 1/x$.

Solution First, note that $f(a + h) = 1/(a + h)$ and $f(a) = 1/a$

$$\frac{f(a+h) - f(a)}{h} = \frac{\dfrac{1}{a+h} - \dfrac{1}{a}}{h} = \frac{1}{h}\left(\frac{a - (a+h)}{a(a+h)}\right) = \frac{-1}{a(a+h)}$$ ■

Exercises Section 3.3

Which of the expressions in Exercises 1–8 define functions? (Assume that y is dependent on x.)

1. $y = 2x + 5$ **2.** $y = x^2$ **3.** $y = 10$

4. $y < 3x$ **5.** $y = \sqrt[3]{x}$ **6.** $y^2 = x^3$

7. $y^2 = 5x$ **8.** $y = 1/x$

Which of the sets or tables in Exercises 9–12 define y as a function of x?

9. $\{(2, 3), (-1, 4), (3, 0), (0, 4)\}$

10. $\{(-1, 0), (2, 3), (2, -2)\}$

11.

x	1	1	2	3
y	2	3	4	7

12.

x	2	7	8
y	3	9	3

13. Which of the following diagrams define functions?

a.

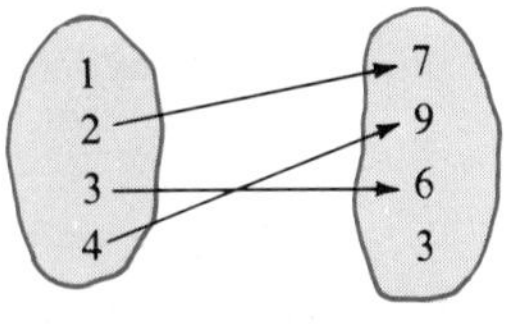

b.

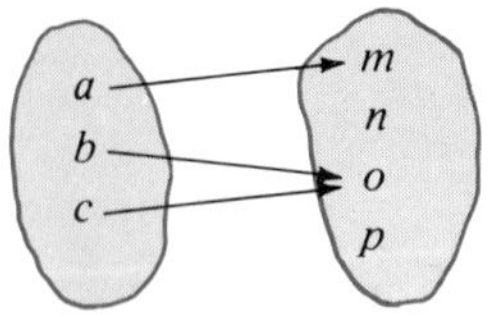

c.

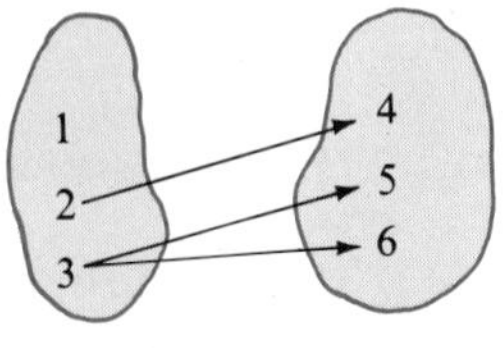

Find the domain and the range of each of the real valued functions in Exercises 14–24.

14. $y = 2x$ **15.** $y = 4 - 3x$

16. $y = 3t^2 + 5$ **17.** $y = \sqrt{x}$

18. $y = 1/x^2$ **19.** $y = x^{1/3}$

20. $\{(1, 2), (3, 5), (7, 1), (12, -2)\}$

21. $f(x) = \sqrt{-x}$ **22.** $f(x) = \sqrt{-x^2}$

23. $f(x) = \sqrt{x - 1}$ **24.** $f(x) = \sqrt{1 - x}$

25. Suppose that the function f has the rule $f(x) = 3x + 1$. Compute the following:
a. $f(3)$ **b.** $f(\pi)$
c. $f(z)$ **d.** $f(x - h)$
e. The element in the domain that maps onto 10
f. The range of the function
g. The difference quotient of f.

26. Suppose that the function G has the rule $G(t) = t^2 - 2t + 1$. Compute the following:
a. $G(2)$ **b.** $G(-1)$ **c.** $G(x^2)$
d. $G(x - h)$ **e.** $G(\sqrt{t})$
f. The difference quotient of G.

Compute the difference quotient for the functions in Exercises 27–32. See Example 10.

27. $f(x) = x^2$ **28.** $f(x) = 2x^2$

29. $f(x) = x^2 - 2x$ **30.** $f(x) = x^3$

31. $f(x) = x^3 - 1$ **32.** $f(x) = 1/x^2$

In Exercises 33–40, identify the given function as even, odd, or neither even nor odd.

33. $f(x) = -3x^5$ **34.** $f(x) = 2x + 5$

35. $f(x) = 2x - x^3$ **36.** $f(x) = 5x^4$

37. $f(x) = x^4 - 3x$ **38.** $f(x) = x^2 + 10$

39. $y = \sqrt{x^2 + 4}$ **40.** $y = (x^2 - 1)/x^2$

41. Given that $g(x) = 2x - 7$, find and expand $g(x - 4) \cdot g(x - 1)$.

42. Given that $h(t) = t^2$, find and expand $h(t+2) \cdot h(\sqrt{t})$.

43. Given that $F(x) = 3x^2$, find and expand $F(x) \cdot F(x-3)$.

44. Let $f(x) = x - 3$. Solve the equation $f(x+2) \cdot f(x-1) = 0$.

45. Let $f(x) = x^2 + 2x$. Solve the equation $f(x) - 3 = 0$.

46. Let $h(t) = t^2 - 9$. Solve the equation $h(t-1) + 9 = 0$.

47. Let $f(x) = 2x - x^2$. Solve the equation $f(x) - f(2x) = 0$.

48. Suppose that y is directly proportional to x; that is, $y = f(x) = kx$.
  a. Compute $f(x_1)/f(x_2)$ for any two numbers x_1 and x_2. ($f(x_2) \neq 0$).
  b. Compare $f(1/x)$ with $1/f(x)$.
  c. Compare $f(x^2)$ with $[f(x)]^2$.
  d. Find the difference quotient.
  e. Compare $f(x) + 1$ with $f(x+1)$.
  f. Compare $f(x_1 + x_2)$ with $f(x_1) + f(x_2)$.
  g. Compare $af(x)$ with $f(ax)$, where a is a constant.

49. Suppose that y is inversely proportional to x; that is, $y = f(x) = k/x$. Answer the questions in Exercise 48 for this function.

50. Let $f(x) = mx + b$, where m and b are constants.
  a. Compare $f(ax)$ with $af(x)$.
  b. Compare $f(x) + 1$ with $f(x+1)$.

Use a calculator to find the indicated range value in Exercises 51–54.

51. Given $f(s) = 3.101s^2 + 29.46s$, find $f(-0.415)$.

52. Given $g(t) = 4356t(3.7 + t)$, find $g(287.7)$.

53. The current i in a resistor is found to vary with time according to

$$i(t) = 1.196t^2 + 0.076t$$

where i is in amperes and t is in seconds. Find $i(1.375)$.

54. The equation of motion of a rocket is given by

$$h(t) = 150.6t - 16.1t^2$$

where h is altitude in feet when t is measured in seconds. Find $h(0.45)$.

55. Jim must pay taxes of 12% to the IRS, 10% to Social Security, 6% to the state, and 1.5% to the city. In addition, \$150 is withheld from each paycheck for retirement. Write a function that gives Jim's take-home pay, P, as a function of his gross wages, w.

56. The insurance premium for a company health plan is presently \$25,000. The company controller estimates that this cost will increase each year by an amount equal to the square root of gross revenues. Write an expression for insurance premium, P, as a function of gross revenue, U.

3.4 The Graph of a Function

The **graph of a function f** is the set of points (x, y) in the plane whose coordinates satisfy the equation $y = f(x)$. The first number in the ordered pair is the domain element and the second number is the range element. Domain values are plotted along the horizontal axis and range values along the vertical axis.

EXAMPLE 1 The graph of the function defined by $f = \{(1, 3), (-2, 2), (5, -1)\}$ is shown in Figure 3.16.

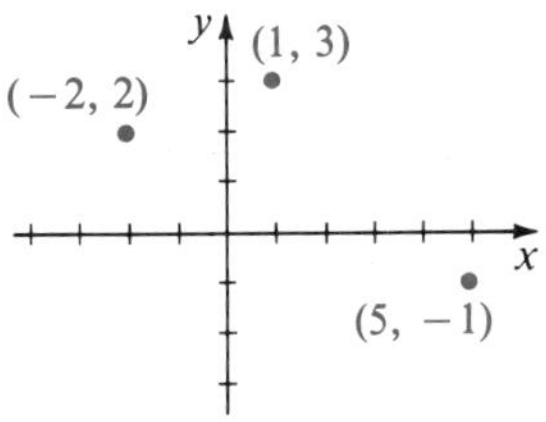

Figure 3.16 ■

EXAMPLE 2 Draw the graph of the function g if the domain of g is $\{0, 1, 4, 9\}$ and the rule of correspondence is $g(x) = -\sqrt{x}$.

Solution From the given conditions, we have $g = \{(0, 0), (1, -1), (4, -2), (9, -3)\}$. The graph of g is shown in Figure 3.17.

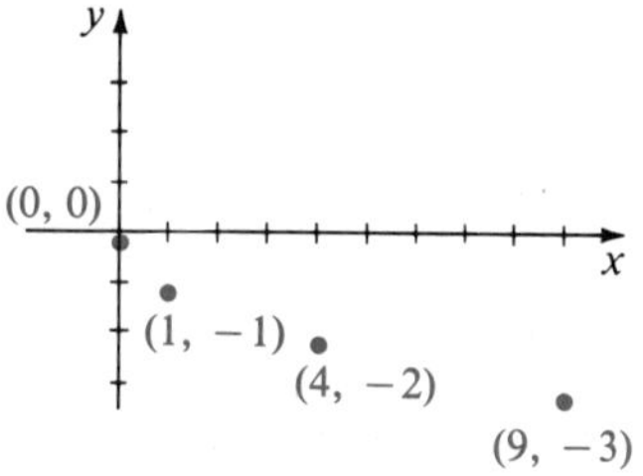

Figure 3.17

■

The domain of a function is usually an interval of real numbers. The graphs of such functions can be constructed by plotting all points in the plane whose coordinates satisfy the function. However, this approach is impractical since there is no limit to the number of such points that can be plotted. In practice, the graph of such a function is constructed by plotting a few selected points and connecting these points with a smooth curve. As an illustration, consider the function defined by $y = x^2$, whose domain is the entire set of real numbers. By assigning values to x, we obtain the following set of ordered pairs.

x	-3	-2	-1	0	1	2	3
y	9	4	1	0	1	4	9

Now plot the set of ordered pairs in the Cartesian plane, as shown in Figure 3.18(a). The representation of the graph of $y = x^2$ can then be obtained by connecting the points with a smooth curve, as in Figure 3.18(b). This graph is, of course, only an approximation of the actual graph of the function. Its accuracy depends on the number of points plotted and the care taken in drawing the smooth curve connecting the points.

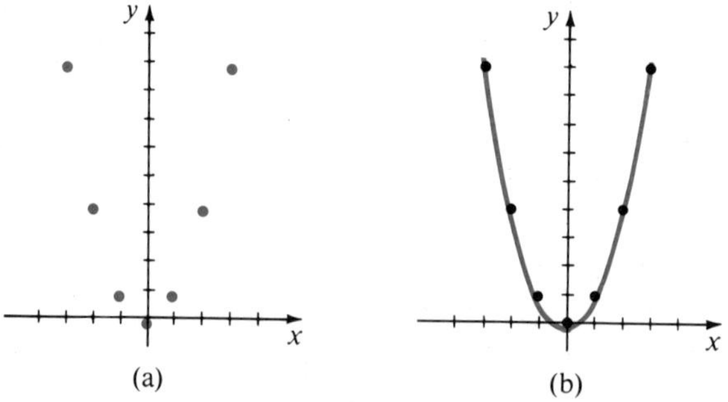

Figure 3.18

Usually only a segment of the graph in the vicinity of the origin is plotted, even though the graph may extend much farther. For instance, in Figure 3.18 only the portion of the curve from $x = -3$ to $x = 3$ is plotted, although the domain of the function is the set of all real numbers.

When graphing a function it is always helpful to determine the domain beforehand since the domain determines the extent of the graph with respect to the x-axis.

EXAMPLE 3 Graph the function $y = \sqrt{4 - x}$.

Solution The domain consists of all real numbers x for which $4 - x \geq 0$. Otherwise, the range values would not be real numbers. Hence the domain is the set of all real numbers x such that $x \leq 4$. This means that the graph must be to the left of the vertical line $x = 4$, except for the point (4, 0), which *is* part of the graph, as you can see in Figure 3.19.

$y = \sqrt{4 - x}$

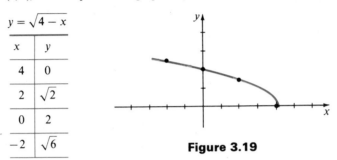

x	y
4	0
2	$\sqrt{2}$
0	2
−2	$\sqrt{6}$

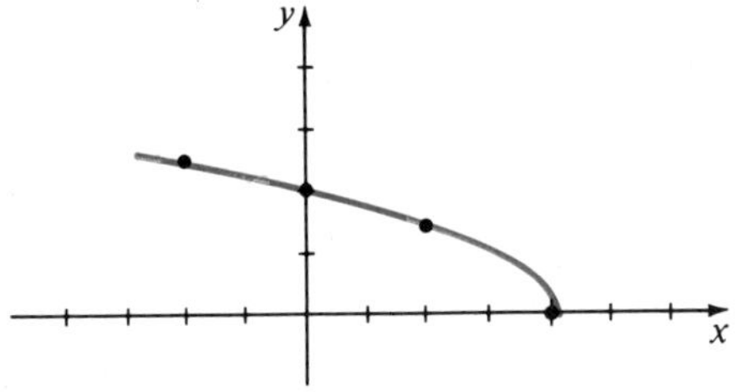

Figure 3.19

In many physical situations, the nature of the problem restricts the domain of the function. For instance, the height above ground of a ball thrown upward from ground level with an initial velocity of 32 ft/sec is described by the function $h = 32t - 16t^2$, where t is the elapsed time in seconds and h is the vertical height in feet. The ball will strike the ground when $h = 0$; that is, when $32t - 16t^2 = 0$, or $t = 2$ sec after the ball is thrown upward. The domain of this function is $0 \leq t \leq 2$, since the equation has no meaning before the ball is thrown or after it hits the ground.

EXAMPLE 4 Draw the graph of $h = 32t - 16t^2$ on $0 \leq t \leq 2$.

Solution The table and graph in Figure 3.20 result from computing some convenient values of h in the interval $0 \leq t \leq 2$. The graph shows that the maximum height to which the ball rises is 16 ft.

$h = 32t - 16t^2$

t	h
0	0
.5	12
1.0	16
1.5	12
2.0	0

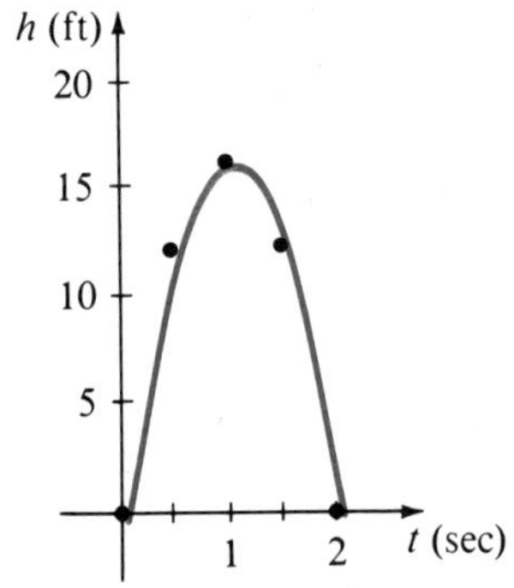

Figure 3.20

In business, the relationship between the price of an item and the number of items purchased by the consumer (in a fixed period of time) is called the **demand function.** The relation between the price and the number of items supplied by the producer is called the **supply function.** If n is the number of items and p is the price, we can express either a supply or demand function in the form

$$p = f(n)$$

Typical demand and supply curves are shown in the next example.

EXAMPLE 5 a. Draw the demand curve corresponding to $p = 8000 - \frac{1}{2}n^2$ for $0 \le n \le 100$.

b. Draw the supply curve corresponding to $p = 100 + 5\sqrt{n}$ for $0 \le n \le 900$.

Solution Some convenient values of n are used to compute the values in the tables and the curves drawn from these tabled values. Although the graphs of demand and supply functions consist of sets of discrete points, it is common practice to show a smooth curve through these points, as in Figure 3.21. ■

The two curves shown in Figure 3.21 characterize the conditions in a free market: the demand curve shows that as price decreases, the demand for the item will increase; and the supply curve shows that as the price increases, the supply will also increase.

$p = 8000 - \frac{1}{2}n^2$

n	p
0	8000
20	7800
40	7200
60	6200
80	4800
100	3000

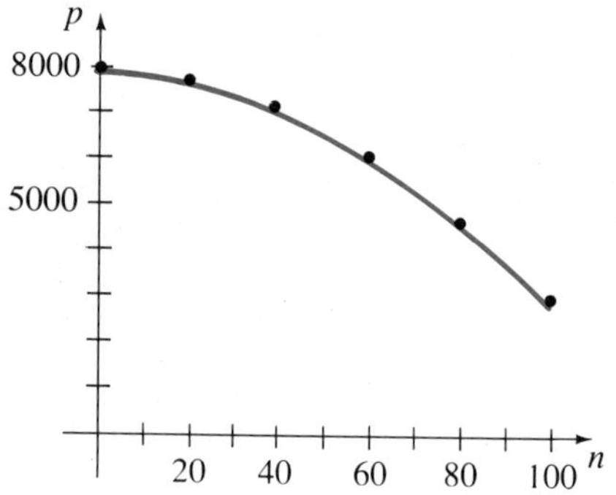

(a) Demand curve

$p = 100 + 5\sqrt{n}$

n	p
0	100
100	150
400	200
900	250

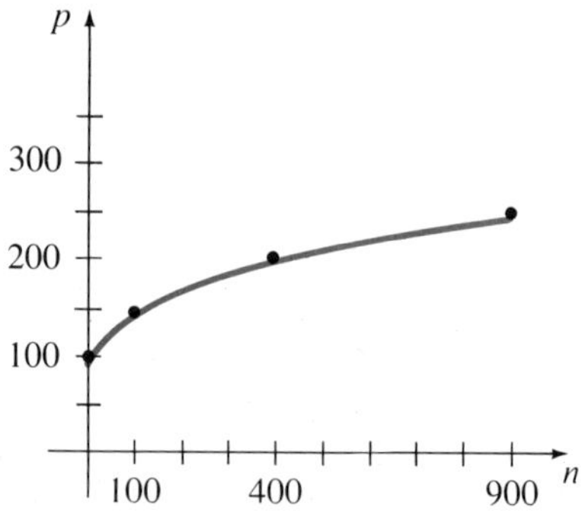

(b) Supply curve

Figure 3.21

Comment: Example 5 shows how the graph of a function can reveal important features of a function.

The graphs of even and odd functions have an interesting kind of symmetry with respect to the coordinate axes.

- Given that f is an even function, then $y = f(x) = f(-x)$ for every x in the domain of f. This means that if (x, y) is on the graph of the function f, then so is $(-x, y)$. See Figure 3.22. A graph that has this property is said to be **symmetric with respect to the y-axis.**

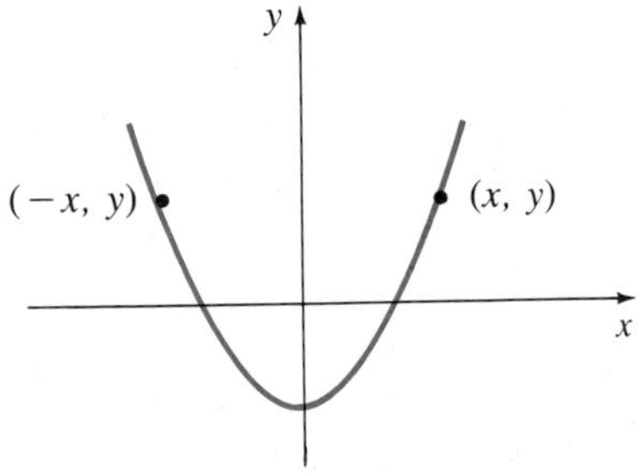

Figure 3.22 Even function

- Given that f is an odd function, then if (x, y) is on the graph of the function f, so is $(-x, -y)$. See Figure 3.23. A graph that has this property is said to be **symmetric with respect to the origin.**

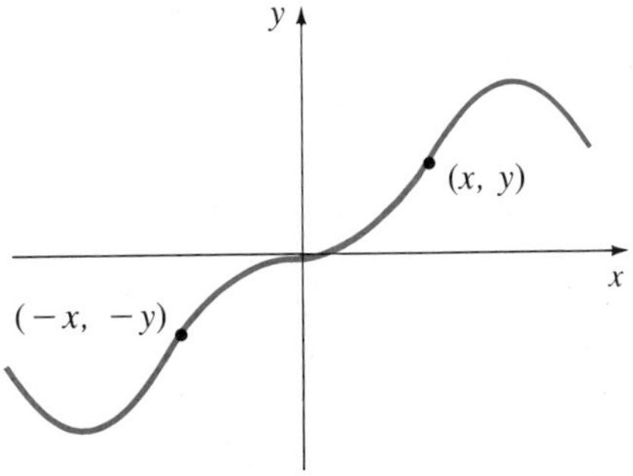

Figure 3.23 Odd function

We can use our knowledge of the symmetry of a graph to assist us in the sketching process. For example, the function given in Figure 3.18 is even; so we could have drawn the graph by plotting points from $x = 0$ to $x = 3$ and then used its symmetry with respect to the y-axis to obtain the segment from $x = -3$ to $x = 0$.

Using a Graph to Define a Function

A set of ordered pairs of real numbers is represented graphically by points in the Cartesian plane. Conversely, a graph determines a set of ordered pairs of real numbers corresponding to the coordinates of the points on the graph. The set of ordered pairs determined by a graph may or may not define a function.

There is a simple test, called the **vertical line test,** to tell if a graph defines a function. Draw vertical lines on the graph. If no vertical lines can be drawn to intersect the graph in more than one point, the graph defines a function because for each x there is exactly one y. Figures 3.24(a) and (b) define y as a function of x. On the other hand, Figures 3.24(c) and (d) do not define functions since some vertical lines intersect these graphs in two or more points, indicating that there is more than one value of y for some values of x.

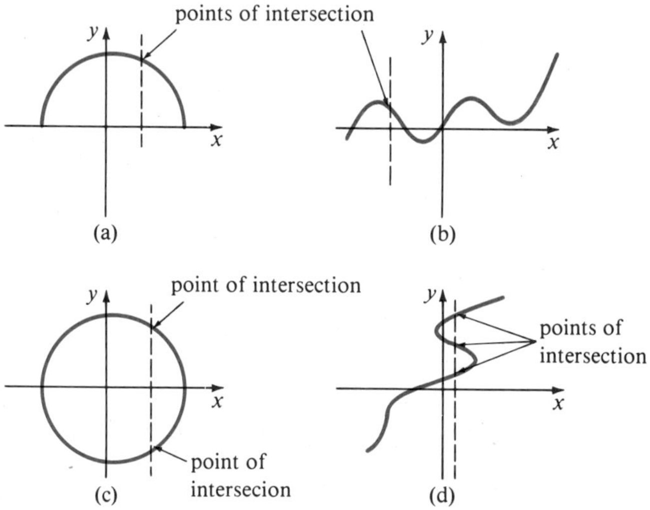

Figure 3.24

Increasing and Decreasing Functions

A function f whose graph rises from left to right is said to be an increasing function. See Figure 3.25(a). This means that as x increases, $f(x)$ also increases. A function f whose graph falls from left to right is said to be a decreasing function. See Figure 3.25(b). In this case, $f(x)$ decreases as x increases. In general, we speak of a function increasing or decreasing on some interval as in the following definition.

Definition

1. A function f is **increasing** on the interval $[a, b]$ if $f(x_1) < f(x_2)$ whenever $x_1 < x_2$ in $[a, b]$.
2. A function f is **decreasing** on the interval $[a, b]$ if $f(x_1) > f(x_2)$ whenever $x_1 < x_2$ in $[a, b]$.

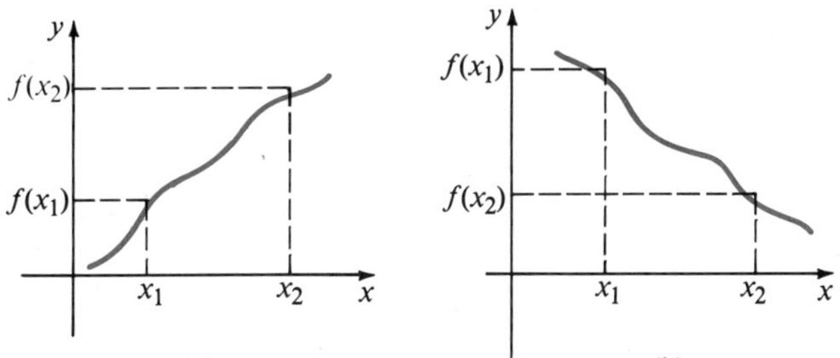

(a) (b)

Figure 3.25

EXAMPLE 6 Increasing and decreasing functions are illustrated in Figure 3.26.

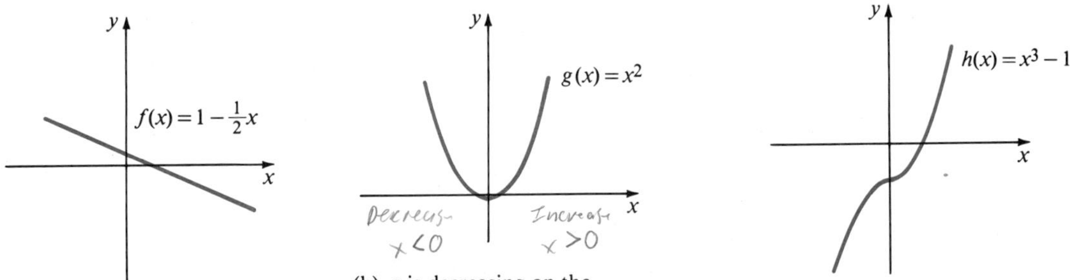

(a) f is decreasing for all x in the domain

(b) g is decreasing on the interval $(-\infty, 0]$ and increasing on the interval $[0, \infty)$

(c) h is increasing for all x in the domain

Figure 3.26 ■

The Zeros of a Function

A **zero** of a function is any domain value whose corresponding range value is 0. Thus, if $f(C) = 0$, where C is a number in the domain of the function f, then C is called a zero of f. The concept of a zero of a function has a simple graphical analog: *The zeros of a function correspond to the abscissas of the points at which the graph of the function crosses the x-axis.* The abscissas of these points are called **x-intercepts.** In Figure 3.27(a), the values x_1, x_2, and x_3 are zeros of the function. Figure 3.27(b) shows a function that has no zeros. The zeros should be indicated on the graph, at least approximately.

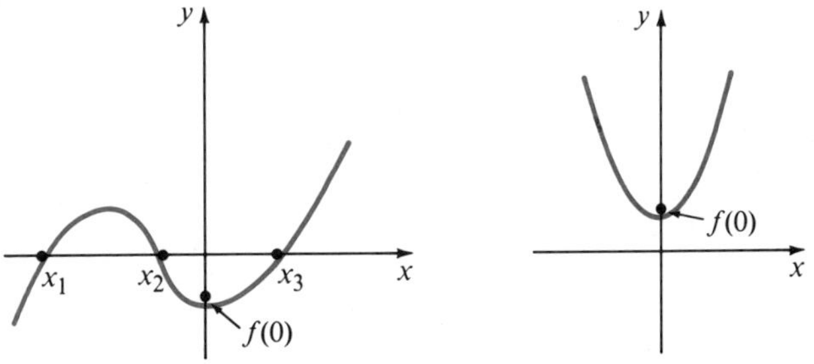

(a) (b)

Figure 3.27

Comment: Be sure to distinguish carefully between the zeros of a function and the value of the function when $x = 0$. The x-intercepts are the zeros, while the value of the y-intercept is $f(0)$.

EXAMPLE 7 Draw the graph of $f(x) = x^2 - 3x + 1$ and indicate the zeros.

Solution Computing $f(x)$ for some convenient values of x, we get the graph shown in Figure 3.28.

$f(x) = x^2 - 3x + 1$

x	$f(x)$
-1	5
0	1
1	-1
2	-1
3	1
4	5

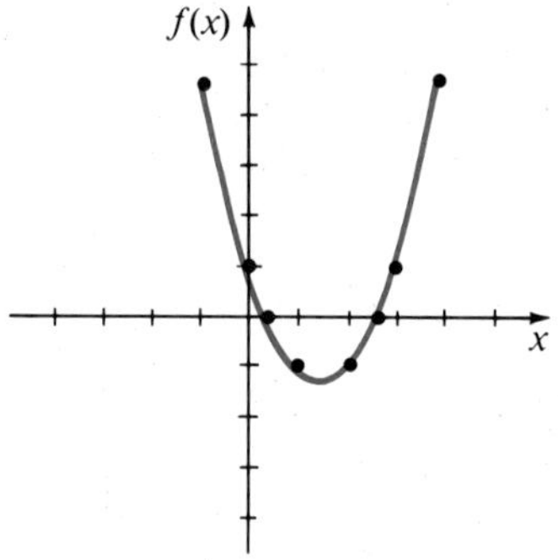

Figure 3.28

Here the graph crosses the x-axis at approximately $x = 0.4$ and $x = 2.6$. Therefore, these points are the zeros of the function. By using a graphical method, we can estimate the zeros. Analytically, the zeros are obtained by setting $f(x) = 0$. Therefore,

$$x^2 - 3x + 1 = 0$$

whose roots, using the quadratic formula, are found to be

$$x = \frac{3 \pm \sqrt{5}}{2}$$

These two roots of the quadratic equation give the exact zeros of the function. ■

Exercises Section 3.4

In Exercises 1–4, indicate those graphs that define functions.

1. a.

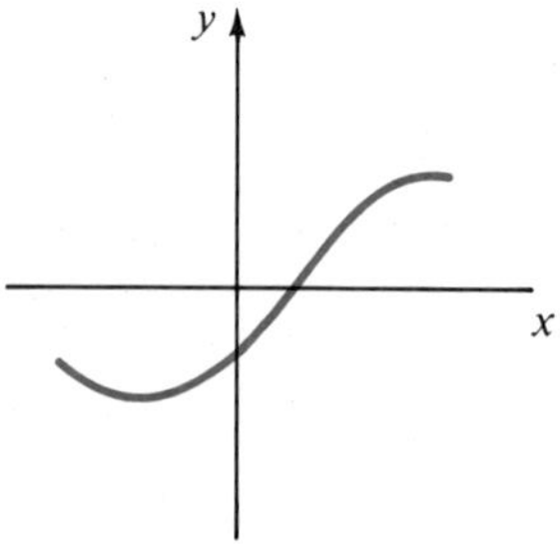

b.

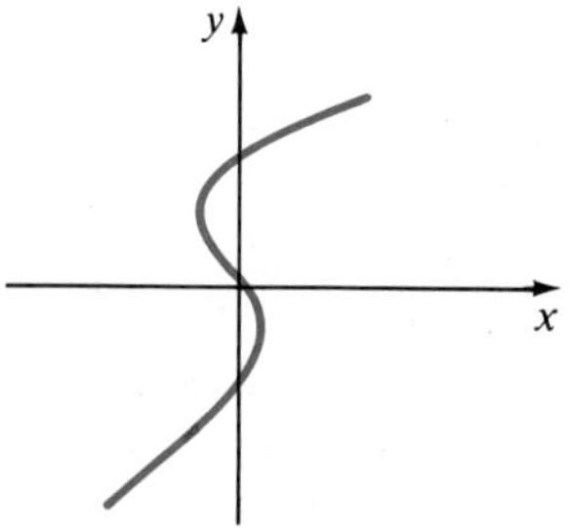

2. a.

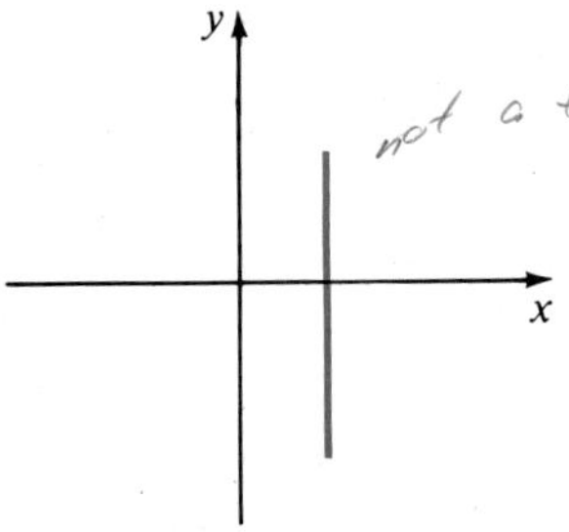

b.

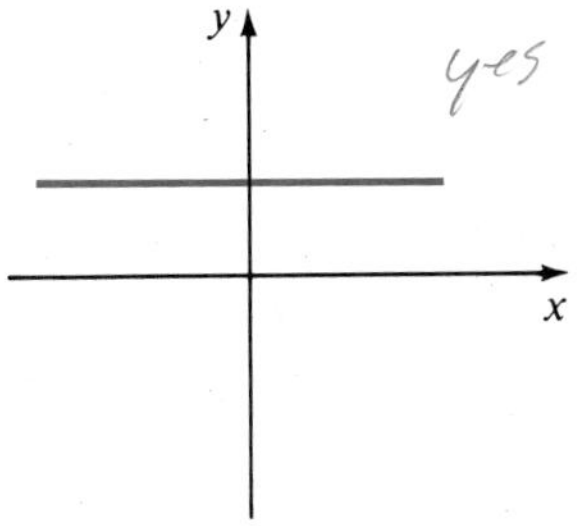

3. a.

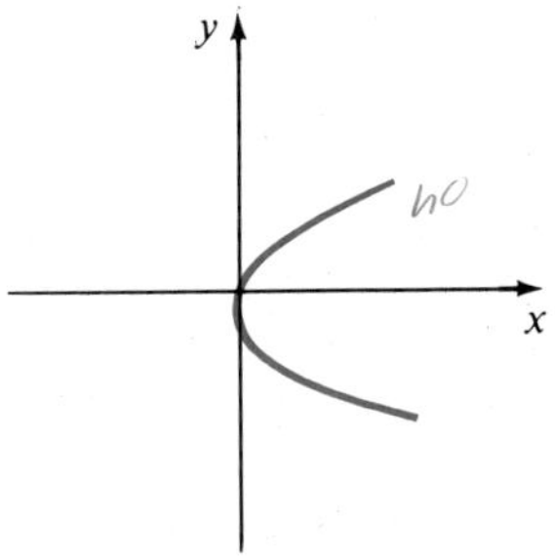

b.

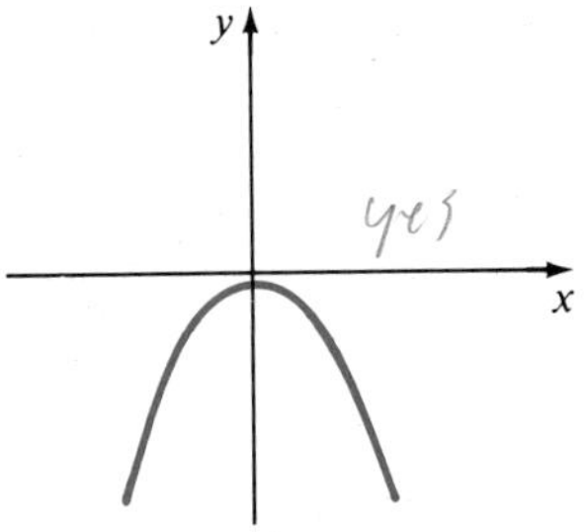

4. a.

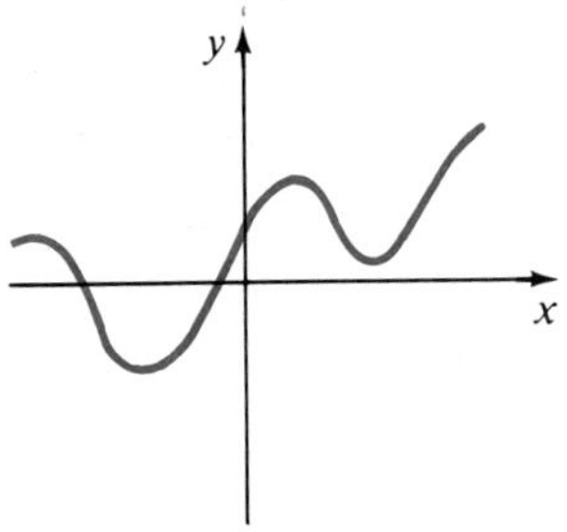

b.

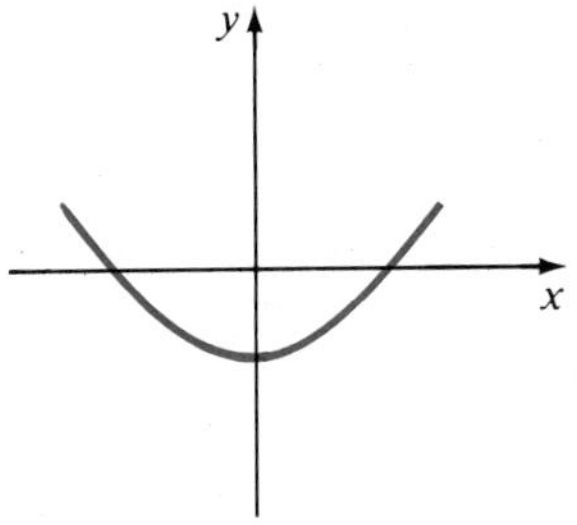

5. Indicate the intervals on which f is increasing and the intervals on which it is decreasing.

a.

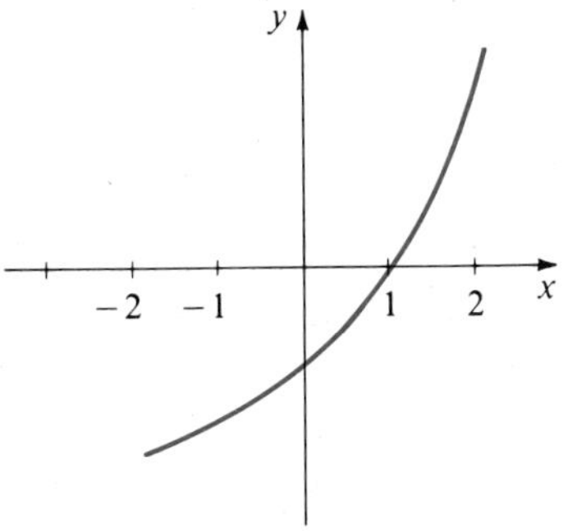

b.

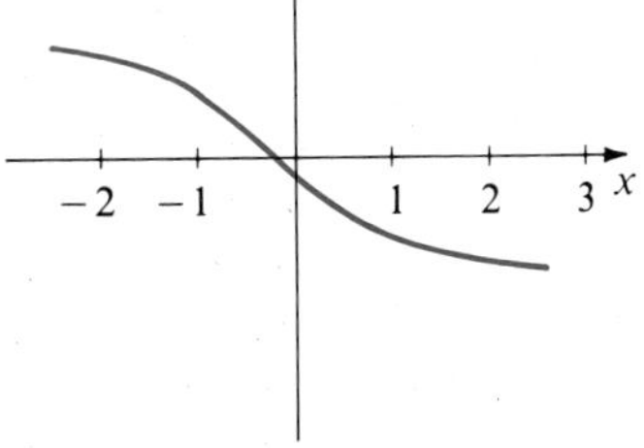

c.

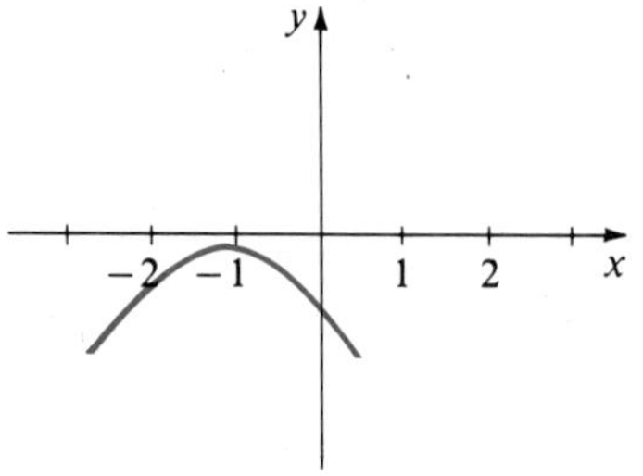

6. Indicate the intervals on which f is increasing and the intervals on which it is decreasing.

a.

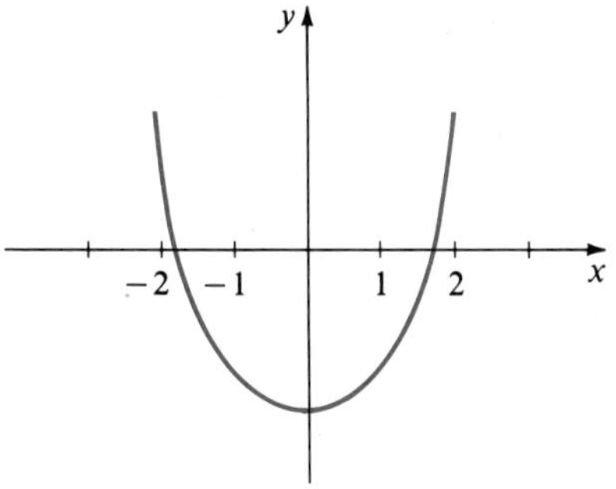

b.

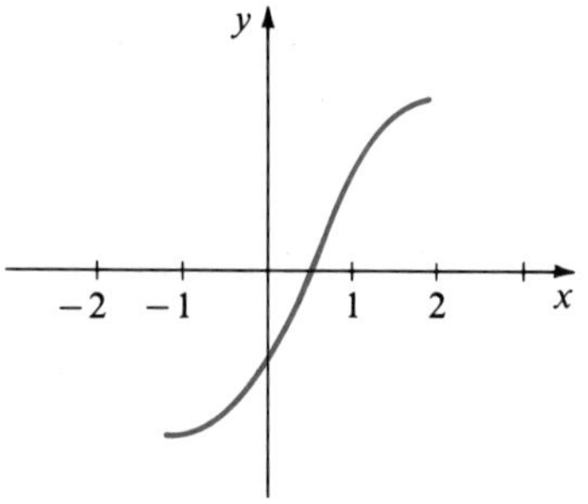

c.

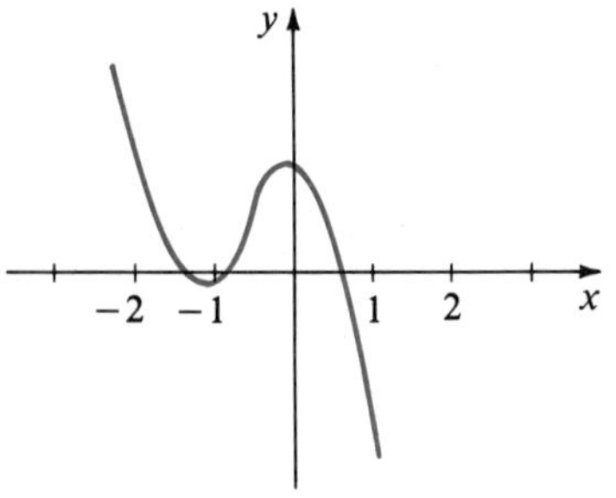

Graph the functions in Exercises 7–28. Indicate the domain and range. Where appropriate, find the value of the zeros.

7. $\{(-2, 3), (0, 4), (2, 5)\}$
8. $\{(-1, 0), (0, 0), (1, 2), (3, -4)\}$
9. $f(x) = 3x + 5$
10. $y = 2 - \frac{1}{2}x$
11. $y = x^3$
12. $f(x) = -x^2$
13. $z = t^2 + 4$
14. $i = r - r^2$
15. $y(x) = \sqrt{x}$
16. $\phi = \dfrac{w^2}{2}$
17. $p = z^2 - z - 6$
18. $v = 10 + 2t$
19. $y = \sqrt{16 - 4x^2}$
20. $y = \sqrt{25 - x^2}$
21. $\alpha = \theta^{1/3}$
22. $z = \sqrt[3]{t^2}$
23. $y(x) = \sqrt{x - 2}$
24. $y = \sqrt[3]{2 - x}$
25. $v = s^3 - 4s^2$
26. $a = \frac{1}{4}b^4$
27. $y = -x^3$
28. $\beta = -\alpha^{1/2}$
29. The work w done in moving an object varies with the distance s according to $w = \sqrt[3]{2s}$. Show this relationship graphically.
30. The path of a certain projectile is described by the function $h = 100x - 2x^2$, where h is the vertical height in feet and x is the horizontal displacement in feet. Draw the path of the projectile.
31. An office machine is supposed to be serviced once a month. If it is not serviced, the cost of repairs is \$20 plus five times the square of the number of months the machine goes unserviced. Express the cost of repairs as a function of the number of months the machine goes unserviced and draw the graph.
32. A typical demand curve in economics is given by

$$D(x) = \frac{50}{x + 10}$$

Sketch this function for $0 \le x \le 10$.

33. A typical supply function in economics is given by

$$S(x) = \frac{1}{2}x^2 + 20$$

Sketch this function for $0 \le x \le 6$.

34. The following table describes the functional relationship between the safe speed at which a car can round a curve and the degree of the curve. Draw the graph of safe speed as a function of the degree of the curve.

Degrees of curve	5	10	15	20	25	30	35
Safe speed (mph)	70	68	66	63	58	50	34

35. A thermocouple generates a voltage in millivolts when its two ends are kept at different temperatures. In laboratory experiments the cold end of the thermocouple is usually kept at 0° C while the temperature of the other end varies. The next table represents the results of an experiment in which the output voltage of the thermocouple was recorded for various thermocouple temperatures. Draw the graph of voltage versus temperature.

T(°C)	0	50	100	150	200	250
V(mv)	0	2.1	4.1	5.9	7.0	7.8

36. The following table shows men's height and corresponding normal weight in pounds. Draw the graph of weight vs. height.

Ht.	5′2″	5′4″	5′6″	5′8″	5′10″	6′0″	6′2″	6′4″
Wt.	130	136	144	152	161	170	184	196

3.5 Composite and Inverse Functions

Composite Functions

We found previously that functions can be combined by arithmetic operations. In this section, we look at another method of combining functions, called composition.

Definition

If f and g are two functions such that the range of g is contained in the domain of f, the **composite function of f with g** is denoted by $f \circ g$ and defined by

$$(f \circ g)(x) = f(g(x))$$

for every x in the domain of g.

The notation $f(g(x))$ is read "f of g of x."

Note the important assumption that $g(x)$ is in the domain of f; otherwise $f(g(x))$ does not make sense. The process of composition is represented in diagram form in Figure 3.29.

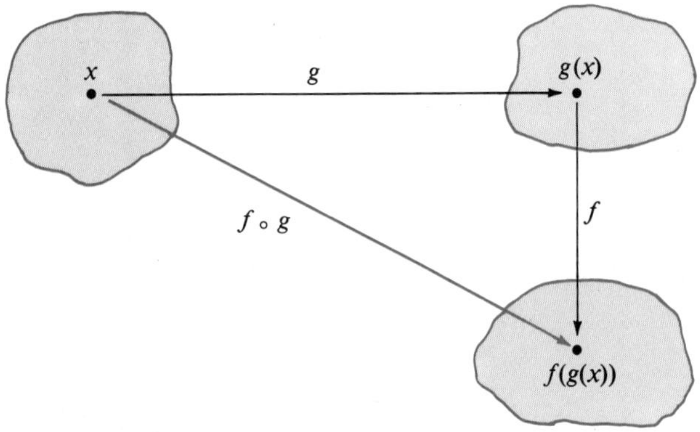

Figure 3.29

The diagram shows that we first apply the rule for $g(x)$ followed by the rule for $f(x)$ in order to obtain the composition $f \circ g$.

EXAMPLE 1 Find the composition $f \circ g$ and $g \circ f$ if $f(x) = 3x + 1$ and $g(x) = x - 4$.

Solution
$f \circ g = f(g(x)) = f(x - 4) = 3(x - 4) + 1 = 3x - 11$
$g \circ f = g(f(x)) = g(3x + 1) = (3x + 1) - 4 = 3x - 3$

Notice that $f(g(x)) \neq g(f(x))$ here. This is typical of the composition of functions; so we say that composition is not commutative. ■

Warning: The composition of two functions f and g should not be confused with the product $f(x)g(x)$. Using the functions in Example 1 we see that $f(x)g(x) = (3x + 1)(x - 4) = 3x^2 - 11x - 4$, which is not the same as either $f(g(x))$ or $g(f(x))$.

EXAMPLE 2 Let $f(x) = x + 1$ and $g(x) = \sqrt{x}$. Find the composite function $g \circ f$. What is the domain of $g \circ f$?

Solution The composite function is $g(f(x)) = g(x + 1) = \sqrt{x + 1}$. The domain of $g(f(x))$ is $x \geq -1$, since these values and only these values yield real numbers for the range. ■

Comment: Forming the composition of two functions is used extensively in calculus and involves recognizing a functional expression as a composite of more elementary functions.

EXAMPLE 3
a. The function $(x + 1)^2$ may be considered as the composition $f(g(x))$, where $f(x) = x^2$ and $g(x) = x + 1$.
b. The function $(x^5 + 1)^{1/3}$ may be considered as $f(g(x))$, where $f(x) = x^{1/3}$ and $g(x) = x^5 + 1$. ■

Inverse Functions

An element in the range of a function may correspond to more than one element in its domain. For example, if $f(x) = x^2$, then both 2 and -2 have the same range element 4. This is diagrammed in Figure 3.30.

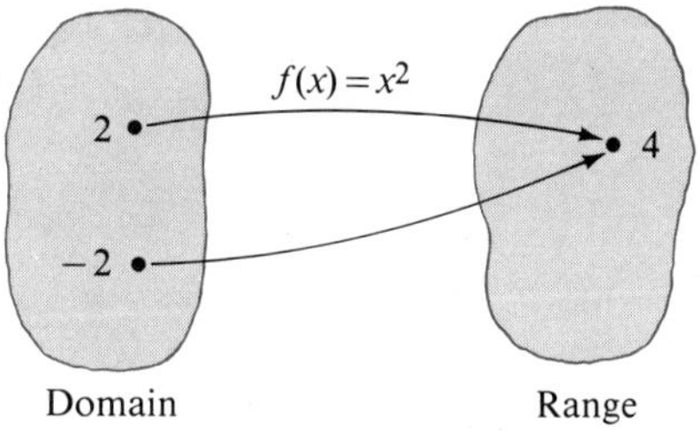

Figure 3.30

If we require that the rule of correspondence assign to every element in the domain a different element in the range, then the function is called a **one-to-one function.** We state the following definition.

Definition

> A function f is one-to-one if for a and b in the domain of f, $f(a) = f(b)$ implies that $a = b$.

The function

$$y = x^2$$

is NOT one-to-one because $f(2) = 4 = f(-2)$, but $2 \neq -2$.

Graphically, a one-to-one function is one for which *both* horizontal and vertical lines intersect the graph in, at most, one point. In Figure 3.31 the first function is one-to-one; the second is not.

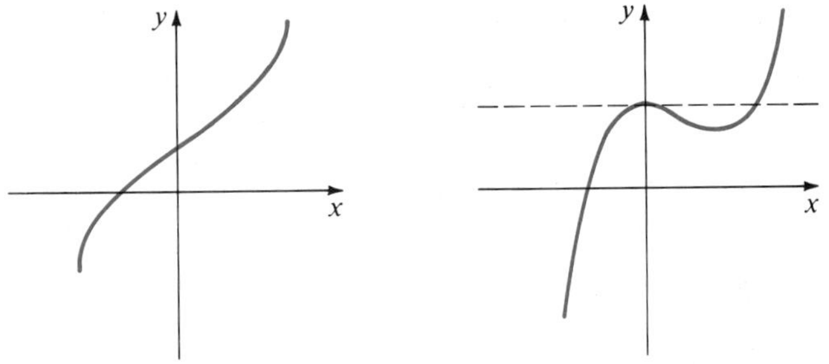

Figure 3.31

By requiring that f be a one-to-one function, we know that each element in the range corresponds to a unique element in the domain. Under this condition, it is possible to define a function g whose domain is the range of f and whose range is the domain of f, such that the correspondence is reversed; that is, $g(f(x)) = x$ for every x in the domain of f.

Definition

> If f is a one-to-one function and g is a function such that $g(f(x)) = x$ for all x in the domain of f and $f(g(x)) = x$ for all x in the domain of g, then g is called the **inverse function** of f. The domain of f is the range of g and the range of f is the domain of g. The inverse function of f is usually denoted by f^{-1}.

Warning: The notation f^{-1} does NOT mean f to an exponent of -1. The inverse of a function is NOT its reciprocal; that is,

$$f^{-1}(x) \neq \frac{1}{f(x)}$$

The relationship between f and f^{-1} is shown in diagram form in Figure 3.32.

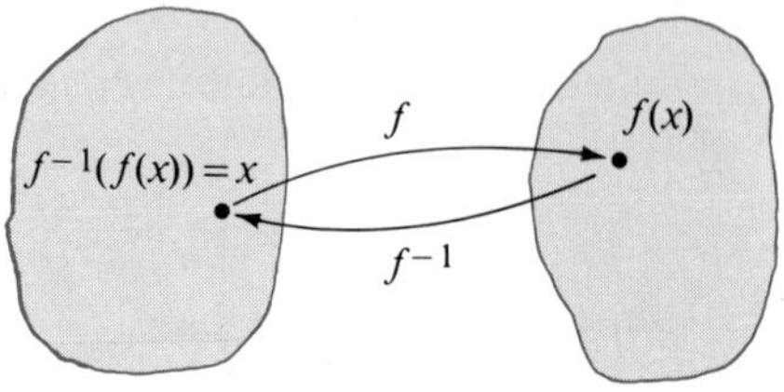

Figure 3.32

By definition of an inverse, the composition of a function and its inverse is equal to x. Specifically, if f is a one-to-one function and f^{-1} is its inverse, then

$$f(f^{-1}(x)) = x = f^{-1}(f(x))$$

We can use this fact to show that two functions are inverses of one another.

EXAMPLE 4 Use composition to show that $f(x) = 2x + 1$ and $g(x) = (x - 1)/2$ are inverse functions.

Solution

$$f(g(x)) = f\left(\frac{x-1}{2}\right) = 2\left(\frac{x-1}{2}\right) + 1 = x$$

$$g(f(x)) = g(2x + 1) = \frac{(2x + 1) - 1}{2} = x$$

Therefore, f and g are inverses. ■

The definition of an inverse function also gives rise to an algebraic procedure for finding an inverse when the rule of correspondence is given by a formula.

EXAMPLE 5 Let $f(x) = 2x + 4$. Find the inverse of f.

Solution Let g be the inverse of f. Then, by the definition of an inverse, we write

$$f(g(x)) = x$$

In this particular case $f(x) = 2x + 4$, so

$$2g(x) + 4 = x$$

Solving for $g(x)$, we have

$$g(x) = \frac{1}{2}x - 2$$

which is the inverse of f. ■

EXAMPLE 6 Let $f(x) = (2x + 1)/(x + 3)$. Find the inverse of f.

Solution Let $g(x)$ be the inverse. Then, $f(g(x)) = x$ yields

$$\frac{2g(x) + 1}{g(x) + 3} = x$$

$$xg(x) + 3x = 2g(x) + 1 \qquad \text{Multiplying both sides by } g(x) + 3$$

$$xg(x) - 2g(x) = 1 - 3x \qquad \text{Adding } -3x - 2g(x) \text{ to both sides}$$

$$(x - 2)g(x) = 1 - 3x \qquad \text{Factoring}$$

$$g(x) = \frac{1 - 3x}{x - 2} \qquad \text{Dividing by } x - 2$$

which is the inverse of f. Note that the domain of the inverse is the set of all real numbers except $x = 2$. ■

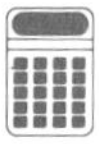

Scientific calculators have an inv *or* arc *button, but the operation of this button applies to only a few selected preprogrammed functions and will not perform the inverse operation in general.*

Comment: The graphs of f and f^{-1} have an interesting relationship. As the next two examples show, the graphs of f and f^{-1} are mirror reflections of each other in the line bisecting the first and third quadrants.

EXAMPLE 7 Draw the graphs of $y = 2x + 4$ and $y = \frac{1}{2}x - 2$ on the same coordinate axes.

Solution Several solution pairs for each equation are given in the respective tables and the graphs plotted in Figure 3.33. Notice that each graph is the mirror reflection in the dashed line of the other. The inverse nature of these functions was established in Example 5.

$y = 2x + 4$

x	y
−6	−8
−4	−4
−2	0
0	4
2	8

$y = \frac{1}{2}x - 2$

x	y
−8	−6
−4	−4
0	−2
4	0
8	2

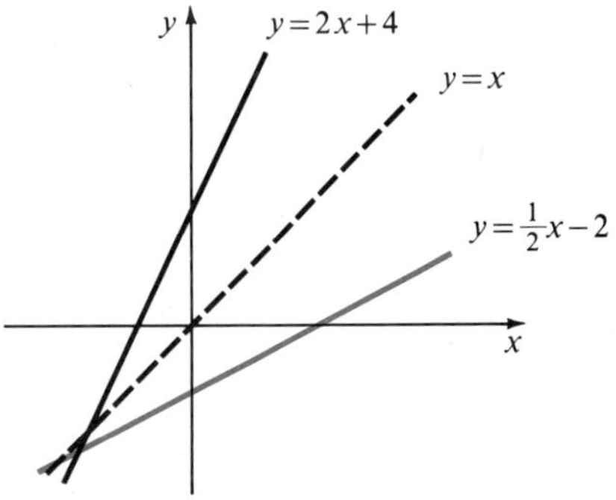

Figure 3.33

■

If a one-to-one function f is given by a set of ordered pairs, the inverse f^{-1} is obtained by interchanging the elements in each functional pairing. A typical function is shown in the next example.

EXAMPLE 8 Find the inverse of $f = \{(2, 1), (-3, 2), (0, 5)\}$ and draw the graphs of f and f^{-1}.

Solution The inverse f^{-1} is obtained by interchanging the elements of f. Thus,

$$f^{-1} = \{(1, 2), (2, -3), (5, 0)\}$$

The graphs are shown in Figure 3.34. Note that the points in the graphs are mirror reflections in the line $y = x$.

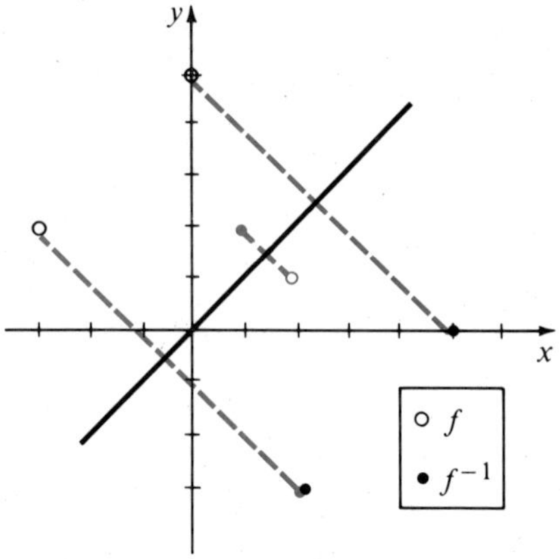

Figure 3.34

■

Exercises Section 3.5

In the statements in Exercises 1–8, find $f \circ g$ and $g \circ f$.

1. $f(x) = x - 5, g(x) = 3 - 2x$

2. $f(x) = 2x + 3, g(x) = 5x - 1$

3. $f(x) = 3x + 4, g(x) = 2x$

4. $f(x) = 1/(x + 1), g(x) = x + 1$

5. $f(x) = x, g(x) = x^2$

6. $f(x) = \sqrt{x}, g(x) = x^2$

7. $f(x) = x^3 - 1, g(x) = x^{1/3}$

8. $f(x) = 1/(x^2 + 1), g(x) = 1/x$

9. If $f(x) = 2x + 3$, for what value of x is $f(x) = 6$?

10. If $f(x) = 4/x$, for what value of x is $f(x) = 3$?

11. If $v = 10 + 4t$, for what value of t is $v = 20$?

Determine graphically which of the pairs of functions in Exercises 12–19 are inverses of one another.

12. $y = 3x, y = \frac{1}{3}x$

13. $y = -2x, y = -\frac{1}{2}x$

14. $y = 6 - 3x, y = -\frac{1}{3}x + 2$

15. $y = x + 1, y = x - 2$

16. $y = \frac{1}{2}x + 1, y = 2x - 1$

17. $y = 5(x + 1), y = \frac{1}{5}x - 1$

18. $y = x^2, y = \sqrt{x}$

19. $y = x^3, y = \sqrt[3]{x}$

20. Suppose that f and f^{-1} are defined by identical formulas. What can you say about the graph of f?

For each pair of functions in Exercises 21–25, compute the composition $f \circ g$ to show that f and g are inverses.

21. $f(x) = -2x, g(x) = -x/2$

22. $f(x) = 3x, g(x) = x/3$

23. $f(x) = 6 - 3x, g(x) = -\frac{1}{3}x + 2$

24. $f(x) = \dfrac{1}{2x + 1}, g(x) = \dfrac{1 - x}{2x}$

25. $f(x) = 5(x + 1), g(x) = \frac{1}{5}x - 1$

For each function in Exercises 26–31, find the inverse function of f, if it exists.

26. $f(x) = 3x + 2$

27. $f(x) = x - 3$

28. $f(x) = \frac{1}{2}x + 5$

29. $f(x) = \dfrac{1}{x + 1}$

30. $f(x) = \dfrac{2x - 1}{3x + 5}$

31. $f(x) = \dfrac{x - 1}{x + 1}$

32. If $f = \{(3, 0), (2, 6), (1, 5)\}$, for which x is $f(x) = 5$? For which x is $f(x) = 0$?

33. If $f = \{(0, 1), (2, 5), (3, 8), (5, 6)\}$, for which x is $f(x) = 8$? For which x is $f(x) = 3$?

Determine the inverse function in Exercises 34–41 *if it exists.*

34. $\{(2, 6), (3, 5), (0, 4)\}$

35. $\{(3, 7), (5, 9), (7, 3), (9, 5)\}$

36. $\{(-1, 2), (2, 3), (6, -2)\}$

37. $\{(1, 2), (2, 2)\}$

38. $\{(3, 2), (5, 4), (7, 2), (9, 8)\}$

39. $\{(-2, 3), (-1, 4), (0, 0)\}$

40. $\{(0, 1), (1, 0)\}$

41. $\{(0, 3), (1, 5), (2, 3), (6, 7)\}$

Review Exercises Chapter 3

1. Graph the set $\{(2, -1), (4, 1), (6, 3), (8, 5)\}$.
2. Graph the set $\{(0, 2), (\frac{1}{2}, 1), (1, 0)\}$.
3. Find the distance between the points (3, 7) and $(-2, -1)$.
4. Find the distance between the points $(2, -2)$, and $(7, -5)$.
5. Pressure is defined as the ratio of applied force to the area over which it is applied. What is the pressure exerted by a force of 16 lb over an area of 2.4 ft^2?
6. Newton's second law of motion states that the magnitude of a force causing motion is directly proportional to the acceleration of the object. If a force of 12 lb causes an acceleration of 5 ft/sec^2, how much force must be applied to cause an acceleration of 8 ft/sec^2?
7. The marginal cost of manufacturing a product is the ratio of the variable cost to the number of units produced. Find the marginal cost of producing 750,000 units if the variable cost is $300,000.
8. The force between two electrically charged particles is inversely proportional to the square of the distance between them. If a force of 10^{-6} newtons is exerted when two particles are 5×10^{-2} cm apart, how much force will be exerted when they are 5×10^{-3} cm apart?
9. The breaking load of a rectangular beam supported at both ends is directly proportional to the width and the square of the depth and inversely proportional to the distance between the supports. If a 6 in. × 8 in. × 12 ft beam has a breaking load of 2500 lb, what is the breaking load of a 6 in. × 8 in. × 15 ft beam? Assume the width is the smaller dimension.

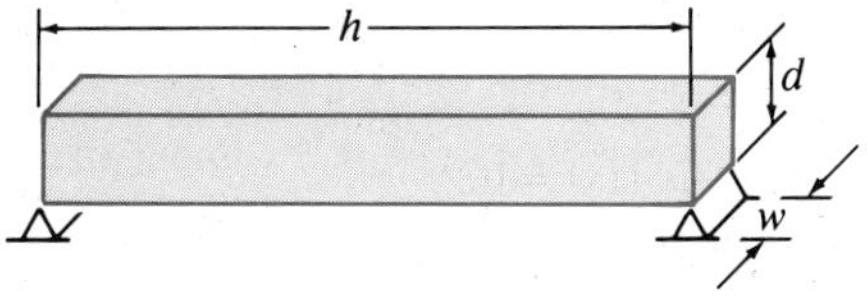

In Exercises 10–20, tell whether the given equation, table, or diagram defines a function.

10. $y = 3x$

11. $y = x^4$

12. $y = x \pm 5$

13. $y < 2$

14. $y = 1/x^2$

15. $y = x - x^{-1}$

16.

x	2	-1	4	7
y	3	0	7	-3

17.

x	0	5	7	8	10	5
y	0	3	4	2	-1	-3

18.

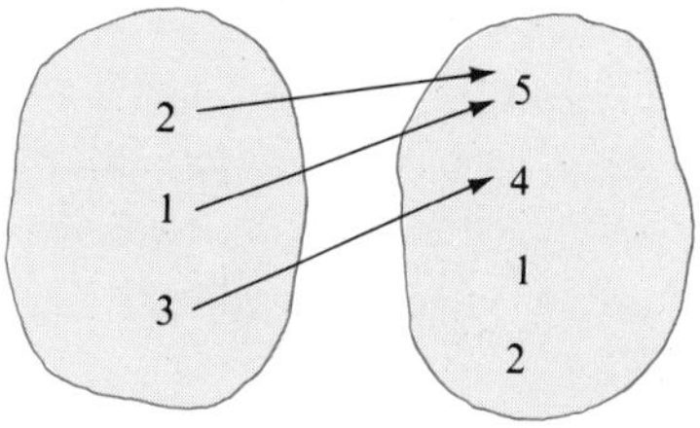

19.

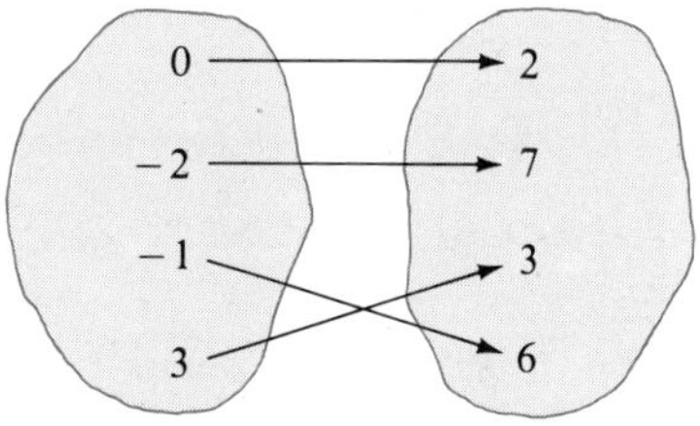

20.

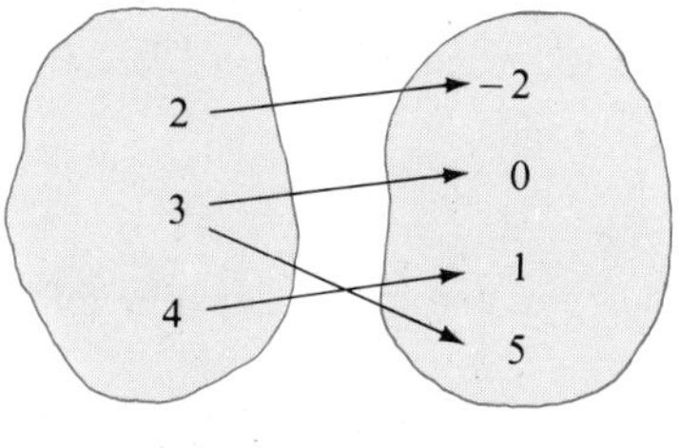

21. Find the range and domain of $f(x) = 2x^2$.

22. Find the range and domain of $y = 7 + 2x$.

23. Find the range and domain of $g(x) = \sqrt{x - 3}$.

24. Find the range and domain of $h(x) = \dfrac{3}{x + 5}$.

In Exercises 25–30, draw the graph and indicate the zeros of the function.

25. $y = 4 - 2x$

26. $y = 1 - x^2$

27. $F(x) = -\sqrt{x} + 2$

28. $s = t^2 - 3t$

29. $y = \sqrt{-x}$

30. $M = \sqrt{2(t - 3)}$

Determine the inverse function in Exercises 31–36.

31. $\{(2, 5), (-1, 0), (7, 3)\}$

32. $\{(0, -1), (1, 1), (5, -2)\}$

33. $f(x) = 2x + 5$

34. $f(x) = 2 - 3x$

35. $g(x) = 1/(x + 2)$

36. $F(x) = x/(x + 1)$

In Exercises 37–40, find $f \circ g$ and $g \circ f$.

37. $f(x) = 3x - 1, g(x) = 4 - x$

38. $f(x) = 1/x, g(x) = 2x + 5$

39. $f(x) = 1/(x - 1), g(x) = 1/x$

40. $f(x) = x^2 + 1, g(x) = \sqrt{x}$

Test 1 Chapter 3

Answer True or False to Exercises 1–10.

1. If $a > 0$ and $b < 0$, then the point (a, b) is in quadrant IV.
2. The distance from a to b on the number line is the same as that from b to a.
3. For any function f, $f(x + y) = f(x) + f(y)$.
4. $f(x) = x^2$ is a function.
5. $x^2 + y^2 = 1$ represents a function.
6. $x + y = 1$ represents a function.
7. In order for a formula to represent a function, there must exist a real value of $f(x)$ for every real x.
8. Only one-to-one functions have inverse functions.
9. If y varies directly as x and x varies directly as t, then y varies directly as t.
10. The range of a real valued function is a subset of the real numbers.
11. The amount of money a man earns is directly proportional to the number of hours he works. If he makes \$18.80 in an 8-hour day, write a formula for the amount of money he makes as a function of the hours he works.
12. Let $f(x) = x^2 + 5x + 2$. Find and simplify $[f(2 + h) - f(2)]/h$.
13. Make a careful sketch of the graph of the function $f(x) = x^2 - 3x$ on the interval $-1 \le x \le 4$.
14. Find the domain and range of each of the following real valued functions.
    a. $f(x) = x$ b. $f(x) = 1/x$ c. $f(x) = \sqrt{x}$
15. Find the distance from $(2, \sqrt{2})$ to $(-2, 0)$.
16. Graph $x = 1$. Is this a function?
17. Find the inverse function for $f(x) = (x - 1)/(2x + 5)$.

Test 2 Chapter 3

1. If s varies directly with t and if $s = 2$ when $t = 5$, find s when $t = 7$.
2. Find the distance between the points $(-2, -2)$ and $(-5, 3)$.
3. Graph $\{(2, -1), (3, 0), (3, -1), (2, 0)\}$.
4. Which of the following expressions define y as a function of x?
    a. $y = 2 + x$ b. $y^2 = x$
    c. $y < 3x + 2$ d. $y = 3 - x^2$
5. Find the domain and range for the following functions.
    a. $y = x^2$
    b. $y = 5x - 2$
    c. $y = \sqrt{x - 3}$
6. Given $f(t) = 3t^2 - 4t + 6$, find $f(-2)$ and $f(x^2)$.
7. Draw the graph of $y = \sqrt{x - 5}$.
8. Draw the graph of $y = 6 + x - x^2$. What are the zeros?
9. Determine the inverse function for $y = 5x + 3$.
10. Given $f(x) = 4/x^2$ and $g(x) = 3x$, find $f(g(x))$ and $g(f(x))$.

4

Elementary Functions

4.1 Linear Functions

In this chapter we concentrate on the study of several elementary functions that are extremely important in applied work, so you should know as much as you can about them. To "know a function" means to be able to determine

1. The domain of the function.
2. The range of the function.
3. The rule of correspondence (usually given by some formula).
4. The graph of the function.

By a **linear function,** we mean a function expressible in the form

$$f(x) = ax + b \tag{4.1a}$$

where a and b are constants. If we replace $f(x)$ with the letter y, the linear function can be written in the form

$$y = ax + b \tag{4.1b}$$

In this form, it is called a **linear equation in the two variables *x* and *y*.** More generally, any equation in the variables x and y that can be arranged into the form $y = ax + b$ is a linear equation. Thus,

$$ax + by = c \tag{4.2}$$

is a linear equation since, if $b \neq 0$, it can be written $y = (-a/b)x + (c/b)$. If $b = 0$, we get $ax = c$, which is not a linear function but is still considered to be a linear equation.

A remark here about the domain and range of $y = ax + b$: if $a \neq 0$, then both the domain and the range are the set of all real numbers. If $a = 0$, then $y = b$. In this case, the domain is still the set of all real numbers (that is, the independent variable is not restrained in any way) while the range is the one number, $y = b$.

To graph a linear function, calculate some of the ordered pairs, plot the corresponding points, and then, since the domain consists of all real numbers, connect these points with a smooth curve.

EXAMPLE 1 Draw the graph of $y = 2 - 2x$.

Solution The usual method is to assign values to x and find the corresponding values of y. Thus, when $x = 0$, then $y = 2$; when $x = 1$, then $y = 0$, and so on. See Figure 4.1.

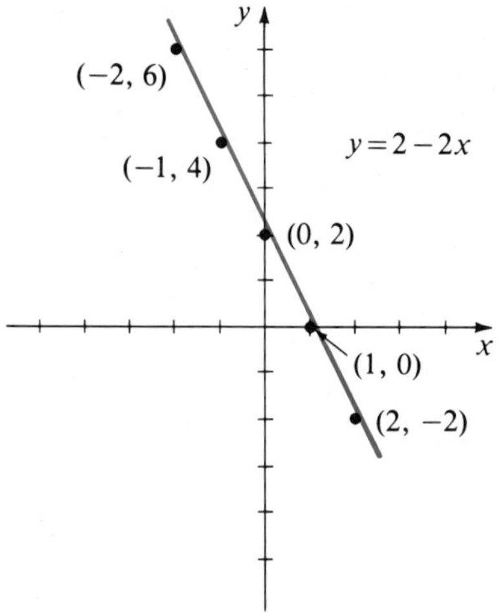

Figure 4.1 ■

Figure 4.1 suggests that the graph of the linear function $y = 2 - 2x$ is a straight line. More generally, **the graph of every linear function is a straight line.** We will not prove this fact. Suffice it to say that the terms *linear function* and *linear equation* are chosen to suggest the geometric nature of their graphs.

Since the graph of every linear function is a straight line, the work of graphing it can be considerably shortened. From geometry we know that a straight line is determined by two distinct points, so any two ordered pairs (x_1, y_1) and (x_2, y_2) that satisfy a given linear equation may be used to determine its graph. Although any two points may be used, we usually choose those that correspond to the intercepts of the line with the x- and y-axes, called the **x-intercept** and **y-intercept,** respectively.

- To find the x-intercept of the graph of a linear function, let $y = 0$ and solve for x.*
- To find the y-intercept of the graph of a linear function, let $x = 0$ and solve for y.

EXAMPLE 2 Graph $y = 2x - 4$.

Solution Letting $x = 0$ gives $y = -4$ and letting $y = 0$ gives $x = 2$. Thus, the graph passes through $(0, -4)$ on the y-axis and $(2, 0)$ on the x-axis. The graph of this equation is shown in Figure 4.2.

* Recall from Section 3.4 that an x-intercept is the geometric counterpart of a zero of a function.

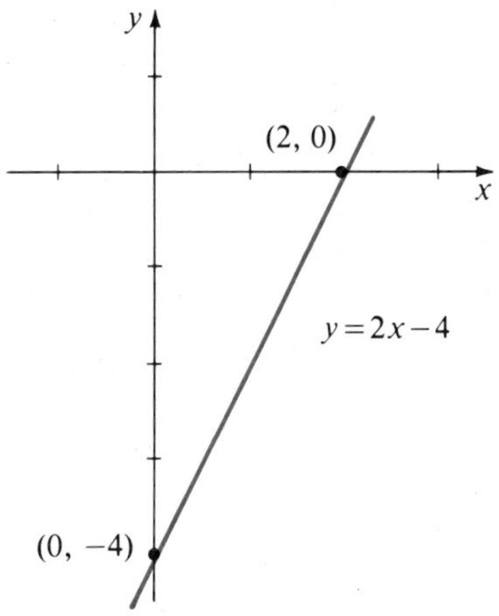

Figure 4.2 ■

Slope of a Straight Line

If you were asked to describe the graph in Figure 4.2, you would say that the graph is a straight line that crosses the x-axis at $x = 2$ and the y-axis at $y = -4$. In addition, you might say that the line rises from left to right. Another bit of information that would be useful is a measure of the steepness of the graph. The line in Figure 4.2 rises two units for every one unit moved to the right. Implicit in this description of steepness is a quantity called the **slope** of the line.

The slope of a straight line is defined as the ratio of the vertical rise of the line to the corresponding horizontal run; that is,

$$\text{slope} = \frac{\text{vertical rise}}{\text{horizontal run}}$$

Applying this definition to the line segment P_1P_2 in Figure 4.3, the slope m is given by

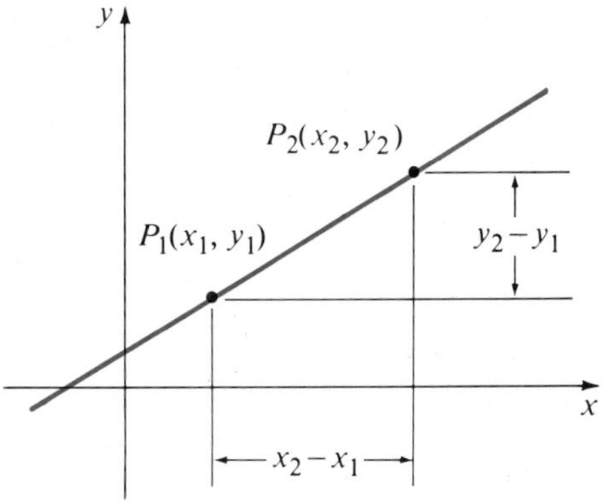

Figure 4.3

the equation

$$m = \frac{y_2 - y_1}{x_2 - x_1} \tag{4.3}$$

where $y_2 - y_1$ is the vertical distance between the given points and $x_2 - x_1$ is the horizontal distance between the points.

EXAMPLE 3 Find the slope of the straight line passing through the points $(-5, 1)$ and $(2, -3)$ in Figure 4.4.

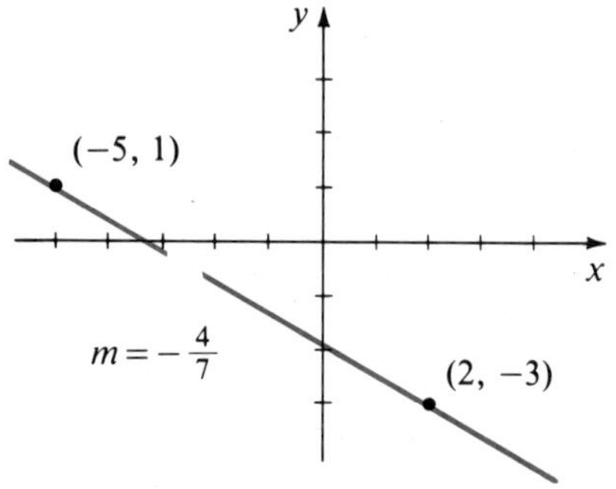

Figure 4.4

Solution Letting $(x_1, y_1) = (-5, 1)$ and $(x_2, y_2) = (2, -3)$ and using Equation 4.3, we obtain the desired slope:

$$m = \frac{y_2 - y_1}{x_2 - x_1} = \frac{-3 - 1}{2 - (-5)} = \frac{-4}{7} = -\frac{4}{7}$$

If we interchange the labels of the given points and let $(x_1, y_1) = (2, -3)$ and $(x_2, y_2) = (-5, 1)$, the result is

$$m = \frac{y_2 - y_1}{x_2 - x_1} = \frac{1 - (-3)}{-5 - 2} = \frac{4}{-7} = -\frac{4}{7}$$

Hence, the order in labeling the given points is immaterial. We interpret a slope of $-4/7$ to mean that for every 7 units moved to the right, the straight line moves down 4 units, or, for every 7 units moved to the left, the straight line moves up 4 units. ■

In working with straight lines, the following generalizations about slopes are useful.

- The slope of a straight line is positive if, as you follow the curve from left to right, you move up. See Figure 4.5(a).
- The slope of a straight line parallel to the x-axis is zero because the rise is zero for any run. See Figure 4.5(b).
- The slope of a straight line is negative if, as you follow the curve from left to right, you move down. From Figure 4.5(c), we see that when the run is positive, the rise is negative, and when the run is negative, the rise is positive. The ratio of rise to run (that is, slope) in this case must be negative.

- The slope of a straight line parallel to the y-axis is undefined because the run is zero for any rise. Therefore, to apply Equation 4.3, we would have to divide by zero. (Remember, division by zero is an undefined operation.) See Figure 4.5(d).
- Parallel straight lines have equal slopes.
- Perpendicular straight lines have slopes that are negative reciprocals. That is, $\boldsymbol{m_1 = -1/m_2} \cdot (m_2 \neq 0)$

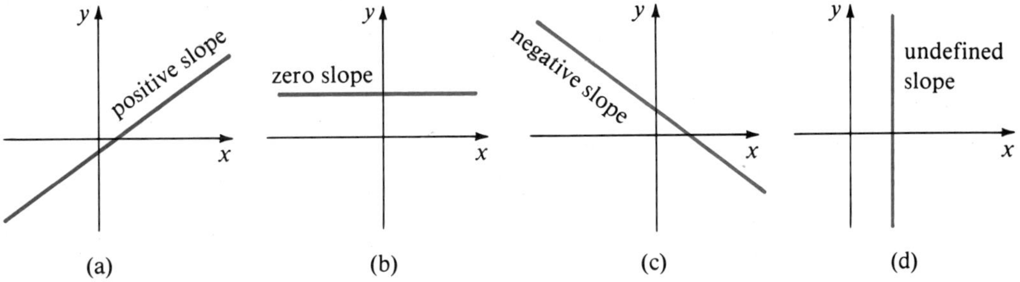

Figure 4.5

EXAMPLE 4 a. Find the slope of a line passing through (2, 1) and (−4, 6).
b. Find the slope of a line drawn perpendicular to the given line at (2, 1) (see Figure 4.6).

Solution a. The slope m of the given line is

$$m = \frac{y_2 - y_1}{x_2 - x_1} = \frac{6 - 1}{-4 - 2} = -\frac{5}{6}$$

b. The slope m' of a line perpendicular to the given line is

$$m' = -\frac{1}{m} = -\frac{1}{-5/6} = \frac{6}{5}$$

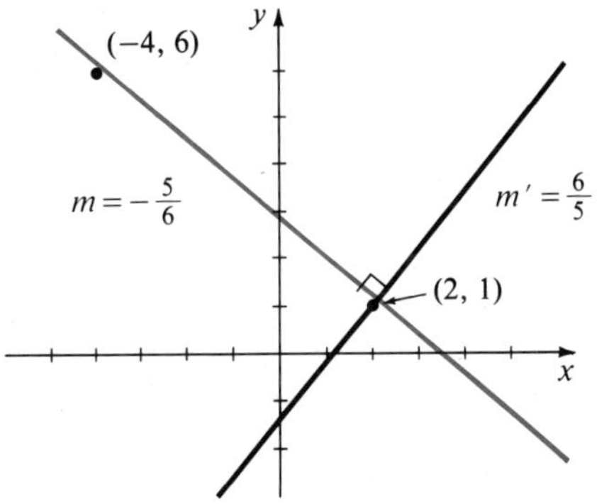

Figure 4.6

■

Methods of Describing a Line

Whereas every straight line can be represented by a linear equation of the general form $ax + by + c = 0$, sometimes certain other forms of representation are significant. Two important forms of a straight line are the point-slope form and the slope-intercept form. Each form shows two properties of a line that can be determined by inspection of the equation.

The **point-slope form** of a straight line is used when we know the slope and one point on the line. See Figure 4.7. To obtain the point-slope form of a straight line,

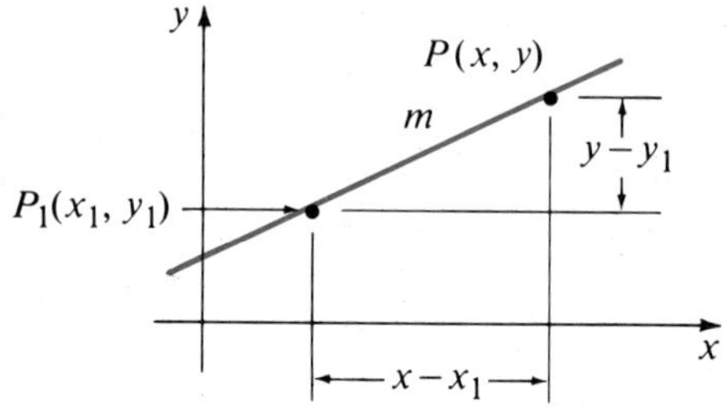

Figure 4.7

choose an arbitrary point $P(x, y)$ different from $P(x_1, y_1)$ on the straight line. Then, by the definition of the slope of a straight line, we have

$$\frac{y - y_1}{x - x_1} = m$$

Rearranging the terms yields

The Point-Slope Form of a Straight Line

The equation of a straight line passing through (x_1, y_1) with slope m is

$$y - y_1 = m(x - x_1) \qquad (4.4)$$

Comment: Note that, since *any* fixed point (x_1, y_1) may be used in Equation 4.4, the equation will *appear* different for various choices of the point, but the resulting equations are equivalent.

EXAMPLE 5 The point-slope form of the equation representing the line that passes through (2, 1) with slope $\frac{1}{3}$ is

$$y - 1 = \frac{1}{3}(x - 2)$$

However, the two points $(0, \frac{1}{3})$ and $(-1, 0)$ are also on the line so that two other point-slope forms of the same line are

$$y - \frac{1}{3} = \frac{1}{3}(x - 0) \quad \text{and} \quad y = \frac{1}{3}(x + 1)$$

Infinitely many other point-slope forms of this equation are possible. Note that the general form of this line is

$$x - 3y + 1 = 0$$

■

If the point used in the point-slope form is (0, b), we have the special case of the **slope-intercept form.** Substituting $x_1 = 0$ and $y_1 = b$ into the point-slope form yields

$$\frac{y - b}{x} = m$$

Solving for y, we have

The Slope-Intercept Form of a Straight Line

The equation of a straight line passing through (0, b) with slope m is

$$y = mx + b \tag{4.5}$$

Comment: When an equation is in slope-intercept form, the constant on the right-hand side is the y-intercept and the coefficient of x is the slope. Given any linear equation, a few simple manipulations can represent the line in any desired form.

EXAMPLE 6 Rearrange the linear equation $3x + 2y = -5$ into slope-intercept form and draw its graph.

Solution To rearrange into slope-intercept form, solve for y. Thus,

$$2y = -3x - 5$$

and

$$y = \underbrace{-\frac{3}{2}}_{m}x + \underbrace{\left(-\frac{5}{2}\right)}_{b}$$

from which we recognize the slope as $-\frac{3}{2}$ and the y-intercept as $-\frac{5}{2}$. (See Figure 4.8.)

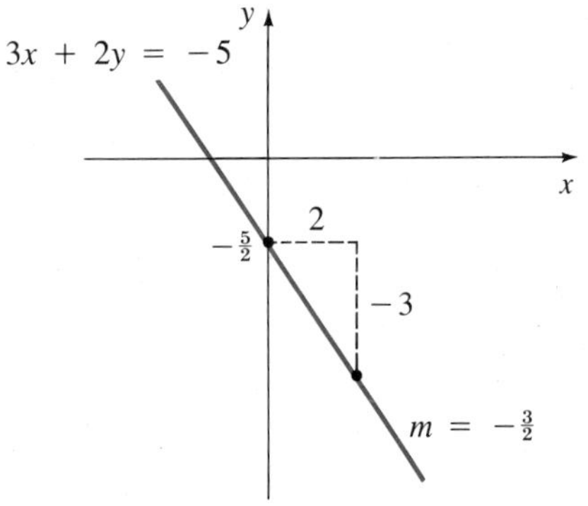

Figure 4.8

■

EXAMPLE 7 Write the equation of the line perpendicular to $x - 3y = 7$ at the point $(4, -1)$.

Solution First, we rewrite the given equation in slope-intercept form; that is,

$$y = \frac{1}{3}x - \frac{7}{3}$$

From this form of the given equation we see that the slope of its graph is $m = \frac{1}{3}$. Denoting the slope of the perpendicular line by m', we have

$$m' = -\frac{1}{m} = -\frac{1}{\frac{1}{3}} = -3$$

Finally, using the point-slope form of a straight line, the equation of the perpendicular line is

$$y - (-1) = -3(x - 4)$$
$$y + 1 = -3x + 12$$
$$y = -3x + 11$$

The general form of the line is $3x + y - 11 = 0$. ■

The general relationship between equations of lines that are perpendicular to each other is given in Exercise 53 of the following exercise set. Before looking at Exercise 53, see if you can find any relationship between the given equation and that of the perpendicular line.

Exercises Section 4.1

In Exercises 1–12, sketch the graph of the given linear equation.

1. $x + y = 1$ **2.** $x - y = 1$

3. $x = 5$ **4.** $y = -2$

5. $2x - y = 5$ **6.** $3x + 2y = 5$

7. $4x - y + 1 = 0$ **8.** $x = 7 - y$

9. $3y - 4x = 4$ **10.** $y = \frac{1}{2}x - 3$

11. $y = \dfrac{x - 2}{3}$ **12.** $15(x + y) = 10$

In Exercises 13–20, sketch the straight line through the pairs of points and compute the slope.

13. $(1, 2), (5, 4)$ **14.** $(-5, 2), (3, -7)$

15. $(-1, -1), (3, -6)$ **16.** $(7, 3), (0, 5)$

17. $(-2, -3), (-5, -7)$ **18.** $(3, -2), (7, 6)$

19. $(-2, 3), (5, 3)$ **20.** $(\frac{1}{2}, \frac{1}{2}), (\frac{1}{3}, -\frac{2}{5})$

In Exercises 21–24, sketch the line passing through the given point with the given slope and then determine its equation.

21. $(2, 5), m = \frac{1}{2}$ **22.** $(-1, -3), m = 3$

23. $(5, -2), m = -7$ **24.** $(3, 4), m = -\frac{2}{5}$

In Exercises 25–30, draw the line through the given points and then find its equation.

25. $(1, 3), (6, 2)$ **26.** $(2, 5), (-3, -7)$

27. $(-1, -1), (1, 2)$ **28.** $(0, 0), (3, -2)$

29. $(0, 2), (-5, 0)$ **30.** $(\frac{1}{2}, \frac{1}{3}), (-\frac{1}{2}, \frac{1}{3})$

Find the slope and the y-intercept of the graph of the equations in Exercises 31–42 and then draw the line.

31. $2x - 3y = 5$ **32.** $3x + 4y = 0$

33. $x + y = 2$ **34.** $5x + 2y = -3$

35. $4y - 2x + 8 = 0$ **36.** $-5x - y - 2 = 0$

37. $2y = x + 5$ **38.** $3x + 6 = 2y$

39. $y = 5$ **40.** $x + y = 1$

41. $x - 5y + 7 = 0$ **42.** $y = 1 - x$

In Exercises 43–52, write the equation of the line perpendicular to the given line at the indicated point.

43. $3x + 2y = 7$ at $(1, 2)$ **44.** $x + 3y = 11$ at $(2, 3)$

45. $x - y = 2$ at $(5, 3)$

46. $2x - 5y = 2$ at $(-4, -2)$

47. $2y - 3x = 1$ at $(1, 2)$ **48.** $y = x$ at $(0, 0)$

49. $5x - 7y = 0$ at $(0, 0)$

50. $5x - 7y = 3$ at $(2, 1)$

51. $-x + 3y = 5$ at $(-2, 1)$

52. $-2y - x = 3$ at $(-1, -1)$

53. Show that the equation of the line perpendicular to $Ax + By = C$ at (x_1, y_1) is

$$Bx - Ay = Bx_1 - Ay_1$$

Hint: Use the fact that the product of the slopes equals -1.

54. Show that the equation of a line with x-intercept a and y-intercept b may be written in the form

$$\frac{x}{a} + \frac{y}{b} = 1 \qquad (a \neq 0, b \neq 0)$$

This form of a line is known as the **intercept form** of a line.

55. Write the equation $x + 3y = 2$ in intercept form.

56. Write the equation $2x - y = 5$ in intercept form.

4.2 Mathematical Models

Representing the relation between two or more physical variables by a mathematical equation is called *mathematical modeling.* If the relation is represented by a linear equation, the model is called a **linear model.**

In economics, the total cost C in dollars of producing x units of a product is represented by a linear **cost-unit model** of the form

$$C = mx + b$$

where m and b are constants to be described. A typical graph of this model is shown in Figure 4.9. The vertical intercept b corresponds to the cost of operation when zero units are produced—that is, the cost of utilities, insurance, mortgage interest, and so on. Cost of this type is called **fixed cost.** Cost such as that for labor and materials is called **variable cost.**

The ratio of variable cost to the number of units made is called **marginal cost.** Thus, marginal cost corresponds to the slope of the graph of the linear function $C = mx + b$. Marginal cost is constant when we are using this linear model.

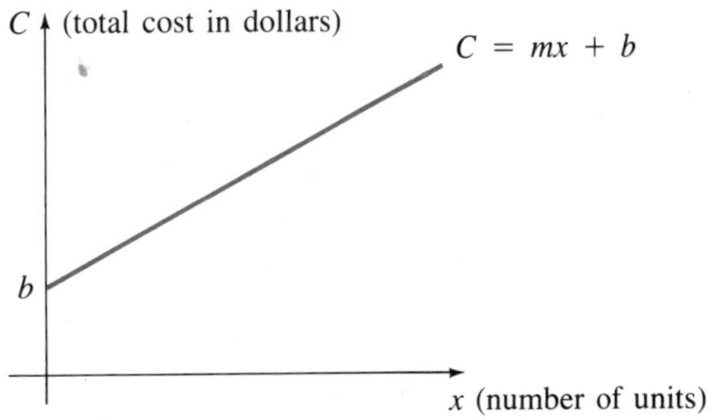

Figure 4.9

Total cost divided by the number of units produced is referred to as the **average cost** of a unit. Example 1 shows that average cost declines as the number of units produced increases when the simple linear model is used.

EXAMPLE 1 The manufacturing cost C (in dollars) when x units are produced by a company is given by $C = 0.2x + 5000$.

a. Sketch the graph of total cost versus units produced.
b. What is the marginal cost?
c. Compute the average cost for the 100th unit; for the 200th unit.

Solution a. The graph is shown in Figure 4.10.

b. The marginal cost is \$0.20. Marginal cost is numerically equal to the slope of the cost-unit equation.

c. The average cost of the 100th unit is

$$\frac{5020}{100} = \$50.20$$

The average cost of the 200th unit is

$$\frac{5040}{200} = \$25.20$$

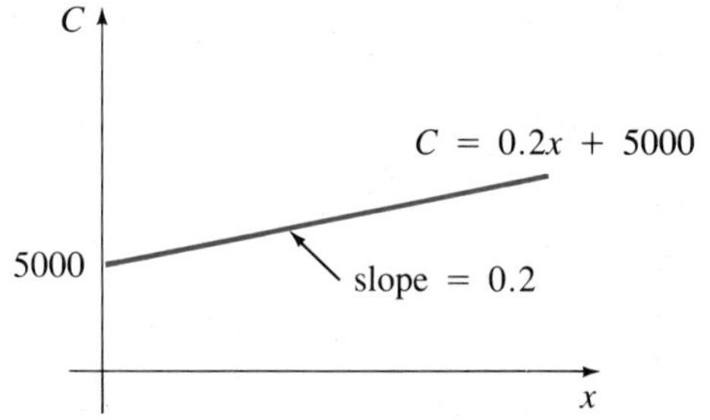

Figure 4.10 ■

Profit can be determined from the cost-unit model if the unit sales price is known. Since the revenue from selling x units at a unit price of u dollars is $u \cdot x$ and the profit is given by

profit = total revenue − total cost

we replace total revenue with ux and total cost with $mx + b$, and the result is

$$\begin{aligned} P &= ux - (mx + b) \\ &= ux - mx - b \\ P &= (u - m)x - b \end{aligned}$$

The value of x for which $P = 0$ is called the **break-even point.**

EXAMPLE 2 Suppose the variable costs of producing a small electric motor are \$5 per unit and the fixed costs are \$3000 per month. The company plans to sell the motors for \$20 each. Determine the monthly revenue, cost, and profit functions for this company. Graph the profit function and indicate the break-even point.

Solution If we let x equal the number of motors sold each month, the monthly revenue function is $R = 20x$. The monthly cost function is $C = 5x + 3000$, and the profit function is $P = (20 - 5)x - 3000 = 15x - 3000$. The break-even point is found by setting $P = 0$ and solving for x. Thus,

$$0 = 15x - 3000$$

or

$$x = 200 \text{ motors}$$

The profit function is shown graphically in Figure 4.11. Notice that the break-even point corresponds to the x-intercept.

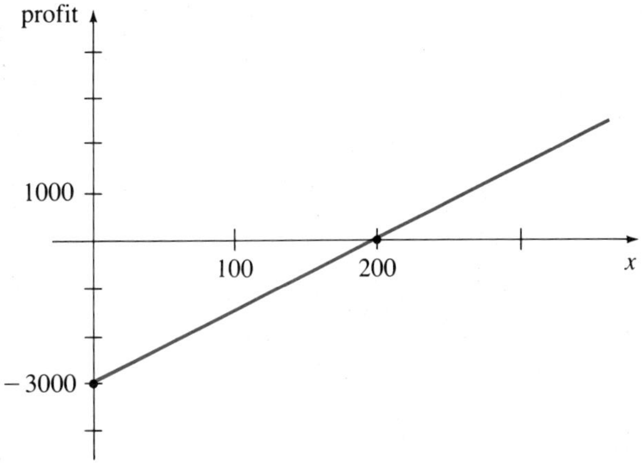

Figure 4.11 ■

In the final example, a linear model is used to represent the physical problem of a spring being stretched by an applied force. Problems of this type are studied in physics.

EXAMPLE 3 The length of a spring can be expressed as a linear function of the applied force. Find the equation relating the length d of a spring to applied force f, if the length of the spring is 5 in. when a 6-lb weight is applied and 7 in. when a 14-lb weight is applied. Assume $f \geq 0$.

Solution Since spring length is a linear function of applied force, its graph is a straight line. Figure 4.12 shows this graphically. The slope of the straight line between these two points is then given by

$$m = \frac{d_2 - d_1}{f_2 - f_1} = \frac{7 - 5}{14 - 6} = \frac{2}{8} = \frac{1}{4}$$

The point-slope form of this straight line can be written in the form

$$d - d_1 = m(f - f_1)$$

Now, letting $(f_1, d_1) = (6, 5)$ and $m = \frac{1}{4}$, we have

$$d - 5 = \frac{1}{4}(f - 6)$$

or

$$d = \frac{1}{4}f + \frac{7}{2}$$

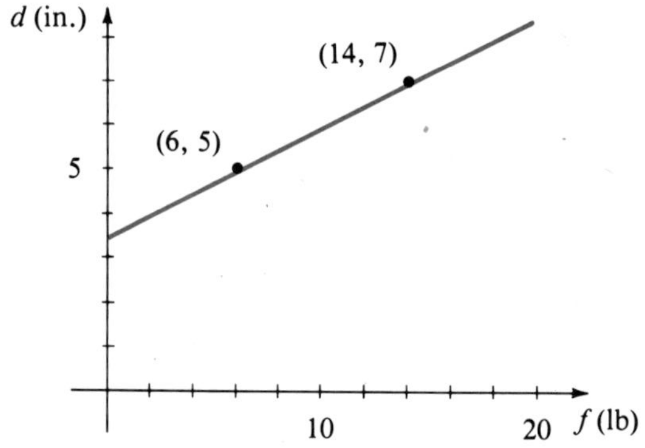

Figure 4.12

In physics, the slope of a graph such as Figure 4.12 is called the **spring constant.** Also, the **free length** of a spring equals the vertical intercept of this graph. In the language of the physicist, the spring in Example 3 has a spring constant of $\frac{1}{4}$ and a free length of 3.5 in.

Exercises Section 4.2

1. If the total factory cost C of making x units of a product is $C = 5x + 400$, what are the values for the following?
   a. The cost of making 300 units.
   b. The average cost per unit of making 300 units.
   c. The average cost per unit of making 500 units.
   d. The marginal cost per unit.
   e. The number of units that can be made for a cash outlay of $2000.
2. If the marginal cost of producing a unit is constant at $0.50 and the fixed cost is $500:
   a. Write the cost-unit equation.
   b. What is the marginal cost of producing the 100th unit?
   c. What is the cost of producing 100 units?
   d. What is the average cost per unit of producing 100 units?
3. If the cost-unit function is $C = 2x + 300$:
   a. What is the marginal cost of the 100th unit?
   b. What is the variable cost for 100 units?
   c. How does the fixed cost change from the 100th to the 101st unit?
   d. How many units can be made for a cash outlay of $100? of $500? of $1000?
4. If the cost-unit function is $C = 0.5x + 175$:
   a. What is the variable cost for 300 units?
   b. What is the fixed cost?
   c. What is the average cost per unit to produce 100 units?
   d. What is the average cost per unit to produce 200 units?
5. A small company reconditions car batteries and sells them for $30. For 1987, fixed costs were $24,000 and marginal costs were $8 per battery on sales of 2810 batteries.
   a. Determine the revenue for the year.
   b. Determine the profit for the year.
   c. Determine the break-even point.

6. Suppose the cost-unit function for a company is $C = 0.25x + 1200$.
a. Determine the marginal cost.
b. Determine the revenue on sales of 10,000 units at \$0.60 per unit.
c. Determine the profit for these sales figures.
d. Determine the break-even point.

7. Suppose the cost-unit function for a company is $C = 0.37x + 18{,}000$.
a. Determine the variable costs on sales of 50,000 units.
b. If each unit sells for \$0.62, determine the profit on these sales.
c. Determine the break-even point.

8. Express degrees Celsius as a linear function of degrees Fahrenheit if 0° C corresponds to 32° F and 100° C corresponds to 212° F.

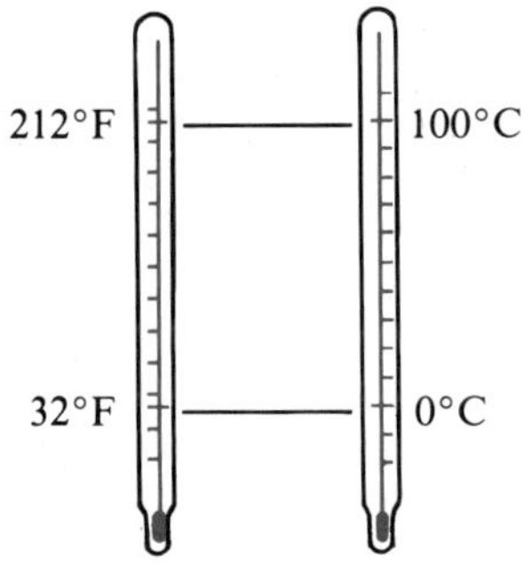

9. The current I in a resistor is a linear function of the applied voltage V. Find the equation relating the current to the voltage if the current is $\frac{1}{4}$ amp when the voltage is 6 volts and $\frac{2}{3}$ amp when the voltage is 8 volts.

10. In an experiment to determine the coefficient of friction, it is found that a 10-lb block has a frictional force of 3 lb and a 25-lb block has a frictional force of 7.5 lb. Find the equation relating frictional force to weight if the frictional force is a linear function of weight.

11. *Linear depreciation* is one of several methods approved by the Internal Revenue Service for depreciating business property. If the original cost of the property is C dollars and if it is depreciated linearly over N years, its value V remaining at the end of n years is given by

$$V = C - \frac{C}{N}n$$

Find the value after five years of a typewriter whose initial cost of \$300 is to be depreciated over 20 years.

12. If you borrow P dollars at the simple interest rate i, the annual interest is $P \cdot i$. Hence, the amount A owed at the end of n years is given by

$$A = P(1 + i \cdot n)$$

Find the amount you owe after five years if you borrow \$2000 at 8% simple interest.

13. Mr. Smith wants to borrow \$4000 to buy a new car. He wishes to pay off the loan with monthly payments stretching over three years. If he is charged 12% simple interest and if he computes the monthly payments by dividing the total amount due in three years by 36, how much will Mr. Smith have to pay each month?

14. A manufacturer of fountain pens can expect to sell 21,000 felt-tip pens if he charges \$0.80 per pen but only 10,000 if he raises the price to \$1.00. Assuming that the relationship is linear, find the equation of the line relating the number of pens to their price. How many felt-tip pens can he sell if he charges \$0.90?

15. The error E of a radar varies with slant range R according to the equation $5E - R = 3$. Graphically show the relationship between radar error and slant range.

16. The pressure at a point below the surface of a body of water is given by $P = 0.04D + 14.7$, where P is the pressure in psi and D is the depth in inches. Draw the graph of the relationship.

4.3 Quadratic Functions: The Parabolic Graph

Functions that can be put into the form

$$f(x) = ax^2 + bx + c$$

where a, b, and c are constants and $a \neq 0$ are called **quadratic functions.** Functions of this type arise naturally in describing physical quantities such as the path of a projectile, the shape of a radar antenna, and the area of a circle.

EXAMPLE 1 a. $f(x) = x^2 - 2x + 1$ is a quadratic function with $a = 1, b = -2$, and $c = 1$.
b. $g(x) = 9 - x^2$ is a quadratic function with $a = -1, b = 0$, and $c = 9$.
c. $h(x) = x^2 + 3x$ is a quadratic function with $a = 1, b = 3$, and $c = 0$. ■

The graph of a quadratic function is a U-shaped curve called a **parabola.** The parabola is the graph of the quadratic function just as the straight line is the graph of the linear function. The graphs of $y = x^2$ and $y = -x^2$, which are shown in Figure 4.13, typify the parabolic shape. The parabola in Figure 4.13(a) opens upward and the one in 4.13(b) opens downward. The low (or high) point of the parabola is called the **vertex.** The parabola is **symmetric** about a vertical line through its vertex.

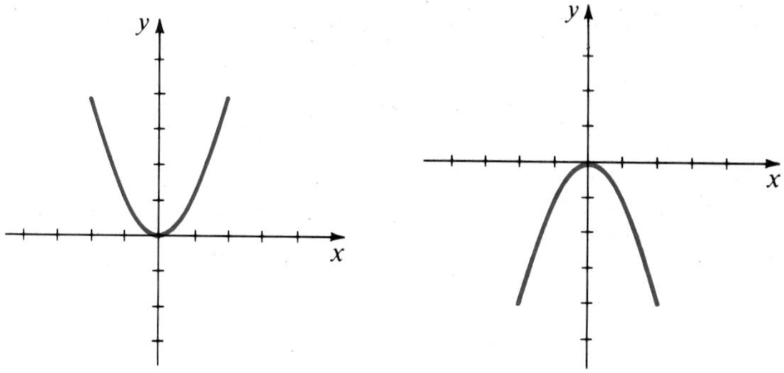

(a) $y = x^2$ (b) $y = -x^2$

Figure 4.13

The constants a, b, and c determine the shape and location of the parabola. We can sketch the graph of a quadratic function by plotting some points and then connecting them with a smooth curve. Usually a few points near the vertex are all that are needed since we know the graph is a parabola.

EXAMPLE 2 Sketch the graph of $y = x^2 + 1$.

Solution The graph is shown in Figure 4.14.

$y = x^2 + 1$

x	y
-2	5
-1	2
0	1
1	2
2	5

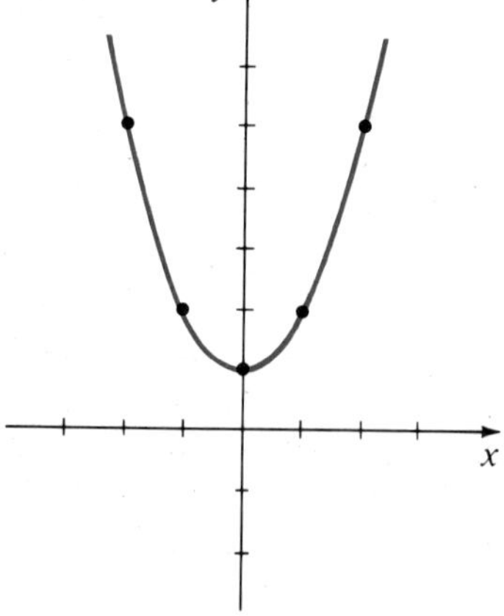

Figure 4.14 ■

EXAMPLE 3 Sketch the graph of $y = 2x - \frac{1}{2}x^2$.

Solution The graph is shown in Figure 4.15. Notice from the graph that the vertex is at (2, 2) and the zeros of the functions are $x = 0$ and $x = 4$.

$y = 2x - \frac{1}{2}x^2$

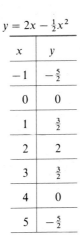

x	y
-1	$-\frac{5}{2}$
0	0
1	$\frac{3}{2}$
2	2
3	$\frac{3}{2}$
4	0
5	$-\frac{5}{2}$

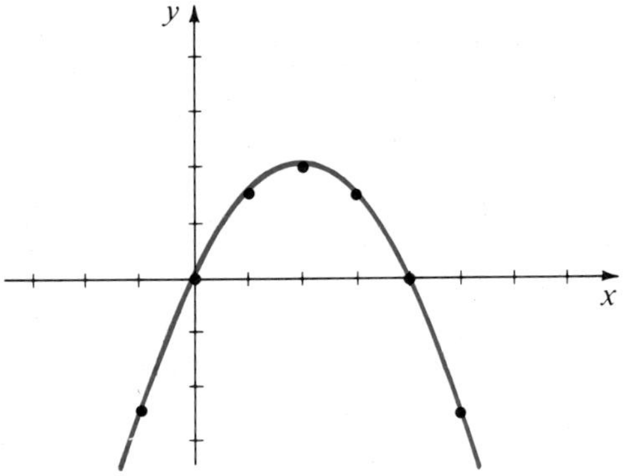

Figure 4.15 ■

The point plotting method used in Examples 2 and 3 is time consuming and gives you only a starting point. The important observation to be made in Figures 4.14 and 4.15 is that each graph is a parabola and that the vertex is not always at the origin. As a matter of fact, the vertex is at the origin only if b and c are zero.

The vertex of the parabola in Example 3 can be found by completing the square on $2x - \frac{1}{2}x^2$ as follows. Factoring $-\frac{1}{2}$ from $2x - \frac{1}{2}x^2$, we get

$$y = -\frac{1}{2}(x^2 - 4x)$$

Next, we complete the square on the quantity in the parentheses by adding 4 inside the parentheses and $(-\frac{1}{2})(4) = 2$ outside. This procedure yields

$$y = -\frac{1}{2}(x^2 - 4x + 4) + 2$$

or

$$y = -\frac{1}{2}(x - 2)^2 + 2$$

In this form, we see that the maximum value of $y = 2$ occurs at $x = 2$ since $-\frac{1}{2}(x - 2)^2 + 2$ is less than 2 for all $x \neq 2$. Therefore, the vertex must be located at (2, 2).

The coordinates of the vertex of the graph of the general quadratic are found by applying the same procedure to

$$y = ax^2 + bx + c$$

After factoring a from $ax^2 + bx$, we complete the square on $x^2 + (b/a)x$ by adding

$(b/2a)^2$ as follows:

$$y = a\left(x^2 + \frac{b}{a}x + \left(\frac{b}{2a}\right)^2\right) + c - a\left(\frac{b}{2a}\right)^2$$
$$= a\left(x + \frac{b}{2a}\right)^2 + c - \frac{b^2}{4a}$$

We see from this result that if $x = -b/2a$, the value of $y = f(-b/2a)$ is either a minimum or a maximum depending on whether a is negative or positive. In either case, $y = c - b^2/4a$. Thus, **the coordinates of the vertex of the parabola corresponding to $y = ax^2 + bx + c$ are**

$$x = -\frac{b}{2a}, \qquad y = f\left(-\frac{b}{2a}\right) = c - \frac{b^2}{4a}$$

EXAMPLE 4 The vertex of the graph of $y = 2x^2 - 6x$ is located at $(\frac{3}{2}, -\frac{9}{2})$ since

$$x = \frac{-(-6)}{2(2)} = \frac{3}{2}, \qquad y = 2\left(\frac{3}{2}\right)^2 - 6\left(\frac{3}{2}\right) = -\frac{9}{2}$$

See Figure 4.16. The value of y can also be found by using

$$y = c - \frac{b^2}{4a} = 0 - \frac{(-6)^2}{4(2)} = -\frac{9}{2}$$

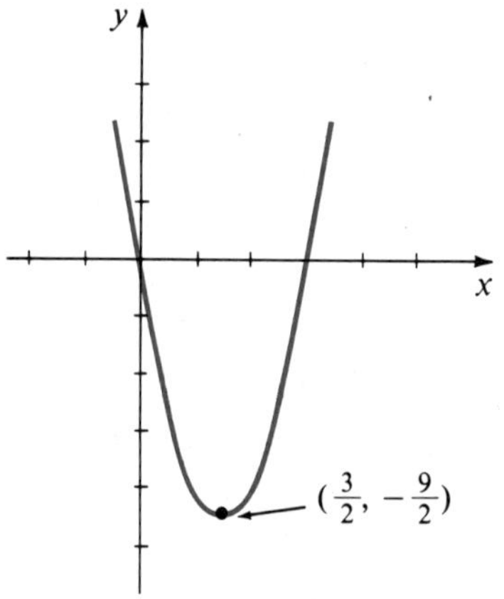

Figure 4.16 ■

The procedure outlined in Example 4 may be used to graph any quadratic function. To make an accurate sketch of the graph of a quadratic function, use the procedure outlined on page 125.

Procedure for Sketching the Graph of $f(x) = ax^2 + bx + c$

1. Determine the sign of the x^2 coefficient. If $a > 0$, the parabola opens upward; if $a < 0$, it opens downward.
2. Determine the y-intercept by letting $x = 0$. That is, $f(0) = c$ is the y-intercept.
3. Determine the x-intercepts by letting $f(x) = 0$. The x-intercepts are given by

$$x = \frac{-b \pm \sqrt{b^2 - 4ac}}{2a}$$

   If $b^2 - 4ac > 0$, the graph has two x-intercepts; if $b^2 - 4ac = 0$, the graph has one x-intercept; if $b^2 - 4ac < 0$, the graph has no x-intercepts and, therefore, does not cross the x-axis. If $f(x)$ can be factored as $k(x - x_1)(x - x_2)$, where k is a constant, then the x-intercepts are $x = x_1$ and $x = x_2$.
4. Determine the location of the vertex by $x = \dfrac{-b}{2a}$ and $y = f\left(-\dfrac{b}{2a}\right) = c - \dfrac{b^2}{4a}$.
5. If the graph has no x-intercepts, then locate a few more points to the left and right of the vertex.

EXAMPLE 5 Sketch the graph of $f(x) = x^2 - x - 6$.

Solution First note that $a = 1$, $b = -1$, and $c = -6$.

1. The parabola opens upward since $a > 0$.
2. The y-intercept is $f(0) = -6$.
3. The x-intercepts are found by letting $f(x) = 0$. Thus,

$$x^2 - x - 6 = 0$$

   Observing that the quadratic is factorable, we have

$$(x - 3)(x + 2) = 0$$

   Therefore, the x-intercepts are $x = 3$ and $x = -2$.
4. To locate the vertex, note that

$$x = -\frac{b}{2a} = -\frac{-1}{2(1)} = \frac{1}{2} \quad \text{and} \quad y = f\left(\frac{-b}{2a}\right) = \left(\frac{1}{2}\right)^2 - \frac{1}{2} - 6 = -\frac{25}{4}$$

   Hence, the vertex is located at $(\frac{1}{2}, -\frac{25}{4})$.

The graph of $f(x) = x^2 - x - 6$ is shown in Figure 4.17. From the figure we see that the domain is $-\infty < x < \infty$ and the range is $f(x) \geq -25/4$.

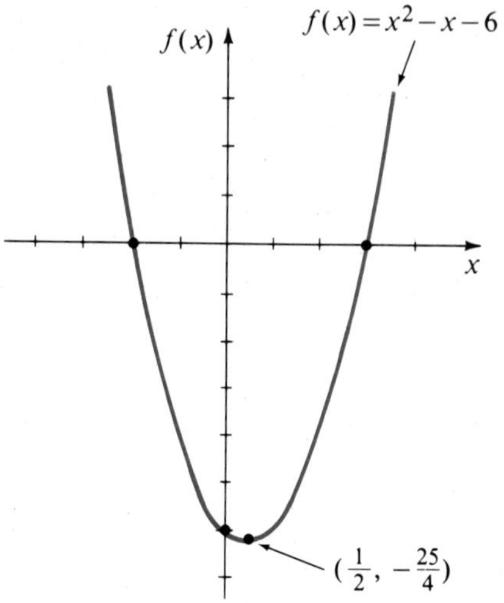

Figure 4.17

■

EXAMPLE 6 Sketch the graph of $y = x^2 + 3x$.

Solution Here, $a = 1$, $b = 3$, and $c = 0$.

1. The parabola opens upward since $a > 0$.
2. The y-intercept is $y(0) = 0$.
3. The x-intercepts are obtained from $x^2 + 3x = 0$. Since $x^2 + 3x$ factors into $x(x + 3)$, we conclude that the x-intercepts are $x = 0$ and $x = -3$.
4. The vertex is at

$$-\frac{b}{2a} = -\frac{3}{2(1)} = -\frac{3}{2}$$

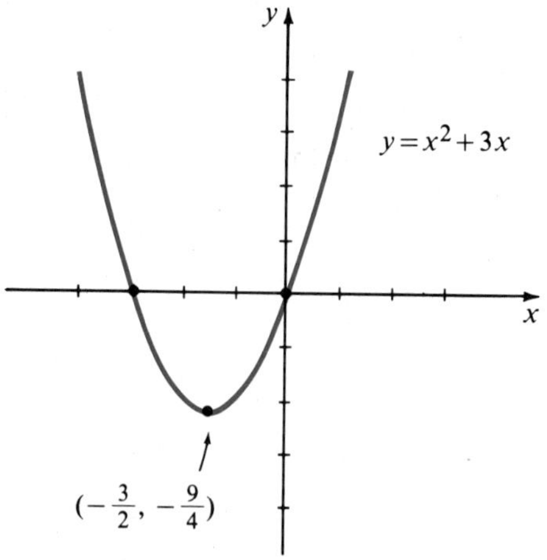

Figure 4.18

and

$$f\left(\frac{-b}{2a}\right) = f\left(-\frac{3}{2}\right) = \left(-\frac{3}{2}\right)^2 + 3\left(-\frac{3}{2}\right) = \frac{9}{4} - \frac{9}{2} = -\frac{9}{4}$$

These points and our knowledge of the parabolic shape yield the graph in Figure 4.18. From the figure the domain is $-\infty < x < \infty$ and the range is $y \geq -9/4$. ■

EXAMPLE 7 Sketch the graph of $G(t) = -t^2 + 2t - 2$.

Solution

1. Since $a < 0$, the parabola opens downward.
2. The y-intercept is $G(0) = -2$.
3. There are no x-intercepts since the discriminant

   $$b^2 - 4ac = (2)^2 - 4(-1)(-2) = -4$$

   which is negative. This means that the graph does not cross the x-axis.
4. Since $-\dfrac{b}{2a} = -\dfrac{2}{2(-1)} = 1$, the vertex is located at $(1, G(1))$, where

   $$G(1) = -(1)^2 + 2(1) - 2 = -1$$

5. Since there are no x-intercepts, we locate a couple of additional points corresponding to $t = -1$ and $t = 2$. The graph is shown in Figure 4.19. The domain of the function is $-\infty < t < \infty$ and the range is $G(t) \leq -1$.

t	$G(t)$
-1	-5
2	-2

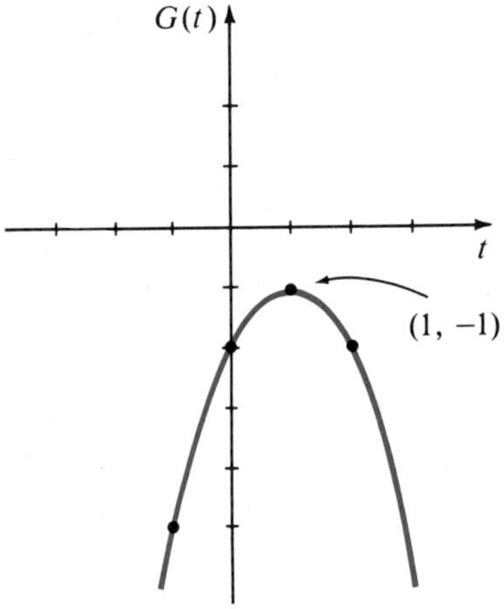

Figure 4.19 ■

Sometimes we want to find a quadratic function whose graph has x-intercepts at $x = a$ and $x = b$. Then the function has linear factors $(x - a)$ and $(x - b)$; hence, the quadratic function has the form $f(x) = k(x - a)(x - b)$, where k is a constant. The value of k can be determined if an additional point on the parabola is known.

EXAMPLE 8 Determine the quadratic function whose graph is shown in Figure 4.20.

Solution

1. The x-intercepts are 5 and -3. Hence the form of the function is

   $$y = k(x - 5)(x + 3)$$

2. Since the y-intercept is -4, substitute $x = 0$ and $y = -4$ into the functional expression to get

$$-4 = k(-5)(3) \quad \text{or} \quad k = \frac{4}{15}$$

The desired function is then

$$y = \frac{4}{15}(x-5)(x+3) = \frac{4}{15}(x^2 - 2x - 15) = \frac{4}{15}x^2 - \frac{8}{15}x - 4$$

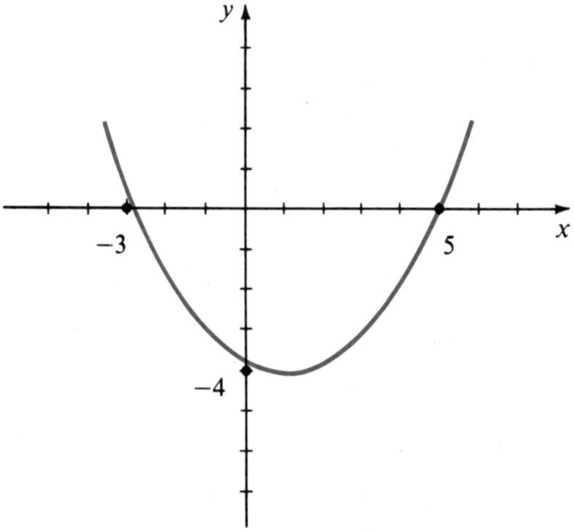

Figure 4.20

■

Exercises Section 4.3

In Exercises 1–20, sketch the graph of the given quadratic function. Give the domain and range and the intercepts of the graph. Be sure to indicate the vertex of each.

1. $f(x) = x^2 - 4$
2. $y = 2x^2 - 6$
3. $y = x^2 + 1$
4. $g(t) = t^2 + 5$
5. $f(x) = 9 - x^2$
6. $y = x^2 + 2x$
7. $x(t) = t^2 - 3t$
8. $s = 3t - 16t^2$
9. $y = x^2 - 5x + 6$
10. $y = x^2 + 7x + 12$
11. $y = 3x^2 + 2x + 1$
12. $y = x^2 + 7x + 13$
13. $y = 2 - x^2 + x$
14. $y = x - x^2 - 1$
15. $f(x) = 2x^2 - 3x - 5$
16. $f(t) = -2t^2 - 4t + 5$
17. $y = 3 + x - x^2$
18. $g(x) = 3 + x + x^2$
19. $G(x) = 1 + x + x^2$
20. $f(x) = \frac{1}{2}x^2 - x - 2$

In Exercises 21–30, determine the quadratic function of the given graph.

21.

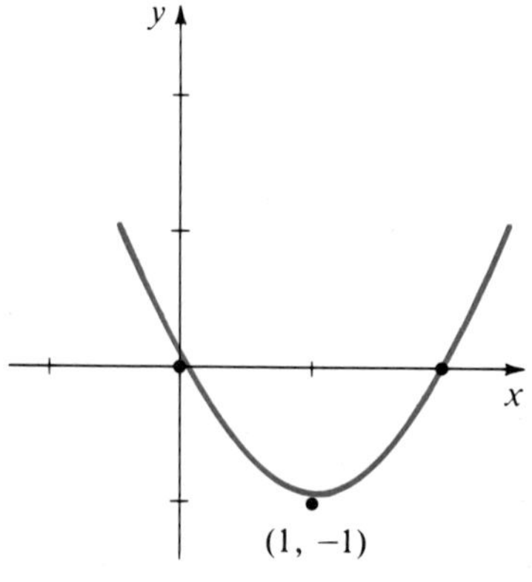

22.

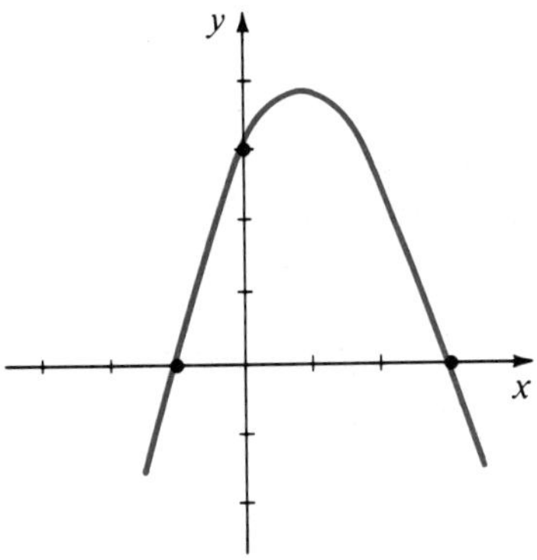

23.

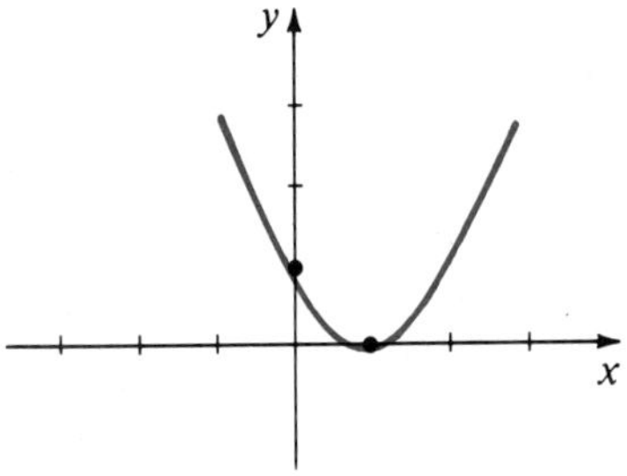

24.

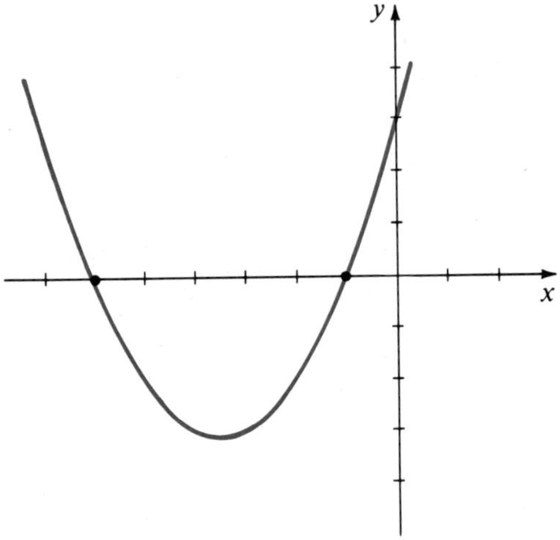

25.

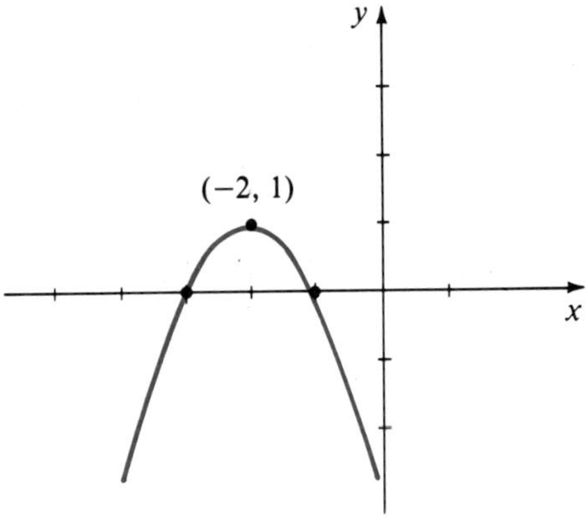

26.

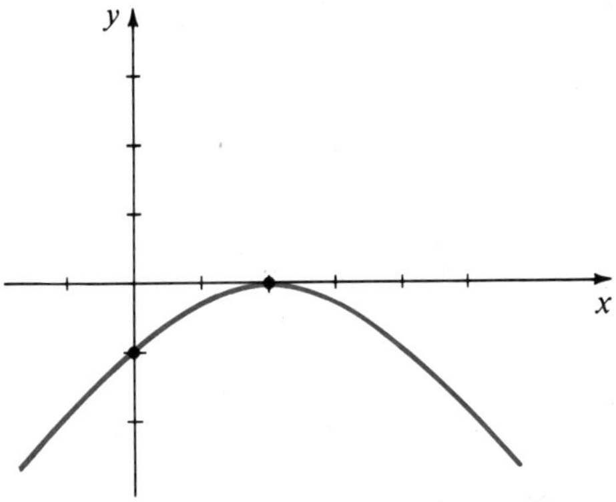

27.

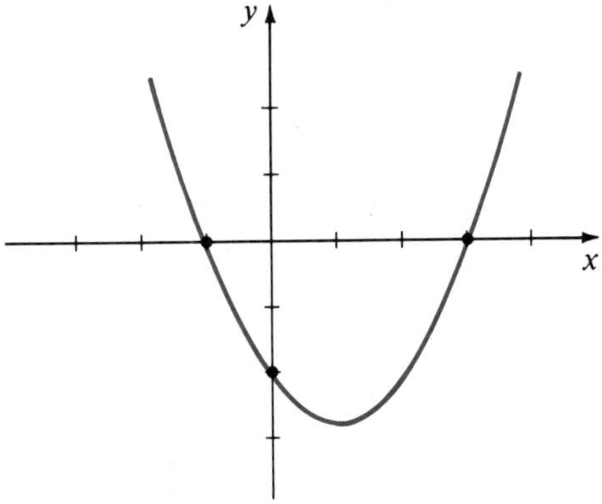

28.

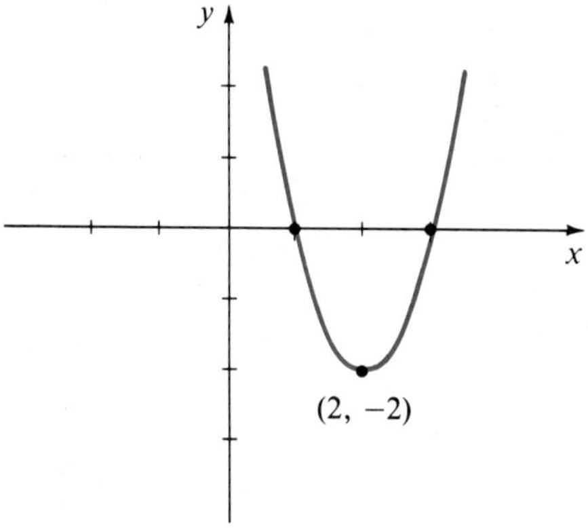

29.

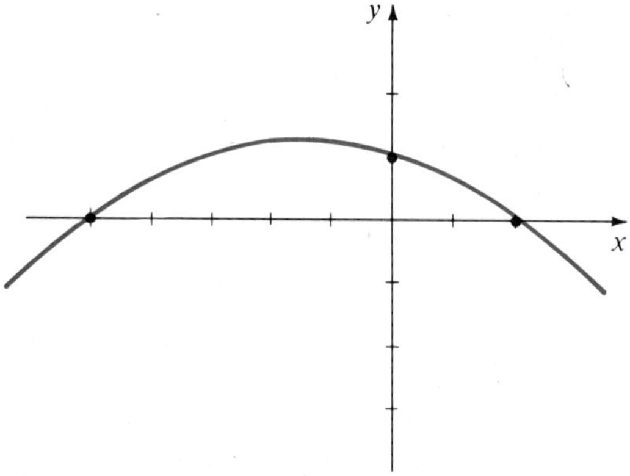

30.

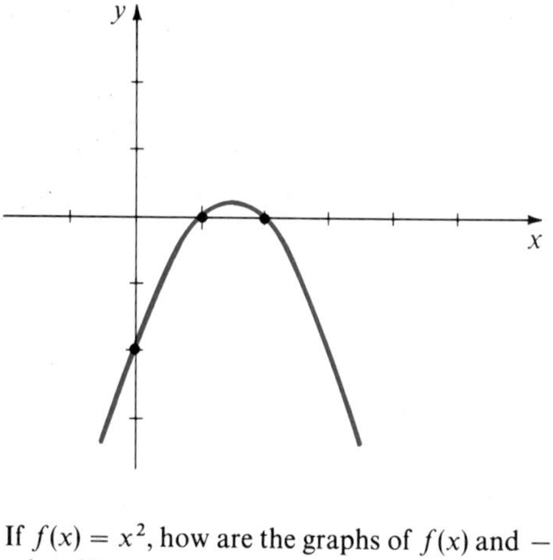

31. If $f(x) = x^2$, how are the graphs of $f(x)$ and $-f(x)$ related?

32. If $f(x) = x^2$, how are the graphs of $f(x)$ and $f(-x)$ related?

33. A radar antenna is to be built with a cross-section that is described by the function $y = 0.05x^2$, where x and y are in feet. Draw the cross-section of the antenna if it has a diameter of 15 ft.

34. When an object is thrown into the air, its height above the ground is a quadratic function of time. Sketch the graph of height versus time from $t = 0$ to $t = 3$ if the functional relationship is $h = 48t - 16t^2$. What is the object's maximum height?

35. The profit function of a small retail firm is given by

$$P(t) = 45t - 3t^2$$

where t is the number of hours per day the business remains open.

a. Sketch the graph of the profit for $0 \le t \le 24$.
b. For which numbers of hours is the company making money?
c. For which numbers of hours is the company losing money?
d. If profit were the only motive, how many hours should the business stay open?

36. A cost function for manufacturing a certain product is given by

$$C(t) = 0.5t^2 - 3t + 8$$

a. Make a sketch of this cost function versus t.
b. For which value of t is the cost lowest?

37. The velocity of a certain rocket varies with time according to $v = 100 + 200t - 25t^2$, where v is in ft/sec when t is in seconds. Sketch the graph of the velocity function for $t \ge 0$. What is the maximum velocity of the rocket? At what time is the velocity equal to zero?

38. Using the graph from Exercise 37, estimate the time it takes for the velocity of the rocket to equal its initial velocity.

39. Determine whether the composition of a quadratic function with a quadratic function is quadratic.

4.4 Polynomial Functions

Linear and quadratic functions are special cases of a class of functions called **polynomial** functions. In general, a function defined by the rule

$$f(x) = a_n x^n + a_{n-1}x^{n-1} + \cdots + a_1 x + a_0, \qquad a_n \neq 0$$

is called a polynomial function of degree n if n is a positive integer and $a_n, a_{n-1}, \ldots, a_0$ are arbitrary but constant real numbers. Using this definition, you can see that a quadratic function is a polynomial function of degree two and a linear function is a polynomial function of degree one.

Functions that include negative or fractional exponent terms are not polynomials. For instance, neither

$$f(x) = x + \frac{1}{x} \quad \text{nor} \quad g(x) = \sqrt{x}$$

is a polynomial.

Graphing general polynomials is best done with the aid of calculus, so we will limit our discussion to certain special polynomials. The idea is to learn to make quick sketches of certain polynomial functions without plotting an excessive number of points.

Single-Term Polynomials

We begin our discussion of graphing polynomials by describing the characteristics of single-term polynomials of the form $y = x^n$, where n is a positive integer. The basic shape of the graph of $y = x^n$ depends upon whether n is odd or even. If n is odd, the value of y is positive when x is positive and negative when x is negative. Also, y becomes very large and positive when x becomes very large and positive, and y becomes very large and negative when x becomes very large and negative. If n is odd and greater than 1, the characteristic shape of $y = x^n$ is typified by the graphs of $y = x^3$ and $y = x^5$, as shown in Figure 4.21(a). The graph of $y = x$, which is a

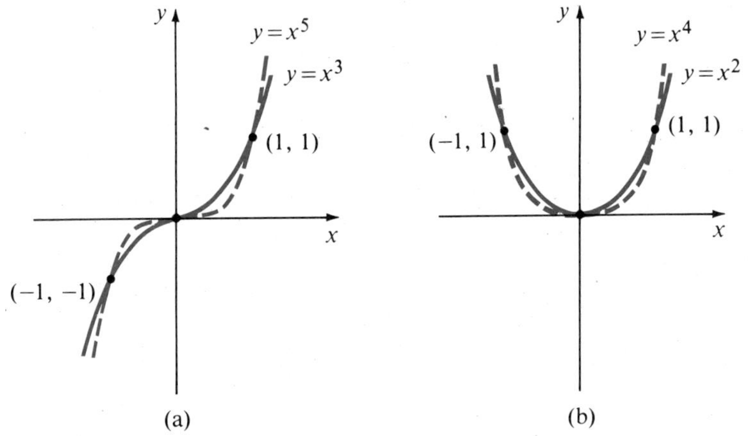

Figure 4.21

straight line, is not shown in the figure because it is not typical of the shape of polynomials of higher degree.

If n is even, the values of y are positive for both positive and negative values of x. Further, y becomes very large and positive when x becomes either very large and positive or very large and negative. The characteristic shape of a graph of $y = x^n$, for n even, is typified by the graphs of $y = x^2$ and $y = x^4$, as shown in Figure 4.21(b).

Reflection and Translation

Once the basic shapes of the graphs of $y = x^n$ are known, we can draw the graphs of other polynomials such as $y = -x^n$, $y = x^n + c$, and $y = (x - c)^n$ by identifying their geometric relation to $y = x^n$.

A Reflection of the Graph in the x-axis

The graph of $y = -x^n$ is obtained from that of $y = x^n$ by changing the sign of y for each x and plotting the resulting points. Since (x, y) and $(x, -y)$ are mirror reflections of one another in the x-axis, it follows that the graph of $y = -x^n$ is the reflection of $y = x^n$ in the x-axis. Figure 4.22 shows the graphs of $y = x^3$ and $y = -x^3$.

x	x^3	$-x^3$
-1	-1	1
0	0	0
1	1	-1

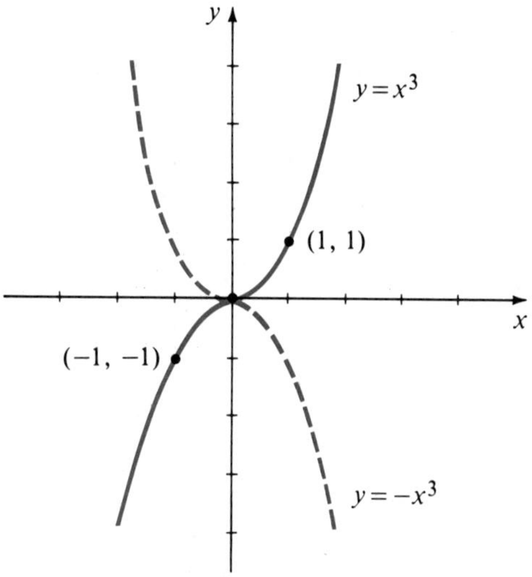

Figure 4.22

A Vertical Translation of the Graph

The graph of $y = x^n + c$ is obtained from that of $y = x^n$ by adding c to y for each x. Then the graph of $y = x^n + c$ is c units higher $(c > 0)$ or lower $(c < 0)$ than that of $y = x^n$. We say that the graph of $y = x^n$ has been **translated** vertically c units. Figure 4.23 shows the graphs of $y = x^4$ and $y = x^4 - 1$.

x	x^4	$x^4 - 1$
-1	1	0
0	0	-1
1	1	0

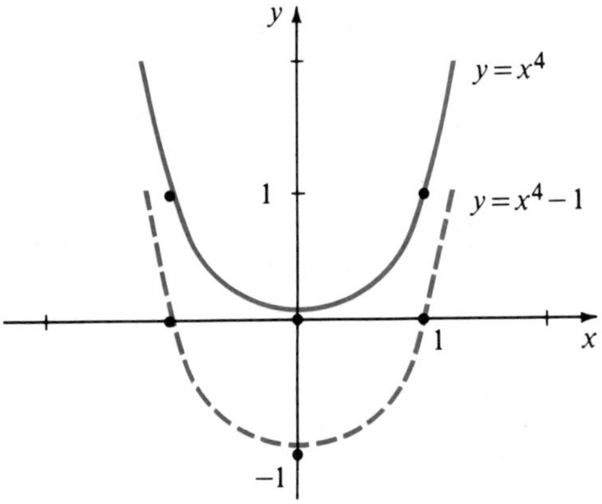

Figure 4.23

A Horizontal Translation of the Graph

The functions $y = x^n$ and $y = (x - c)^n$ have the same domain and range. Note, however, that for $y = x^n$, $y = 0$ when $x = 0$; whereas for $y = (x - c)^n$, $y = 0$ when $x = c$. For instance, $y = x^3 = 0$ when $x = 0$, but $y = (x - 2)^3 = 0$ when $x = 2$. We conclude that the graph of $y = (x - c)^n$ is the same shape as that of $y = x^n$ but shifted c units to the right for $c > 0$ and c units to the left for $c < 0$. Figure 4.24 shows the graphs of $y = x^3$, $y = (x - 2)^3$, and $y = (x + 2)^3$.

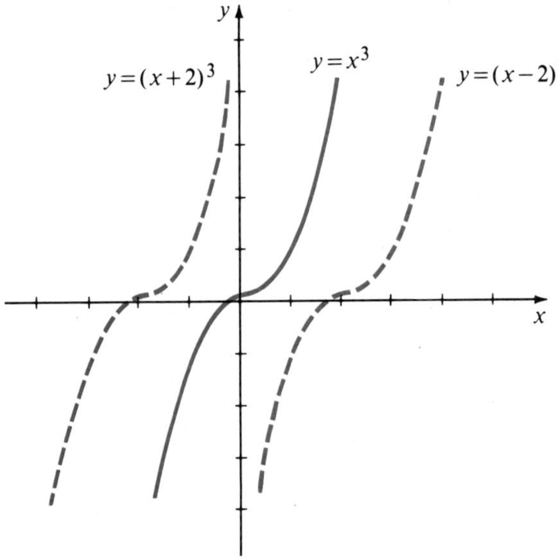

Figure 4.24

Comment: Although the discussion of reflection and translation was given in the context of polynomial functions, it applies to functions in general. Thus, we note that

- The graph of $y = -f(x)$ is the reflection in the x-axis of the graph of $y = f(x)$.
- The graph of $y = f(x) + c$, or $y - c = f(x)$, is the graph of $y = f(x)$ translated vertically by c units. The graph of $y = f(x) + c$ is c units higher than that of $y = f(x)$ if $c > 0$ and c units lower if $c < 0$.
- The graph of $y = f(x - c)$ is the graph of $y = f(x)$ translated horizontally by c units. The graph of $y = f(x - c)$ is c units to the right of the graph of $y = f(x)$ if $c > 0$ and c units to its left if $c < 0$.

EXAMPLE 1 Sketch the graph of $y = 2 - x^5$.

Solution We interpret this to be the graph of $y = x^5$, but reflected in the x-axis and translated 2 units upward. Figure 4.25 shows how to obtain the graph by means of a sequence of operations on the graph of $y = x^5$.

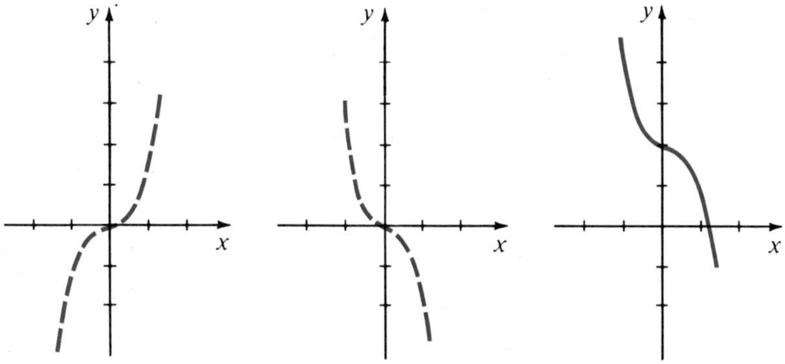

(a) $y=x^5$ (b) $y=-x^5$ Reflection (c) $y=2-x^5$ Vertical translation

Figure 4.25

■

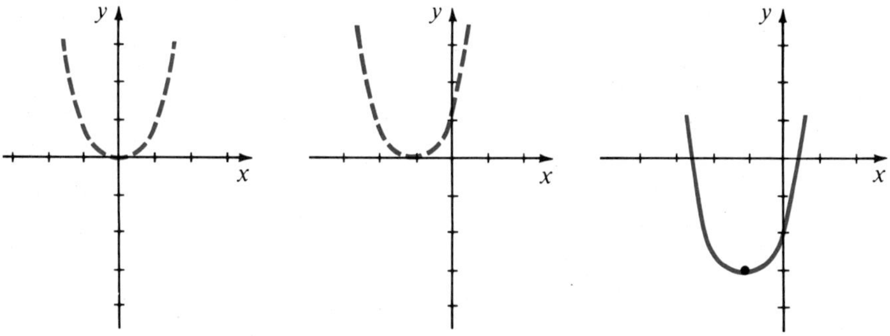

(a) $y=x^4$ (b) $y=(x+1)^4$ Horizontal translation (c) $y=(x+1)^4-3$ Vertical translation

Figure 4.26

EXAMPLE 2 Sketch the graph of $y = (x + 1)^4 - 3$.

Solution This is the graph of $y = x^4$ shifted 1 unit to the left and 3 units downward. See Figure 4.26. ■

Factored Polynomials

If a polynomial is written as a product of linear and irreducible quadratic factors, the x-intercepts can be obtained. This helps considerably in making the sketch.

EXAMPLE 3 Sketch the graph of $y = x^3 - 4x$.

Solution This can be written as $y = x(x - 2)(x + 2)$. The x-intercepts are at $x = 0$, $x = 2$, and $x = -2$. The value of y alternates in sign, as shown on the accompanying sign diagram. The graph is shown in Figure 4.27.

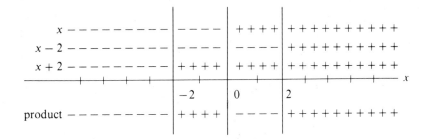

x	− − − − − − − − −	− − − −	+ + + +	+ + + + + + + + + +
$x - 2$	− − − − − − − − −	− − − −	− − − −	+ + + + + + + + + +
$x + 2$	− − − − − − − − −	+ + + +	+ + + +	+ + + + + + + + + +
x		−2	0	2
product	− − − − − − − − −	+ + + +	− − − −	+ + + + + + + + + +

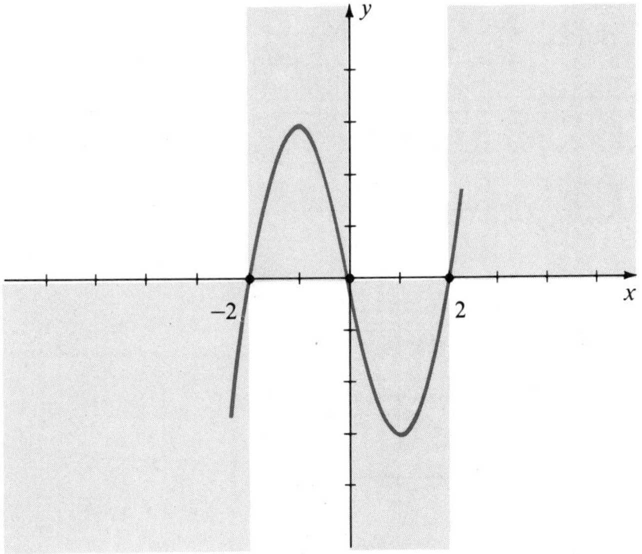

Figure 4.27 ■

Our basic strategy in sketching factored polynomials is based upon finding intercepts and using the sign diagram.

Sketching Factored Polynomials

1. Factor the polynomial as much as possible into real factors. (Do not factor quadratic factors into factors that use complex numbers.) The zeros of each of these factors are the x-intercepts.
2. Determine the y-intercept by setting $x = 0$.
3. Construct a sign diagram. On the intervals where the function is positive, the graph lies above the x-axis; on the intervals where it is negative, the graph is below the x-axis.
4. If necessary, you can compute the ordinate for selected values of x between some of the intercepts.
5. Determine the behavior of y for large positive and negative values of x. (This will be a check on your work.)

EXAMPLE 4 Sketch the graph of $y = x^2(x + 1)(x + 2)$.

Solution Figure 4.28 shows the graph of this function. The points on the x-axis for $x = 0, -1$, and -2 are easily obtained. The graph does not cross the x-axis at $x = 0$ because x^2 is always nonnegative in the vicinity of $x = 0$.

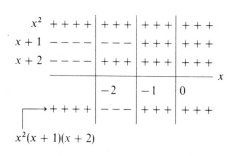

x^2	+ + + +	+ + +	+ + +	+ + +
$x + 1$	− − − −	− − −	+ + +	+ + +
$x + 2$	− − − −	+ + +	+ + +	+ + +
x		-2	-1	0
$x^2(x + 1)(x + 2)$	+ + + +	− − −	+ + +	+ + +

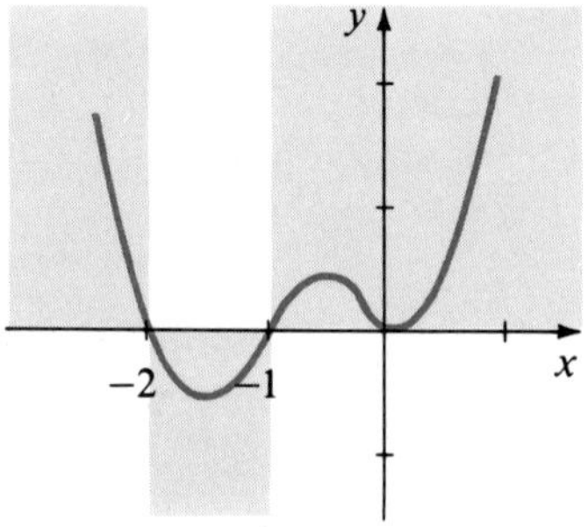

Figure 4.28 ■

Exercises Section 4.4

Sketch the graphs of the polynomials given in Exercises 1–30.

1. $y = x^3 + 1$
2. $y = (x - 1)^3$
3. $y = 1 - x^4$
4. $y = x^4 - 1$
5. $y = 3 + (x - 1)^3$
6. $y = -(x - 2)^4 + 1$
7. $y = (x + 1)^5 - 2$
8. $y = 27 - (x - 2)^3$
9. $y = 1 - (x - 2)^4$
10. $y = (x - 2)^5 + 1$
11. $y = x^3 - x$
12. $y = x^3 - x^2$
13. $y = x^4 - x^2$
14. $y = x^3 + x$
15. $y = x^5 - 4x^3$
16. $y = x^4 + x^2$
17. $y = 3x^3 - 81$
18. $y = x^6 - 1$
19. $y = x^4 - 2x^2 + 1$
20. $y = x^4 - 4x^2 + 4$
21. $y = x(x - 1)(x + 3)$
22. $y = (x - 1)(x + 4)(x - 10)$

23. $y = (x + 1)^2(x)(x - 1)$
24. $y = (x^2 - 3x + 2)(x^2 - 9)$
25. $y = (x^2 - 9)(x^2 + 4)$
26. $y = (x^2 - 1)(x + 1)^2$
27. $y = (x + 2)(x - 3)(x + 5)$
28. $y = (x + 5)(x + 2)(x - 1)x$
29. $y = (x^2 - 6x + 5)(x^2 + 4x + 4)$
30. $y = x^2(x^2 - 1)(x + 2)$

4.5 Rational Functions

Functions that are the ratio of two polynomials are called **rational functions.** Specifically, if $N(x)$ and $D(x)$ are polynomials without common factors, then

$$f(x) = \frac{N(x)}{D(x)}, \qquad D(x) \neq 0$$

is called a rational function of x. Notice the similarity between rational functions and rational numbers. Rational numbers are quotients of integers, whereas rational functions are quotients of polynomials. Some examples of rational functions are

$$\frac{3x^5 + 5}{20x^3 + x - 16} \qquad \frac{4}{x^2 - 4} \qquad \frac{3x^2 + 5x - 6}{(x - 5)(x + 3)}$$

If the degree of N is less than that of D, then N/D is called a **proper rational function;** otherwise, N/D is *improper.* Using the division process, we may express any improper function as a polynomial quotient plus a remainder that is a proper rational function.

We will use the function

$$f(x) = \frac{1}{x}$$

to illustrate the typical characteristics of graphs of rational functions. $f(x) = 1/x$ is not defined at $x = 0$; however, it is defined for all other values of x. To determine the behavior of the graph, note that as x approaches zero from the right, $f(x)$ is positive and increases indefinitely. We say that $f(x)$ **increases without bound.** Similarly, as x approaches zero from the left, $f(x)$ is negative and decreases indefinitely. Using this knowledge and computing some points on either side of $x = 0$ yields the graph shown in Figure 4.29. The vertical line at $x = 0$ is called a **vertical asymptote** of the graph.

Figure 4.29 also shows that the graph comes closer to the x-axis as x increases. In fact, as x increases, the value of $1/x$ approaches zero. (But no matter how large x becomes, $1/x$ will not equal zero.) The same observation holds as x decreases. The line $y = 0$ is called a **horizontal asymptote** of the graph.

From the foregoing discussion you can see that the asymptotes of a rational function are very helpful in sketching its graph. Use the following rule to determine the vertical asymptotes of a rational function in which $N(x)$ and $D(x)$ have no common factors.

x	y
-3	$-\frac{1}{3}$
-2	$-\frac{1}{2}$
-1	-1
$-\frac{1}{2}$	-2
$-\frac{1}{4}$	-4
$\frac{1}{4}$	4
$\frac{1}{2}$	2
1	1
2	$\frac{1}{2}$
3	$\frac{1}{3}$

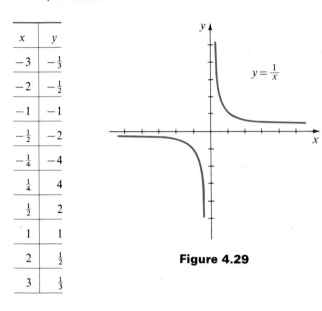

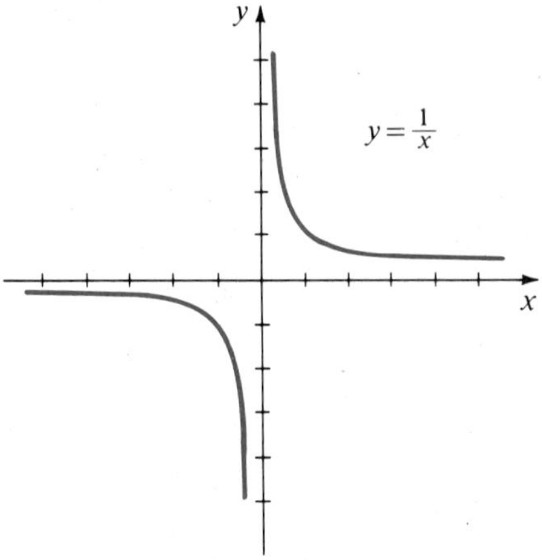

Figure 4.29

> **Vertical Asymptote**
>
> If $D(x)$ represents the denominator function and if $D(k) = 0$, then $x = k$ is a vertical asymptote for the graph of $f(x) = N(x)/D(x)$, where N and D have no common factors.

A rational function may have more than one vertical asymptote, determined by the zeros of the denominator function. Thus, the function $y = (2x^2 + 5)/(x^2 - 9)$ has two vertical asymptotes, the lines $x = 3$ and $x = -3$.

The graph of a rational function may have at most one horizontal asymptote. To find the horizontal asymptote, or to determine that one does not exist, use the following rule.

> **Horizontal Asymptote**
>
> Divide the numerator and denominator of the function by x^n, where n is the larger of the degrees of N and D. If the resulting expression approaches a constant c as x becomes large, then $y = c$ is a horizontal asymptote. If the expression becomes large as x becomes large, there is no horizontal asymptote.

To illustrate the technique, consider the function $y = (2x^2 + 5)/(x^2 - 9)$. Dividing the numerator and the denominator of this function by x^2, we get

$$y = \frac{2 + 5/x^2}{1 - 9/x^2}$$

Now as x becomes large, both $5/x^2$ and $9/x^2$ approach zero. Hence, the value of the function approaches 2 as x becomes large, and we conclude that $y = 2$ is a horizontal asymptote. As an example of a rational function that does not have a horizontal asymptote, consider

$$y = \frac{x^3 - 6}{5x + 1}$$

Dividing the numerator and the denominator by x^3, we have

$$y = \frac{1 - 6/x^3}{5/x^2 + 1/x^3}$$

As x becomes large, the numerator is close to 1 and both terms in the denominator approach zero; therefore, the resulting value of y increases without bound as x increases without bound. We conclude that $y = (x^3 - 6)/(5x + 1)$ does not have a horizontal asymptote.

Sketching Graphs of Rational Functions

1. Locate any vertical and horizontal asymptotes by the methods described above. Draw the asymptotes as dashed lines.
2. Plot any x-intercepts of the graph. Find the x-intercepts by equating the numerator to 0 and solving for x.
3. Plot any y-intercept of the graph. Find the y-intercept by equating x to 0.
4. Plot a point or two for values of x near any vertical asymptotes of the graph.
5. Draw the graph through the selected points so that it approaches the asymptotes identified in Step 1.

EXAMPLE 1 Sketch the graph of $y = \dfrac{3x}{x - 2}$.

$$y = \frac{3x}{x - 2}$$

x	y
-1	1
0	0
1	-3
2	undef.
3	9
4	6

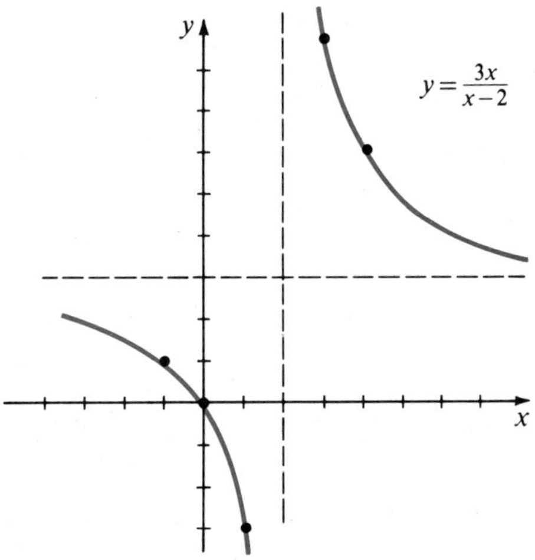

Figure 4.30

Solution *Intercepts:* $x = 0$, $y = 0$.

Vertical Asymptote: The denominator of the function is zero for $x = 2$. Since the numerator and the denominator have no common factors, the line $x = 2$ is a vertical asymptote.

Horizontal Asymptote: To find the horizontal asymptote, divide the numerator and the denominator by x to get

$$y = \frac{3}{1 - 2/x}$$

As x becomes large, the fraction $2/x$ approaches zero and, therefore, the value of y approaches 3. The line $y = 3$ is the horizontal asymptote.

Finally, determine some additional points in the vicinity of the vertical asymptote as shown in the table. The graph is now readily determined. (See Figure 4.30.) ■

EXAMPLE 2 Sketch the graph of $y = \dfrac{2x}{x^2 - 4}$.

Solution *Vertical Asymptotes:* The graph of this function has vertical asymptotes at $x = 2$ and $x = -2$ since these are the zeros of the denominator.

Horizontal Asymptotes: Divide the numerator and denominator by x^2 to get

$$y = \frac{2/x}{1 - 4/x^2}$$

As x becomes large, the fraction $2/x$ approaches zero and the denominator approaches 1. Therefore, $y = 0$ is the horizontal asymptote. The graph is then determined by plotting a few additional points, as shown in the table. See Figure 4.31.

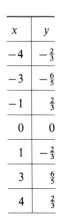

x	y
-4	$-\frac{2}{3}$
-3	$-\frac{6}{5}$
-1	$\frac{2}{3}$
0	0
1	$-\frac{2}{3}$
3	$\frac{6}{5}$
4	$\frac{2}{3}$

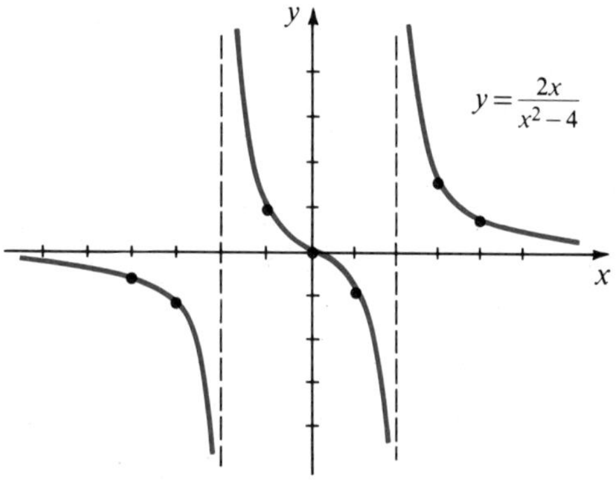

Figure 4.31 ■

EXAMPLE 3 The heat generated by a certain chemical process varies with time according to

$$H = \frac{t}{t^2 + 4}$$

where H is the heat in calories and t is the time in seconds. Draw the graph of this function and find the maximum heat output.

Solution There are no vertical asymptotes since there is no real value of t for which $t^2 + 4 = 0$. However, the t-axis is a horizontal asymptote. Since a negative time has no physical significance, we consider only positive values of t. Plotting a few additional points and drawing the curve so that it approaches the t-axis as t increases, we obtain the graph in Figure 4.32. The graph illustrates that the heat output increases rapidly at first, reaching a peak of 0.25 cal at about 2.0 sec. From this point the heat output decreases gradually toward zero.

$$H = \frac{t}{t^2 + 4}$$

t	H
0	0
2	.25
4	.20
6	.15
8	.12
10	.10

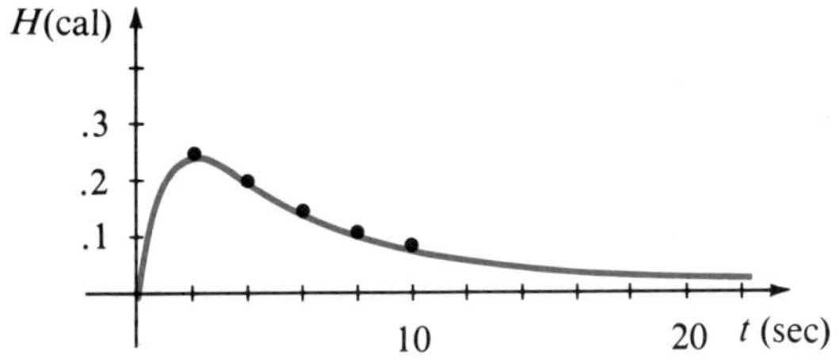

Figure 4.32

■

Exercises Section 4.5

Compute intercepts and locate asymptotes (if any). Then graph the rational functions in Exercises 1–18.

1. $y = -\dfrac{1}{x}$

2. $y = \dfrac{5x + 2}{2 - x}$

3. $y = \dfrac{3x - 2}{x - 4}$

4. $z = \dfrac{2}{t - 1}$

5. $p = \dfrac{1}{w + 1}$

6. $v = \dfrac{t^2 - 1}{t^2 + 1}$

7. $s = \dfrac{5w^2}{4 - w^2}$

8. $m = \dfrac{u + 1}{u^2 - 1}$

9. $y = \dfrac{x^2}{x^2 - 9}$

10. $y = \dfrac{-2x}{x^2 - 4}$

11. $s = \dfrac{(t + 2)^2}{t^2 + 2t}$

12. $w = \dfrac{3x^2}{x^2 - 3x}$

13. $y = \dfrac{3}{w^2 - 9w}$

14. $r = \dfrac{5z + 10}{3z - z^2}$

15. $y = \dfrac{1}{p^2 - 3p - 4}$

16. $n = \dfrac{1 + s^2}{s^2 - s - 2}$

17. $y = \dfrac{5x + 3}{x^2 + x}$

18. $y = \dfrac{x^2 + 3x + 2}{x^2 + x}$

19. A manufacturer of combination locks finds that the number of locks sold varies inversely as the price; that is,

$$N = \frac{k}{P}$$

where N is the number of units sold, P is the unit price in dollars, and k is a constant. Show this relationship graphically for $k = 250{,}000$. Use domain elements of \$0.50, \$1.00, \$1.50, \$2.00, \$2.50, and \$3.00. Note that the number of locks sold is an integer, so the graph will consist of six points.

20. Owing to leakage, the pressure in a hydraulic system varies with time according to $P = 10/(t^2 + 1)$ psi, where t is the time in seconds. Show this pressure variation graphically.

21. The coefficient of friction, μ, of a plastic block sliding on an aluminum table varies according to $\mu = (v^2 + 3)/(4v^2 + 5)$, where v is the velocity of the block in centimeters per second. Draw the graph of this function.

22. What is the horizontal asymptote of any proper rational function?

4.6 Multipart Functions

Many practical situations are described by functions whose graphs contain discontinuities in the form of "jumps," or "gaps." For example, when you mail a letter, you pay \$0.25 for the first ounce and \$0.20 for each extra ounce. The table in Figure 4.33 gives the function describing this situation for weights up to 4 oz. Plotting the graph of this function produces a series of half-open line segments that are separated by discrete "jumps," as shown in Figure 4.33.

x	$f(x)$
Weight (oz)	Postage (cts)
$0 \leq x < 1$	25
$1 \leq x < 2$	45
$2 \leq x < 3$	65
$3 \leq x < 4$	85

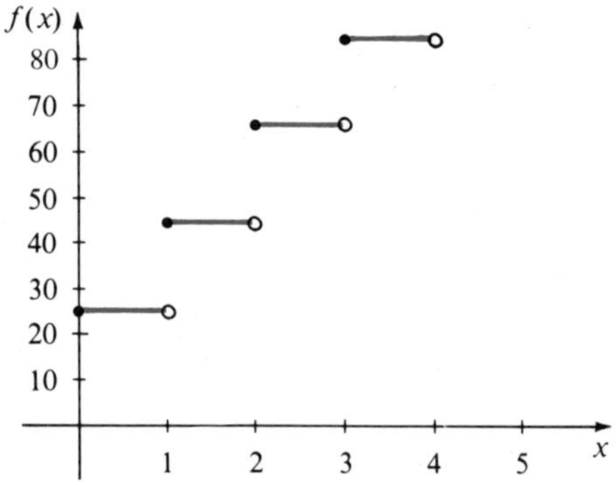

Figure 4.33

The cost of postage is a function, since a vertical line at any x of the domain intersects the graph in only one place.

The following examples illustrate some additional functions that are defined by multipart rules. In each case the rule changes over different subsets of the domain.

EXAMPLE 1 Draw the graph of f if the function is given by

$$f(x) = \begin{cases} 4, & x < 0 \\ -2x + 4, & 0 \leq x \leq 3 \\ -2, & x > 3 \end{cases}$$

Solution Note that the analytic expression given here describes *one* function, even though the rule of correspondence is given in *three* parts. From Section 4.1 we know that the individual rules each describe straight lines; however, these lines must be restricted to their intervals of definition. Figure 4.34 shows the graph of the function. The graphs of $y = 4$, $y = -2x + 4$, and $y = -2$ are first made as dashed curves, and then the portions relevant to this function are made solid, as is shown in Figures 4.34(a) and 4.34(b).

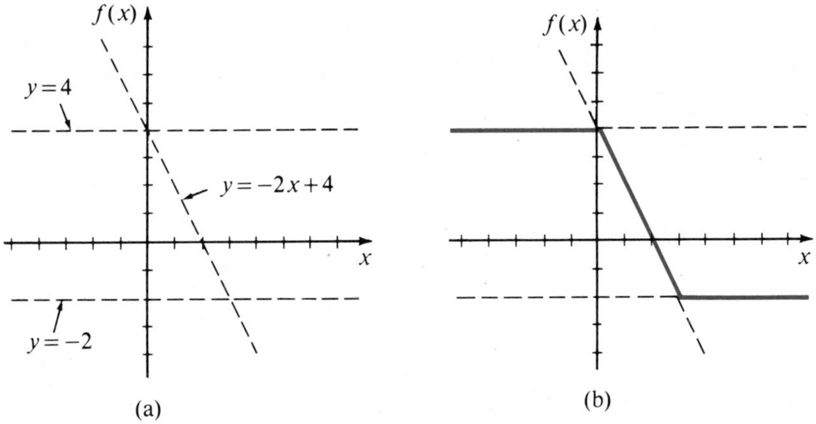

Figure 4.34 ■

EXAMPLE 2 Sketch the graph of the function whose definition is

$$f(x) = \begin{cases} 1, & x < 0 \\ x^2 + 1, & 0 \le x < 2 \\ -x + 7, & 2 \le x \end{cases}$$

Solution The graphs of $y = 1$, $y = x^2 + 1$, and $y = -x + 7$ are drawn in dashed lines in Figure 4.35. The portions of these curves that constitute the given function are shown as a solid line.

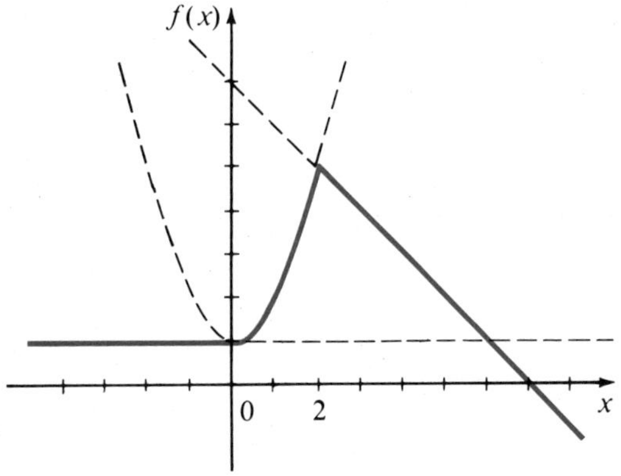

Figure 4.35 ■

Comment: The next example shows how multipart functions can be used to describe physical situations.

EXAMPLE 3 The yearly maintenance cost for a water purification system is expected to vary with time according to

$$C(t) = \begin{cases} 20t, & 0 \le t < 10 \\ 30t - 100, & 10 \le t \le 25 \end{cases}$$

where C is in dollars and t is in years. Plot the graph of this function.

Solution The graph of $C = 20t$ is a straight line through the origin, but only the portion for $0 \le t < 10$ is a part of the graph of the given function. The equation $C = 30t - 100$ is another straight line and represents the function for $10 \le t \le 25$. The function is undefined for $t < 0$ and for $t > 25$. Its graph is shown in Figure 4.36.

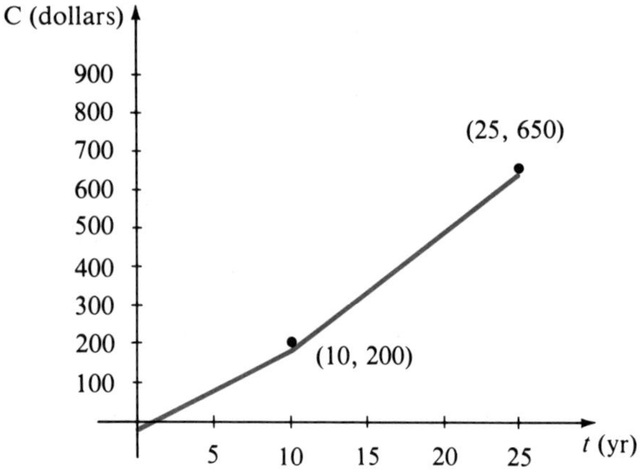

Figure 4.36

■

The Absolute Value Function

One of the most useful multipart functions is the absolute value function $f(x) = |x|$, where $|x|$ is called the "absolute value of x" and is defined as follows.

Definition

The absolute value of x, denoted by $|x|$, is given by

$$|x| = \begin{cases} x, & x \ge 0 \\ -x, & x < 0 \end{cases}$$

When we consider $|x|$, we sometimes say that we are "taking the absolute value of x." Quite obviously this means to consider the numerical value of x independently of the positive or negative quality. Thus, since the domain of the absolute value of x is the set of all real numbers, the range is the set of nonnegative real numbers.

The graph of $f(x) = |x|$ consists of a combination of the graphs of $y = -x$ (for $x < 0$) and $y = x$ (for $x \ge 0$). These two graphs are shown in Figure 4.37 with the portion relevant to the given function drawn as solid lines.

More generally, we often want to take the absolute value of entire algebraic quantities. The absolute value of the quantity $u(x)$ is

$$|u(x)| = \begin{cases} u(x), & u(x) \ge 0 \\ -u(x), & u(x) < 0 \end{cases}$$

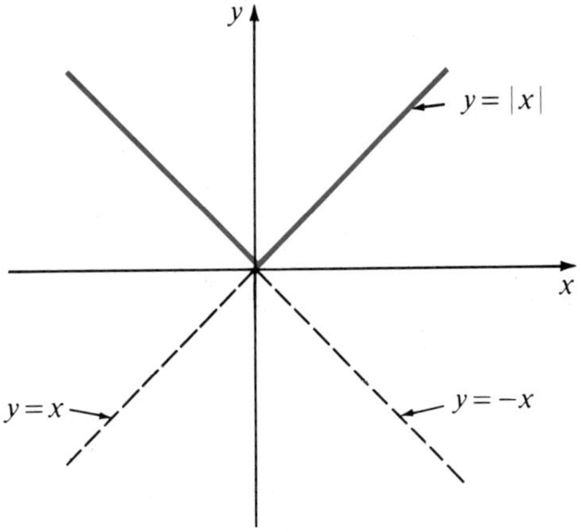

Figure 4.37

EXAMPLE 4 Sketch the graph of $f(x) = |x - 2|$.

Solution This function is given by the two-part rule

$$f(x) = \begin{cases} x - 2, & x - 2 \geq 0 \text{ (that is, for } x \geq 2) \\ -(x - 2), & x - 2 < 0 \text{ (that is, for } x < 2) \end{cases}$$

Thus, the graph consists of a part of $y = x - 2$ and a part of $y = -x + 2$. See Figure 4.38. Note that this is the graph of $y = |x|$ translated two units to the right.

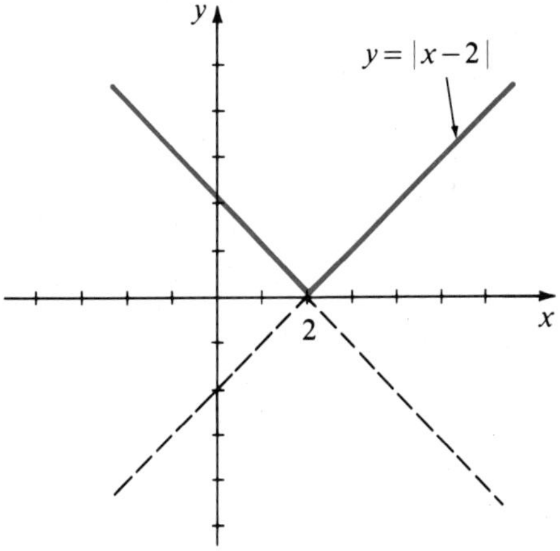

Figure 4.38 ■

EXAMPLE 5 Sketch the graph of $f(x) = |x^2 + x - 6|$.

Solution In this case

$$f(x) = \begin{cases} x^2 + x - 6 & \text{if } x^2 + x - 6 \geq 0 \\ -x^2 - x + 6 & \text{if } x^2 + x - 6 < 0 \end{cases}$$

It should be easy for you to show that $f(x)$ has the equivalent definition

$$f(x) = \begin{cases} (x+3)(x-2) & \text{for} \quad x \le -3 \quad \text{or} \quad x \ge 2 \\ -(x+3)(x-2) & \text{for } -3 < x < 2 \end{cases}$$

Effectively, you are asked to sketch the parabola, $y = x^2 + x - 6$, and reflect any negative portion in the x-axis. The graph is shown in Figure 4.39.

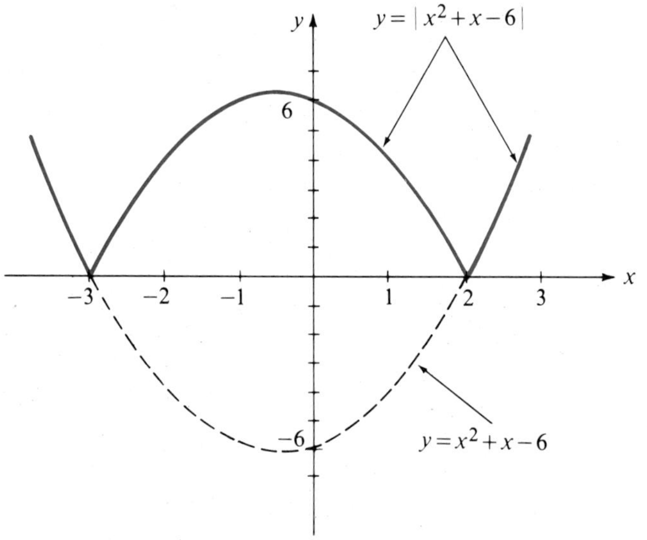

Figure 4.39 ■

Exercises Section 4.6

In Exercises 1–16, graph the specified function.

1. $f(x) = \begin{cases} 2, & x < 0 \\ 3, & x \ge 0 \end{cases}$

2. $g(x) = \begin{cases} -1, & x < 0 \\ 1, & x \ge 0 \end{cases}$

3. $F(t) = \begin{cases} 0, & t \le 0 \\ t, & t > 0 \end{cases}$

4. $f(x) = \begin{cases} x, & x < 0 \\ -2, & x \ge 0 \end{cases}$

5. $h(x) = \begin{cases} 0, & x < 2 \\ 2x - 4, & x \ge 2 \end{cases}$

6. $H(t) = \begin{cases} -2, & t < 0 \\ t - 2, & t \ge 0 \end{cases}$

7. $G(x) = \begin{cases} 0, & x < 0 \\ 1, & 0 < x < 2 \\ 0, & x \ge 2 \end{cases}$

8. $f(t) = \begin{cases} 0, & t < 0 \\ 2t, & 0 \le t < 3 \\ 6, & t \ge 3 \end{cases}$

9. $y(x) = \begin{cases} 0, & x < -2 \\ x^2 + 2, & -2 < x < 0 \\ 0, & x > 0 \end{cases}$

10. $z(x) = \begin{cases} x^2, & x < 0 \\ -x^2, & x \ge 0 \end{cases}$

11. $f(x) = \begin{cases} x, & x < 1 \\ -x, & x \ge 1 \end{cases}$

12. $f(x) = \begin{cases} 0, & x \text{ an integer} \\ 1, & x \text{ not an integer} \end{cases}$

13. $f(x) = \begin{cases} x + 2, & x < -2 \\ x^2, & -2 \le x < 3 \\ x - 2, & x \ge 3 \end{cases}$

14. $g(x) = \begin{cases} x, & x \le -2 \\ x^2 - 4, & -2 < x < 1 \\ x, & x \ge 1 \end{cases}$

15. $f(x) = \begin{cases} (x-3)(x+2), & x < -2 \\ x^2 - 4, & x \ge -2 \end{cases}$

16. $f(x) = \begin{cases} x+3, & x \le -3 \\ (x+3)(x-2), & x > -3 \end{cases}$

In Exercises 17–36, sketch the graph of the given function.

17. $f(x) = |x+1|$
18. $y = |x-4|$
19. $H(x) = |2x|$
20. $f(x) = 2|x|$
21. $f(x) = |x| - 3$
22. $G(t) = |t-3|$
23. $y = |x| + 3$
24. $f(x) = |x| - 5$
25. $f(t) = |t^2|$
26. $f(x) = |x|^2$
27. $f(x) = x^2 - |x| + 1$
28. $f(x) = |x^2 - x + 1|$
29. $g(x) = |2x^2 + x - 1|$
30. $y = |x^2 + x + 1|$
31. $y = x^2 + 3|x| + 2$
32. $f(x) = |x^2 + 3x + 2|$
33. $f(x) = (x-1)|x+1|$
34. $F(x) = (x-3)|x+2|$
35. $f(x) = x|x-4|$
36. $f(x) = (x-5)|x+1|$
37. Find values of x and y to show that $f(x+y) \ne f(x) + f(y)$ where $f(x) = |x|$.
38. Compare $f(x) = |x|$ and $g(x) = |x-2|$ by sketching their graphs on the same set of coordinates. How do the two graphs differ?
39. Compare $f(x) = |x|$ and $g(x) = |x| + 2$ by sketching their graphs on the same set of coordinates. How do the two graphs differ?
40. Compare $f(x) = |x|$, $g(x) = |2x|$, and $h(x) = 2|x|$ by sketching their graphs on the same set of coordinates. How do the graphs differ?
41. The load, in kilograms, applied to a tensile specimen varied with time according to

$$F(t) = \begin{cases} 1000t, & 0 \le t \le 5 \text{ min} \\ 5000, & 5 < t \le 60 \text{ min} \end{cases}$$

Sketch the load-time curve.

42. The voltage applied to a given circuit varied with time according to

$$v(t) = \begin{cases} 0 \text{ volts}, & t < 2 \\ 6 \text{ volts}, & t \ge 2 \end{cases}$$

Sketch the voltage-time curve.

43. The cost of concrete to a contractor varies with the number of yards delivered according to

$$c(n) = \begin{cases} 60 \text{ dollars}, & 0 < n \le 3 \\ 20n \text{ dollars}, & 3 < n \le 10 \end{cases}$$

Sketch the graph.

44. A chemical supply house charges \$1.50/gal for muriatic acid on orders up to 10 gal. For orders from 10 to 20 gal, the price is \$1.25/gal and from 20 to 30 gal, the price is \$1.10/gal. Orders in excess of 30 gal cost \$1.00/gal. Write the rule for the function that relates the cost per gallon to the size of the order. Sketch the graph.

The **greatest integer function,** denoted by $[\![x]\!]$, is defined such that for a particular value of x, the value of $[\![x]\!]$ is the largest integer that is less than or equal to x. For example, $[\![2.1]\!] = 2$, $[\![-3.1]\!] = -4$, and $[\![-1]\!] = -1$. More specifically,

$$[\![x]\!] = \begin{cases} \vdots & \\ -3, & -3 \le x < -2 \\ -2, & -2 \le x < -1 \\ -1, & -1 \le x < 0 \\ 0, & 0 \le x < 1 \\ 1, & 1 \le x < 2 \\ 2, & 2 \le x < 3 \\ \vdots & \end{cases}$$

45. Sketch the graph of the greatest integer function.

In Exercises 46–56, sketch the graph of the given function.

46. $f(x) = 2[\![x]\!]$
47. $f(x) = [\![2x]\!]$
48. $f(x) = 2[\![x]\!] - [\![x]\!]$
49. $f(x) = [\![x^2]\!]$
50. $f(x) = [\![x^2 + 1]\!]$
51. $f(x) = [\![x]\!] - 3[\![x]\!]$
52. $f(x) = [\![x^2]\!] + 1$
53. $f(x) = 2[\![x]\!] - 3[\![x]\!] + 1$
54. $f(x) = [\![x - 1]\!]$
55. $f(x) = [\![x]\!]^2$
56. $f(x) = [\![x^2]\!] - [\![x]\!]^2$

Review Exercises Chapter 4

Sketch the straight line determined by the pairs of points in Exercises 1–4 and compute the slope of the line.

1. $(-1, 3), (0, -2)$ **2.** $(2, -7), (-1, -4)$

3. $(3, 2), (1, -5)$ **4.** $(8, 0), (0, -3)$

5. Draw the straight line passing through $(-1, 2)$ with a slope of $\frac{2}{5}$.

6. Draw the straight line passing through $(0, -3)$ with a slope of 4.

7. Find the slope of a line that is perpendicular to the line through $(5, 4)$ and $(-1, -1)$.

8. Find the slope of a line that is perpendicular to the line through $(-2, 0)$ and $(-2, 5)$.

9. Determine the equation of the line passing through $(3, -1)$ with a slope of -2.

10. Determine the equation of the line passing through the point $(-5, 2)$ with a slope of $\frac{1}{3}$.

11. Determine the equation of the line passing through $(7, 2)$ and $(-1, 4)$.

12. Determine the equation of the line passing through $(1, 3)$ and $(-1, -2)$.

In Exercises 13–16, find the slope and the y-intercept and then draw the line.

13. $2x + 7y = -3$ **14.** $-3x + y = 2$

15. $3(x - 2y) = 1$ **16.** $\frac{1}{2}y - x = 0.25$

In Exercises 17–20, find the equation of the line perpendicular to the given line at the indicated point.

17. $x - 2y = -5$ at $(0, \frac{5}{2})$

18. $-4y - 3 = 3x$ at $(1, -\frac{3}{2})$

19. $x - 3y = 7$ at $(1, -2)$

20. $5x - 2y = 4$ at $(2, 3)$

In Exercises 21–26, sketch the graph of the given quadratic function. Be sure to show the vertex of each.

21. $y = x^2 + 7$ **22.** $y = 3 - x^2$

23. $f(x) = 2x^2 - x - 3$ **24.** $g(t) = t^2 + 3t - 5$

25. $s = 2 + t - t^2$ **26.** $y = 5x^2 + 3x + 7$

In Exercises 27–30, determine the quadratic function whose graph is given.

27.

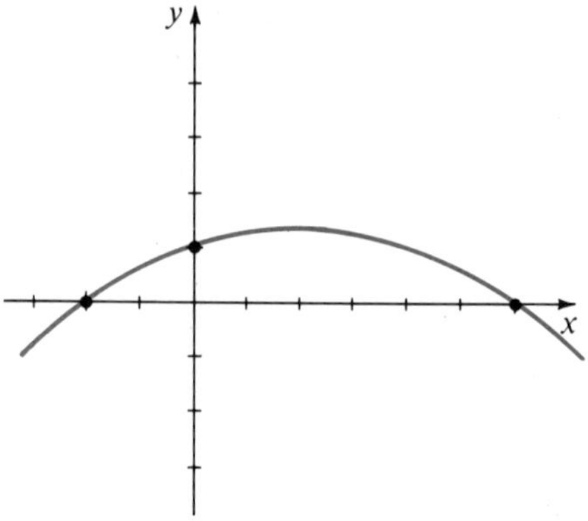

28.

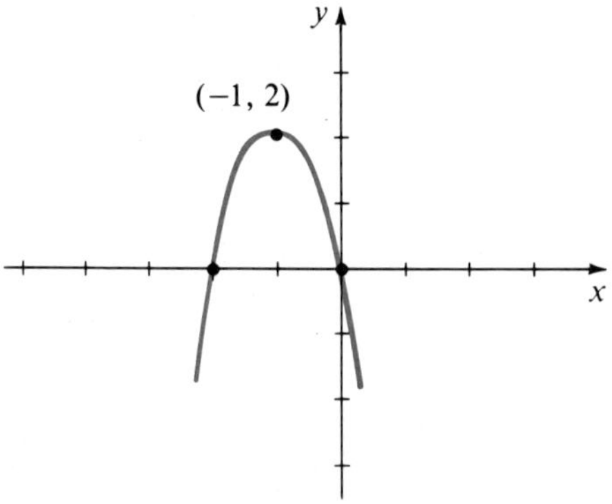

29.

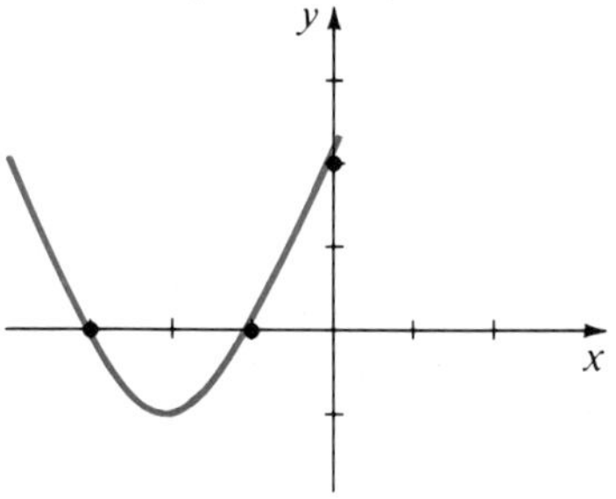

30.

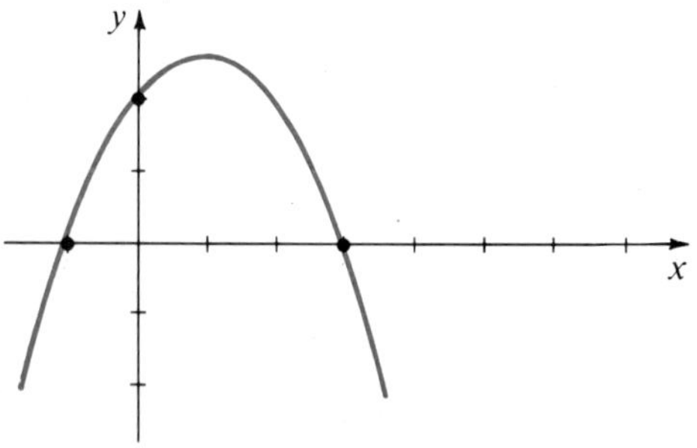

Sketch the graph of each of the functions in Exercises 31–52.

31. $y = 2 - x^3$

32. $y = x^4 + 1$

33. $y = x(x + 1)(x + 5)$

34. $y = (x - 2)(x + 1)(x + 3)$

35. $y = (x - 2)(x + 1)^2$

36. $y = x^2(x + 2)(x - 3)$

37. $y = \dfrac{3}{x + 2}$

38. $s = \dfrac{3}{t - 5}$

39. $p = \dfrac{2x}{x^2 - 4}$

40. $y = \dfrac{1}{x^2 - x - 6}$

41. $y = \begin{cases} 1, & \text{if } x < 0 \\ -1, & \text{if } x \geq 0 \end{cases}$

42. $f(x) = \begin{cases} -1, & \text{if } x < 0 \\ x - 1, & \text{if } x \geq 0 \end{cases}$

43. $g(x) = \begin{cases} x, & \text{if } x < 0 \\ x^2, & \text{if } x \geq 0 \end{cases}$

44. $y = \begin{cases} 2 - x, & \text{if } x < 0 \\ 2, & \text{if } x \geq 0 \end{cases}$

45. $F(x) = |x - \frac{1}{2}|$

46. $y = |2 - x|$

47. $y = |t| + 2$

48. $m(t) = |t| - 0.5$

49. $s = t^2 + 2t$

50. $y = x^2 + 5x + 4$

51. $y = x^2 - x$

52. $m = r^2 + r$

53. Graph $f(x) = 3 - x$. Determine the graphs of $f(-x)$ and $-f(x)$ from this graph.

54. Graph $g(x) = x^2 + 1$. Determine the graphs of $g(-x)$ and $-g(x)$ from this graph.

55. Graph $f(x) = \frac{1}{2}x$. Determine the graphs of $f(x + 2)$ and $f(x) + 2$ from this graph.

56. Graph $f(x) = x^2$. Determine the graphs of $f(x - 1)$ and $f(x) - 1$ from this graph.

57. The velocity of an object is 25 cm/sec at 4 sec after release, and 38 cm/sec at 10 sec after release. Find the velocity-time equation of the object if velocity is known to be a linear function of time.

58. The force required to stretch a spring is a linear function of the displacement of the spring. What is the force-displacement equation for a spring if it is 15 in. long when no force is applied and 18 in. long when a 2-lb force is applied?

59. In surveying for a new coal mine, a geologist drills two holes 500 ft apart. One hole contacts the vein at a depth of 225 ft and the other at a depth of 315 ft. Find the slope of the vein of coal, assuming that the depth of the vein is a linear function of the distance between the two holes.

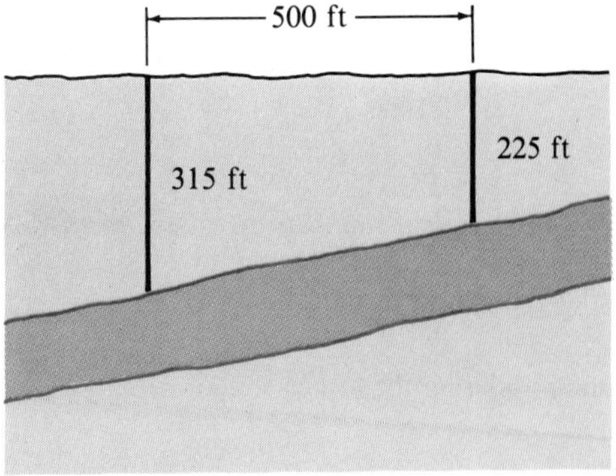

60. The input voltage across a 50 Ω resistor is given by $v = 2t + 3$ volts, where t is the elapsed time in seconds. Sketch the voltage as a function of time. What is the initial voltage across the resistor?

61. A new advertising agency's estimated profit during the first five years is given by

$$P(t) = 10(2t - 3)$$

where P is in thousands of dollars and t is the time in years.

a. Sketch P as a function of time for $0 \leq t \leq 5$ years.

b. When does the agency begin earning a profit?

62. The cost of renting a car is \$20/day plus \$0.15 for each mile driven over 100 miles.

a. Express this cost as a functional relation.

b. Graph the cost vs. the mileage driven for the first 300 miles.

63. The admission price to a concert in an 850-seat theater is \$12.

a. Given that the cost of the performance is \$5500, write a formula showing profit as a function of paid admissions, n.

b. Sketch the graph of this function for $0 \leq n \leq 850$.

c. Use the graph to determine how many tickets must be sold to break even.

64. The total cost C (in dollars) of making n units of a product is given by

$$C = \begin{cases} 2n + 100, & 0 \leq n \leq 1000 \\ n + 1100, & 1000 < n \leq 5000 \end{cases}$$

a. Sketch the graph of C.

b. Determine the cost of making 300 units.

c. Use the graph to determine how many units can be built for \$4000.

65. A political analyst finds that the number of registered independents voting for Democratic candidates seems to vary with the inflation rate according to the function

$$D = \frac{100{,}000}{1 + \sqrt{i}}$$

where D is the number of independents voting Democratic and i is the inflation rate in percent. Sketch the graph of this function for $0 \le i \le 10\%$.

66. A sociologist finds that the number of enlistees per month joining the armed forces increases with the unemployment rate. Assume this relationship is given by the function

$$N = \begin{cases} 10{,}000 + 1000u^2, & 0 \le u \le 6\% \\ 40{,}000 + 1000u, & 6 < u \le 10\% \end{cases}$$

where N is the enlistment rate per month and u is the unemployment rate.

a. Sketch the graph of this function.

b. What is the enlistment rate when the inflation rate is 7.5%?

Test 1 Chapter 4

Answer True or False to the statements in Exercises 1–10.

1. $x + \frac{1}{x} = 0$ is a linear equation.

2. The slope of a straight line is a constant.

3. If a line passes through the origin, one of its forms is $ax + by = 1$.

4. If $f(x) = |x|$, then $f(x^2) = x^2$.

5. The slope of a line parallel to the line $x = 4$ is 1.

6. The graph of a quadratic function is a parabola.

7. The graph of a quadratic function with real coefficients always intersects the y-axis.

8. If a quadratic function has real zeros, the value of the x-coordinate of the vertex is the average of these zeros.

9. The function $f(x) = (x - 1)(1 + x)$ is a quadratic.

10. Any quadratic function with real zeros can be written as a product of real linear factors.

11. Write the equation of the line that is perpendicular to $x - 3y = 7$ at the point $(1, -2)$.

12. Write the equation of the line that passes through $(1, 3)$ and $(-1, -2)$. Express in slope-intercept form and sketch the line.

13. Make a careful sketch of the function

$$f(x) = \begin{cases} x^2, & x \le 0 \\ 2, & 0 < x < 3 \\ -x, & 3 \le x \end{cases}$$

14. Sketch the graph of $y = \frac{2}{x^2 - 2x}$.

15. Sketch the graph of $y = 3 + x - x^2$ after locating the x-intercepts, if any, the y-intercept, and the vertex.

16. Sketch the graph of $f(x) = |(x - 3)(2 + x)|$.

Test 2 Chapter 4

1. Draw the graph of $2x + 3y = -6$.

2. Find the equation of the line through $(-1, 3)$ and $(0, -5)$.

3. Draw the graph of $y + |x| = 2$.

4. Sketch the graph of $y = x^2 - x - 12$ indicating intercepts and vertex.

5. Sketch the graph of $y = x(x + 2)x - 3)$.

6. Sketch the graph of

$$f(x) = \begin{cases} 2, & x < -1 \\ x, & -1 \le x < 2 \\ 2 - x, & x \ge 2 \end{cases}$$

7. Write the equation of the line perpendicular to $5x - 2y = 4$ at $(2, 3)$.

8. Write the equation of the quadratic function whose graph has x-intercepts $(-3, 0)$ and $(1, 0)$ and y-intercept $(0, 2)$.

9. Let $f(x) = |x - 2|$. Give the domain, range, and graph of the function.

10. Sketch the graph of $y = \frac{x + 2}{x - 3}$.

5

Exponential and Logarithmic Functions

5.1 Exponential Functions

In Chapter 1 we introduced the concept of an exponent and gave meaning to a^x, $a > 0$, when x is a rational number. Recalling our discussion from Section 1.3, we define $a^{1/n}$ to be the number whose nth power is a, where n is a nonzero integer. Also, if p/q is in lowest terms, $a^{p/q}$ means the pth power of the qth root of a.

EXAMPLE 1

a. $81^{1/4} = 3$ because $3^4 = 81$.
b. $8^{4/3} = 16$ because $(8^{1/3})^4 = 2^4 = 16$.
c. $32^{1.2} = 64$ because $32^{1.2} = 32^{6/5} = (32^{1/5})^6 = 2^6 = 64$. ■

Calculators with a $\boxed{y^x}$ *key can perform the exponentiation operation for rational numbers. See the Calculator Comment in Section 1.3.*

For convenience, we restate three important rules for manipulating numbers with exponents.

Rule 1	$a^m a^n = a^{m+n}$
Rule 2	$(a^m)^n = a^{mn}$
Rule 3	$a^m \div a^n = a^{m-n}$

EXAMPLE 2 Use the laws of exponents to solve the equation $4^{x+1} = 8$.

Solution Since $4 = 2^2$ and $8 = 2^3$, the given equation can be written in the equivalent form

$$(2^2)^{x+1} = 2^3 \quad \text{or} \quad 2^{2(x+1)} = 2^3$$

For these two expressions to be equal, the exponents must be equal. Therefore,

$$2(x + 1) = 3$$
$$2x + 2 = 3$$
$$x = \frac{1}{2}$$

■

In this chapter we extend the concept of an exponent to include all real numbers. This topic is more properly covered in a course in calculus, but we can give some idea of the meaning of an irrational number exponent. First, let us consider the meaning of 2^π. We know that π is an irrational number that has the unending decimal expansion

$$3.141592653\ldots$$

Now, consider the sequence of rational numbers 3, 3.1, 3.14, 3.141, 3.1415, and so forth. Each of these rational numbers is an approximation of the irrational number π, the more decimal places the better the approximation. In the same way, the corresponding rational powers of 2, namely,

$$2^3,\ 2^{3.1},\ 2^{3.14},\ 2^{3.141},\ 2^{3.1415}$$

and so forth become better approximations of 2^π as more accurate estimates of π are used. In this way we see that irrational exponents have a definite interpretation to which the exponential laws apply. Accepting the fact that a^x has meaning for all real x, if $a > 0$, we formulate the following definition:

Definition

If a is any positive fixed constant, $a \neq 1$, then the **exponential function with base *a*** is defined by

$$f(x) = a^x$$

The domain of the exponential function is the set of all real numbers and the range is the set of positive real numbers.

If $y = f(x)$ is an exponential function, then y is said to *vary exponentially* as x. The next example shows the characteristic shape of the graph of an exponential function.

EXAMPLE 3 Sketch the graph of 2^x and $(\frac{1}{2})^x$.

Solution Figure 5.1 shows a table of values for each of the functions along with the graph.

x	$(\frac{1}{2})^x$
-2	4
-1	2
0	1
1	$\frac{1}{2}$
2	$\frac{1}{4}$

x	2^x
-2	$\frac{1}{4}$
-1	$\frac{1}{2}$
0	1
1	2
2	4

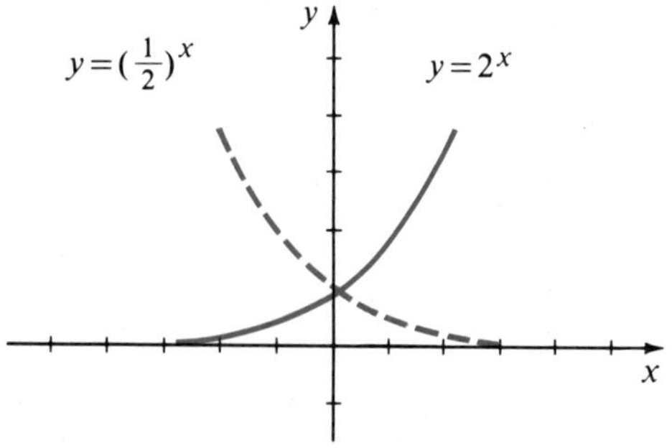

Figure 5.1

Notice that if we let $f(x) = 2^x$, then $f(-x) = 2^{-x} = (\frac{1}{2})^x$. Thus, the graphs of 2^x and $(\frac{1}{2})^x$ are reflections in the y-axis. ■

We make the following observations about the function $f(x) = a^x$ and its graph.

Properties of $f(x) = a^x$, $a > 1$

1. The domain of the function consists of all real numbers and since $a^x > 0$ for all x, the range consists of all positive real numbers.
2. When $x = 0$, $a^0 = 1$. Hence, the graph has a y-intercept at (0, 1).
3. When $x = 1$, $a^1 = a$. Hence, the graph passes through $(1, a)$.
4. As x increases without bound, a^x increases without bound.
5. As x decreases without bound, a^x approaches 0. Hence, the graph is asymptotic to the negative x-axis.
6. If $x_1 < x_2$, then $a^{x_1} < a^{x_2}$. Hence, a^x is an increasing function.

If $0 < a < 1$, then properties (4)–(6) become

4′. As x increases without bound, a^x approaches 0. In this case the positive x-axis is a horizontal asymptote.
5′. As x decreases without bound, a^x increases without bound.
6′. If $x_1 < x_2$, then $a^{x_1} > a^{x_2}$. Hence, a^x is a decreasing function.

A different exponential function is obtained for each value of a, although the shape of the graph remains basically the same and the same kind of functional properties as (1)–(6) continue to hold.

Figure 5.2 shows the graph of a^x for $a = \frac{1}{4}, \frac{1}{2}, 1, 2,$ and 4. We exclude the value of $a = 1$ because not only is the graph of 1^x trivial, but it is not of exponential shape. Further, $f(x) = 1^x$ does not obey the functional properties (1) through (6), which are ordinarily associated with exponential functions. Henceforth, the only acceptable bases will be $a > 0$, $a \neq 1$.

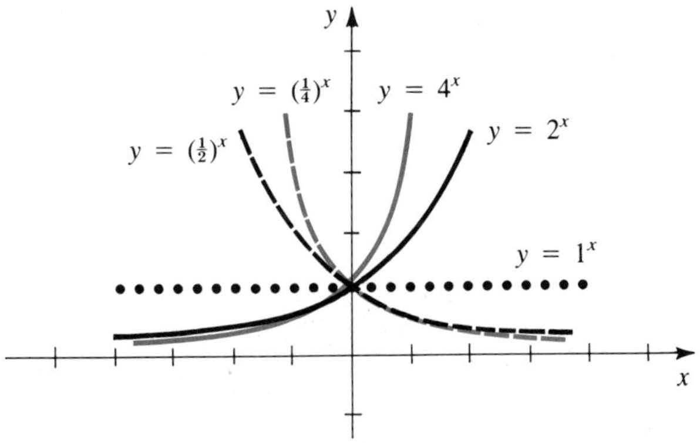

Figure 5.2

Warning: Be aware of the fact that -3^x and $(-3)^x$ have different meanings (for example, $-3^2 = -9 \neq (-3)^2 = 9$). The latter is an "unacceptable" exponential function since $-3 < 0$, while -3^x is merely the negative of 3^x. (See Figure 5.3.)

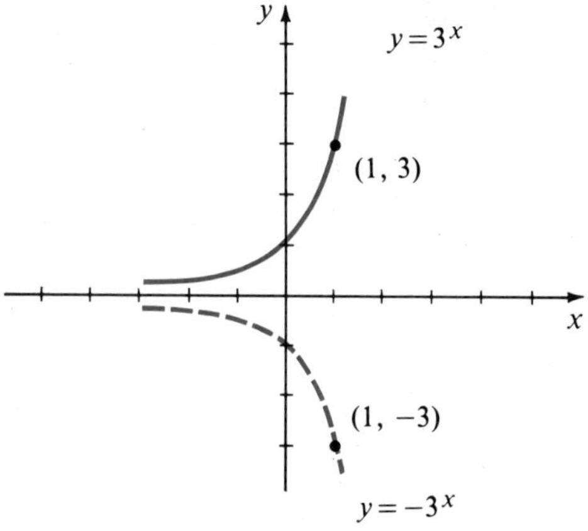

Figure 5.3

Applications of Exponential Functions

The exponential function is one of the most useful functions for describing physical and social phenomena, of which the following are just a few.

- Electric current
- Atmospheric pressure
- Decomposition of uranium
- Population growth
- Learning process
- Compound interest

If a physical quantity obeys a law that is described by an exponential function and is increasing, it is said to *increase exponentially*. If it is exponential in character but is decreasing, it is said to *decrease or decay exponentially*.

EXAMPLE 4 A company finds that the net sales of its product double every year. Write this fact as an exponential function.

Solution Let $s(t)$ represent sales at any time t and let s_0 be the initial sales. Then we can write

$$s(0) = s_0$$
$$s(1) = 2s_0$$
$$s(2) = 2s(1) = 2^2 s_0$$
$$s(3) = 2s(2) = 2^3 s_0$$

We could continue this process but we would not gain any new information. It is obvious from what we have done that

$$s(t) = s_0 2^t$$

is the desired expression. ■

EXAMPLE 5 An approximate rule for atmospheric pressure at altitude less than 50 mi is the following: *Standard atmospheric pressure,* 14.7 *lb/in.*^{2}, *is halved for each* 3.25 *mi of vertical ascent.*

a. Write an exponential function to express this rule.

b. Compute the atmospheric pressure at an altitude of 19.5 mi.

Solution a. If we let P denote the atmospheric pressure at less than 50 mi and h the altitude in miles, the general expression will be of the form

$$P = P_0 a^{kh}$$

where P_0 is the value of P when $h = 0$; that is, 14.7 lb/in.^{2}. Since the pressure is halved for each 3.25 mi of ascent, $a = \frac{1}{2}$. Since the halving is accomplished every 3.25 mi, $k = 1/3.25$. Hence,

$$P = 14.7\left(\frac{1}{2}\right)^{h/3.25}$$

This function is shown graphically in Figure 5.4.

b. Using the expression for P and letting $h = 19.5$, we get

$$P = 14.7\left(\frac{1}{2}\right)^{19.5/3.25}$$

14,7 × (.5) yˣ (19,5 ÷ 3,25)

$$= 14.7\left(\frac{1}{2}\right)^{6} = \frac{14.7}{64} \approx 0.23 \text{ lb/in.}^2$$

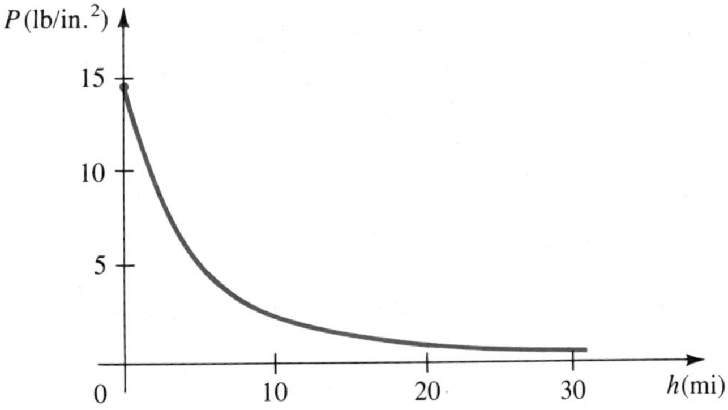

Figure 5.4 ■

Another important exponential function arises in computing compound interest on a sum of money P, called the **principal.** The principal earns compound interest if the interest paid each interest period is allowed to accumulate so that it earns additional interest during the next interest period.

Suppose a principal P is invested at an interest rate r for each period, compounded over n periods. The total amount A_1 at the end of the first interest period is

$$A_1 = P + rP = P(1 + r)$$

At the end of the second period, the total amount is

$$A_2 = A_1 + rA_1 = P(1 + r) + rP(1 + r) = P(1 + r)^2$$

At the end of the third period, the total amount is

$$A_3 = A_2 + rA_2 = P(1 + r)^2 + rP(1 + r)^2 = P(1 + r)^3$$

By continuing this process for n interest periods, we obtain the compound interest formula.

Compound Interest Formula

The formula for computing **compound interest** is

$$A_n = P(1 + r)^n$$

where

A_n = value after n interest periods
P = principal
r = interest rate for each interest period
n = number of interest periods

EXAMPLE 6 A principal of \$1000 is invested at an annual interest rate of 9%. Calculate the value of the investment after five years if (a) the interest is compounded annually and (b) the interest is compounded monthly.

Solution a. For annual compounding, the interest period is one year, so the interest rate for the period is $r = 0.09$ and the number of interest periods is $n = 5$. Substituting these values into the compound-interest formula, we have

$$A_5 = 1000(1 + 0.09)^5 = 1000 \boxed{\times} 1.09 \boxed{y^x} 5 \boxed{=} \text{1538.623955} = \$1538.62$$

b. Here, the value is to be compounded monthly, so the interest period is 1/12 year. The interest rate for one period is then $r = 0.09/12 = 0.0075$ and the number of periods is $n = 5(12) = 60$. The value of the investment after five years is then

$$A_{60} = 1000(1 + 0.0075)^{60} = \text{1565.681027} = \$1565.68$$

Clearly, more interest is earned by compounding monthly. ■

Exercises Section 5.1

Solve for x in Exercises 1–10.

1. $x^{-3/2} = \frac{27}{8}$
2. $27^{-2/3} = x$
3. $27^{x+2} = 9^{2-x}$
4. $2^{x+4} = 8$
5. $(-2)^{x+2} = -8$
6. $(-x)^{-3} = \frac{27}{64}$
7. $((3)^x)^x = 1$
8. $(2^x)^{x-1} = 64$
9. $3^{x^2+4x} = \frac{1}{81}$
10. $4^{x^2-3x} = 256$

Sketch the graphs of the exponential functions in Exercises 11–26.

11. $y = 5^x$
12. $h = 10^x$
13. $y = 3^{-x}$
14. $p = 10^{-t}$
15. $s = 3 \cdot 2^x$
16. $y = 2 + 2^x$
17. $y = 2 - 2^x$
18. $y = (\sqrt{2})^x$
19. $m(t) = 3^{3-t}$
20. $y = 1 + 2^x$
21. $y = 10^{x/2}$
22. $y = 10 + 4^{x/2}$

23. $f(t) = 3^{-(t-1)}$ **24.** $z = 2(3^T)$

25. $y = 2^{x+2}$ **26.** $y = 2^{1-x}$

27. Make a careful sketch of the graph of $y = 2^x$. Using this graph, approximate the values of (a) $2^{\sqrt{2}}$; (b) 2^{π}; (c) $2^{3/2}$; (d) $2^{-3/2}$; (e) $2^{1/3}$.

28. Why is the base of exponential functions restricted to positive numbers?

29. Discuss the exponential function with base 1.

In Exercises 30–35, say how the graph of the given exponential compares with the graph of $y = 2^x$. In each case make a sketch to show the comparison.

30. 2^{-x} **31.** -2^x **32.** $2^{|x|}$

33. $|2^x|$ **34.** $3 + 2^x$ **35.** 2^{x+3}

36. The population of spider mites on a pond is estimated to double every month. If there are initially 10,000 mites on the pond, estimate the size of the population at the end of six months.

37. Radioactive materials decay with time; that is, the mass of the substance decreases as particles are emitted. The **half-life** of a radioactive substance is the time it takes the substance to decay to one half its original value. Write an expression for the mass m of radioactive substance if its initial mass is m_0 and its half-life is one hour.

38. Suppose that each year an automobile loses one fourth of the value it had at the beginning of the year. If a new car costs \$10,000, write an expression for its value at the end of t years. How much is the car worth at the end of five years?

39. The rate at which a certain chemical reaction takes place is known to double each time the temperature increases by 10° C. Write an expression for the rate of the reaction R as a function of temperature T. Assume the initial rate is R_0.

40. Referring to Example 5, calculate the atmospheric pressure at altitudes of five miles and ten miles.

41. In the absence of promotional activity, the sales of a company's product decreases by 2% each year. If the company is presently selling 500,000 units of its product, write an expression for future sales S as a function of time in years t. How many units can it expect to sell after four years?

In Exercises 42–48, use the compound-interest formula.

42. If \$2000 is invested at 8.3% compounded annually, what is its value at the end of ten years?

43. If \$500 is invested at 4.5% compounded annually, how much interest will it earn in five years?

44. If a bank pays 5% interest compounded annually, how much interest is earned on \$2000 invested for three years?

45. Suppose \$1000 is invested at 7% compounded semiannually. How much will the investment total at the end of five years?

46. At the birth of their son, Mr. and Mrs. Profitt invested \$100 for him at 8% compounded quarterly. When the son is 21 years old, how much will their investment have amounted to?

47. A woman invests \$5000 at 6% compounded quarterly. How much interest will the investment earn in two years?

48. A principal of \$2000 is invested at 10% interest for five years. Compare the annual to the semiannual method of compounding interest.

5.2 Exponential Functions with Base *e*

Exponential functions are essential to the description and understanding of growth and decay processes such as population size, radioactive decay, and compound interest. The most important base for exponential functions is the irrational number e, which is approximated to three decimal places by 2.718. Remember that irrational numbers do not have a finite decimal representation, so 2.718 is only an approximation of e. The purpose of this section is to give you some idea of why the number e is chosen as a base for exponential functions.

An indication of the importance of the exponential function is that most scientific calculators have an [e^x] *button. To find* e^x *for any number, enter* x *and push the* [e^x] *button. Thus you find that* $e^{3.1}$ = 22.19795128 *by entering* 3.1 *and pushing the* [e^x] *button. Note also that if you enter* 1 *and then push* [e^x], *the display will show* 2.718281828, *which is e approximated to nine decimal places.*

To initiate our discussion of why e is used as a base for exponential functions, consider the following problem. Assume that the size of a population, P, grows at a rate $r = 1/n$, where n is the number of growth periods. Using the same approach that we used to derive the compound-interest formula, we note that if the initial population size is P_0, then the size of the population at the end of one period is given by

$$P_1 = P_0 + \frac{1}{n}P_0 = P_0\left(1 + \frac{1}{n}\right)$$

At the end of the second period it is

$$P_2 = P_1 + \frac{1}{n}P_1 = P_0\left(1 + \frac{1}{n}\right) + \frac{1}{n}P_0\left(1 + \frac{1}{n}\right) = P_0\left(1 + \frac{1}{n}\right)^2$$

Continuing in this way, at the end of n periods the population size is

$$P_n = P_0\left(1 + \frac{1}{n}\right)^n$$

We see that the size of the population depends upon the value of $(1 + 1/n)^n$. We are interested in what happens to the value of $(1 + 1/n)^n$ as the number of periods increases. We approach this problem by calculating values for $(1 + 1/n)^n$ for progressively larger and larger values of n. Table 5.1 shows the results obtained from a calculator.

As you study Table 5.1, you can see that the value of $(1 + 1/n)^n$ increases rapidly at first and then more slowly as n increases. It is clear that the digits 2.718 do not change after $n = 10{,}000$ and the digits 2.71828 do not change after $n = 1{,}000{,}000$. The table seems to indicate that the value of $(1 + 1/n)^n$ is getting closer and closer to some fixed number. In fact, it can be proved that the value of $(1 + 1/n)^n$ gets closer and closer to e as n gets larger and larger. For this reason, the number is a very natural choice as the base for exponential functions.

Exponential functions of the form $y = e^x$ have the properties described in the previous section. We conclude the section with some examples that use e^x.

TABLE 5.1

n	$(1 + 1/n)^n$
1	2.00000000
10	2.59374246
100	2.704813829
1000	2.716923932
10,000	2.718145927
100,000	2.718268237
1,000,000	2.718280469
10,000,000	2.718281693
100,000,000	2.718281815

EXAMPLE 1 Sketch the graph of $y = 2 + e^x$.

Solution The indicated table was constructed using a calculator. The graph is shown in Figure 5.5.

x	e^x	$2 + e^x$
-3	.05	2.05
-2	.14	2.14
-1	.37	2.37
0	1.00	3.00
1	2.72	4.72
2	7.39	9.39

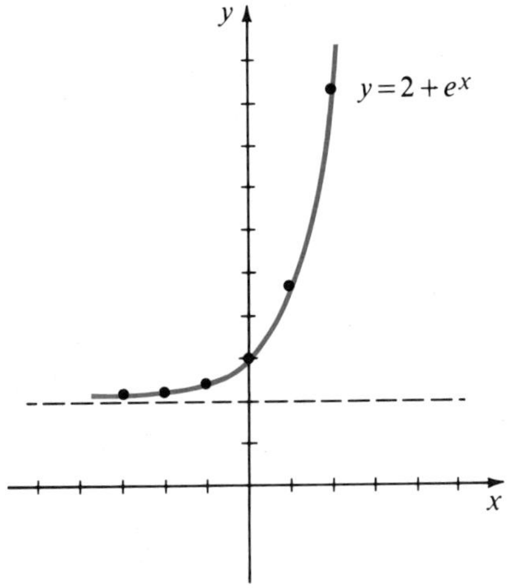

Figure 5.5

Note that as x decreases, $2 + e^x$ approaches 2. This is indicated in the figure by the dashed line. ■

EXAMPLE 2 A psychologist finds that the number of different mazes, R, a laboratory animal can learn to run is represented by the exponential function $R = 5(1 - e^{-t})$, where t is the time in days spent training the animal. Graph this function for $t \geq 0$, assuming that its domain is the set of all positive real numbers.

Solution Letting $t = 0$ in the expression for R, we obtain

$$R(0) = 5(1 - e^{-0}) = 5(1 - 1) = 0$$

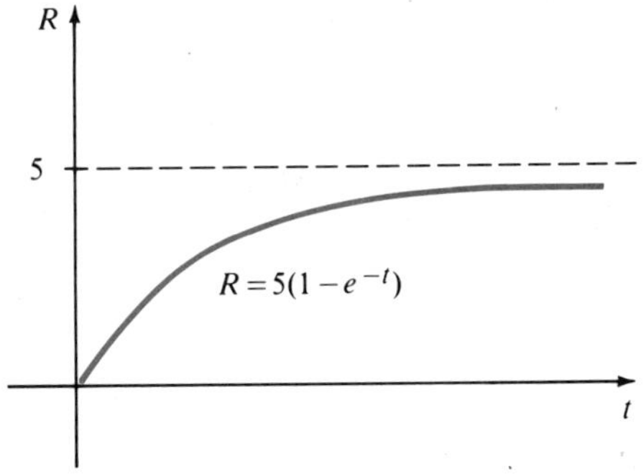

Figure 5.6

As t increases, e^{-t} decreases and, hence, $1 - e^{-t}$ approaches the value 1; consequently, R approaches 5. The graph in Figure 5.6 shows that the ability of the animals to learn increases rapidly at first and then levels off at 5 as t becomes large. This curve is called a **learning curve.** ■

EXAMPLE 3 An unmanned satellite has a radioisotope power supply whose power output in watts is given by the equation

$$P = 50e^{-t/260}$$

where t is the time in days that the battery has been in operation. How much power will be available at the end of one year? Give the answer to one decimal place.

Solution Applying the given formula with $t = 365$,

$$P = 50e^{-365/260} = \boxed{12.28251678} = 12.3 \text{ w}$$ ■

EXAMPLE 4 Population growth is described by an exponential function of the form

$$P = P_0e^{kt}$$

where P_0 is the initial population size, t is the elapsed time, and k is a constant. Estimate the population of the asteroid Malthus in 2025 and 2075 if the population in 1975 was 500. Assume $k = 0.032$.

Solution The growth equation for this population is

$$P = 500e^{0.032t}$$

Using this formula with $t = 50$, we have

$$P = 500e^{1.6} = \boxed{2476.516212} = 2477$$

If $t = 100$, the population is

$$P = 500e^{3.2} = \boxed{12266.2651} = 12{,}267$$

Thus, in 2025 the population of the asteroid is 2477, or almost five times what it was in 1975. By 2075 the population has increased to 12,267, which is about 25 times the population in 1975. ■

Exercises Section 5.2

In Exercises 1–10, use your knowledge of the properties of exponential functions to sketch the graph of the indicated function.

1. $y = 0.5e^x$

2. $y = 2e^{-x}$

3. $m = e^x - 3$

4. $y = 1 + e^x$

5. $y = e^{x/2}$

6. $y = 10 + e^{3x/2}$

7. $f(t) = e^{1-t}$

8. $z = 2e^T$

9. $y = e^{x+2}$

10. $g(x) = e^{1-x}$

Use a calculator to evaluate Exercises 11–20.

11. Find the velocity of a rocket when $t = 2.75$ sec, if $v = 10.772e^{2.032t}$ m/sec.

12. If the mass of a radioactive material varies with time according to $m = 558.76e^{-.01749t}$ g, what is the mass when (a) $t = 3.95$; (b) $t = 5.50$.

13. Find the temperature of an object when $t = 7.5$ min, if the temperature T varies according to $T = 198.6 + 95.3e^{-0.147t}$.

14. In the absence of promotional activity, the sales of a product decrease at a rate described by the exponential function

$$A(t) = A_0e^{-kt}$$

where A_0 is the amount of the sales when $t = 0$, and k is the *sales decay constant*. Find the sales after one year if $A_0 = 10{,}000$ for a sales decay constant of 0.5.

15. The mass m of a certain radioactive substance decays with time according to

$$m = 100e^{-0.1t} \text{ kilograms}$$

where t is the time in days. Using a calculator to evaluate the expression, draw an accurate sketch of mass versus time for $t > 0$. Using this graph, estimate the half-life of the substance. *Hint:* The **half-life** is the time in which a substance decays to one half of its original value.

16. A company has found that a person new to the assembly line produces items according to the function

$$N = 50 - 50e^{-0.5t}$$

where t is the number of days he has worked on the line. How many items will the new worker produce on the fifth day? Graph this function for $t > 0$, assuming it to be a function of real numbers, not just of the positive integers.

17. Given $f(t) = \sqrt{t + 3.346e^{0.0178t}}$, find $f(30.542)$.

18. Given $g(t) = t^3e^{t^2} + 156.79$, find $g(2.069)$.

19. Given $H(x) = (e^{0.15x} + e^{-0.15x})e^{3.19-x}$, find the value of $H(0.7683)$.

20. Given $r(n) = 0.00156(8013.6 - 13.607e^{1.116n})/n$, find $r(9.0075)$.

5.3 The Logarithm Function*

A horizontal line will intersect the graph of the exponential function $y = a^x$ only once. Hence, the function is one-to-one; that is, for each value of x, there is at most one value of y and for each value of y, there is a unique x. Using this property we can define another important function.

Definition

Let $a > 0$ and $a \neq 1$. Then for $x > 0$,

$$\mathbf{y = \log_a x \quad \text{means } x = a^y}$$

The function $\log_a x$ is called the **logarithm function** of x to the base a.

Thus, the value of $\log_a x$ is the exponent to which the base a must be raised to give the value x. In other words, **every logarithm is an exponent of the base.** The next example shows how the logarithm of a number is found directly from the definition.

EXAMPLE 1
a. $\log_2 16 = 4$ because $2^4 = 16$.
b. $\log_2 (\frac{1}{8}) = -3$ because $2^{-3} = \frac{1}{8}$.
c. $\log_{10} (1/1000) = -3$ because $10^{-3} = 1/1000$.
In each of the cases, note that the logarithm is an exponent. ■

EXAMPLE 2 Find $\log_2 32$.

Solution Let $y = \log_2 32$. Then $32 = 2^y$, or $y = 5$. ■

EXAMPLE 3 Find b, given that $\log_b 4 = -\frac{1}{2}$.

Solution Writing this in exponential form, we have $4 = b^{-1/2}$. Solving $4 = 1/b^{1/2}$ for b, we find that $16 = 1/b$ and $b = \frac{1}{16}$. ■

* Section 3.5 should be reviewed before reading this section.

EXAMPLE 4 Solve $3 = \log_4 (x^2 + 2)$ for x.

Solution

$3 = \log_4 (x^2 + 2)$	
$4^3 = x^2 + 2$	Definition of the logarithm
$x^2 = 62$	Subtracting 2 from both sides
$x = \pm\sqrt{62}$	Taking the square root

■

EXAMPLE 5 Determine the values of x for which

$$1 < \log_3 (2x + 5) < 2$$

Solution We use the fact that

$$1 < \log_3 u < 2 \quad \text{when} \quad 3^1 < u < 3^2$$

Thus, we are to solve the inequality

$$3 < 2x + 5 < 9$$

Subtracting 5 from each member, we have

$$-2 < 2x < 4$$

which gives

$$-1 < x < 2$$

■

EXAMPLE 6 The intensity (energy) level β of a soundwave with intensity I is defined to be

$$\beta = 10 \log_{10} (I/I_0) \text{ db (decibels)}$$

where I_0 is the minimum intensity detectable by the human ear. (When two sounds differ in intensity by a factor of 10, they differ in loudness by 1 bel; a difference of 100 means a loudness difference of 2 bels. In practice, the unit used is the decibel, one tenth of a bel.) Solve for I.

Solution Dividing both sides of $\beta = 10 \log_{10} (I/I_0)$ by 10, we have

$$\frac{\beta}{10} = \log_{10} (I/I_0)$$

Using the fact that $y = \log_b x$ means $x = b^y$, we have

$$\frac{I}{I_0} = 10^{\beta/10}$$

from which

$$I = I_0\, 10^{\beta/10}$$

■

EXAMPLE 7 The relationship between the velocity, v, of a space vehicle, its exhaust velocity, c, and its mass ratio, R, is given by the exponential relationship

$$R = e^{v/c}$$

Write this expression logarithmically by solving for v.

Solution Using the fact that $y = e^x$ may also be written as $x = \log_e y$, we have

$$\frac{v}{c} = \log_e R$$

from which

$$v = c \log_e R$$ ■

Because of the definition, the domain and the range of the logarithm function are the same as the range and the domain of the exponential function, respectively. Thus, the domain of $y = \log_a x$ is the set of all positive reals (sometimes we say that the logarithm of a nonpositive number is undefined) and the range is the set of all real numbers. A diagram of these relationships is shown below.

Exponential function		Logarithm function
$y = a^x$		$y = \log_a x$
Domain	⟶ all real numbers ⟵	Range
Range	⟶ all positive reals ⟵	Domain

We may sketch the graph of the logarithm function by first constructing a table of values. The tables for $y = \log_2 x$ and $y = \log_{10} x$ are included below and the corresponding graphs are presented in Figure 5.7.

x	$\frac{1}{8}$	$\frac{1}{4}$	$\frac{1}{2}$	1	2	4	8
$\log_2 x$	-3	-2	-1	0	1	2	3

x	$\frac{1}{1000}$	$\frac{1}{100}$	$\frac{1}{10}$	1	10	100
$\log_{10} x$	-3	-2	-1	0	1	2

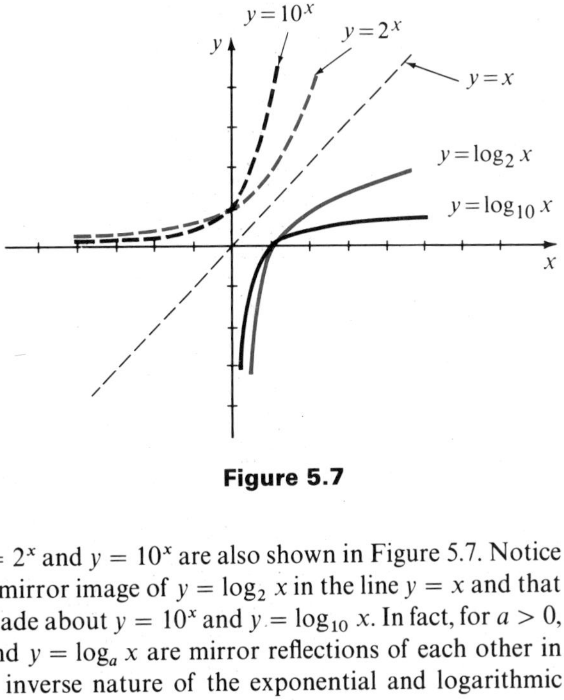

Figure 5.7

Comment: The graphs of $y = 2^x$ and $y = 10^x$ are also shown in Figure 5.7. Notice that the graph of $y = 2^x$ is the mirror image of $y = \log_2 x$ in the line $y = x$ and that the same observation can be made about $y = 10^x$ and $y = \log_{10} x$. In fact, for $a > 0$, $a \neq 1$, the graphs of $y = a^x$ and $y = \log_a x$ are mirror reflections of each other in $y = x$. This demonstrates the inverse nature of the exponential and logarithmic functions.

Each of the solid curves of Figure 5.7 is characteristic of what is called **logarithmic shape.** The figure clearly demonstrates the following properties of the logarithm function for $a > 1$. Any function that has these properties is said to behave logarithmically.

Properties of $f(x) = \log x$, $a > 1$

1. $\text{Log}_a\, x$ is not defined for $x \leq 0$, so the domain is the set of positive real numbers.
2. $\text{Log}_a\, 1 = 0$.
3. $\text{Log}_a\, a = 1$.
4. The value of $\log_a x$ is negative for $0 < x < 1$ and positive for $x > 1$. Hence, the range is the set of all real numbers.
5. As x approaches 0, $\log_a x$ decreases without bound. The graph is asymptotic to the negative y-axis.
6. As x increases without bound, $\log_a x$ increases without bound.
7. If $x_1 < x_2$, then $\log_a x_1 < \log_a x_2$. Hence, $\log_a x$ is an increasing function.

Although the base of a logarithm may theoretically be any positive number except 1, in practice we seldom use bases other than 10 and e. Logarithms with base 10 are called **common logarithms.** Conventionally, $\log_{10} x$ is often written $\log x$, with the subscript 10 understood. However this convention is far from universal, so use it with care. Logarithms with base e, called **natural logarithms,** are often denoted with the alternate notation **ln *x*.** That is, $\log_e x$ and $\ln x$ mean the same thing.

Most scientific calculators have both a [log] *and an* [ln] *button, or if not, the capability of making these computations. Consult your user's manual for specific directions.*

More generally, we must work with functions of the type $y = \log [g(x)]$, where $g(x)$ is some function of x.

EXAMPLE 8 Sketch the graph of the function $y = \log_2 (-x)$.

Solution At first glance you might conclude that this function is undefined since the logarithm of a negative number is undefined. However, $-x$ is positive when $x < 0$, so $\log_2 (-x)$ has a domain of $x < 0$. The graph passes through $(-2, 1)$ and $(-1, 0)$ since $\log_2 (-(-2)) =$

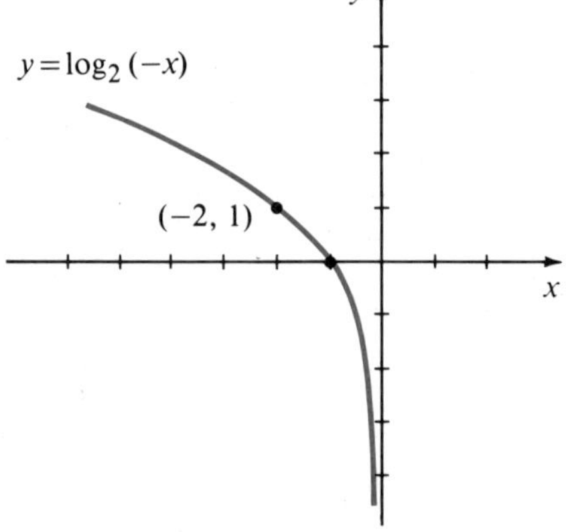

Figure 5.8

$\log_2 2 = 1$ and $\log_2(-(-1)) = \log_2 1 = 0$. The graph is shown in Figure 5.8. Notice that the characteristic logarithmic shape of $\log_2(-x)$ is the mirror reflection of $\log_2 x$ in the y-axis. ■

EXAMPLE 9 Sketch the graph of $y = \ln x$.

Solution Recall that $\ln x$ means $\log_e x$. The graph passes through $(1, 0)$ and $(e, 1) \approx (2.7, 1)$ since $\ln 1 = 0$ and $\ln e = 1$. The graph is shown in Figure 5.9.

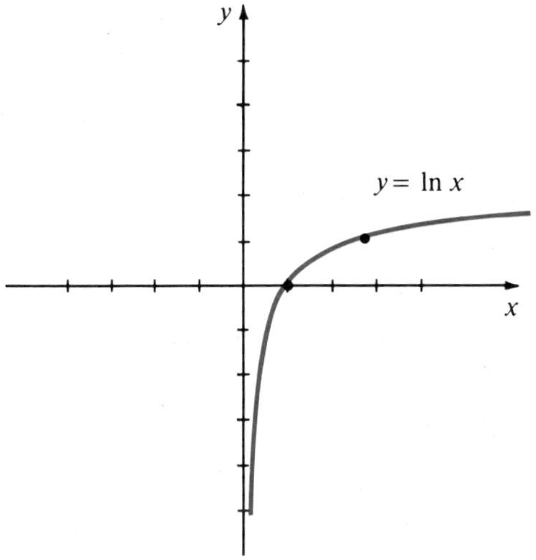

Figure 5.9 ■

EXAMPLE 10 Sketch the graph of $y = \log_5(2x - 1)$.

Solution Here we note that the function is *not* defined for values of $x \leq \frac{1}{2}$. Furthermore, when $x = 1$, $y = \log_5 1 = 0$, and when $x = 3$, $y = \log_5 5 = 1$. These facts are summarized in the table and the graph drawn in Figure 5.10.

$y = \log_5(2x - 1)$

x	y
$\frac{1}{2}$	undef.
1	0
3	1
increasing w/o bound	increasing w/o bound

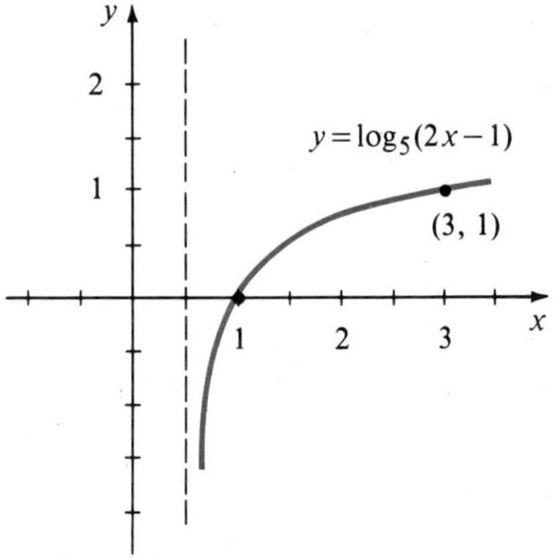

Figure 5.10 ■

Exercises Section 5.3

Write a logarithmic expression equivalent to the exponential expression given in Exercises 1–5.

1. $x = 2^3$ **2.** $y = 3^8$ **3.** $M = 5^{-3}$

4. $N = 10^{-2}$ **5.** $L = 7^2$

In Exercises 6–10, write an exponential expression equivalent to the given logarithmic expression. In each case find the base of the logarithm function.

6. $\log_b 8 = 3$ **7.** $\log_b 4 = 2$

8. $\log_b 0.25 = -2$ **9.** $\log_b 100 = 2$

10. $\log_b b = 1$

In Exercises 11–30, solve for the unknown.

11. $\log_{10} x = 4$ **12.** $\log_5 N = 2$

13. $\log_x 10 = 1$ **14.** $\log_x 25 = 2$

15. $\log_x 64 = 3$ **16.** $\log_{16} x = 2$

17. $\log_{27} x = \frac{2}{3}$ **18.** $\log_2 \frac{1}{8} = x$

19. $\log_3 9 = x$ **20.** $\log_{10} 10^7 = x$

21. $\log_b b^a = x$ **22.** $\log_b x = b$

23. $\log_x 2 = \frac{1}{3}$ **24.** $\log_x 0.0001 = -2$

25. $\log_x 6 = \frac{1}{2}$ **26.** $\log_b x = 0$

27. $6^{\log_6 x} = 6$ **28.** $x^{\log_x x} = 3$

29. $\log_2 (x + 3) = -1$ **30.** $\log_2 (x - 1) = 3$

In Exercises 31–34, solve the given logarithmic inequalities.

31. $\log_3 (x + 1) < 2$ **32.** $\log_2 (2 - x) > -1$

33. $2 \le \log_2 x \le 3$ **34.** $0 < \log x < 1$

Sketch a graph of the functions in Exercises 35–43. (Remember that $\log x$ means $\log_{10} x$.)

35. $f(x) = \ln x$ **36.** $f(x) = -\log x$

37. $f(x) = \log |x|$ **38.** $f(x) = \log (x - 1)$

39. $f(x) = \log 2x$ **40.** $g(x) = \log_3 (-x)$

41. $f(x) = \log_2 (1 - x)$ **42.** $f(x) = \log_2 (1 + x)$

43. $f(x) = \log_2 |1 + x|$

In Exercises 44–49, describe how the graph of the given logarithmic function is related to the graph of $y = \log x$. In each case make a sketch to show the comparison.

44. $\log (-x)$ **45.** $-\log x$ **46.** $\log |x|$

47. $|\log x|$ **48.** $3 + \log x$ **49.** $\log (x + 3)$

Find the base of the logarithm function $y = \log_a x$ whose graphs contain the points in Exercises 50–54.

50. (100, 2) **51.** (4, 2) **52.** (64, 3)

53. (0.1, −1) **54.** (0.5, −1)

55. Let $f_b(x) = \log_b x$. For any acceptable base the graph of $f_b(x)$ passes through a point independent of b. What is that point?

56. Let $f(x) = \log_3 x$. Find $f(9)$, $f(\frac{1}{27})$, and $f(81)$.

57. Let $f(x) = \log_2 x$. By example show that
- **a.** $f(x + y) \ne f(x) + f(y)$
- **b.** $f(ax) \ne af(x)$

58. On the same set of axes, sketch $\log_2 x$ and $\log_3 x$ and
- **a.** solve the equation $\log_2 x = \log_3 x$.
- **b.** solve the inequality $\log_2 x > \log_3 x$.

59. How are the graphs of $y = \log_2 x$ and $y = 2^x$ related?

In Exercises 60–67, use a calculator to approximate the given logarithm.

60. $\log 2.67$ **61.** $\log 0.5$

62. $\log 5000$ **63.** $\log 5 + \log 2$

64. $\ln 10$ **65.** $\ln e^{-1}$

66. $\ln 1000$ **67.** $\ln 0.5$

68. A power supply has a power output in watts approximated by the equation

$$P = 64e^{-3t}$$

where t is in days. Solve this expression for t.

69. A certain radioactive material decays exponentially by the equation

$$A(t) = A_0 e^{-t/5}$$

Find the half-life of the material. (See Exercise 37, Section 5.1.)

5.4 Basic Properties of Logarithms

There are three rules for simplifying logarithmic expressions. These three properties of logarithms correspond to the three fundamental rules for exponents and are necessary consequences of them.

Rule 1

$$\log_a MN = \log_a M + \log_a N$$

Proof Let $u = \log_a M$ and $v = \log_a N$. Then,

$$a^u = M \quad \text{and} \quad a^v = N$$

from which

$$MN = a^u a^v = a^{u+v}$$

Reexpressing in terms of logarithms, we have

$$\log_a MN = u + v = \log_a M + \log_a N$$

Rule 2

$$\log_a M^c = c \log_a M \quad \text{where } c \text{ is any real number}$$

Proof Let $u = \log_a M$. Then,

$$a^u = M \quad \text{and} \quad (a^u)^c = a^{uc} = M^c$$

In terms of logarithms, this may be expressed as

$$\log_a M^c = uc = c \log_a M$$

Rule 3

$$\log_a (M/N) = \log_a M - \log_a N$$

Proof $M/N = M(N)^{-1}$. Now apply the previous two rules.

In words, Rule 1 states that the logarithm of a product is equal to the sum of the logarithms of the individual factors; Rule 2 states that the logarithm of a number to a power is the power times the logarithm of the number; and Rule 3 states that the logarithm of a quotient is the difference of the logarithms of the numerator and denominator. Examine these rules carefully and notice where they apply as well as where they do *not* apply. For example, there is *no* rule for simplifying expressions of the form $\log_a (x + y)$ or $\log_a (x - y)$.

Warning: $\log_a (x + y)$ IS NOT EQUAL TO $\log_a x + \log_a y$. The following example shows why.

$$\log_2 (8 + 8) = \log_2 16 = 4$$
$$\log_2 8 + \log_2 8 = 3 + 3 = 6 \neq 4$$

EXAMPLE 1 a. $\log_2 (8)(64) = \log_2 8 + \log_2 64 = \log_2 2^3 + \log_2 2^6 = 3 + 6 = 9$
b. $\log_3 \sqrt{243} = \log_3 243^{1/2} = \frac{1}{2} \log_3 243 = \frac{1}{2}(5) = 2.5$
c. $\log_2 (\frac{3}{5}) = \log_2 3 - \log_2 5$
d. $\log (4 \cdot 29/5) = \log 4 + \log 29 - \log 5$ ■

EXAMPLE 2 Given that $\log 2 = 0.3010$ and $\log 3 = 0.4771$, find $\log 45$.

Solution Since $45 = 9 \cdot 5$, we have

$$\begin{aligned}\log 45 &= \log 9 + \log 5\\ &= \log 3^2 + \log (\tfrac{10}{2})\\ &= 2 \log 3 + \log 10 - \log 2\\ &= 2(0.4771) + 1 - 0.3010\\ &= 1.6532\end{aligned}$$ ■

EXAMPLE 3 Write the expression $\log x - 2 \log x + 3 \log (x + 1) - \log (x^2 - 1)$ as a single term.

Solution Proceed as follows:

$$\log x - 2 \log x + 3 \log (x + 1) - \log (x^2 - 1)$$
$$= \log x - \log x^2 + \log (x + 1)^3 - \log (x^2 - 1) \quad \text{Rule 2}$$
$$= \log \frac{x(x + 1)^3}{x^2(x^2 - 1)} = \log \frac{(x + 1)^2}{x(x - 1)} \quad \text{Rules 1 and 3 and the cancellation law}$$ ■

EXAMPLE 4 Given $\log_a x = 3$, find $\log_a (1/x)$.

Solution $\log_a (1/x) = \log_a x^{-1}$
$= -\log_a x$
$= -3$ ■

Exercises Section 5.4

Evaluate the logarithms in Exercises 1–8.

1. $\log_2 32 \cdot 16$
2. $\log_2 16^5$
3. $\log_5 25^{1/4}$
4. $\log_3 27$
5. $\log_3 27 \cdot 9 \cdot 3$
6. $\log_2 64 \cdot 32 \cdot 8$
7. $\log_2 (8 \cdot 32)^3$
8. $\log_3 (9 \cdot 81)^8$

Given $\log 2 = 0.3010$, $\log 3 = 0.4771$, and $\log 7 = 0.8451$, find the logarithms in Exercises 9–20.

9. $\log \frac{3}{2}$
10. $\log 4$
11. $\log 12$
12. $\log 30$
13. $\log 90$
14. $\log \sqrt{2}$
15. $\log \sqrt{5}$
16. $\log 21^{1/3}$
17. $\log 2400$
18. $\log 0.00018$
19. $\log 0.0014$
20. $\log 42000$

In Exercises 21–28, write the given expression as a single logarithmic term.

21. $\log_2 x^2 - \log_2 x$
22. $\log_2 (x^2 - 1) - \log_2(x - 1)$
23. $\log x + \log (1/x)$

24. $\log 3x + 3\log(x+2) - \log(x^2-4)$

25. $\log 5t + 2\log(t^2-4) - \frac{1}{2}\log(t+3)$

26. $\log z - 3\log 3z - \log(2z-9)$

27. $3\log u - 2\log(u+1) - 5\log(u-1)$

28. $\log t + 7\log(2t-8)$

29. Let $\ln I = (-R/L)t + \ln I_0$. Show that $I = I_0 e^{-Rt/L}$.

30. If y is directly proportional to x^p, what relation exists between $\log y$ and $\log x$?

31. Compare the functions $f(x) = \log x^2$ and $g(x) = 2\log x$. In what way are they the same? In what way different?

32. Let $f(x) = \log_a x$ and $g(x) = \log_{1/a} x$. Show that $g(x) = f(1/x)$.

33. If $\log_a x = 2$, find $\log_{1/a} x$ and $\log_a(1/x)$.

34. Compare the graphs of the functions $f(x) = \log_2 2x$, $g(x) = \log_2 x$, $h(x) = \log_2 \sqrt{x}$, and $m(x) = \log_2 x^2$.

35. Given the graph of $y = \log x$, explain a convenient way to obtain the following graphs.

a. $\log x^p$ **b.** $\log px$

c. $\log(x+p)$ **d.** $\log(x/p)$

36. If $f(x) = \log_b x$, is $f(x+y) = f(x) + f(y)$?

In Exercises 37–47, use a calculator to verify the given statement.

37. $\ln 6 = \ln 2 + \ln 3$

38. $\ln 100 = \ln 50 + \ln 2$

39. $\ln 9 = 2\ln 3$

40. $\ln[16\sqrt{2}] = 2\ln 4 + \frac{1}{2}\ln 2$

41. $\ln[(62.3)(28.6)] = \ln 62.3 + \ln 28.6$

42. $\ln e^{\pi} = \pi$

43. $\ln 12 = \ln 36 - \ln 3$

44. $\log[25 \cdot 34] = \log 25 + \log 34$

45. $\log[16 \cdot \pi] = \log 16 + \log \pi$

46. $\log \frac{125}{73} = \log 125 - \log 73$

47. $\log \frac{17}{35} = \log 17 - \log 35$

5.5 Exponential and Logarithmic Equations

Equations in which the variable occurs as an exponent are called **exponential equations.** To solve these equations, we use the fact that the logarithm is a one-to-one function. Thus, $\log x = \log y$ if and only if $x = y$. Hence, if both sides are positive, taking the logarithm of both sides yields an equivalent equation.

EXAMPLE 1 Solve the exponential equation $3^x = 2^{2x+1}$.

Solution Taking the common logarithm of both sides, we write

$$\log 3^x = \log 2^{2x+1}$$

$$x\log 3 = (2x+1)\log 2 \qquad \text{Using Rule 2}$$

$$x(\log 3 - 2\log 2) = \log 2 \qquad \text{Expanding and collecting like terms}$$

$$x = \frac{\log 2}{\log 3 - 2\log 2} \qquad \text{Solving for } x$$

$$= -2.40942084 \qquad \text{Using a calculator}$$

$$x = -2.41 \qquad \text{Rounding off to two decimals}$$

■

EXAMPLE 2 The expression $(e^x - e^{-x})/2$ is called the hyperbolic sine of x and is denoted by $\sinh x$. Solve the equation $\sinh x = 3$. Round off the answer to two decimal places.

Solution

$$\frac{e^x - e^{-x}}{2} = 3 \qquad \text{Replacing } \sinh x \text{ by its equal}$$

$$e^x - e^{-x} = 6 \qquad \text{Multiplying both sides by 2}$$

$e^{2x} - 6e^x - 1 = 0$ Adding -6 to both sides and multiplying by e^x

$u^2 - 6u - 1 = 0$ Letting $u = e^x$

$u = \dfrac{6 \pm \sqrt{40}}{2} = 3 \pm \sqrt{10}$ Using the quadratic formula

Since $u = e^x$ is always positive, discard the root $3 - \sqrt{10}$, which is negative. Thus,

$$e^x = 3 + \sqrt{10}$$

Then

$$x = \ln(3 + \sqrt{10}) = \boxed{1.818446459} = 1.82$$

is the desired solution. ■

Equations involving logarithms are called **logarithmic equations.** The use of one of the rules of logarithms frequently gives the needed simplification to allow you to solve such an equation.

EXAMPLE 3 Solve the logarithmic equation $\log(x^2 - 1) - \log(x - 1) = 3$.

Solution Simplifying the left-hand side by combining the two logarithm terms, we get

$$\log \frac{x^2 - 1}{x - 1} = 3$$

$\log(x + 1) = 3$ Canceling $x - 1$ in $x^2 - 1$

$x + 1 = 10^3$ $\log M = N$ means $M = 10^N$

$x = -1 + 10^3 = 999$ Adding -1 to both sides ■

EXAMPLE 4 Solve the equation

$$x^{\log x} = \frac{x^3}{100}$$

Solution Taking the common logarithm of both sides, we have

$$\log x^{\log x} = \log \frac{x^3}{100}$$

$(\log x)(\log x) = \log x^3 - \log 100$ Using Rules 2 and 3

$(\log x)^2 - \log x^3 + \log 100 = 0$ Collecting terms on the left

$(\log x)^2 - 3 \log x + 2 = 0$ $\log x^3 = 3 \log x$ and $\log 100 = 2$

$(\log x - 2)(\log x - 1) = 0$ Factoring

$\log x = 2$, or $\log x = 1$ Solving for $\log x$

Thus, $x = 100$ or 10. ■

EXAMPLE 5 A certain power supply has a power output in watts governed by the equation

$$P = 50e^{-t/250}$$

where t is the time in days. If the equipment aboard a satellite requires 10 w of power to operate properly, what is the operational life of the satellite?

Solution Letting $P = 10$, we solve the equation $10 = 50e^{-t/250}$ for t. Dividing both sides by 50, we have

$$e^{-t/250} = 0.2$$

$$\frac{-t}{250} = \ln 0.2 \qquad e^y = x \text{ means } y = \ln x$$

$$t = -250 \ln 0.2 \qquad \text{Multiplying both sides by } -250$$

$$= 402.3594781 \qquad \text{Using a calculator}$$

$$= 402 \qquad \text{To three significant figures}$$

Hence, the operational life of the satellite is 402 days. ■

Exercises Section 5.5

Solve for x in Exercises 1–26.

1. $7^{x+1} = 2^x$

2. $3^x 2^{2x+1} = 10$

3. $10^{x^2} = 2^x$

4. $8^x = 10^x$

5. $2^{1+x} = 3$

6. $3^{1-x} = 7^x$

7. $2^{x+5} = 3^{x-2}$

8. $(1/2)^x > 3$

9. $2^{x+1} > 5$

10. $5^{-(1+x)} < 8$

11. $2^{\log x} = 2$

12. $\log \log \log x = 1$

13. $(\log x)^{1/2} = \log \sqrt{x}$

14. $(\log x)^2 = \log x^2$

15. $(\log x)^3 = \log x^3$

16. $x^{\log x} = 10$

17. $\log (x + 15) + \log x = 2$

18. $\log 3x - \log 2x = \log 3 - \log x$

19. $\log (x - 2) - \log (2x + 1) = \log (1/x)$

20. $\log (x^2 + 1) - \log (x - 1) - \log (x + 1) = 1$

21. $\log (x + 2) - \log (x - 2) - \log x + \log (x - 3) = 0$

22. $\log x + \log (x - 99) = \log 2$

23. $\log x + \log (x^2 - 4) - \log 2x = 0$

24. $3 \log (x - 1) = \log 3(x - 1)$

25. $\log (x + 1) - \log x < 1$

26. $\log (x + 1) + \log (x - 1) < 2$

27. The expression $(e^x + e^{-x})/2$ is called the hyperbolic cosine of x and is denoted by $\cosh x$. Solve the equation $\cosh x = 2$. *Hint:* Let $u = e^x$.

28. Solve the two equations $y = 50e^{-2x}$ and $y = 2^x$ simultaneously by making a sketch of each of the two equations on the same coordinate system.

29. Explain why if $\log u(x) = v(x)$, then $u(x) = 10^{v(x)}$.

30. Show that if $y = e^{\ln f(x)}$, then $y = f(x)$.

31. The radioactive chemical element strontium 90 has a half-life of approximately 28 years. The element obeys the radioactive decay formula, $A(t) = A_0 e^{-kt}$, where A_0 is the original amount and t is the time in years. Find the value of k.

32. Repeat Exercise 31 for the element iodine, whose decay formula is the same type. Express t in days. The half-life is 8 days.

33. What is the half-life of the power supply of Example 5?

34. The difference in intensity level of two sounds with intensities I and I_0 is defined by $10 \log (I/I_0)$ db. Find the intensity level in decibels of the sound produced by an electric motor that is 175.6 times greater than I_0.

35. As previously pointed out, the population growth curve is given by $P = P_0 e^{kt}$, where P_0 is the initial size, t is time in hours, and k is a constant. If $k = 0.0132$ for a bacteria culture, how long does it take for the culture to double in size?

Review Exercises Chapter 5

In Exercises 1–14, solve for x.

1. $2^{x-5} = 3^x$

2. $x^{-1.2} = 18$

3. $2^{x^2-3x} = 16$

4. $3^{\log x} = 2$

5. $3^{1-x} = 5$

6. $\log 2^x = x^2 - 2$

7. $\log x = 3$

8. $\log_2 x = 5$

9. $\log_3 81 = x$

10. $\log_5 (\frac{1}{25}) = x$

11. $\log_x 64 = 6$

12. $\log_x 27 = 3$

13. $x^{4.3} = 2.1$

14. $\log_x (0.01) = -2$

In Exercises 15–24, make a sketch of the graph of the given function.

15. $y = e^{-(1-x)}$

16. $y = 2e^{-x} + 3$

17. $y = 2^2 2^t$

18. $y = (0.5)^{-x}$

19. $y = (2/3^x)$

20. $y = 2 - 5e^{-(x-1)}$

21. $y = -\log(x - 2)$

22. $y = 1 + \log x$

23. $y = 2 - \log x^3$

24. $y = \log(-x) - 3$

In Exercises 25–30, write the given expression as a single logarithmic term.

25. $\log x + \log x^2$

26. $\log 2x - \log x$

27. $\log_2 2x + 3 \log_2 x$

28. $3 \log_2 x - \log_2 x$

29. $3 \log_5 x - \log_5 (2x - 3)$

30. $5 \log(x + 2) - 2 \log x$

Solve each of the equations in Exercises 31–40.

31. $2^{x+2} = 10$

32. $5^{3-x} = 8$

33. $3^{x+1} = 4^x$

34. $2^x = 3^{x-1}$

35. $\log(\log x) = 1$

36. $(\log x)^2 = \log x$

37. $\log x + \log(x + 1) = \log 6$

38. $\log(x - 2) + \log x = \log 8$

39. $\log x + \log(x - 3) = 1$

40. $\log 5x + \log 2x = 2 + \log x$

41. Find the half-life of a radioactive material that decays exponentially according to the equation $A(t) = A_0 e^{-t/4}$, where t is the time in years.

42. A colony of bacteria increases according to the law:

$$N(t) = N(0)e^{kt}$$

If the colony doubles in five hours, find the time needed for the colony to triple.

43. A bacteria colony population is given by $N(t) = 2000\, e^{1.3t}$. Plot a graph of N as a function of t.

44. A principal of \$5000 is invested at the rate of 9.2% per year **compounded continuously.** The law governing continuous compounding is $P = P_0 e^{rt}$, where t is the time in years. What will be the amount after 20 years?

45. In the dye-dilution procedure for measuring cardiac output, the amount in milligrams of dye in the heart at any time, t, in minutes is given by

$$D(t) = D(0)e^{-rt/V}$$

where $D(0)$ is the amount in milligrams of dye injected, r is a constant representing the outflow of blood and dye in liters per minute, and V is the volume of the heart in liters. Find the amount of dye in the heart after 5 sec, given that $V = 450$ mL, $r = 1.4$ L/min, and $D(0) = 2.3$ mg. *Hint:* Use consistent units.

Test 1 Chapter 5

Answer True or False to Exercises 1–10.

1. If $f(x) = 2^x$, then $f(x + y) = f(x) \cdot f(y)$.

2. If $f(x) = 2^x$, then if $x_1 < x_2$, $f(x_1) > f(x_2)$.

3. If $a > b$, $a^x > b^x$.

4. $\log 0 = 1$

5. $\log(x + y) = \log x + \log y$

6. For all $x > 0$, $y = \log x$ is an increasing function.

7. $2^{\log_2 7} = 7$

8. The domain of $\log(-x)$ is the empty set.

9. The domain of $\log(-x^2)$ is the empty set.

10. The logarithm function is the reciprocal of the exponential function.

11. Make a careful sketch of $y = 2^x$, $y = 2^{x+3}$, and $y = 2^x + 3$ on the same coordinate axes.

12. Make a careful sketch of $y = \log x$, $y = -\log x$, and $y = \log(-x)$ on the same coordinate axes.

13. If $\log v = 5.4371$, find the value of v.

14. Find x if $10^{x^2-4} = 7$.

15. **a.** Solve for x: $2^{x+1} > 0$.
b. Solve for x: $\log(x + 1) > 0$.

16. Find x if $x^{4.3} = 2.1$.

Test 2 Chapter 5

1. Sketch the graph of
a. $y = 2^{x-3}$ **b.** $y = \log_2 (x - 5)$

2. Solve for x if (a) $\log_x 8 = -3$; (b) $\log_3 x = 4$.

3. Express as a single logarithmic term:

$$3 \log x - \log(x^2 - 2) + 2 \log(x + 1)$$

4. Evaluate
a. $\log_5 (125 \cdot 625)$
b. $\log_2 (128 \cdot 64)$

5. Solve for x if $3^x = 2^{x+1}$.

6. Solve for x if $\log x + \log (x - 3) = 1$.

7. Given $m = ce^{-kt}$, find k if $m = 50$ and $c = 20$, when $t = 2$.

8. If a bank pays 6.6% interest compounded monthly, how much interest is earned on an investment of $5000 for three years?

9. Suppose a new car loses 20% of its value each year after it is purchased. In how many years will the car be worth one half its original value? Give answer to the nearest tenth of a year.

6

Systems of Equations and Inequalities

A solution to an equation in two variables consists of any ordered pair of numbers that satisfy the equation. For example, the ordered pairs (1, 2), (2, −1), (3, −4), (0, 5), and so on are solutions to the equation $3x + y = 5$. Similarly, (8, 1), (−1, −8), (10, 3), (3, −4), and so on are solutions to $x - y = 7$. Inspection of the two solution sets reveals the interesting fact that (3, −4) satisfies both equations. When considered together like this, the two equations are referred to as a **system of equations** and any common solution is called a **simultaneous solution** to the system of equations.

You can get an idea of what it means to solve a system of equations by drawing the graph of each equation on the same set of coordinates. Figure 6.1 shows the graphs of $3x + y = 5$ and $x - y = 7$. The ordered pair (3, −4) appears as the point of intersection of the two curves. Simultaneous solutions of systems of two equations in two unknowns can always be represented in this way. We sometimes use this fact to solve a system of equations "graphically," especially when the system contains one or more nonlinear equations.

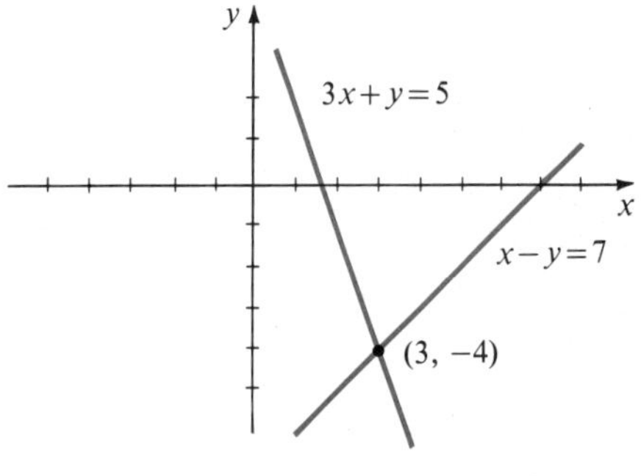

Figure 6.1

A **linear** system of equations is one in which each equation is linear. A system that is not linear is called **nonlinear.** For example, the equations

$$3x + y = 5$$
$$x - y = 7$$

form a linear system, while the equations

$$x + 5y = 10$$
$$x^2 - 13y = 4$$

form a nonlinear system. Most of our effort in this chapter is directed toward solving linear systems, although some of the techniques are applicable to nonlinear systems as well. Our discussion is further limited to systems for which the number of unknowns and the number of equations are the same.

As we noted earlier, any system of two equations in two unknowns may be solved graphically simply by sketching the curve corresponding to each equation and determining the coordinates of the points of intersection. However, graphical methods are tedious and generally yield only approximate results. Therefore, we will concentrate on certain algebraic methods, using the graphs of the equations to support and check the solution.

6.1 Linear Systems of Equations

Perhaps the most widely used method of solving a system of equations is altering the given system algebraically until one of the equations involves only one unknown. Before explaining how this is done, we introduce some preliminary ideas.

Two systems of equations are **equivalent** if both systems have precisely the same solutions. Thus, the systems

$$\text{I}\begin{cases} 2x - y = 5 \\ x - 2y = 4 \end{cases} \quad \text{and} \quad \text{II}\begin{cases} x + y = 1 \\ 3x - y = 7 \end{cases}$$

are equivalent systems since $x = 2$, $y = -1$ is the only solution of both. Figure 6.2(a) shows the graph of System I and Figure 6.2(b) shows the graph of System II. Notice that the point $(2, -1)$ is the point of intersection in both cases.

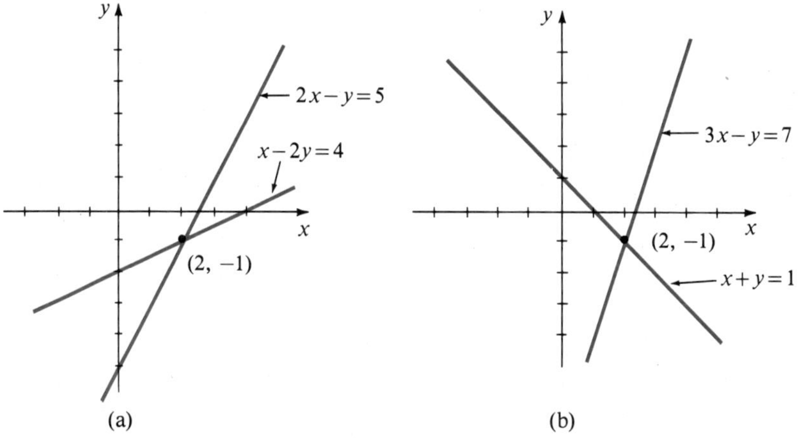

Figure 6.2

An operation that transforms a system of equations into an equivalent system is said to be **allowable.** Three allowable operations for systems of equations are:

1. The position of any two equations can be changed. Thus,

$$\begin{matrix} 3x + 5y = 6 \\ x - 3y = 4 \end{matrix} \quad \text{and} \quad \begin{matrix} x - 3y = 4 \\ 3x + 5y = 6 \end{matrix}$$

   are equivalent systems.
2. Any equation of a system may be replaced by a nonzero multiple of itself. Thus, the systems

$$\text{I}\begin{cases} x - 5y = 3 \\ 2x + 3y = 1 \end{cases} \qquad \text{II}\begin{cases} x - 5y = 3 \\ 4x + 6y = 2 \end{cases} \qquad \text{III}\begin{cases} x - 5y = 3 \\ -6x - 9y = -3 \end{cases}$$

   are equivalent since the lower equation in each system is a constant multiple of the others.
3. Any equation of a system may be replaced by the sum of any two equations in the system. For example, the systems

$$\text{I}\begin{cases} 3x + 5y = 2 \\ x - 3y = 1 \end{cases} \quad \text{and} \quad \text{II}\begin{cases} 3x + 5y = 2 \\ 4x + 2y = 3 \end{cases}$$

   are equivalent systems since the upper equation in each system is the same and the lower equation in System II is obtained by adding together the equations in System I.

Elimination of a Variable by Addition or Subtraction

Operations corresponding to items 2 and 3 are used to solve systems of equations in a technique called **elimination of a variable by addition or subtraction:** you multiply each of the equations by just the right constants so that after adding the two equations, the coefficients of one of the variables vanishes. In this way, the number of variables is essentially reduced by one. If there are only two variables initially, this process will yield one equation in one unknown that can be solved.

Comment: Elimination of a variable by addition or subtraction is called **Gaussian elimination.**

EXAMPLE 1 Use the method of elimination of a variable by addition or subtraction to solve the system of equations

$$\begin{aligned} 3x + 2y &= 5 \\ x - 2y &= 3 \end{aligned}$$

Sketch a figure showing the solution.

Solution First, decide which variable can most easily be eliminated by adding or subtracting the two given equations. In this case, the y variable can be eliminated by simply adding the two equations. Thus, the system

$$\begin{cases} 3x + 2y = 5 \\ x - 2y = 3 \end{cases} \quad \text{is equivalent to the system} \quad \begin{cases} 3x + 2y = 5 \\ 4x = 8 \end{cases}$$

Solving $4x = 8$ for x yields $x = 2$. Now find the value of y by substituting $x = 2$ into $3x + 2y = 5$. Thus,

$$3(2) + 2y = 5$$

and

$$y = -\frac{1}{2}$$

Therefore, the solution of the given system of equations is $x = 2$, $y = -\frac{1}{2}$. Figure 6.3 shows the graph of the system.

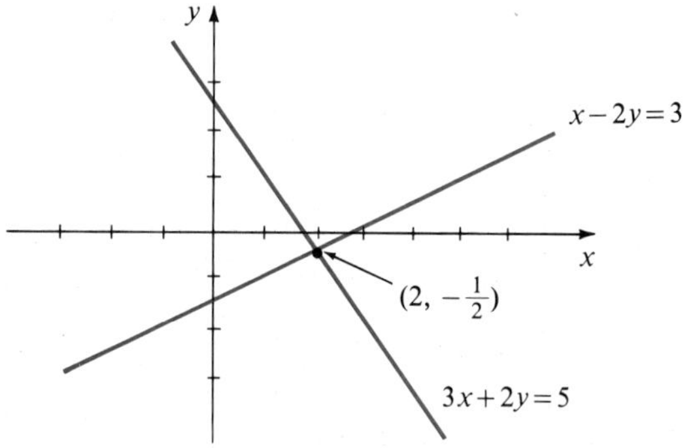

Figure 6.3 ■

EXAMPLE 2 Use the method of elimination of a variable to solve the system

$$3a + 2b = -4$$
$$4a + 9b = 1$$

Solution Inspection of this system of equations reveals that neither of the variables will be eliminated by adding the two equations. However, we can eliminate the a variable by multiplying the first equation by 4 and the second by 3. Thus, we have

$$\begin{cases} 12a + 8b = -16 \\ 12a + 27b = 3 \end{cases}$$

Now subtracting the second equation from the first yields the equivalent system

$$\begin{cases} 12a + 8b = -16 \\ \quad -19b = -19 \end{cases}$$

Thus, $b = 1$. Substituting this value into the first of the original equations yields

$$3a + 2(1) = -4$$

Solving for a, we get

$$a = -2$$

Therefore, the desired solution is $a = -2$, $b = 1$. ■

Elimination of a Variable by Substitution

Another way to eliminate a variable from a system is to solve one of the equations for one variable in terms of the other and substitute it into the remaining equation. This method of eliminating a variable is called the **method of substitution.**

EXAMPLE 3 Solve the following system of equations by the method of substitution.

(1) $3x + 2y = 5$

(2) $x - 2y = 3$

Solution Begin with either equation, solving for either variable in terms of the other. We choose to solve the second equation for x since this choice eliminates the need for fractions. Thus, Equation 2 becomes

$$x = 2y + 3$$

Substituting this result into Equation 1, we get

$$3(2y + 3) + 2y = 5$$

Solving for y yields

$$y = -\frac{1}{2}$$

Substituting this result into Equation 2, we have

$$x = 2\left(-\frac{1}{2}\right) + 3 = 2$$

Therefore, the desired solution is $x = 2$, $y = -\frac{1}{2}$. ■

Solutions of Linear Systems

Since the linear systems presented so far have had precisely one solution, you may think that this is always the case. However, as the next example shows, a linear system can have infinitely many solutions or no solution.

EXAMPLE 4 Find the solution to each of the following linear systems.

$$\text{I}\begin{cases} x + y = 2 \\ x + 2y = 3 \end{cases} \qquad \text{II}\begin{cases} x - 2y = 6 \\ 2x - 4y = 12 \end{cases} \qquad \text{III}\begin{cases} 2x + y = 4 \\ 6x + 3y = -6 \end{cases}$$

Solution Figure 6.4 shows a sketch of each of the three systems.

The two straight lines of System I cross at (1, 1). Thus, the solution is $x = 1$, $y = 1$, which can easily be checked by direct substitution. Since the equations of System II have the same intercepts, the two lines coincide, and the solution set is the infinite set of ordered pairs given by the coordinates of the points on the line. In System III, the lines do not intersect; that is, they are parallel. Hence, the system has no solution.

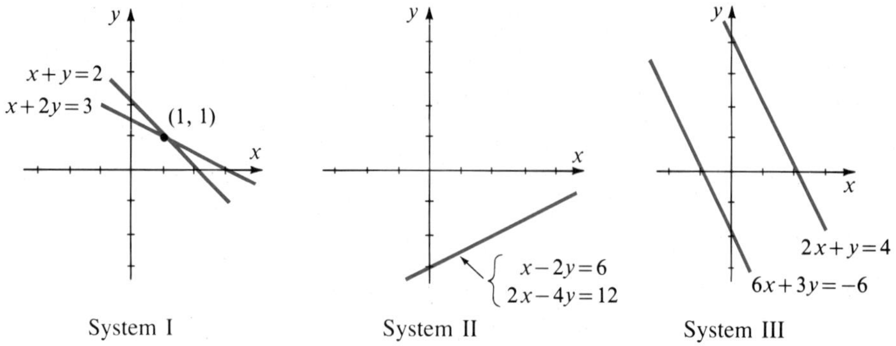

Figure 6.4

The same conclusions can be obtained by algebraic methods if we proceed as follows:

System I: Subtract the first equation from the second to obtain

$$\begin{array}{r} x + 2y = 3 \\ -x - y = -2 \\ \hline y = 1 \end{array}$$

This leads to the solution $x = 1$, $y = 1$.

System II: Multiply the first equation by -2 and add it to the second equation to get

$$\begin{array}{r} -2x + 4y = -12 \\ 2x - 4y = 12 \\ \hline 0 = 0 \end{array}$$

Since $0 = 0$ is true for all values of x and y, we conclude that this system has infinitely many solutions. Particular solutions can be obtained by letting y be a value and finding $x = 6 + 2y$. For example, if $y = -1$, $x = 6 + 2(-1) = 4$, so $(4, -1)$ is a solution.

System III: Multiply the first equation by -3 and add it to the second equation to get

$$\begin{array}{r} -6x - 3y = -12 \\ 6x + 3y = -6 \\ \hline 0 = -18 \end{array}$$

Since $0 = -18$ can never be true, we conclude that there is no solution to this system. ■

Example 4 shows the only three possibilities for linear systems of two equations in two unknowns. Since the graph of each of the equations is a straight line, one of the following statements must be true.

1. The lines intersect at one point. (The system is said to be **consistent.**)
2. The lines are parallel. (The system is said to be **inconsistent.**)
3. The lines coincide. (The system is said to be **dependent.**)

More generally, linear systems are said to be consistent, inconsistent, or dependent as their simultaneous solution sets consist of a single element, of no elements, or of infinitely many elements. *Caution:* This terminology applies only to *linear* systems.

Applications of Linear Systems

The next examples show how systems arise. There is no general technique or set of rules for converting a written problem into a system of equations. Example 5 requires a rudimentary understanding of trigonometry. (See the appendix for the basic definitions.)

EXAMPLE 5 Two observers who are 4250 feet apart measure the angle of elevation to the top of a mountain to be 18.7° and 25.3°, respectively. (See Figure 6.5.) Find the height of the mountain. The angle of elevation is the angle between a horizontal line and the line of sight when looking up at an object.

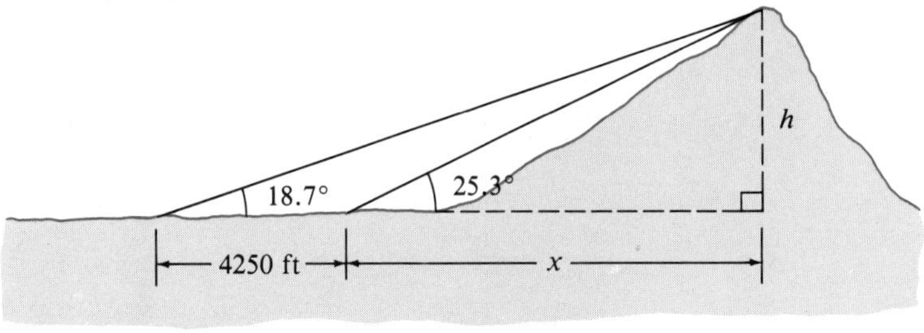

Figure 6.5

Solution From Figure 6.5 we can write the following two equations:

$$(1)\quad \tan 18.7^\circ = \frac{h}{x + 4250}$$

$$(2)\quad \tan 25.3^\circ = \frac{h}{x}$$

The only two unknowns in these two equations are x and h. Solving Equation 2 for x, we get

$$x = \frac{h}{\tan 25.3^\circ} = h \cot 25.3^\circ$$

Substituting this expression into Equation 1, we have

$$\tan 18.7^\circ = \frac{h}{h \cot 25.3^\circ + 4250}$$

To solve this equation for h, we proceed as follows:

$$(h \cot 25.3^\circ + 4250) \tan 18.7^\circ = h$$

$$h \cot 25.3^\circ \tan 18.7^\circ + 4250 \tan 18.7^\circ = h$$

$$(1 - \cot 25.3^\circ \tan 18.7^\circ)h = 4250 \tan 18.7^\circ$$

$$h = \frac{4250 \tan 18.7^\circ}{1 - \cot 25.3^\circ \tan 18.7^\circ} = \boxed{5066.421507}$$

This rounds off to 5070 to three significant figures. Thus, the top of the mountain is 5070 feet above the observers. ■

In business, the relationship between the price of an item p and the number of items purchased by the consumer in a fixed period n is called a demand function. The relationship between the price p and the number of items supplied by the producer n is called a supply function. For many business applications, we assume that supply and demand functions are linear. Figure 6.6 shows typical linear supply and demand curves drawn on the same coordinate axes. Although the graphs of supply and demand functions consist of sets of discrete points, it is common practice to treat them as continuous functions and draw their graphs as smooth curves.

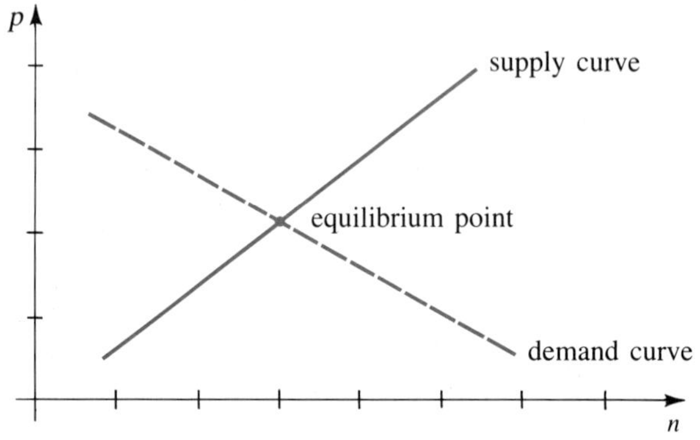

Figure 6.6

The graph shows that producers are much more willing to supply an item priced high and, conversely, consumers are more willing to buy when prices are low. This tension of the two principal market forces causes either a surplus of the item or a shortage, both undesirable. Market equilibrium results when there is no surplus or shortage. This equilibrium is represented by the point at which the supply and demand curves meet. The coordinates of the point give the equilibrium quantity and price.

EXAMPLE 6 Find the equilibrium quantity and price for a VCR market in which a group of wholesalers will buy 200 VCRs if the price is \$150 and 50 if the price is \$400, while the manufacturer will supply 50 units at \$100 and 200 units at \$300. Assume linear supply and demand functions.

Solution Letting x be the number of the items produced or supplied and p the price, we have the following chart:

Demand:	$x = 200,$	$p = 150$	Supply:	$x = 50,$	$p = 100$
	$x = 50,$	$p = 400$		$x = 200,$	$p = 300$

The equation of the demand line is obtained by using the point-slope form of a straight line.

$$\frac{p - 150}{x - 200} = \frac{400 - 150}{50 - 200} = -\frac{5}{3}$$

which may be written $3p + 5x = 1450$.

Similarly, the supply function is

$$\frac{p-100}{x-50}=\frac{300-100}{200-50}=\frac{4}{3}$$

which may be written $3p - 4x = 100$.

We solve the equations $3p + 5x = 1450$ and $3p - 4x = 100$ simultaneously by taking the negative of the second equation and adding it to the first:

$$9x = 1350$$
$$x = 150$$

which is the equilibrium number of VCRs to be supplied (and demanded). The corresponding price is obtained by substituting 150 for x in either of the two equations to obtain $p = \$233$, which is the equilibrium price. ■

EXAMPLE 7 A chemist has two acid solutions, one containing 10% acid and the other 4% acid. See Figure 6.7. How many liters of each solution are needed to make 200 liters of a solution that is 6% acid?

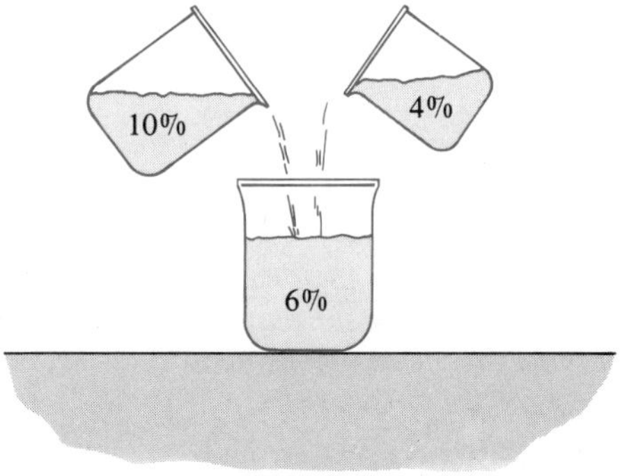

Figure 6.7

Solution Let x = the number of liters of 10% acid solution and let y = the number of liters of 4% acid solution. Since the amount of the 10% solution plus the amount of the 4% solution must equal 200 liters, we have the following equation:

$$(1)\quad x + y = 200$$

A second equation is generated by observing that the amount of acid in x liters of the 10% solution is $0.10x$, the amount of acid in y liters of the 4% solution is $0.04y$, and the amount of acid in the final 6% solution is $200(0.06) = 12$. Since the amount of acid from the two sources must equal the amount of acid in the final solution, we write the following equation:

$$(2)\quad 0.10x + 0.04y = 12$$

The solution to this system of equations is found by solving Equation 1 for y and substituting the result into Equation 2. Thus,

$$0.10x + 0.04(200 - x) = 12$$
$$0.10x + 8 - 0.04x = 12$$
$$x = 66\tfrac{2}{3} \text{ liters}$$

From Equation 1, we get $y = 133\frac{1}{3}$ liters. ■

Exercises Section 6.1

Solve the systems of equations in Exercises 1–14 by the method of elimination of a variable by addition or subtraction. Indicate whether the system is consistent, inconsistent, or dependent. In each case, draw the graph of the system.

1. $2x - 4y = 2$
$-2x + y = 4$

2. $x + 5y = 4$
$x + 3y = 6$

3. $3x + 4y = 23$
$x - 3y = -1$

4. $x + y = 4$
$x - y = 2$

5. $x - 4y = 8$
$2x - 8y = 16$

6. $3x + 2y - 6 = 0$
$x - 3y - 3 = 0$

7. $3x + 4y = 10$
$6x + 8y = -2$

8. $3x + 5y = 2$
$6x + 10y = 4$

9. $3x - y = 2$
$2x + y = 6$

10. $2x + 3y = 7$
$6x - y = 1$

11. $3x + y = 0$
$2x - 2y = 2$

12. $x + 5y = 0$
$3x + 15y = 3$

13. $x + 7y - 7 = 0$
$8x - 7y - 3 = 0$

14. $3x + 5y = 4$
$\frac{3}{2}x + \frac{5}{2}y = 2$

Solve the systems of equations in Exercises 15–29 by the method of elimination of a variable by substitution. Indicate whether the system is consistent, inconsistent, or dependent.

15. $r - s = 3$
$r - 2s = 5$

16. $2x - y - 2 = 0$
$x + y + 5 = 0$

17. $x + 3y = 7$
$2x + 6y = 9$

18. $2s - t = 5$
$6s + 2t = -5$

19. $5y - x = 2$
$2y + 3x = 11$

20. $x + y = 8$
$-19x + 8y = 10$

21. $4x + 5y = -6$
$3x - 2y = -16$

22. $4x = 10 - 5y$
$7x = 41 + 3y$

23. $6x - 8y = 14$
$3x - 4y = 7$

24. $4x + 3y - 6 = 0$
$2x + 5y + 4 = 0$

25. $3x + 5y = 5$
$x + 4y = 11$

26. $4x - 7y = 29$
$6x + 5y = -3$

27. $9z - 13w + 3 = 0$
$6z - 7w = 3$

28. $5x + 4y = 0$
$3x + 5y + 13 = 0$

29. $2x + 3y = -10$
$3x - 2y = -2$

In the remainder of this exercise set, use the most convenient method of eliminating variables to solve the systems of equations.

30. The velocity-time equation of car A is $v = 3t + 20$ ft/sec, where t is the time in seconds. If the velocity-time equation for car B is $v = 6t + 5$ ft/sec, at what time do both cars have the same velocity? What is this velocity?

31. A company buys a total of 25 grinders from two different companies. It buys 3 more Brand A grinders than Brand B. The total number of each brand of grinder can be found by solving the system of equations

$$A + B = 25$$
$$A - B = 3$$

Can you explain how these equations are derived? Solve for A and B.

32. The sum of the tens digit and the units digit of a two-digit number is 11. The value of the number is seven less than 30 times the units digit. Find the number.

33. The sum of two numbers is 12 and the difference is 4. Find the two numbers.

34. Some 20-lb containers and 30-lb containers are used to load 160 lb of salt. The number of 20-lb containers is one more than twice the number of 30-lb containers. How many of each kind of container are used?

35. The graph of $ax + by^2 = 2$ passes through the points $(4, -2)$ and $(-2, 2)$. Determine the coefficients a and b.

36. The resistance of a wire is given by $R = aT + K$, where a and K are constants and T is the temperature in degrees Celsius. Find a and K if $R = 25$ ohms when $T = 10°$ C and $R = 30$ ohms when $T = 100°$ C.

37. A boat travels 60 mi upstream in 10 hr. If it returns in 8 hr, find the rate of the current and the boat. Assume that both rates are constant during the trip.

38. A truck enters a freeway traveling 50 mph. One hour later a car enters the freeway by the same ramp traveling 80 mph. How long does it take for the car to overtake the truck?

39. A technician needs 10 lb of an alloy that is 60% lead and 40% zinc by weight. If she has an alloy that is 80% lead and 20% zinc and another that is 50% lead and 50% zinc, how many pounds of each must she use to obtain the desired alloy?

40. Two water pipes running at the same time can fill a swimming pool in 6 hr. If both pipes run for 2 hr and the first is then shut off, the second pipe will take 5 hr more to fill the pool. How long does it take each pipe to fill the pool by itself?

41. A collection of nickels and dimes amounts to \$2.50. If there are 35 coins in all, find the number of dimes.

42. An airplane flying with a tail wind takes 2 hr to make a trip of 1240 mi. If the return trip against the wind takes 2.5 hr, what is the speed of the airplane relative to the air? What is the wind speed?

43. Two computers can complete a series of calculations in 10 min when they are used together. After 6 min, one of the computers breaks down and the other takes 9 min to finish the job. How long does it take for each computer to do the series of calculations working alone?

44. A fishing boat sailing due north sites a lighthouse as 16.2° east of north. If 12.7 miles later the lighthouse is sited as 43.7° east of north, how close will the boat come to the lighthouse?

45. An observer at the base of a hill knows that the television antenna on top of the hill is 550 ft high. If the angle of elevation from the observer to the base of the antenna is 16.4° and to the top of the antenna is 29.1°, how high is the hill?

46. A manufacturer will supply an item as follows: 10 if the price is \$50; 40 if it is \$100. The corresponding demand is 250 if the price is \$25 and 50 if it is \$125. Assume that the supply and demand functions are linear.

a. Write the supply function.

b. Write the demand function.

c. Determine the equilibrium amount and price.

47. A group of wholesalers will buy 100 television sets if the price is \$400 each and 150 if it is \$250. The manufacturer is willing to supply 75 sets at a price of \$300 each or 150 sets at \$350 each. Write the linear supply and demand functions and determine the equilibrium values.

48. A small video store rents movies at \$3 per movie. Its monthly revenue function is therefore $R(x) = 3x$ where x is the number of movies rented in a month's time. Its cost function is $C(x) = 1600 + x$. Graph the revenue and cost functions on the same axes. What does the point of intersection represent? What are those values?

6.2 Nonlinear Systems

Sometimes the process of elimination of a variable can be used for systems of nonlinear equations, too. The approach is basically the same as that for systems of linear equations.

EXAMPLE 1 Solve the system

$$2x - y = 4$$
$$x^2 - y = 4$$

by the method of substitution.

Solution Solving the linear equation for y, we get

$$y = 2x - 4$$

Substituting into the quadratic yields

$$x^2 - (2x - 4) = 4$$

Expanding and collecting like terms, we have

$$x^2 - 2x = 0$$
$$x(x - 2) = 0$$

from which $x = 0$ and $x = 2$. Substituting these values into the given linear equation, we have $x = 0$, $y = -4$ and $x = 2$, $y = 0$ as the solutions. A picture of the system is shown in Figure 6.8.

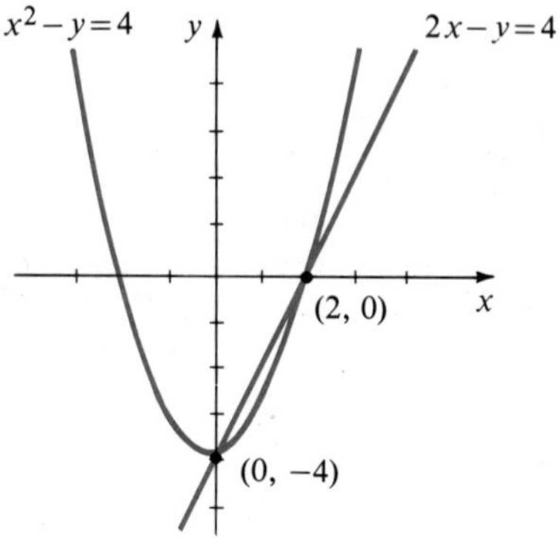

Figure 6.8

■

EXAMPLE 2 Solve the system

$$x^2 + y^2 = 4$$
$$x^2 + 4y^2 = 8$$

Solution Multiplying the first of these equations by -1 and adding gives $3y^2 = 4$, from which

$$y = \pm\frac{2}{\sqrt{3}} = \pm\frac{2\sqrt{3}}{3}$$

Using this in the first equation, we get

$$x^2 = 4 - \frac{4}{3} = \frac{8}{3}$$

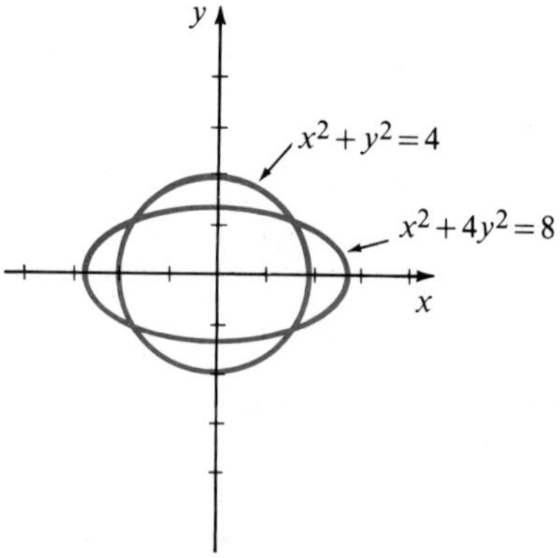

Figure 6.9

from which

$$x = \pm\sqrt{\frac{8}{3}} = \pm\frac{2\sqrt{6}}{3}$$

The solution set consists of the four ordered pairs

$$\left(\frac{2\sqrt{6}}{3}, \frac{2\sqrt{3}}{3}\right), \left(\frac{2\sqrt{6}}{3}, \frac{-2\sqrt{3}}{3}\right), \left(\frac{-2\sqrt{6}}{3}, \frac{2\sqrt{3}}{3}\right), \left(\frac{-2\sqrt{6}}{3}, \frac{-2\sqrt{3}}{3}\right)$$

The graph of this system is shown in Figure 6.9, in which you can see the four points of intersection corresponding to the four ordered pairs of the solution set. ■

EXAMPLE 3 Solve the system

$$2x + y = 3$$
$$x^2 + y + x = 2$$

Solution Solving the first equation for y and substituting into the second, we have

$$x^2 + (3 - 2x) + x = 2$$

or

$$x^2 - x + 1 = 0$$

Using the quadratic formula, we get

$$x = \frac{1 \pm \sqrt{-3}}{2}$$

which is not real. Therefore, we conclude that there is no real solution to this system. ■

Exercises Section 6.2

Solve the nonlinear systems of Exercises 1–11. In each case, sketch both equations of the system showing graphically the simultaneous solution.

1. $y - x = 0$, $y - x^2 = 0$
2. $x - x^2 + y = 0$, $x - y + 3 = 0$
3. $x^2 - x - y = -1$, $x - y = 0$
4. $x^2 - 3x - y = -2$, $x - y = 1$
5. $2x - y = 1$, $2x^2 + x - y = 1$
6. $x + y = 0$, $-y + x^2 + 3x = -3$
7. $x + 2y = 3$, $x^2 + y + x = 0$
8. $x - y + 2 = 0$, $2x^2 + 3y - 2 = 0$
9. $2x + y - 5 = 0$, $x^2 - y + 3 = 0$
10. $x^2 - 4x + y = 2$, $2x - y = 2$
11. $x^2 - y - 4 = 0$, $2y + x^2 = 1$

Solve the nonlinear systems given in Exercises 12–32 for all *real* simultaneous solutions.

12. $x^2 + y^2 = 1$, $x^2 - y^2 = 1$
13. $x^2 + y^2 = 4$, $4x^2 + y^2 = 4$
14. $2x^2 + 3y^2 = 4$, $x^2 + 2y^2 = 10$
15. $x^2 + 4y^2 = 2$, $x^2 - y^2 = 3$
16. $x^2 + y^2 = 1$, $x^2 + 2y^2 = 2$
17. $x^2 + y^2 = 1$, $2x^2 - y^2 = 2$
18. $2y^2 + x^2 = 9$, $y^2 = x^2 + 3$
19. $y - x = 1$, $x^2 - y^2 = 10$
20. $x^2 - 4y^2 = 25$, $x - 2y = -1$
21. $y^2 + 2x^2 = 2$, $x^2 + y^2 = 2$
22. $y - x^2 = 2$, $x^2 + y = 10$
23. $2a^2 - 4b^2 = 7$, $a^2 + 2b^2 = 3$
24. $xy = 4$, $2x + y = 0$
25. $ab = 16$, $a - b = 0$
26. $x^2 + 4y^2 = 1$, $4x^2 + y^2 = 1$
27. $xy = 1$, $x^2 + y^2 = 1$

28. $x^2 - y^2 = 1$
$\quad xy = 1$

29. $x^2 + y^2 = 16$
$\quad y = 2$

30. $x + y = 7$
$\quad x^2 + y = 4$

31. $x + y = 1$
$\quad x^2 - y^2 = 1$

32. $x^2 - y^2 = 1$
$\quad y^2 - x^2 = 1$

33. Two integers have a sum of 30 and a product of 225. Find the integers.

34. The area of a field is 540 sq yd with a perimeter of 128 yd. Find the dimensions of the field.

35. If the supply function for a commodity is $p = x + 6$ and the corresponding demand function is $p = 208/(x + 3)$, determine the market equilibrium. (See Example 6 of Section 6.1.)

36. If the supply function of a commodity is $p = x^2 + 4$ and the corresponding demand function is $p = 36 - x^2$, determine the market equilibrium. (See Example 6 of Section 6.1.)

6.3 Higher-Order Linear Systems: Matrix Notation

Matrices

Groupings of numbers such as

$$\begin{array}{c} 7 \\ 8 \\ 3 \\ -1 \end{array} \qquad \begin{array}{ccccc} & & 4 & & \\ & 2 & & -1 & \\ 7 & & 6 & & 0 \end{array} \qquad \begin{array}{cccc} 2 & 3 & 5 & 2 \\ 6 & 7 & 8 & 9 \\ 3 & -2 & 0 & 6 \end{array}$$

(a) (b) (c)

are called **arrays.** A rectangular array is called a **matrix.** Thus, of the arrays above, only (a) and (c) are matrices. A matrix has no numerical *value,* but is a notation for conveniently listing or cataloging numbers. In fact, applications of matrices range from use as a filing system to the solution of large systems of equations.

The **dimension** of a matrix is indicated by giving the number of rows followed by the number of columns. Thus, an $m \times n$ (read "m by n") matrix is a rectangular array having m rows and n columns. A rectangular array of $m \times n$ and one of $n \times m$ are not considered to be the same size unless $m = n$.

Of the preceding arrays, the first is a 4×1 matrix, the second is nonrectangular and thus not a matrix, and the third is a 3×4 matrix. We denote matrices by capital letters and display them by enclosing them in brackets. Thus,

$$A = \begin{bmatrix} 7 \\ 8 \\ 3 \\ -1 \end{bmatrix} \quad \text{and} \quad B = \begin{bmatrix} 2 & 3 & 5 & 2 \\ 6 & 7 & 8 & 9 \\ 3 & -2 & 0 & 6 \end{bmatrix}$$

describe the two matrices mentioned earlier.

A **square matrix** has the same number of rows and columns. In this case the number of rows (or columns) is called the **order** of the matrix. Thus,

$$\begin{bmatrix} 2 & 1 \\ 0 & -3 \end{bmatrix} \quad \text{and} \quad \begin{bmatrix} 0 & 5 & -2 \\ 2 & 3 & 0 \\ -1 & 7 & 9 \end{bmatrix}$$

are matrices of orders 2 and 3, respectively.

The theory of matrices includes the study of the algebraic operations between two or more matrices. However, in this section our study of matrices will be restricted to showing how they are used to describe and solve linear systems of equations.

Higher-Order Linear Systems

An equation of the form $ax + by + cz = d$ is called a linear equation in three variables x, y, and z, where a, b, c, and d are constants. A *solution* to this equation is an ordered triple of numbers corresponding to values of x, y, and z that make the equation true. A *system* of three linear equations in three unknowns will be of the form

$$\begin{aligned} a_1x + b_1y + c_1z &= d_1 \\ a_2x + b_2y + c_2z &= d_2 \\ a_3x + b_3y + c_3z &= d_3 \end{aligned}$$

A *solution* to such a system is any ordered triple that simultaneously satisfies each equation of the system.

The technique of Gaussian elimination used for solving systems of two equations can be used for higher-order systems. For example, consider a system of three linear equations. Choose any pair of equations and eliminate one of the variables by one of the standard techniques, usually by adding multiples of two of the equations together. This yields an equivalent equation in two variables. Now eliminate the same variable in a different pair of equations. In this way the original three equations are essentially reduced to two linear equations in two variables—a system we know how to solve.

As with systems of two linear equations, higher-order linear systems are

- **Consistent** if there is a unique simultaneous solution.
- **Inconsistent** if there is no simultaneous solution.
- **Dependent** if there are infinitely many simultaneous solutions.

When a third-order system in the variables x, y, and z has been reduced to an equivalent system in which the third equation involves only the z variable, and the second equation involves only the y and perhaps the z variables, the system is said to be in **triangular** form. An example of a system in triangular form is

$$\begin{aligned} x - 6y + 3z &= -2 \\ 9y - 5z &= 2 \\ z &= 5 \end{aligned}$$

A system in triangular form is easy to solve for x, y, and z. Thus, it is clear that $z = 5$. Substituting $z = 5$ into the second equation $9y - 5z = 2$ yields $y = 3$. Finally, substituting $z = 5$ and $y = 3$ into $x - 6y + 3z = -2$, we get $x = 1$. The next example shows how to use Gaussian elimination to reduce a linear system to triangular form.

EXAMPLE 1 Use Gaussian elimination to reduce the system to triangular form. Solve the system

$$\begin{aligned} x - 6y + 3z &= -2 \\ 2x - 3y + z &= -2 \\ 3x + 3y - 2z &= 2 \end{aligned}$$

Solution Since the manipulations required to reduce three equations to triangular form are more involved than for two equations, we introduce special notation.

First label each equation in the system. For instance, suppose we number the equations in the given system.

$$\begin{aligned} &① \quad x - 6y + 3z = -2 \\ &② \quad 2x - 3y + z = -2 \\ &③ \quad 3x + 3y - 2z = 2 \end{aligned}$$

Then, the notation

$$a① + ② \rightarrow ②$$

means "multiply Equation ① by a, add it to Equation ②, and replace Equation ② with this sum." Notice that this transformation affects only Equation ②, while Equations ① and ③ are unaltered. We show the use of this notation in the context of the given system.

$$\left.\begin{aligned} x - 6y + 3z &= -2 \\ 2x - 3y + z &= -2 \\ 3x + 3y - 2z &= 2 \end{aligned}\right\} \xrightarrow{-2① + ② \rightarrow ②} \left.\begin{aligned} x - 6y + 3z &= -2 \\ 9y - 5z &= 2 \\ 3x + 3y - 2z &= 2 \end{aligned}\right\} \xrightarrow{-3① + ③ \rightarrow ③}$$

$$\left.\begin{aligned} x - 6y + 3z &= -2 \\ 9y - 5z &= 2 \\ 21y - 11z &= 8 \end{aligned}\right\} \xrightarrow{-\frac{7}{3}② + ③ \rightarrow ③} \left.\begin{aligned} x - 6y + 3z &= -2 \\ 9y - 5z &= 2 \\ \frac{2}{3}z &= \frac{10}{3} \end{aligned}\right\}$$

From Equation ③ of the triangular form, we get $z = 5$. Substituting $z = 5$ in $9y - 5z = 2$ yields $y = 3$. Finally, substituting $y = 3$ and $z = 5$ in $x - 6y + 3z = -2$, we get $x = 1$. Hence, the solution is $x = 1$, $y = 3$, $z = 5$. ■

The Augmented Matrix

The effort required to reduce a linear system to triangular form can be simplified if we avoid the needless rewriting of variables. We easily eliminate the variable names by using a matrix to keep track of the coefficients of a system. For example, the system in Example 1 can be represented by the matrix

$$\left[\begin{array}{rrr|r} 1 & -6 & 3 & -2 \\ 2 & -3 & 1 & -2 \\ 3 & 3 & -2 & 2 \end{array}\right]$$

This matrix is called the **matrix of the system,** or the **augmented matrix.** We have inserted the dashed line to emphasize the matrix of the coefficients of the variables, which alone is called the **coefficient matrix.** Notice that *the form of the augmented matrix assumes that each equation in the system is written in the form* $ax + by +$

$cz = d$. If an equation of a system is not given in this form, it must be so written before it can be used in the augmented matrix.

Once the matrix of a system of equations is written, we treat the rows of the matrix just as we treat the equations they represent. Of course, we must make a mental note that the numbers in the first column represent the coefficients of x; those in the second column, the coefficients of y; and those in the third column, the coefficients of z.

A system of equations written in matrix form is solved using the same operations as in the method of Gaussian elimination. The use of *equivalent matrices* corresponds to equivalent systems.

Operations on Matrices

Two matrices are equivalent if

1. The position of any two rows is interchanged.
2. A row of one matrix is a nonzero multiple of the other.
3. A row of one matrix is the sum of two rows of the other.

The following examples show the use of the method of elimination along with matrix notation to solve a system of equations.

EXAMPLE 2 Use matrix notation to solve the system

$$\begin{aligned} 3x + 2y &= 10 \\ x - 3y &= -4 \end{aligned}$$

Solution This system is represented by the matrix

$$\left[\begin{array}{rr|r} 3 & 2 & 10 \\ 1 & -3 & -4 \end{array}\right]$$

The following transformation yields the desired solution.

$$\left[\begin{array}{rr|r} 3 & 2 & 10 \\ 1 & -3 & -4 \end{array}\right] \xrightarrow{①-3②\to②} \left[\begin{array}{rr|r} 3 & 2 & 10 \\ 0 & 11 & 22 \end{array}\right]$$

The resulting matrix is the matrix for the system

$$\begin{aligned} 3x + 2y &= 10 \\ 11y &= 22 \end{aligned}$$

We get $y = 2$ from the equation $11y = 22$. Substituting $y = 2$ into $3x + 2y = 10$, we get $x = 2$. The solution is then $x = 2$, $y = 2$. ■

Comment: Notice in Example 2 that row ① remained unchanged although we used it to operate on row ②. In this case, we call line ① the *operative line* of the operation. In matrices of three or more rows, we can perform more than one operation at a time *provided* that the operative line is the same for all uses of the operation. This is shown in the next example.

EXAMPLE 3 Use matrix notation to solve the system

$$\begin{aligned} x - 6y + 3z &= -2 \\ 2x - 3y + z &= -2 \\ 3x + 3y - 2z &= 2 \end{aligned}$$

This is the same system that was solved in Example 1 of this section.

Solution The given system is represented by the augmented matrix

$$\left[\begin{array}{ccc|c} 1 & -6 & 3 & -2 \\ 2 & -3 & 1 & -2 \\ 3 & 3 & -2 & 2 \end{array}\right]$$

The following steps yield the desired form.

$$\left[\begin{array}{ccc|c} 1 & -6 & 3 & -2 \\ 2 & -3 & 1 & -2 \\ 3 & 3 & -2 & 2 \end{array}\right] \xrightarrow[(-3)①+③\to③]{(-2)①+②\to②} \left[\begin{array}{ccc|c} 1 & -6 & 3 & -2 \\ 0 & 9 & -5 & 2 \\ 0 & 21 & -11 & 8 \end{array}\right]$$

$$\xrightarrow{7②-3③\to③} \left[\begin{array}{ccc|c} 1 & -6 & 3 & -2 \\ 0 & 9 & -5 & 2 \\ 0 & 0 & -2 & -10 \end{array}\right]$$

Notice that this is the matrix of the triangular form of the given system; that is,

$$\begin{aligned} x - 6y + 3z &= -2 \\ 9y - 5z &= 2 \\ -2z &= -10 \end{aligned}$$

Solving the last equation, we get $z = 5$. Substituting $z = 5$ into the middle equation yields $y = 3$. Finally, we find that $x = 1$ by substituting $y = 3$ and $z = 5$ into the upper equation. The solution $x = 1$, $y = 3$, $z = 5$ agrees with that in Example 1. ■

EXAMPLE 4 Solve the system

$$\begin{aligned} x + y - z &= -1 \\ 2x - y + z &= 2 \\ x - 5y + 5z &= 7 \end{aligned}$$

Solution The given system is represented by the augmented matrix

$$\left[\begin{array}{ccc|c} 1 & 1 & -1 & -1 \\ 2 & -1 & 1 & 2 \\ 1 & -5 & 5 & 7 \end{array}\right]$$

The following steps lead to the solution.

$$\left[\begin{array}{ccc|c} 1 & 1 & -1 & -1 \\ 2 & -1 & 1 & 2 \\ 1 & -5 & 5 & 7 \end{array}\right] \xrightarrow[(-1)①+③\to③]{(-2)①+②\to②} \left[\begin{array}{ccc|c} 1 & 1 & -1 & -1 \\ 0 & -3 & 3 & 4 \\ 0 & -6 & 6 & 8 \end{array}\right]$$

$$\xrightarrow{(-2)②+③\to③} \left[\begin{array}{ccc|c} 1 & 1 & -1 & -1 \\ 0 & -3 & 3 & 4 \\ 0 & 0 & 0 & 0 \end{array}\right]$$

The third row of all zeros shows that x, y, and z are related only by the equations that the first two rows represent. The system is therefore *dependent*. Any of the infinitely many solutions may be found by assigning a value to z and solving for x and y. For example, if we let $z = 1$, then $x = \frac{1}{3}$ and $y = -\frac{1}{3}$. If $z = 0$, then $x = \frac{1}{3}$ and $y = -\frac{4}{3}$. In general, if $z = c$, the second row yields $y = c - \frac{4}{3}$ and the first row yields $x = \frac{1}{3}$. ■

EXAMPLE 5 Solve the system

$$\begin{aligned} x - y + z &= 8 \\ 2x + y - z &= -2 \\ -x - 5y + 5z &= 10 \end{aligned}$$

Solution The augmented matrix of the system is

$$\left[\begin{array}{rrr|r} 1 & -1 & 1 & 8 \\ 2 & 1 & -1 & -2 \\ -1 & -5 & 5 & 10 \end{array}\right]$$

The reduction of this matrix to triangular form follows.

$$\left[\begin{array}{rrr|r} 1 & -1 & 1 & 8 \\ 2 & 1 & -1 & -2 \\ -1 & -5 & 5 & 10 \end{array}\right] \xrightarrow[\textcircled{1} + \textcircled{3} \to \textcircled{3}]{(-2)\textcircled{1} + \textcircled{2} \to \textcircled{2}} \left[\begin{array}{rrr|r} 1 & -1 & 1 & 8 \\ 0 & 3 & -3 & -18 \\ 0 & -6 & 6 & 18 \end{array}\right]$$

$$\xrightarrow{(2)\textcircled{2} + \textcircled{3} \to \textcircled{3}} \left[\begin{array}{rrr|r} 1 & -1 & 1 & 8 \\ 0 & 3 & -3 & -18 \\ 0 & 0 & 0 & -18 \end{array}\right]$$

The last row represents

$$0x + 0y + 0z = -18$$

which is impossible for any x, y, and z. Hence, the system is inconsistent. ■

The matrix method can be used for linear systems of any order. The following example is typical for fourth-order systems.

EXAMPLE 6 Solve the system

$$\begin{aligned} x - y + 2z + w &= -3 \\ 2x + y - 3z - w &= 4 \\ 4x + 3y - z + 2w &= 9 \\ 3x - y + 5z - 2w &= -9 \end{aligned}$$

Solution This system is represented by the augmented matrix

$$\left[\begin{array}{rrrr|r} 1 & -1 & 2 & 1 & -3 \\ 2 & 1 & -3 & -1 & 4 \\ 4 & 3 & -1 & 2 & 9 \\ 3 & -1 & 5 & -2 & -9 \end{array}\right]$$

The following sequence of operations leads to the solution.

$$\left[\begin{array}{cccc|c} 1 & -1 & 2 & 1 & -3 \\ 2 & 1 & -3 & -1 & 4 \\ 4 & 3 & -1 & 2 & 9 \\ 3 & -1 & 5 & -2 & -9 \end{array}\right] \xrightarrow[\substack{-3(1)+(4)\to(4)}]{\substack{-2(1)+(2)\to(2)\\ -4(1)+(3)\to(3)}}$$

$$\left[\begin{array}{cccc|c} 1 & -1 & 2 & 1 & -3 \\ 0 & 3 & -7 & -3 & 10 \\ 0 & 7 & -9 & -2 & 21 \\ 0 & 2 & -1 & -5 & 0 \end{array}\right] \xrightarrow[\substack{-\frac{2}{3}(2)+(4)\to(4)}]{\substack{-\frac{7}{3}(2)+(3)\to(3)}}$$

$$\left[\begin{array}{cccc|c} 1 & -1 & 2 & 1 & -3 \\ 0 & 3 & -7 & -3 & 10 \\ 0 & 0 & \frac{22}{3} & 5 & -\frac{7}{3} \\ 0 & 0 & \frac{11}{3} & -3 & -\frac{20}{3} \end{array}\right] \xrightarrow{-\frac{1}{2}(3)+(4)\to(4)} \left[\begin{array}{cccc|c} 1 & -1 & 2 & 1 & -3 \\ 0 & 3 & -7 & -3 & 10 \\ 0 & 0 & \frac{22}{3} & 5 & -\frac{7}{3} \\ 0 & 0 & 0 & -\frac{11}{2} & -\frac{11}{2} \end{array}\right]$$

The last row gives the solution $w = 1$. If we use this value for w, the third row yields $z = -1$. Continuing, we get $y = 2$ and $x = 0$. ■

Comment: In each of the preceding examples, we use a triangular form in which the zeros are below the main diagonal. We could just as easily have used a triangular form with the zeros above the main diagonal. Either way, the solution is the same.

Exercises Section 6.3

In Exercises 1–20, use matrix notation to determine if the given linear system is consistent, dependent, or inconsistent. If the system is consistent, give the unique solution.

1. $x + 2y = 10$
$x - 2y = -6$

2. $5x + 2y = 6$
$3x + 4y = 12$

3. $3x - y = 5$
$x + 4y = 6$

4. $x - 2y + z = 3$
$2x + y - z = 7$
$3x - y + 2z = 6$

5. $8x + 5y = 4$
$5y - 3z = 1$
$12x + 5z = 6$

6. $2x + y - z = 2$
$x - y + z = 4$
$y - z = -2$

7. $3x + 5y - 3z = 31$
$2x - 3y + 2z = 13$
$5x + 2y - 5z = 20$

8. $-x + 3y - z = 0$
$2x + y + 2z = 2$
$-x + 7y - z = -2$

9. $2x - 5z = 2$
$9y - 4z = 7$
$3x - 12y = -2$

10. $x - 2y + z = 7$
$2x + 3z = 4$
$y + 2z = 1$

11. $x + y + 2z = 3$
$3x - y - z = 1$
$x + 5y + 9z = 11$

12. $6x - 8y + 3z = -5$
$15x + 12y + 7z = 12$
$9x + 20y - 4z = 25$

13. $2x + y - z = 9$
$x - y + z = 0$
$-x + 3y - 2z = 5$

14. $x + 2y - z = 1$
$y + z = 3$
$x - y = 2$

15. $x - y = 2$
$y - z = -3$
$3x + 2y - 5z = 1$

16. $x - 2y + 3z = 7$
$2x - y - z = -4$
$-x + 3y - 4z = -5$

17. $x - 3y + 2z = 0$
$2x + y - z = -3$
$10x - 2y = -12$

18. $-x - 2y + z = -7$
$x - 3y + 4z = 2$
$2x - 5y - 7z = 5$

19. $x + y + z = 3$
$x - 2y - 3z = 4$
$2x + y + 2z = 9$

20. $3x + y - 2z = 0$
$x - y + z = 1$
$-2x + 6y - 7z = -2$

The systems in Exercises 21–24 are consistent. Find their unique solution by using matrix methods.

21. $$\begin{aligned} 3x - 2y + z + w &= 10 \\ x + y - z - w &= -5 \\ 2x + y + z + 5w &= 18 \\ -x - 2y + 5z - 2w &= 5 \end{aligned}$$

22. $$\begin{aligned} 2x - 5y + z - w &= -5 \\ x + 4y - z - 2w &= -7 \\ -x - 7y + 3z + w &= -5 \\ -3x + 8y - 6z - 3w &= -6 \end{aligned}$$

23. $$\begin{aligned} 3x + y + z - w &= -2 \\ -5x + 2y - 3z - 3w &= -1 \\ 7x + 5y + 4z - w &= -1 \\ 4x - y - 2z + 3w &= 7 \end{aligned}$$

24. $$\begin{aligned} 2x + 5y - 2z + w &= -11 \\ x - 8y - z + 3w &= -18 \\ -3x - 9y + 3z + 2w &= -1 \\ 6x + 7y + 5z + 8w &= 8 \end{aligned}$$

In the remaining problems, obtain the system of equations from the statement of the problem.

25. The total number of nickels, dimes, and quarters in a box is 900. There are 20 more nickels than there are dimes and the number of nickels and dimes together is 44 more than the number of quarters. How many coins of each denomination are in the box?

26. A triangle has a perimeter of 50 in. The longest side is 3 in. longer than the next longest and 10 in. longer than the shortest. Find the length of each side.

27. A company runs three production lines that together have an output of 45 parts/hr. Twice the production of the first line is equal to the sum of the other two lines, and the output of the second line is four parts per hour more than the third line. Find the production rate of each line.

28. A laboratory produces an alloy of copper, tin, and zinc having a weight of 37 g. If the copper in the alloy weighs 3 g more than the zinc and the zinc weighs 8 g more than the tin, how much of each element is in the alloy?

6.4 The Algebra of Matrices

The concept of a matrix was introduced in the previous section in connection with systems of linear equations. There are additional applications of matrices, but before we discuss them we must become familiar with matrix algebra. For convenience, we restate the definition of a matrix.

Definition

Matrix

A **matrix** is a rectangular array of numbers.

We denote matrices by capital letters and display them by enclosing the array in square brackets. The **dimensions** of a matrix are indicated by the number of rows and the number of columns in the array. We specify the number of rows first, followed by the number of columns. Thus, an $m \times n$ (read "m by n") matrix has m rows and n columns.

EXAMPLE 1 $A = \begin{bmatrix} 2 & 1 & -1 \\ 3 & 0 & 4 \end{bmatrix}$ is a 2×3 matrix. $B = \begin{bmatrix} 0 & 0 & 1 \\ 1 & 0 & 1 \\ 0 & -1 & 0 \\ 1 & 1 & 1 \\ 1 & 0 & 0 \end{bmatrix}$ is a 5×3 matrix. ■

If a matrix has only one row, it is called a **row matrix;** if a matrix has only one column, it is called a **column matrix.** As we noted in Section 6.3, a matrix that has the same number of rows or columns is called a **square matrix.** For a square matrix, the number of rows and columns is called the **order** of the matrix. If all the entries in a matrix are zeros, the matrix is called the **zero matrix** and is denoted by **0.**

To identify specific entries, or elements, within a matrix, we use a lower-case letter with a double subscript to indicate each element's row and column location. The first number of the subscript refers to the row location and the second to the column location. Thus, the notation a_{ij} means the element in the ith row and the jth column of the matrix A. The following 3×4 matrix shows how this notation is used:

$$A = \begin{bmatrix} a_{11} & a_{12} & a_{13} & a_{14} \\ a_{21} & a_{22} & a_{23} & a_{24} \\ a_{31} & a_{32} & a_{33} & a_{34} \end{bmatrix}$$

Elements such as a_{11}, a_{22}, and a_{33}, which have the same row and column number, are called **main diagonal elements.**

We also write the matrix A as

$$A = [\, a_{ij} \,]$$

where i is the row and j is the column.

Two matrices are equal if they have the same order or dimensions and if their corresponding elements are equal. We formalize the equality of matrices in the following definition.

Definition

Equality of Matrices

The $m \times n$ matrices A and B are **equal** if

$$a_{ij} = b_{ij}$$

for $i = 1$ to m and $j = 1$ to n.

EXAMPLE 2 a. The following matrices are equal:

$$\begin{bmatrix} 2 & 1 \\ -1 & 7 \end{bmatrix} = \begin{bmatrix} \sqrt{4} & 1 \\ -1 & \frac{21}{3} \end{bmatrix}$$

b. The following matrices have the same dimensions but are *not* equal:

$$\begin{bmatrix} 3 & 5 & 0 \\ 2 & 3 & -2 \end{bmatrix} \neq \begin{bmatrix} 3 & 5 & 7 \\ 2 & 1 & -2 \end{bmatrix}$$

■

Two matrices can be added together if they have the same dimensions. The sum of two matrices having the same dimensions is defined as follows.

Definition

Matrix Addition

If A and B are $m \times n$ matrices, then $C = A + B$ is given by

$$c_{ij} = a_{ij} + b_{ij}$$

for $i = 1$ to m and $j = 1$ to n.

EXAMPLE 3 a. $\begin{bmatrix} 2 & 5 \\ -3 & 1 \end{bmatrix} + \begin{bmatrix} -2 & 2 \\ 1 & 0 \end{bmatrix} = \begin{bmatrix} 2+(-2) & 5+2 \\ -3+1 & 1+0 \end{bmatrix} = \begin{bmatrix} 0 & 7 \\ -2 & 1 \end{bmatrix}$

b. $\begin{bmatrix} 3 & 1 \\ -2 & 4 \end{bmatrix} + \begin{bmatrix} 5 \\ 2 \end{bmatrix}$ is undefined because the dimensions of these matrices are not the same. ■

The operation of multiplying each element of a matrix A by a number c is called **scalar multiplication.** The next definition describes the process.

Definition

Scalar Multiplication

If A is an $m \times n$ matrix and c is a real number, then the **scalar multiplication** of A by c is denoted by cA and given by

$$cA = [\, ca_{ij} \,]$$

for $i = 1$ to m and $j = 1$ to n.

EXAMPLE 4 Let $A = \begin{bmatrix} 1 & 2 \\ -1 & 3 \end{bmatrix}$. Then

$$2A = \begin{bmatrix} 2 \cdot 1 & 2 \cdot 2 \\ 2 \cdot (-1) & 2 \cdot 3 \end{bmatrix} = \begin{bmatrix} 2 & 4 \\ -2 & 6 \end{bmatrix}$$

and

$$(-1)A = \begin{bmatrix} -1 \cdot 1 & -1 \cdot 2 \\ -1 \cdot (-1) & -1 \cdot 3 \end{bmatrix} = \begin{bmatrix} -1 & -2 \\ 1 & -3 \end{bmatrix}$$ ■

Comment: By convention, $(-1)A$ is written $-A$. In this way, subtraction of matrices is included in the definition of matrix addition. That is,

$$A - B = A + (-B)$$

Next we consider the process of matrix multiplication. From the process for adding matrices, it might seem natural to multiply matrices by multiplying corresponding entries. However, such a definition is not useful; instead we use the following definition of matrix multiplication.

Definition

Matrix Multiplication

Let A be an $m \times p$ matrix and B be a $p \times n$ matrix. Then $C = AB$ is an $m \times n$ matrix for which

$$c_{ij} = a_{i1}b_{1j} + a_{i2}b_{2j} + \cdots + a_{ip}b_{pj}$$

That is, each entry c_{ij} in the product matrix C is obtained by multiplying each element in the ith row of A by its corresponding element in the jth column of B and then adding these products. We demonstrate this process in detail in the following examples.

Comment: The definition of AB requires that the number of *columns* of A be equal to the number of *rows* of B. If the dimensions of A are $m \times p$ and the dimensions of B are $p \times n$, then the dimensions of the product matrix C are $m \times n$. That is, we have the following:

$$A_{m \times p} \cdot B_{p \times n} = C_{m \times n}$$

EXAMPLE 5 Let $A = \begin{bmatrix} 2 & 1 \\ 3 & 0 \end{bmatrix}$ and $B = \begin{bmatrix} 1 & 2 & 1 \\ 0 & 1 & 4 \end{bmatrix}$. Find AB and BA.

Solution Since there are two columns in A and two rows in B, we can form the product AB. The product matrix AB will be a 2×3 matrix. The six elements in the product $C = AB$ are generated as follows:

$$c_{11} = \begin{bmatrix} 2 & 1 \\ 3 & 0 \end{bmatrix} \begin{bmatrix} 1 & 2 & 1 \\ 0 & 1 & 4 \end{bmatrix} = 2 \cdot 1 + 1 \cdot 0 = 2$$

$$c_{12} = \begin{bmatrix} 2 & 1 \\ 3 & 0 \end{bmatrix} \begin{bmatrix} 1 & 2 & 1 \\ 0 & 1 & 4 \end{bmatrix} = 2 \cdot 2 + 1 \cdot 1 = 5$$

$$c_{13} = \begin{bmatrix} 2 & 1 \\ 3 & 0 \end{bmatrix} \begin{bmatrix} 1 & 2 & 1 \\ 0 & 1 & 4 \end{bmatrix} = 2 \cdot 1 + 1 \cdot 4 = 6$$

$$c_{21} = \begin{bmatrix} 2 & 1 \\ 3 & 0 \end{bmatrix} \begin{bmatrix} 1 & 2 & 1 \\ 0 & 1 & 4 \end{bmatrix} = 3 \cdot 1 + 0 \cdot 0 = 3$$

$$c_{22} = \begin{bmatrix} 2 & 1 \\ 3 & 0 \end{bmatrix} \begin{bmatrix} 1 & 2 & 1 \\ 0 & 1 & 4 \end{bmatrix} = 3 \cdot 2 + 0 \cdot 1 = 6$$

$$c_{23} = \begin{bmatrix} 2 & 1 \\ 3 & 0 \end{bmatrix} \begin{bmatrix} 1 & 2 & 1 \\ 0 & 1 & 4 \end{bmatrix} = 3 \cdot 1 + 0 \cdot 4 = 3$$

The product matrix is

$$C = AB = \begin{bmatrix} 2 & 5 & 6 \\ 3 & 6 & 3 \end{bmatrix}$$

■

Comment: For Example 5, the product BA cannot be obtained since B has three columns and A has only two rows.

EXAMPLE 6 Let $A = \begin{bmatrix} 2 & 1 & -1 \end{bmatrix}$ and $B = \begin{bmatrix} 1 \\ 5 \\ -2 \end{bmatrix}$. Find AB and BA.

Solution A is a 1×3 matrix, and B is a 3×1 matrix. Since A has three columns and B has three rows, the product AB can be formed. AB is a 1×1 matrix:

$$AB = \begin{bmatrix} 2 & 1 & -1 \end{bmatrix} \begin{bmatrix} 1 \\ 5 \\ -2 \end{bmatrix} = \begin{bmatrix} 2 \cdot 1 + 1 \cdot 5 + (-1) \cdot (-2) \end{bmatrix} = \begin{bmatrix} 9 \end{bmatrix}$$

From the dimensions of A and B, we note that the product BA is a 3×3 matrix:

$$BA = \begin{bmatrix} 1 \\ 5 \\ -2 \end{bmatrix} \begin{bmatrix} 2 & 1 & -1 \end{bmatrix} = \begin{bmatrix} 1 \cdot 2 & 1 \cdot 1 & 1 \cdot (-1) \\ 5 \cdot 2 & 5 \cdot 1 & 5 \cdot (-1) \\ -2 \cdot 2 & -2 \cdot 1 & -2 \cdot (-1) \end{bmatrix}$$

$$= \begin{bmatrix} 2 & 1 & -1 \\ 10 & 5 & -5 \\ -4 & -2 & 2 \end{bmatrix}$$ ■

We see from the preceding two examples that the products AB and BA of matrices A and B are not necessarily the same. In Example 5, the product BA was undefined; in Example 6, the product AB was not the same size as BA. The next example shows that even when both AB and BA are defined and of the same size, they may not be equal.

EXAMPLE 7 Let $A = \begin{bmatrix} 1 & -1 \\ 2 & 0 \end{bmatrix}$ and $B = \begin{bmatrix} 0 & 1 \\ 1 & -1 \end{bmatrix}$. Find AB and BA.

Solution $$AB = \begin{bmatrix} 0 + (-1) & 1 + 1 \\ 0 + 0 & 2 + 0 \end{bmatrix} = \begin{bmatrix} -1 & 2 \\ 0 & 2 \end{bmatrix}$$

$$BA = \begin{bmatrix} 0 + 2 & 0 + 0 \\ 1 - 2 & -1 + 0 \end{bmatrix} = \begin{bmatrix} 2 & 0 \\ -1 & -1 \end{bmatrix}$$ ■

Comment: The preceding examples show that matrix multiplication is not commutative. However, matrix multiplication is associative; that is, $A(BC) = (AB)C$. Matrix multiplication is also distributive over matrix addition; that is, $A(B + C) = AB + AC$.

We conclude this section with a discussion of how matrix multiplication helps in simplifying the writing of systems of equations. Recall from Section 6.3 that we can use augmented matrices to solve systems of equations. Matrix notation can also be used to represent systems of equations in the form of matrix equations. To illustrate this notation, consider the following system of equations:

$$\begin{aligned} x - 6y + 3z &= -2 \\ 2x - 3y + z &= -2 \\ 3x + 3y - 2z &= 2 \end{aligned}$$

This is the same system solved in Example 1 in Section 6.3. We let A be the 3×3 matrix of coefficients

$$A = \begin{bmatrix} 1 & -6 & 3 \\ 2 & -3 & 1 \\ 3 & 3 & -2 \end{bmatrix}$$

and B be the 3×1 matrix of constants

$$B = \begin{bmatrix} -2 \\ -2 \\ 2 \end{bmatrix}$$

Finally, we represent the variables x, y, and z by x_1, x_2, and x_3, respectively, and write the unknowns as a 3×1 matrix:

$$X = \begin{bmatrix} x_1 \\ x_2 \\ x_3 \end{bmatrix}$$

The given system of equations may then be written as a matrix equation of the form

$$AX = B$$

or

$$\begin{bmatrix} 1 & -6 & 3 \\ 2 & -3 & 1 \\ 3 & 3 & -2 \end{bmatrix} \begin{bmatrix} x_1 \\ x_2 \\ x_3 \end{bmatrix} = \begin{bmatrix} -2 \\ -2 \\ 2 \end{bmatrix}$$

Solving the matrix equation $AX = B$ means finding the values of the elements in the matrix X. Any matrix X that satisfies the equation $AX = B$ is called a **solution** of the matrix equation. We know from Example 1 in Section 6.3 that $x = 1$, $y = 3$, and $z = 5$ is a solution of the given system of equations. Consequently,

$$X = \begin{bmatrix} 1 \\ 3 \\ 5 \end{bmatrix}$$

is a solution of $AX = B$ for the given coefficient matrices. Example 8 demonstrates that this is a correct solution.

EXAMPLE 8 Let $A = \begin{bmatrix} 1 & -6 & 3 \\ 2 & -3 & 1 \\ 3 & 3 & -2 \end{bmatrix}$ and $B = \begin{bmatrix} -2 \\ -2 \\ 2 \end{bmatrix}$. Show that $X = \begin{bmatrix} 1 \\ 3 \\ 5 \end{bmatrix}$ is a solution of $AX = B$.

Solution

$$\begin{bmatrix} 1 & -6 & 3 \\ 2 & -3 & 1 \\ 3 & 3 & -2 \end{bmatrix} \begin{bmatrix} 1 \\ 3 \\ 5 \end{bmatrix} = \begin{bmatrix} 1 \cdot 1 + (-6) \cdot 3 + 3 \cdot 5 \\ 2 \cdot 1 + (-3) \cdot 3 + 1 \cdot 5 \\ 3 \cdot 1 + 3 \cdot 3 + (-2) \cdot 5 \end{bmatrix} = \begin{bmatrix} -2 \\ -2 \\ 2 \end{bmatrix} = B$$

This shows that the given matrix X is a solution of $AX = B$. ■

Exercises Section 6.4

In Exercises 1–10, find $A + B$, $A - B$, and $2A$, or tell why the operation cannot be done.

1. $A = \begin{bmatrix} 5 & 0 \\ 1 & 1 \end{bmatrix}$, $B = \begin{bmatrix} -1 & 2 \\ 1 & 0 \end{bmatrix}$

2. $A = \begin{bmatrix} 0 & 1 \\ -1 & 2 \end{bmatrix}$, $B = \begin{bmatrix} 2 & 1 \\ 1 & 2 \end{bmatrix}$

3. $A = \begin{bmatrix} 1 & 2 & 3 \\ 4 & 0 & 1 \end{bmatrix}$, $B = \begin{bmatrix} 1 & 0 & 2 \\ 0 & 5 & 6 \end{bmatrix}$

4. $A = \begin{bmatrix} -1 \\ 5 \end{bmatrix}$, $B = \begin{bmatrix} 2 \\ 0 \end{bmatrix}$

5. $A = \begin{bmatrix} 1 \\ 0 \\ 2 \end{bmatrix}$, $B = \begin{bmatrix} 7 \\ -1 \\ 5 \end{bmatrix}$

6. $A = [\,1 \quad 6\,]$, $B = [\,5 \quad 2\,]$

7. $A = [\,0 \quad 3 \quad 1\,]$, $B = [\,-1 \quad 2 \quad 0\,]$

8. $A = [\,8\,]$, $B = [\,2\,]$

9. $A = \begin{bmatrix} 1 & 0 \\ 5 & 2 \end{bmatrix}$, $B = \begin{bmatrix} 1 \\ 2 \end{bmatrix}$

10. $A = \begin{bmatrix} 1 & 0 \\ 0 & 1 \end{bmatrix}$, $B = \begin{bmatrix} 0 & 1 \\ 1 & 0 \end{bmatrix}$

In Exercises 11–20, find AB and BA, or tell why the product is undefined.

11. $A = \begin{bmatrix} 5 & 0 \\ 1 & 1 \end{bmatrix}$, $B = \begin{bmatrix} -1 & 2 \\ 1 & 0 \end{bmatrix}$

12. $A = \begin{bmatrix} 0 & 1 \\ -1 & 2 \end{bmatrix}$, $B = \begin{bmatrix} 2 & 1 \\ 1 & 2 \end{bmatrix}$

13. $A = \begin{bmatrix} 1 & 2 & 3 \\ 4 & 0 & 1 \end{bmatrix}$, $B = \begin{bmatrix} 1 & 0 & 2 \\ 0 & 5 & 6 \end{bmatrix}$

14. $A = \begin{bmatrix} -1 \\ 5 \end{bmatrix}$, $B = \begin{bmatrix} 2 \\ 0 \end{bmatrix}$

15. $A = \begin{bmatrix} -1 \\ 5 \end{bmatrix}$, $B = [\,2 \quad 0\,]$

16. $A = \begin{bmatrix} 2 \\ 0 \\ 1 \end{bmatrix}$, $B = [\,-5 \quad 5 \quad 3\,]$

17. $A = \begin{bmatrix} 2 & 1 \\ 1 & -1 \end{bmatrix}$, $B = \begin{bmatrix} 1 \\ 2 \end{bmatrix}$

18. $A = [\,3\,]$, $B = [\,2 \quad 5\,]$

19. $A = \begin{bmatrix} 2 & 0 & 5 \\ 6 & 1 & 4 \\ -2 & 1 & 1 \end{bmatrix}$, $B = \begin{bmatrix} 1 & 0 \\ -1 & 1 \\ 2 & 3 \end{bmatrix}$

20. $A = \begin{bmatrix} 2 & -3 & 1 \\ 1 & 0 & -2 \\ -1 & 5 & 2 \end{bmatrix}$, $B = \begin{bmatrix} -2 & 2 \\ 1 & 3 \\ 3 & -2 \end{bmatrix}$

In Exercises 21–26, show that X is a solution of $AX = B$.

21. $A = \begin{bmatrix} 2 & 1 \\ 1 & -1 \end{bmatrix}$, $B = \begin{bmatrix} 1 \\ 2 \end{bmatrix}$, $X = \begin{bmatrix} 1 \\ -1 \end{bmatrix}$

22. $A = \begin{bmatrix} 5 & 2 \\ 1 & -3 \end{bmatrix}$, $B = \begin{bmatrix} 8 \\ 5 \end{bmatrix}$, $X = \begin{bmatrix} 2 \\ -1 \end{bmatrix}$

23. $A = \begin{bmatrix} 2 & 1 & 1 \\ 1 & -1 & 1 \\ 1 & -2 & 2 \end{bmatrix}$, $B = \begin{bmatrix} 6 \\ 3 \\ 5 \end{bmatrix}$, $X = \begin{bmatrix} 1 \\ 1 \\ 3 \end{bmatrix}$

24. $A = \begin{bmatrix} 2 & 2 & -3 \\ 1 & -1 & 2 \end{bmatrix}$, $B = \begin{bmatrix} 1 \\ 2 \end{bmatrix}$, $X = \begin{bmatrix} 1 \\ 1 \\ 1 \end{bmatrix}$

25. $A = \begin{bmatrix} 2 & 1 & 3 \\ 1 & -2 & -1 \end{bmatrix}$, $B = \begin{bmatrix} 3 \\ -\frac{7}{2} \end{bmatrix}$, $X = \begin{bmatrix} -\frac{1}{2} \\ 1 \\ 1 \end{bmatrix}$

26. $A = \begin{bmatrix} 1 & 1 & 0 \\ 0 & 1 & 0 \\ 0 & 0 & 0 \end{bmatrix}$, $B = \begin{bmatrix} 0 \\ 0 \\ 0 \end{bmatrix}$, $X = a\begin{bmatrix} 0 \\ 0 \\ 1 \end{bmatrix}$

27. Let $A = \begin{bmatrix} 1 & 2 \\ -1 & 0 \end{bmatrix}$, $B = \begin{bmatrix} 0 & 1 \\ 5 & 2 \end{bmatrix}$, and $C = \begin{bmatrix} 3 & 5 \\ 0 & 2 \end{bmatrix}$. Show that $A(BC) = (AB)C$. Which property does this result demonstrate?

28. Let A, B, and C be the matrices given in Exercise 27. Show that $A(B + C) = AB + AC$. Which property does this result demonstrate?

29. Let A and B be the matrices given in Exercise 27. Show that $A^2 - B^2 \neq (A - B)(A + B)$. (*Note:* $A^2 = AA$, $B^2 = BB$.)

30. Let A and B be the matrices given in Exercise 27. Show that $(A + B)^2 \neq A^2 + 2AB + B^2$.

31. Determine an appropriate formula for $(A + B)^2$ that will be valid even when $AB \neq BA$.

32. A square matrix is called a **diagonal matrix** if all entries of the main diagonal are zero. Determine a rule for multiplying diagonal matrices.

33. Let $A = \begin{bmatrix} 0 & 1 \\ 0 & 1 \end{bmatrix}$, $B = \begin{bmatrix} 1 & 1 \\ 1 & 0 \end{bmatrix}$, and $C = \begin{bmatrix} 0 & 0 \\ 1 & 0 \end{bmatrix}$. Show that $AB = AC$ even though $B \neq C$. That is, the cancellation law does not hold for matrix multiplication.

34. Let $A = \begin{bmatrix} 1 & 0 \\ 1 & 0 \end{bmatrix}$ and $D = \begin{bmatrix} 0 & 0 \\ 1 & 1 \end{bmatrix}$. Show that $AD = \mathbf{0}$ even though $A \neq \mathbf{0}$ and $D \neq \mathbf{0}$. Note that this result differs from that of a similar property of real-number multiplication.

6.5 Solving Systems of Equations by Matrix Inversion

In the preceding section, we saw that a system of equations can be represented by a matrix equation of the form

$$AX = B$$

where A is an $n \times n$ matrix of coefficients, B is an $n \times 1$ matrix of constants, and X is an $n \times 1$ matrix of unknowns or variables. In this section, we introduce a method for solving matrix equations of the form $AX = B$. First, we must define some additional matrix properties.

Definition

Identity Matrix

The $n \times n$ square matrix I with ones on the main diagonal and zeros elsewhere is called the **identity matrix of order *n*.**

The identity matrix of order 2 is

$$I = \begin{bmatrix} 1 & 0 \\ 0 & 1 \end{bmatrix}$$

and the identity matrix of order 3 is

$$I = \begin{bmatrix} 1 & 0 & 0 \\ 0 & 1 & 0 \\ 0 & 0 & 1 \end{bmatrix}$$

The result of multiplying the $n \times n$ matrix A by the identity matrix I of order n is the matrix A, *unchanged.* For example,

$$\begin{bmatrix} 2 & -3 \\ 1 & 4 \end{bmatrix} \begin{bmatrix} 1 & 0 \\ 0 & 1 \end{bmatrix} = \begin{bmatrix} 2 & -3 \\ 1 & 4 \end{bmatrix}$$

Comment: An identity matrix is always a square matrix.

EXAMPLE 1 Let $A = \begin{bmatrix} 3 & 5 \\ 2 & 7 \end{bmatrix}$. Then

$$AI = \begin{bmatrix} 3 & 5 \\ 2 & 7 \end{bmatrix} \begin{bmatrix} 1 & 0 \\ 0 & 1 \end{bmatrix} = \begin{bmatrix} 3 & 5 \\ 2 & 7 \end{bmatrix}$$

and

$$IA = \begin{bmatrix} 1 & 0 \\ 0 & 1 \end{bmatrix} \begin{bmatrix} 3 & 5 \\ 2 & 7 \end{bmatrix} = \begin{bmatrix} 3 & 5 \\ 2 & 7 \end{bmatrix}$$

■

The result obtained in Example 1 is true for all square matrices. We state this in the following property.

Identity Property

Let A be a square matrix of order n and let I be the identity matrix of order n. Then

$$AI = IA = A$$

A square matrix A for which a square matrix B can be found so that

$$AB = BA = I$$

is said to be **invertible.** The matrix B is called the *inverse matrix* of A.

Definition

Inverse Matrix

Let A be a square matrix of order n. The **inverse matrix** of A is denoted by A^{-1} and has the property that

$$AA^{-1} = A^{-1}A = I$$

Comment: Since $AA^{-1} = A^{-1}A = I$, if we want to show that a given matrix B is an inverse of A, it is sufficient to show that $AB = I$.

EXAMPLE 2 Let $A = \begin{bmatrix} 2 & 1 \\ 3 & 2 \end{bmatrix}$. Show that the inverse of A is $B = \begin{bmatrix} 2 & -1 \\ -3 & 2 \end{bmatrix}$.

Solution To show that B is the inverse of A, we show that $AB = I$.

$$AB = \begin{bmatrix} 2 & 1 \\ 3 & 2 \end{bmatrix} \begin{bmatrix} 2 & -1 \\ -3 & 2 \end{bmatrix} = \begin{bmatrix} 2 \cdot 2 + 1 \cdot (-3) & 2 \cdot (-1) + 1 \cdot 2 \\ 3 \cdot 2 + 2 \cdot (-3) & 3 \cdot (-1) + 2 \cdot 2 \end{bmatrix}$$

$$= \begin{bmatrix} 1 & 0 \\ 0 & 1 \end{bmatrix} = I$$

We have shown that B is the inverse of A; we have also shown that A is the inverse of B.

■

Comment: Not every square matrix has an inverse. For instance, the matrix

$$\begin{bmatrix} 4 & 6 \\ 2 & 3 \end{bmatrix}$$

does not have an inverse. A square matrix that has an inverse is said to be **nonsingular,** and one that does not have an inverse is said to be **singular.**

We now describe a procedure for finding the inverse matrix of any nonsingular matrix A using an augmented matrix. In this case, we augment the matrix A with the identity matrix I and write

$$[\, A \mid I \,]$$

We then perform row operations (see Section 6.3) on the augmented matrix until A is transformed into the identity matrix. The inverse matrix will then appear on the right within the augmented matrix:

$$[\, A \mid I \,] \rightarrow [\, I \mid A^{-1} \,]$$

EXAMPLE 3 Let $A = \begin{bmatrix} 3 & -7 \\ 6 & 2 \end{bmatrix}$. Find A^{-1}.

Solution We form the augmented matrix

$$\left[\begin{array}{cc|cc} 3 & -7 & 1 & 0 \\ 6 & 2 & 0 & 1 \end{array}\right]$$

Next, we perform row operations on the augmented matrix until we obtain the identity matrix on the left-hand side of the dashed line. First, we multiply the first row by -2, add the result to the second row, and replace the second row with this sum. This operation is expressed by

$$\left[\begin{array}{cc|cc} 3 & -7 & 1 & 0 \\ 6 & 2 & 0 & 1 \end{array}\right] \xrightarrow{-2①+②\rightarrow②} \left[\begin{array}{cc|cc} 3 & -7 & 1 & 0 \\ 0 & 16 & -2 & 1 \end{array}\right]$$

To obtain a 1 in the first row of the first column, we multiply the first row by $\frac{1}{3}$.

$$\left[\begin{array}{cc|cc} 3 & -7 & 1 & 0 \\ 0 & 16 & -2 & 1 \end{array}\right] \xrightarrow{\frac{1}{3}①\rightarrow①} \left[\begin{array}{cc|cc} 1 & -\frac{7}{3} & \frac{1}{3} & 0 \\ 0 & 16 & -2 & 1 \end{array}\right]$$

Next, we multiply the second row by $\frac{1}{16}$.

$$\left[\begin{array}{cc|cc} 1 & -\frac{7}{3} & \frac{1}{3} & 0 \\ 0 & 16 & -2 & 1 \end{array}\right] \xrightarrow{\frac{1}{16}②\rightarrow②} \left[\begin{array}{cc|cc} 1 & -\frac{7}{3} & \frac{1}{3} & 0 \\ 0 & 1 & -\frac{1}{8} & \frac{1}{16} \end{array}\right]$$

Finally, we multiply the second row by $\frac{7}{3}$, add the result to the first row, and replace the first row with this sum.

$$\left[\begin{array}{cc|cc} 1 & -\frac{7}{3} & \frac{1}{3} & 0 \\ 0 & 1 & -\frac{1}{8} & \frac{1}{16} \end{array}\right] \xrightarrow{\frac{7}{3}②+①\rightarrow①} \left[\begin{array}{cc|cc} 1 & 0 & \frac{1}{24} & \frac{7}{48} \\ 0 & 1 & -\frac{1}{8} & \frac{1}{16} \end{array}\right]$$

We now have the identity matrix on the left-hand side. The inverse of A is

$$A^{-1} = \begin{bmatrix} \frac{1}{24} & \frac{7}{48} \\ -\frac{1}{8} & \frac{1}{16} \end{bmatrix}$$

■

Comment: If it is impossible to transform the augmented matrix so that the identity matrix appears on the left-hand side, then A^{-1} does not exist.

EXAMPLE 4 Using the procedure of row operations, find A^{-1} for

$$A = \begin{bmatrix} 2 & 1 & 0 \\ 4 & 1 & -1 \\ 2 & 1 & -1 \end{bmatrix}$$

Solution We form the augmented matrix

$$\left[\begin{array}{ccc|ccc} 2 & 1 & 0 & 1 & 0 & 0 \\ 4 & 1 & -1 & 0 & 1 & 0 \\ 2 & 1 & -1 & 0 & 0 & 1 \end{array}\right]$$

Then, we have the following equivalent matrices:

$$\xrightarrow{\frac{1}{2}① \to ①} \left[\begin{array}{ccc|ccc} 1 & \frac{1}{2} & 0 & \frac{1}{2} & 0 & 0 \\ 4 & 1 & -1 & 0 & 1 & 0 \\ 2 & 1 & -1 & 0 & 0 & 1 \end{array}\right]$$

$$\xrightarrow[(-2)① + ③ \to ③]{(-4)① + ② \to ②} \left[\begin{array}{ccc|ccc} 1 & \frac{1}{2} & 0 & \frac{1}{2} & 0 & 0 \\ 0 & -1 & -1 & -2 & 1 & 0 \\ 0 & 0 & -1 & -1 & 0 & 1 \end{array}\right]$$

$$\xrightarrow[(-1)③ \to ③]{(-1)② \to ②} \left[\begin{array}{ccc|ccc} 1 & \frac{1}{2} & 0 & \frac{1}{2} & 0 & 0 \\ 0 & 1 & 1 & 2 & -1 & 0 \\ 0 & 0 & 1 & 1 & 0 & -1 \end{array}\right]$$

$$\xrightarrow{(-1)③ + ② \to ②} \left[\begin{array}{ccc|ccc} 1 & \frac{1}{2} & 0 & \frac{1}{2} & 0 & 0 \\ 0 & 1 & 0 & 1 & -1 & 1 \\ 0 & 0 & 1 & 1 & 0 & -1 \end{array}\right]$$

$$\xrightarrow{(-\frac{1}{2})② + ① \to ①} \left[\begin{array}{ccc|ccc} 1 & 0 & 0 & 0 & \frac{1}{2} & -\frac{1}{2} \\ 0 & 1 & 0 & 1 & -1 & 1 \\ 0 & 0 & 1 & 1 & 0 & -1 \end{array}\right]$$

The inverse matrix of A is then

$$A^{-1} = \begin{bmatrix} 0 & \frac{1}{2} & -\frac{1}{2} \\ 1 & -1 & 1 \\ 1 & 0 & -1 \end{bmatrix}$$

■

One of the main uses for inverse matrices is in solving a system of n equations in n unknowns. Such a system can be represented by

$$AX = B$$

where A is a square $n \times n$ matrix and X is the $n \times 1$ matrix of unknowns. If A^{-1} exists, we can multiply both sides of the above equation by A^{-1} to obtain

$$A^{-1}(AX) = A^{-1}B$$

The left-hand side of this equation becomes

$$A^{-1}(AX) = (A^{-1}A)X = IX = X$$

Therefore, the solution of $AX = B$ is

$$X = A^{-1}B$$

EXAMPLE 5 Solve the matrix equation $AX = B$, where

$$A = \begin{bmatrix} 2 & 1 & 0 \\ 4 & 1 & -1 \\ 2 & 1 & -1 \end{bmatrix}, \quad X = \begin{bmatrix} x_1 \\ x_2 \\ x_3 \end{bmatrix}, \quad B = \begin{bmatrix} 2 \\ -2 \\ 4 \end{bmatrix}$$

Solution Observing that A is the matrix given in Example 4, we have

$$A^{-1} = \begin{bmatrix} 0 & \frac{1}{2} & -\frac{1}{2} \\ 1 & -1 & 1 \\ 1 & 0 & -1 \end{bmatrix}$$

The solution to $AX = B$ is then

$$X = A^{-1}B = \begin{bmatrix} 0 & \frac{1}{2} & -\frac{1}{2} \\ 1 & -1 & 1 \\ 1 & 0 & -1 \end{bmatrix} \begin{bmatrix} 2 \\ -2 \\ 4 \end{bmatrix} = \begin{bmatrix} 0 - 1 - 2 \\ 2 + 2 + 4 \\ 2 + 0 - 4 \end{bmatrix} = \begin{bmatrix} -3 \\ 8 \\ -2 \end{bmatrix}$$

Thus, $x_1 = -3$, $x_2 = 8$, and $x_3 = -2$. ■

EXAMPLE 6 Solve the system

$$2x + y = 3$$
$$3x + 2y = -4$$

by the method of matrix inversion.

Solution This system can be represented in the form $AX = B$ with

$$A = \begin{bmatrix} 2 & 1 \\ 3 & 2 \end{bmatrix}, \quad X = \begin{bmatrix} x \\ y \end{bmatrix}, \quad B = \begin{bmatrix} 3 \\ -4 \end{bmatrix}$$

Then, from Example 2,

$$A^{-1} = \begin{bmatrix} 2 & -1 \\ -3 & 2 \end{bmatrix}$$

Therefore,

$$X = \begin{bmatrix} 2 & -1 \\ -3 & 2 \end{bmatrix} \begin{bmatrix} 3 \\ -4 \end{bmatrix} = \begin{bmatrix} 10 \\ -17 \end{bmatrix}$$

Thus, $x = 10$ and $y = -17$ is the solution of the given system. ■

The method of matrix inversion is not a time-saver except when we are required to solve several systems of the form

$$AX = B_1, AX = B_2, \ldots, AX = B_n$$

Then, all solutions are easily obtained once A^{-1} has been found. This is more efficient than using the method of Gaussian elimination on each of the systems.

EXAMPLE 7 Solve $AX = B$, if $B = B_1 = \begin{bmatrix} 1 \\ 0 \end{bmatrix}$, $B_2 = \begin{bmatrix} 0 \\ 1 \end{bmatrix}$, $B_3 = \begin{bmatrix} 0 \\ 0 \end{bmatrix}$, and $B_4 = \begin{bmatrix} 1 \\ 5 \end{bmatrix}$, and $A = \begin{bmatrix} 2 & 1 \\ 3 & 2 \end{bmatrix}$.

Solution As in Example 6, $A^{-1} = \begin{bmatrix} 2 & -1 \\ -3 & 2 \end{bmatrix}$, so

$$X_1 = A^{-1}\begin{bmatrix} 1 \\ 0 \end{bmatrix}, \quad X_2 = A^{-1}\begin{bmatrix} 0 \\ 1 \end{bmatrix}, \quad X_3 = A^{-1}\begin{bmatrix} 0 \\ 0 \end{bmatrix}, \quad X_4 = A^{-1}\begin{bmatrix} 1 \\ 5 \end{bmatrix}$$

From this, we obtain

$$X_1 = \begin{bmatrix} 2 \\ -3 \end{bmatrix}, \quad X_2 = \begin{bmatrix} -1 \\ 2 \end{bmatrix}, \quad X_3 = \begin{bmatrix} 0 \\ 0 \end{bmatrix}, \quad X_4 = \begin{bmatrix} -3 \\ 7 \end{bmatrix}$$

■

EXAMPLE 8 Solve the system

$$\begin{aligned} x + 2y - 3z &= 1 \\ y + 4z &= 2 \\ 3x + 4y - 17z &= -1 \end{aligned}$$

Solution The matrix of coefficients is

$$\begin{bmatrix} 1 & 2 & -3 \\ 0 & 1 & 4 \\ 3 & 4 & -17 \end{bmatrix}$$

Attempting to find the inverse, we begin with

$$\left[\begin{array}{ccc|ccc} 1 & 2 & -3 & 1 & 0 & 0 \\ 0 & 1 & 4 & 0 & 1 & 0 \\ 3 & 4 & -17 & 0 & 0 & 1 \end{array}\right]$$

Using the elementary row operation $-3①+③ \to ③$, we get

$$\left[\begin{array}{ccc|ccc} 1 & 2 & -3 & 1 & 0 & 0 \\ 0 & 1 & 4 & 0 & 1 & 0 \\ 0 & -2 & -8 & -3 & 0 & 1 \end{array}\right]$$

Next, using $2②+③ \to ③$, we obtain

$$\left[\begin{array}{ccc|ccc} 1 & 2 & -3 & 1 & 0 & 0 \\ 0 & 1 & 4 & 0 & 1 & 0 \\ 0 & 0 & 0 & -3 & 2 & 1 \end{array}\right]$$

This shows that the given matrix of coefficients does not have an inverse since the bottom row of zeros on the left-hand side prevents us from obtaining the identity matrix. However, this does not mean that the system does not have a solution. We may use Gaussian elimination on the augmented matrix, as described in Section 6.3. Thus,

$$\left[\begin{array}{ccc|c} 1 & 2 & -3 & 1 \\ 0 & 1 & 4 & 2 \\ 3 & 4 & -17 & -1 \end{array}\right] \xrightarrow{-3①+③\to③} \left[\begin{array}{ccc|c} 1 & 2 & -3 & 1 \\ 0 & 1 & 4 & 2 \\ 0 & -2 & -8 & -4 \end{array}\right]$$

$$\xrightarrow{2②+③\to③} \left[\begin{array}{ccc|c} 1 & 2 & -3 & 1 \\ 0 & 1 & 4 & 2 \\ 0 & 0 & 0 & 0 \end{array}\right]$$

This system is solved by setting $z = t$, $y = 2 - 4t$, and $x = 11t - 3$. ■

Comment: Note that if the constant on the right-hand side of the first equation of the system in Example 8 had been anything but 1, the system would have been inconsistent.

Exercises Section 6.5

In Exercises 1–15, compute the inverse matrix if it exists.

1. $\begin{bmatrix} 0 & 1 \\ 1 & 0 \end{bmatrix}$

2. $\begin{bmatrix} 2 & 0 \\ 0 & 3 \end{bmatrix}$

3. $\begin{bmatrix} 2 & 1 \\ 1 & 0 \end{bmatrix}$

4. $\begin{bmatrix} 1 & 0 & 1 \\ 0 & 1 & 0 \\ 0 & 0 & 1 \end{bmatrix}$

5. $\begin{bmatrix} 2 & 0 & 0 \\ 0 & 3 & 0 \\ 0 & 0 & 5 \end{bmatrix}$

6. $\begin{bmatrix} 2 & 0 & 1 \\ 0 & 3 & 1 \\ -2 & 0 & 4 \end{bmatrix}$

7. $\begin{bmatrix} 1 & 0 & 1 \\ 2 & 1 & 2 \\ -1 & 0 & 0 \end{bmatrix}$

8. $\begin{bmatrix} 2 & 4 \\ 1 & 2 \end{bmatrix}$

9. $\begin{bmatrix} 1 & 0 & 2 \\ 0 & 1 & 5 \\ 0 & 0 & 0 \end{bmatrix}$

10. $\begin{bmatrix} 1 & 1 & 0 \\ 1 & 1 & 1 \\ 0 & 0 & 1 \end{bmatrix}$

11. $\begin{bmatrix} a & b \\ 0 & d \end{bmatrix}, \quad a \cdot d \neq 0$

12. $\begin{bmatrix} 2 & 1 & 3 \\ 0 & 1 & 2 \\ 2 & 1 & 5 \end{bmatrix}$

13. $\begin{bmatrix} 2 & 4 & 3 \\ -2 & 4 & -2 \\ 1 & 0 & 1 \end{bmatrix}$

14. $\begin{bmatrix} a & 0 & 0 \\ 0 & b & 0 \\ 0 & 0 & c \end{bmatrix}, \quad abc \neq 0$

15. $\begin{bmatrix} -1 & 2 & 2 \\ -1 & 2 & 5 \\ -2 & 2 & 10 \end{bmatrix}$

In Exercises 16–25, solve each system using the method of matrix inversion.

16. $x - y = 1$
$x + y = 2$

17. $2x + y = 4$
$x - y = 0$

18. $2x + y + 3z = 0$
$y + 2z = 1$
$2x + y + 5z = -1$
(*Hint:* See Exercise 12.)

19. $2x + z = 1$
$3y + z = 2$
$-2x + 4z = 0$
(*Hint:* See Exercise 6.)

20. $3x + 2y = 6$
$x - y = 7$

21. $x + z = 0$
$2x + y + 2z = 2$
$-x = 1$
(*Hint:* See Exercise 7.)

22. $2x + y + 3z = -2$
$y + 2z = -1$
$2x + y + 5z = -4$
(*Hint:* See Exercise 12.)

23. $-x + 2y + 2z = 0$
$-x + 2y + 5z = 0$
$-x + y + 5z = -2$
(*Hint:* See Exercise 15.)

24. $x + y - z = 1$
$x - y + z = 3$
$x + y - 2z = -2$

25. $x + y + 5z = 2$
$3x + 8y + 5z = 0$
$-x - 5y + 3z = 15$
(*Hint:* A^{-1} does not exist.)

26. Find the relation among b_1, b_2, and b_3 such that the following system has a solution.

$$x + 3y + z = b_1$$
$$-x + y - z = b_2$$
$$x - y + z = b_3$$

6.6 Determinants

Of primary interest in this section is an operation on a square matrix that yields a real number called the **determinant** of the matrix. To display the determinant of a matrix, replace the brackets with vertical bars. We denote the determinant of a matrix A by **det** $\mathbf{A}$. Thus, if

$$A = \begin{bmatrix} 3 & 7 \\ -1 & 2 \end{bmatrix}$$

then det A is symbolized by

$$\det A = \begin{vmatrix} 3 & 7 \\ -1 & 2 \end{vmatrix}$$

Restricting ourselves for the moment to 2×2 matrices, we make the following definition for the value of det A.

Definition

Let

$$A = \begin{bmatrix} a_1 & b_1 \\ a_2 & b_2 \end{bmatrix}$$

Then the determinant of A is given by

$$\mathbf{det}\ \boldsymbol{A} = \begin{vmatrix} a_1 & b_1 \\ a_2 & b_2 \end{vmatrix} = a_1 b_2 - a_2 b_1$$

Practically, det A is obtained by multiplying the element in the upper left by that in the lower right and then subtracting the product of the element in the lower left and that in the upper right. Remember, det A is a real number and not an array, whereas A itself is an array and *not* a number.

EXAMPLE 1 If

$$A = \begin{bmatrix} 2 & 3 \\ -1 & 4 \end{bmatrix}$$

then

$$\det A = \begin{vmatrix} 2 & 3 \\ -1 & 4 \end{vmatrix} = 2(4) - (-1)(3) = 11$$

■

EXAMPLE 2 $\begin{vmatrix} 3 & 2 \\ 5 & 3 \end{vmatrix} = 3(3) - (5)(2) = -1$ ■

The definition of determinants of higher-order matrices depends upon the definition of 2×2 determinants. A third-order determinant is defined in terms of a second-order determinant, a fourth-order determinant is defined in terms of a third-order determinant, and, in general, an nth-order determinant is defined in terms of one of order $(n - 1)$.

Recall that an element of a matrix is conveniently located using double-subscript notation, where the first number of the subscript refers to the row of the matrix and the second to the column. Thus, a_{ij} means the element in the ith row and jth column.

Definition

> The determinant obtained from A by deleting the ith row and jth column, called the **minor** of the element a_{ij}, is denoted by M_{ij}.

EXAMPLE 3 Find the minors of a_{12} and a_{33}, given the matrix

$$A = \begin{bmatrix} 3 & 2 & 1 \\ 7 & 6 & -2 \\ 0 & 5 & 9 \end{bmatrix}$$

Solution Find the minor of a_{12} by eliminating the first row and the second column of the given matrix. Thus,

$$M_{12} = \begin{vmatrix} 3 & 2 & 1 \\ 7 & 6 & -2 \\ 0 & 5 & 9 \end{vmatrix} = \begin{vmatrix} 7 & -2 \\ 0 & 9 \end{vmatrix} = 63$$

Similarly, the minor of a_{33} is

$$M_{33} = \begin{vmatrix} 3 & 2 & 1 \\ 7 & 6 & -2 \\ 0 & 5 & 9 \end{vmatrix} = \begin{vmatrix} 3 & 2 \\ 7 & 6 \end{vmatrix} = 4$$

■

Using the definition of a minor, we give the following definition of the value of **an nth-order determinant in terms of minors.**

Definition

> An nth-order determinant is the sum of the n products
>
> $$(-1)^{i+j}a_{ij}M_{ij}$$
>
> in any row or column. The value obtained is independent of the column or row used.

The definition says that a third-order determinant is the sum of the *three products* formed by multiplying each element of any row (or column) by its corresponding minor and assigning to each product a plus sign if the sum of the number of the column and the number of the row in which the element lies is even, and a minus sign if it is odd.

In using the jth column to expand the determinant, we say that we have "expanded the determinant about the jth column." An expansion about the ith row can also be described using similar terminology.

A third-order determinant can be expanded by minors in six different ways. Using elements of the first row, we have

$$\begin{aligned}\det A &= (-1)^{1+1}a_{11}M_{11} + (-1)^{1+2}a_{12}M_{12} + (-1)^{1+3}a_{13}M_{13} \\ &= a_{11}M_{11} - a_{12}M_{12} + a_{13}M_{13}\end{aligned}$$

By elements of the second row,

$$-a_{21}M_{21} + a_{22}M_{22} - a_{23}M_{23}$$

By elements of the third row,

$$a_{31}M_{31} - a_{32}M_{32} + a_{33}M_{33}$$

By elements of the first column,

$$a_{11}M_{11} - a_{21}M_{21} + a_{31}M_{31}$$

By elements of the second column,

$$-a_{12}M_{12} + a_{22}M_{22} - a_{32}M_{32}$$

By elements of the third column,

$$a_{13}M_{13} - a_{23}M_{23} + a_{33}M_{33}$$

Each expansion yields the same value. The complete evaluation is essentially a matter of computing three second-order determinants. The following expansion shows this in only the first case; that is, by elements of the first row.

$$\det A = a_{11}\begin{vmatrix} a_{22} & a_{23} \\ a_{32} & a_{33} \end{vmatrix} - a_{12}\begin{vmatrix} a_{21} & a_{23} \\ a_{31} & a_{33} \end{vmatrix} + a_{13}\begin{vmatrix} a_{21} & a_{22} \\ a_{31} & a_{32} \end{vmatrix}$$

The fact that the value of the determinant is independent of the column or row used for the expansion is a theorem proved in more advanced mathematics courses. The next example demonstrates this independence.

EXAMPLE 4 Find the value of the third-order determinant

$$\begin{vmatrix} 2 & -1 & 5 \\ 1 & 3 & -3 \\ 4 & 0 & 1 \end{vmatrix}$$

using expansion of minors (a) about the first column and (b) about the third row.

Solution a.

$$\begin{aligned}\begin{vmatrix} 2 & -1 & 5 \\ 1 & 3 & -3 \\ 4 & 0 & 1 \end{vmatrix} &= (-1)^{1+1}(2)\begin{vmatrix} 3 & -3 \\ 0 & 1 \end{vmatrix} + (-1)^{2+1}(1)\begin{vmatrix} -1 & 5 \\ 0 & 1 \end{vmatrix} \\ &\quad + (-1)^{3+1}(4)\begin{vmatrix} -1 & 5 \\ 3 & -3 \end{vmatrix} \\ &= 2\begin{vmatrix} 3 & -3 \\ 0 & 1 \end{vmatrix} - \begin{vmatrix} -1 & 5 \\ 0 & 1 \end{vmatrix} + 4\begin{vmatrix} -1 & 5 \\ 3 & -3 \end{vmatrix} \\ &= 2(3-0) - (-1-0) + 4(3-15) \\ &= -41\end{aligned}$$

b. $$\begin{vmatrix} 2 & -1 & 5 \\ 1 & 3 & -3 \\ 4 & 0 & 1 \end{vmatrix} = (-1)^{3+1}(4)\begin{vmatrix} -1 & 5 \\ 3 & -3 \end{vmatrix} + (-1)^{3+2}(0)\begin{vmatrix} 2 & 5 \\ 1 & -3 \end{vmatrix}$$

$$+ (-1)^{3+3}(1)\begin{vmatrix} 2 & -1 \\ 1 & 3 \end{vmatrix}$$

$$= 4\begin{vmatrix} -1 & 5 \\ 3 & -3 \end{vmatrix} - 0 + \begin{vmatrix} 2 & -1 \\ 1 & 3 \end{vmatrix}$$

$$= 4(3 - 15) + (6 - (-1))$$

$$= -41$$

■

Comment: Note the advantage of choosing to expand a determinant about rows or columns containing some zeros.

EXAMPLE 5 Evaluate the determinant of the matrix A.

$$A = \begin{bmatrix} 3 & -7 & 6 \\ 4 & 9 & 0 \\ 0 & -1 & 0 \end{bmatrix}$$

Solution Both the third column and the third row contain two zeros. Evaluating by the elements of the third row gives

$$\det A = -(-1)\begin{vmatrix} 3 & 6 \\ 4 & 0 \end{vmatrix} = -24$$

and expanding using the third column yields

$$\det A = 6\begin{vmatrix} 4 & 9 \\ 0 & -1 \end{vmatrix} = 6(-4) = -24$$

■

In working with determinants, you will find the following properties helpful. In stating these properties, we assume that A is a square matrix of any order.

1. If a row (or column) of A has all zeros, then $\det A = 0$.
2. If A is obtained from B by interchanging two rows (or columns), then $\det A = -\det B$.
3. If any two rows (or columns) of A are equal, then $\det A = 0$.
4. If A and B are identical except that a row (or column) of B is k times the same row (or column) of A, then $\det A = k \det B$.
5. The value of a determinant is unchanged if the rows and the columns of the matrix are interchanged.
6. The value of a determinant is unchanged if a multiple of one row (or column) is added to another row (or column).

Property 6 is particularly useful when expanding by minors. The idea is to apply this property repeatedly until all the elements in a given row (or column) are zero except one. Then, when expanding by minors, you need to evaluate only one determinant, of a lower order. In applying Property 6, we can use the notation employed in Section 10.3 to manipulate rows in matrices.

EXAMPLE 6 Evaluate

$$\det A = \begin{vmatrix} 3 & -4 & 3 \\ 5 & 1 & 2 \\ 2 & 7 & -5 \end{vmatrix}$$

Solution The following *row* operations are used to replace a_{12} and a_{32} by zeros:

$$\begin{vmatrix} 3 & -4 & 3 \\ 5 & 1 & 2 \\ 2 & 7 & -5 \end{vmatrix} \xrightarrow[③ - 7② \to ③]{① + 4② \to ①} \begin{vmatrix} 23 & 0 & 11 \\ 5 & 1 & 2 \\ -33 & 0 & -19 \end{vmatrix}$$

Expanding by elements of the second column, we have

$$\det A = \begin{vmatrix} 23 & 11 \\ -33 & -19 \end{vmatrix} = 23(-19) - 11(-33) = -74$$ ■

The expansion by minors of the third-order determinant

$$A = \begin{vmatrix} a_{11} & a_{12} & a_{13} \\ a_{21} & a_{22} & a_{23} \\ a_{31} & a_{32} & a_{33} \end{vmatrix}$$

yields

$$\det A = a_{11}a_{22}a_{33} + a_{12}a_{23}a_{31} + a_{13}a_{21}a_{32} - a_{13}a_{22}a_{31} - a_{11}a_{23}a_{32} - a_{12}a_{21}a_{33}$$

This result can also be obtained by using the following device: *Rewrite the first two columns to the right of the determinant and form the indicated products, adding or subtracting as shown.*

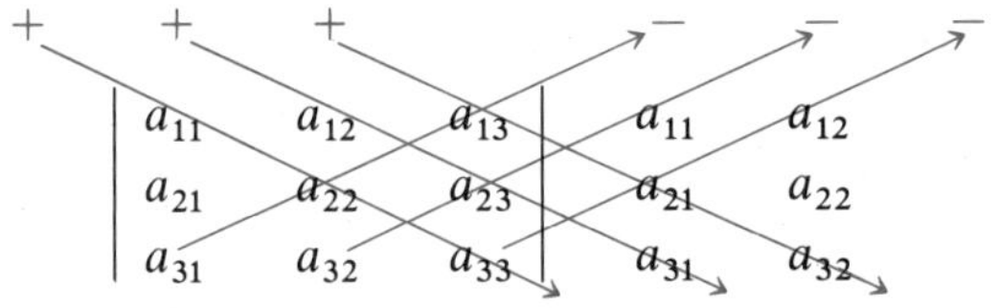

(6.1)

Warning: The device in Equation 6.1 is not used to define a determinant because it cannot be generalized to higher-order determinants; that is, **the device works only for 3 × 3 determinants.**

EXAMPLE 7 Evaluate the determinant in Example 6, using Equation 6.1.

Solution

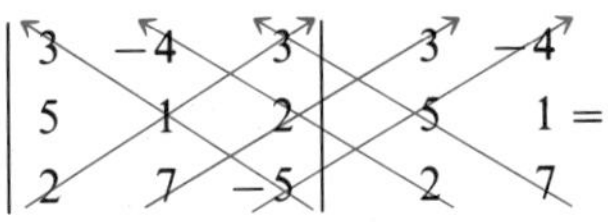

$= (-15) + (-16) + (105) - (6) - (42) - (100) = -74$ ■

EXAMPLE 8 Evaluate

$$\det A = \begin{vmatrix} 6 & 2 & 9 & 1 \\ 8 & 4 & 1 & 4 \\ 2 & 0 & 3 & 5 \\ 2 & 5 & 6 & 2 \end{vmatrix}$$

Solution Notice that we cannot use the method shown in Example 7 since det A is a 4×4 determinant. However, we can use Property 6 of determinants for the following *row* operations.

$$\begin{vmatrix} 6 & 2 & 9 & 1 \\ 8 & 4 & 1 & 4 \\ 2 & 0 & 3 & 5 \\ 2 & 5 & 6 & 2 \end{vmatrix} \xrightarrow[\substack{③ - 5① \to ③ \\ ④ - 2① \to ④}]{② - 4① \to ②} \begin{vmatrix} 6 & 2 & 9 & 1 \\ -16 & -4 & -35 & 0 \\ -28 & -10 & -42 & 0 \\ -10 & 1 & -12 & 0 \end{vmatrix}$$

Therefore

$$\det A = -\begin{vmatrix} -16 & -4 & -35 \\ -28 & -10 & -42 \\ -10 & 1 & -12 \end{vmatrix}$$

We can evaluate this 3×3 determinant, either by the procedure in Example 7 or by transforming all but one element in a row or column to zeros. Either way, the result is

$$\det A = -1552$$

■

Exercises Section 6.6

In Exercises 1–8, evaluate each of the determinants.

1. $\begin{vmatrix} 2 & 4 \\ 3 & 5 \end{vmatrix}$

2. $\begin{vmatrix} -1 & 7 \\ 2 & 1 \end{vmatrix}$

3. $\begin{vmatrix} 0 & 1 \\ 2 & 6 \end{vmatrix}$

4. $\begin{vmatrix} -3 & -4 \\ -2 & -7 \end{vmatrix}$

5. $\begin{vmatrix} 2 & -6 \\ 5 & -3 \end{vmatrix}$

6. $\begin{vmatrix} 4 & 4 \\ -3 & 2 \end{vmatrix}$

7. $\begin{vmatrix} 5 & 10 \\ 2 & 4 \end{vmatrix}$

8. $\begin{vmatrix} -3 & \frac{1}{2} \\ 6 & 4 \end{vmatrix}$

In Exercises 9–17, evaluate the given third-order determinant by two different methods. Compare the results.

9. $\begin{vmatrix} 2 & 0 & 0 \\ 3 & 2 & 4 \\ 1 & -3 & 5 \end{vmatrix}$

10. $\begin{vmatrix} -1 & 6 & 4 \\ -2 & 0 & 5 \\ 3 & 0 & -7 \end{vmatrix}$

11. $\begin{vmatrix} 2 & 3 & -4 \\ 2 & 0 & 3 \\ -1 & 6 & 5 \end{vmatrix}$

12. $\begin{vmatrix} 7 & 2 & 5 \\ 4 & -1 & 8 \\ 3 & 6 & 3 \end{vmatrix}$

13. $\begin{vmatrix} 3 & 1 & 9 \\ 6 & 1 & -2 \\ -4 & 1 & 5 \end{vmatrix}$

14. $\begin{vmatrix} \frac{1}{2} & 6 & 5 \\ 1 & 10 & 2 \\ -2 & 3 & -1 \end{vmatrix}$

15. $\begin{vmatrix} 6 & 7 & 6 \\ 2 & 5 & 2 \\ 3 & 1 & -3 \end{vmatrix}$

16. $\begin{vmatrix} 10 & -6 & 4 \\ 2 & -1 & 2 \\ 5 & 0 & 7 \end{vmatrix}$

17. $\begin{vmatrix} 9 & -6 & 0 \\ -1 & -3 & -1 \\ -5 & -4 & -7 \end{vmatrix}$

18. Solve the equation:
$$\begin{vmatrix} 3 & 1 \\ -1 & x \end{vmatrix} = 0$$

19. Solve the equation:
$$\begin{vmatrix} x & 1 \\ 1 & x \end{vmatrix} = 0$$

20. Solve the inequality:
$$\begin{vmatrix} x & 2 \\ 3 & 5 \end{vmatrix} < \begin{vmatrix} 5 & 2x \\ 4 & 1 \end{vmatrix}$$

21. Compute the following determinant.

$$\begin{Vmatrix} \begin{vmatrix} 3 & 1 \\ -1 & 2 \end{vmatrix} & \begin{vmatrix} 7 & 0 \\ 1 & 2 \end{vmatrix} \\ \begin{vmatrix} 5 & 0 \\ 0 & 1 \end{vmatrix} & \begin{vmatrix} 0 & 0 \\ 0 & 1 \end{vmatrix} \end{Vmatrix}$$

22. Show that a third-order determinant with two identical rows is zero.

23. Solve the equation:

$$\begin{vmatrix} x & 2 & 1 \\ -1 & 3 & 0 \\ 1 & x & 0 \end{vmatrix} = 0$$

24. For what values of k is the following determinant equal to zero?

$$\begin{vmatrix} k & 1 & 0 \\ 0 & 1 & 1 \\ 1 & 0 & 1 \end{vmatrix}$$

25. Evaluate:

$$\begin{vmatrix} 1 & 4 & -2 & 0 \\ 0 & 1 & 1 & 2 \\ -3 & -2 & 1 & 0 \\ -1 & 1 & 2 & 3 \end{vmatrix}$$

26. Evaluate:

$$\begin{vmatrix} 3 & -2 & 0 & 5 \\ -1 & 3 & 6 & 2 \\ 0 & 1 & -1 & 4 \\ 2 & -5 & 1 & 0 \end{vmatrix}$$

27. Prove the six properties of determinants for second-order determinants.

6.7 Solution by Determinants (Cramer's Rule)

Determinants have an immediate and important application to the solution of systems of n equations in n unknowns. For two equations in two unknowns, consider the following system of equations in x and y.

$$a_1x + b_1y = c_1 \tag{6.2}$$

$$a_2x + b_2y = c_2 \tag{6.3}$$

To solve this system algebraically for the x variable, multiply Equation 6.2 by b_2 and Equation 6.3 by $-b_1$ to get

$$a_1b_2x + b_1b_2y = c_1b_2$$

$$-a_2b_1x - b_1b_2y = -c_2b_1$$

Adding the two equations,

$$(a_1b_2 - a_2b_1)x = c_1b_2 - c_2b_1$$

Solving for x on the assumption that $a_1b_2 - a_2b_1 \neq 0$,

$$x = \frac{c_1b_2 - c_2b_1}{a_1b_2 - a_2b_1}$$

By a similar procedure,

$$y = \frac{a_1c_2 - a_2c_1}{a_1b_2 - a_2b_1}$$

Using the definition of a second-order determinant, the numerator and denominator of both expressions may be written in the form

$$x = \frac{\begin{vmatrix} c_1 & b_1 \\ c_2 & b_2 \end{vmatrix}}{\begin{vmatrix} a_1 & b_1 \\ a_2 & b_2 \end{vmatrix}} \qquad y = \frac{\begin{vmatrix} a_1 & c_1 \\ a_2 & c_2 \end{vmatrix}}{\begin{vmatrix} a_1 & b_1 \\ a_2 & b_2 \end{vmatrix}} \tag{6.4}$$

Equation 6.4 is called **Cramer's rule** for the solution of two linear equations in two unknowns. Good practice dictates that in solving a system by this rule, all equations should be expressed in the **standard form** $ax + by = c$. The following observations make Cramer's rule easy to remember when the equations are written in standard form.

- The denominator is the determinant of the coefficient matrix of the system.
- The determinant in the numerator is obtained by replacing the column of coefficients of the variable being determined by the corresponding constant terms.

One of the advantages of Cramer's rule is that the solution of a system of equations may be found with a minimum of algebraic manipulation. If the determinant of the coefficient matrix is nonzero, the system has a unique solution given by Equation 6.4.

EXAMPLE 1 Solve the following system of equations by Cramer's rule.

$$2x + 3y = 11$$
$$-x + 7y = -2$$

Solution

$$x = \frac{\begin{vmatrix} 11 & 3 \\ -2 & 7 \end{vmatrix}}{\begin{vmatrix} 2 & 3 \\ -1 & 7 \end{vmatrix}} = \frac{11(7) - (-2)(3)}{2(7) - (-1)(3)} = \frac{77 + 6}{14 + 3} = \frac{83}{17}$$

$$y = \frac{\begin{vmatrix} 2 & 11 \\ -1 & -2 \end{vmatrix}}{\begin{vmatrix} 2 & 3 \\ -1 & 7 \end{vmatrix}} = \frac{2(-2) - (-1)(11)}{17} = \frac{-4 + 11}{17} = \frac{7}{17}$$

Therefore, the solution is $x = \frac{83}{17}$, $y = \frac{7}{17}$. ■

EXAMPLE 2 Solve the following system of equations by Cramer's rule.

$$-3x + 5y = 2$$
$$7x - 4y = 0$$

Solution

$$x = \frac{\begin{vmatrix} 2 & 5 \\ 0 & -4 \end{vmatrix}}{\begin{vmatrix} -3 & 5 \\ 7 & -4 \end{vmatrix}} = \frac{2(-4) - (0)(5)}{-3(-4) - (5)(7)} = \frac{8}{23}$$

$$y = \frac{\begin{vmatrix} -3 & 2 \\ 7 & 0 \end{vmatrix}}{\begin{vmatrix} -3 & 5 \\ 7 & -4 \end{vmatrix}} = \frac{-3(0) - (2)(7)}{-23} = \frac{14}{23}$$

Therefore, the solution is $x = \frac{8}{23}$, $y = \frac{14}{23}$. ■

Comment: Note that the concepts of consistent, inconsistent, and dependent linear systems may be interpreted in terms of the determinants used in Cramer's rule. If the determinant of the coefficient matrix is zero and the determinants in the numerators of Equation 6.4 are nonzero, the system is *inconsistent;* that is, it has no solution. If both the determinant of the coefficient matrix and all the determinants in the numerators are zero, the system is *dependent*. Otherwise, Cramer's rule gives a unique solution and the system is *consistent*.

EXAMPLE 3 The system

$$\begin{aligned} 3x + 5y &= 2 \\ 6x + 10y &= 1 \end{aligned}$$

is inconsistent since the determinant of the coefficient matrix is

$$\begin{vmatrix} 3 & 5 \\ 6 & 10 \end{vmatrix} = 30 - 30 = 0$$

while the determinants in the numerator expressions of Cramer's rule are easily shown to be nonzero. The system

$$\begin{aligned} -2x + 2y &= 0 \\ x - y &= 0 \end{aligned}$$

is dependent since not only is the determinant of the coefficient matrix equal to zero, but also the determinants in both numerators are zero. Indeed, the solution set in this latter case is the infinite set of ordered pairs of the form (t, t), where t is any real number. ■

Cramer's rule can easily be extended to systems of n equations in n unknowns, but we will be content to show the result of this extension for the case of $n = 3$. The general system of three linear equations in three unknowns,

$$\begin{aligned} a_1x + b_1y + c_1z &= d_1 \\ a_2x + b_2y + c_2z &= d_2 \\ a_3x + b_3y + c_3z &= d_3 \end{aligned}$$

has a solution given by Cramer's rule.

$$x = \frac{\begin{vmatrix} d_1 & b_1 & c_1 \\ d_2 & b_2 & c_2 \\ d_3 & b_3 & c_3 \end{vmatrix}}{\begin{vmatrix} a_1 & b_1 & c_1 \\ a_2 & b_2 & c_2 \\ a_3 & b_3 & c_3 \end{vmatrix}} \quad y = \frac{\begin{vmatrix} a_1 & d_1 & c_1 \\ a_2 & d_2 & c_2 \\ a_3 & d_3 & c_3 \end{vmatrix}}{\begin{vmatrix} a_1 & b_1 & c_1 \\ a_2 & b_2 & c_2 \\ a_3 & b_3 & c_3 \end{vmatrix}} \quad z = \frac{\begin{vmatrix} a_1 & b_1 & d_1 \\ a_2 & b_2 & d_2 \\ a_3 & b_3 & d_3 \end{vmatrix}}{\begin{vmatrix} a_1 & b_1 & c_1 \\ a_2 & b_2 & c_2 \\ a_3 & b_3 & c_3 \end{vmatrix}} \tag{6.5}$$

Notice that Equation 6.5 has the same form as the rule developed for two equations in two unknowns. As in that case, if the equations are written in standard form, $ax + by + cz = d$, the determinants in the denominator are formed from the coefficients of the variables. The determinants in the numerator are formed by replacing the column of coefficients corresponding to the variable of interest by the constant terms on the right side of the equations.

EXAMPLE 4 Solve the following system using Cramer's rule.

$$\begin{aligned} 2x - y + 2z &= 3 \\ x + y - z &= -3 \\ x + z &= 2 \end{aligned}$$

Solution The equations are given in standard form, so Cramer's rule can be used. The determinant in the numerator of y is expanded about the first column, and all others are expanded about the second column to take advantage of the zero element.

$$x = \frac{\begin{vmatrix} 3 & -1 & 2 \\ -3 & 1 & -1 \\ 2 & 0 & 1 \end{vmatrix}}{\begin{vmatrix} 2 & -1 & 2 \\ 1 & 1 & -1 \\ 1 & 0 & 1 \end{vmatrix}}$$

$$= \frac{(-1)(-1)^3\begin{vmatrix} -3 & -1 \\ 2 & 1 \end{vmatrix} + (1)(-1)^4\begin{vmatrix} 3 & 2 \\ 2 & 1 \end{vmatrix} + (0)(-1)^5\begin{vmatrix} 3 & 2 \\ -3 & -1 \end{vmatrix}}{(-1)(-1)^3\begin{vmatrix} 1 & -1 \\ 1 & 1 \end{vmatrix} + (1)(-1)^4\begin{vmatrix} 2 & 2 \\ 1 & 1 \end{vmatrix} + (0)(-1)^5\begin{vmatrix} 2 & 2 \\ 1 & -1 \end{vmatrix}}$$

$$= \frac{(-3 - (-2)) + (3 - 4) - (0)}{(1 - (-1)) + (2 - 2) - (0)} = \frac{-2}{2} = -1$$

$$y = \frac{\begin{vmatrix} 2 & 3 & 2 \\ 1 & -3 & -1 \\ 1 & 2 & 1 \end{vmatrix}}{\begin{vmatrix} 2 & -1 & 2 \\ 1 & 1 & -1 \\ 1 & 0 & 1 \end{vmatrix}} = \frac{2(-3 + 2) - (3 - 4) + (-3 + 6)}{2} = \frac{2}{2} = 1$$

$$z = \frac{\begin{vmatrix} 2 & -1 & 3 \\ 1 & 1 & -3 \\ 1 & 0 & 2 \end{vmatrix}}{\begin{vmatrix} 2 & -1 & 2 \\ 1 & 1 & -1 \\ 1 & 0 & 1 \end{vmatrix}} = \frac{(2 + 3) + (4 - 3)}{2} = \frac{6}{2} = 3$$

Thus, the solution is the ordered triple $(-1, 1, 3)$. ■

EXAMPLE 5 A company buys three kinds of fasteners. Brand *A* fasteners are \$0.30 each, Brand *B* fasteners \$0.15 each, and Brand *C* fasteners \$0.05 each. The total order of 150 fasteners cost \$20.50.

How many of each kind of fastener were purchased if there are twice as many of Brand C as there are of Brand A?

Solution Let

$$N_A = \text{number of Brand } A \text{ fasteners}$$
$$N_B = \text{number of Brand } B \text{ fasteners}$$
$$N_C = \text{number of Brand } C \text{ fasteners}$$

Now form three linear equations in N_A, N_B, and N_C; that is,

$$\begin{aligned} N_A + N_B + N_C &= 150 \quad &&\text{(total number of fasteners)} \\ 30N_A + 15N_B + 5N_C &= 2050 \quad &&\text{(total value of the fasteners in cents)} \\ N_C &= 2N_A \quad &&\text{(relative number of Brands } A \text{ and } C\text{)} \end{aligned}$$

Before using Cramer's rule, write the third equation in the standard form

$$-2N_A + N_C = 0$$

Then

$$N_A = \frac{\begin{vmatrix} 150 & 1 & 1 \\ 2050 & 15 & 5 \\ 0 & 0 & 1 \end{vmatrix}}{\begin{vmatrix} 1 & 1 & 1 \\ 30 & 15 & 5 \\ -2 & 0 & 1 \end{vmatrix}} = \frac{0 - 0 + (2250 - 2050)}{-2(5 - 15) - (0) + (15 - 30)} = \frac{200}{5} = 40$$

$$N_B = \frac{\begin{vmatrix} 1 & 150 & 1 \\ 30 & 2050 & 5 \\ -2 & 0 & 1 \end{vmatrix}}{5} = \frac{-2(750 - 2050) - (0) + (2050 - 4500)}{5} = \frac{150}{5} = 30$$

$$N_C = \frac{\begin{vmatrix} 1 & 1 & 150 \\ 30 & 15 & 2050 \\ -2 & 0 & 0 \end{vmatrix}}{5} = \frac{-2(2050 - 2250) - (0) + (0)}{5} = \frac{400}{5} = 80$$

Consequently, there are 40 Brand A, 30 Brand B, and 80 Brand C fasteners. ■

Exercises Section 6.7

Solve each of the systems of equations in Exercises 1–21 by Cramer's rule.

1. $x - 4y = 2$
   $-2x + y = -4$

2. $2x + 5y = -4$
   $4x + 3y = 6$

3. $3x + 4y = 23$
   $x - 3y = -1$

4. $x + y = 4$
   $x - y = 2$

5. $x - 4y = 8$
   $2x - 8y = 16$

6. $3x + 2y - 6 = 0$
   $x - 3y - 3 = 0$

7. $3x + 4y = 10$
   $6x + 8y = -2$

8. $3x + 5y = 2$
   $6x + 10y = 4$

9. $3x - y - 2 = 0$
   $2x + y - 6 = 0$

10. $r - s = 3$
    $r - 2s = 5$

11. $2x - y - 2 = 0$
    $x + y + 5 = 0$

12. $2s = t + s$
    $6s + 2t = -5$

13. $x + y + z = 8$
$x + y - z = 12$
$x - y + z = 2$

14. $x + 2y - z = 1$
$y + z = 3$
$x - y = 2$

15. $r + 3s + 2t = 2$
$3r + 2s - t = -1$
$r - 3s - 3t = 0$

16. $3x + 4y - 7z = 12$
$6x + 3y + z = 0$
$6x + 8y - 14z = 3$

17. $2x - 3y + 4z = 5$
$5x - 7y + 4z = 4$
$-2x + 3y - 5z = 2$

18. $x + y - z + 3 = 0$
$2x - y + 3z - 12 = 0$
$x + 2y - 3z + 10 = 0$

19. $x + 2y - z = 0$
$x - y + z = 0$
$2x - 3y - 2z = 0$

20. $3m - 5n - 5p = 3$
$m + n - 2p = 7$
$2m - 3n - 2p = 0$

21. $9u - 4v + 2w = 8$
$3u + 2v + w = 1$
$12u - 18w = 17$

22. A company receives a shipment of 25 motors, both AC and DC. There are three more AC than DC motors. How many AC motors are there in the shipment?

23. The width of a rectangle is 6 cm less than its length. If the perimeter of the rectangle is 40 cm, what are the dimensions?

24. A chemist mixes 12 lb of one chemical with 10 lb of another and finds the cost to be \$54. If a mixture of 8 lb of the first chemical and 15 lb of the second costs \$61, what is the price per pound of each chemical used in the mixtures?

25. A rocket traveling at a constant rate of 50 fps passes a checkpoint. One second later a rocket traveling 60 fps passes the same checkpoint. How long does it take for the second rocket to overtake the first?

26. In the following figure, the total number of teeth on two gears is equal to 94. If twice the number of teeth on the small gears is 5 more than the larger, find the number of teeth on each gear.

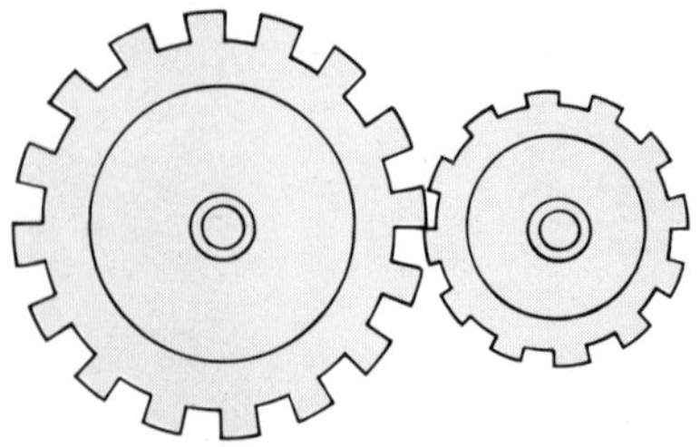

27. A box contains \$19 in nickels, dimes, and quarters. The total number of coins is 100 and there are three times as many nickels as dimes. How many dimes are in the box?

28. The power output of three amplifiers totals 45 w. Twice the power of the first amplifier is equal to the sum of the other two amplifiers together, and the output of the second amplifier is 4 w more than the third. Find the power output of each amplifier.

29. Three antenna wires measure a total length of 50 m. The longest wire is 5 m longer than the next longest and 10 m longer than the shortest. Find the length of each antenna wire.

30. An airplane made a 2000-mile trip with the wind in 3 hr and the return trip against the wind in 4 hr. If the speed of the wind was the same throughout the trip, find the speed of the wind and the average speed of the airplane in still air.

31. The two linear equations

$$R_1(x)u' + Q_1(x)v' = F(x)$$
$$R_2(x)u' + Q_2(x)v' = 0$$

arise in the solution of certain differential equations. Solve for u' and v' using Cramer's rule.

Functions are sometimes specified by their general form and certain points that their graphs must pass through. The following exercises are typical.

32. The graph of $y = ax^2 + bx$ passes through $(4, -2)$ and $(-2, 2)$. Find the values of a and b.

33. Determine the cubic $y = x^3 + ax^2 + bx + c$ whose graph passes through (1, 0), (3, 0), and (0, 1).

34. Determine the cubic that passes through $(-1, 0)$, (0, 0), and (1, 0). See Exercise 33.

35. Determine the specific form of the rational function

$$y = \frac{ax}{x + c}$$

that passes through (1, 2), and (2, 1).

36. Determine the function with general form

$$y = a\frac{x - b}{x - c}$$

that passes through $(2, 0)$, $(0, -1)$, $(-1, 1)$.

6.8 Linear Inequalities in Two Unknowns (Optional)

In Section 2.6 we discussed inequalities in one variable. This section extends the discussion of inequalities to those containing two variables. The operations previously established for inequalities in one variable also apply to inequalities in two variables. The solution set of an inequality in x and y is the set of all ordered pairs (x, y) that satisfy the inequality.

The concept of an inequality in two variables is closely related to the corresponding idea of an equality in two variables. This relationship is best explained in terms of a graphical illustration. Consider the linear equation

$$2x + 3y = -5$$

The graph of this equation is the straight line shown in Figure 6.10. Notice that the line L separates the plane into three disjoint subsets; namely,

1. $L = \{(x, y) \mid 2x + 3y = -5\}$; the set of points making up the line L.
2. $A = \{(x, y) \mid 2x + 3y > -5\}$; the set of points *above* the line L.
3. $B = \{(x, y) \mid 2x + 3y < -5\}$; the set of points *below* the line L.

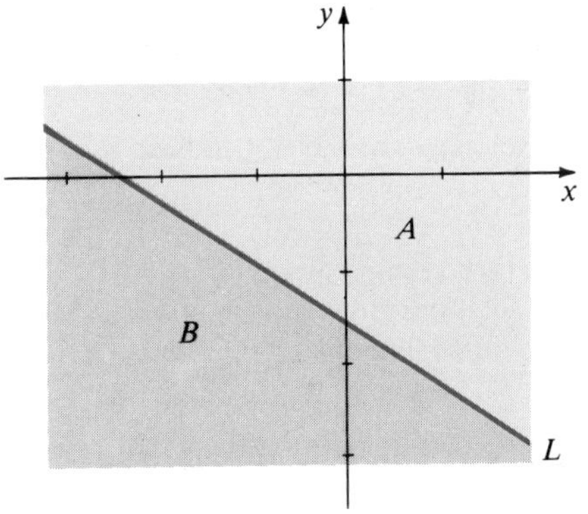

Figure 6.10

Thus, we see that the graph of a linear inequality in two variables corresponds to a *half-plane* composing the region on one side of a straight line. Usually, then, to graph a linear inequality, first draw the line of the corresponding linear equation and decide which half-plane you need. The following examples illustrate how to do this.

EXAMPLE 1 Graph the solution set for the inequality

$$2x + y < 1$$

Solution First draw the line $2x + y = 1$. Figure 6.11 pictures it as a dashed line to indicate its exclusion from the solution set. Now we must decide which side of this line represents the solution set. One way to do this is to select some point (x_1, y_1) not on the line and substitute it into the inequality. If (x_1, y_1) satisfies the inequality, this point lies in the desired region and the half-plane containing (x_1, y_1) is the graph. In this problem, let us use the checkpoint $(0, 0)$.

Since $2(0) + 0 = 0 < 1$ satisfies the inequality, we conclude that the graph of $2x + y < 1$ is the half-plane below the line. The shading in the figure indicates the intended set.

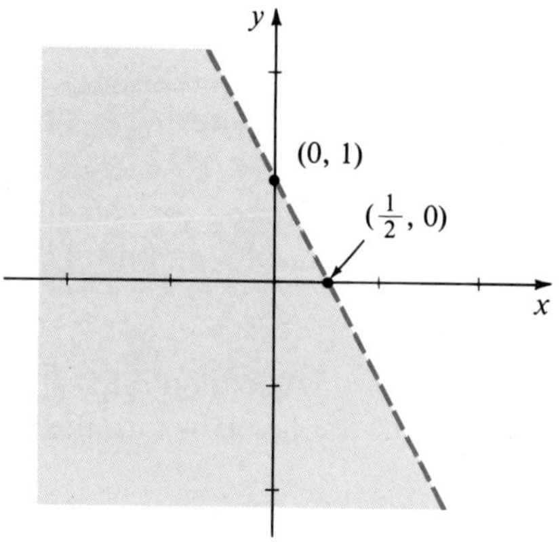

Figure 6.11

■

EXAMPLE 2 Find and graph the solution set for the inequality

$$2x + y - 1 \leq x + 3y + 4$$

Solution By adding $-x - 3y + 1$ to both sides of the inequality, we obtain the equivalent inequality

$$x - 2y \leq 5$$

We then graph $x - 2y = 5$, shown as a solid line in Figure 6.12 to indicate its inclusion in the solution set. At the origin, we find that $x - 2y = 0 < 5$. Therefore, all points on the same side of the line as the origin satisfy $x - 2y \leq 5$. Figure 6.12 shows the solution set.

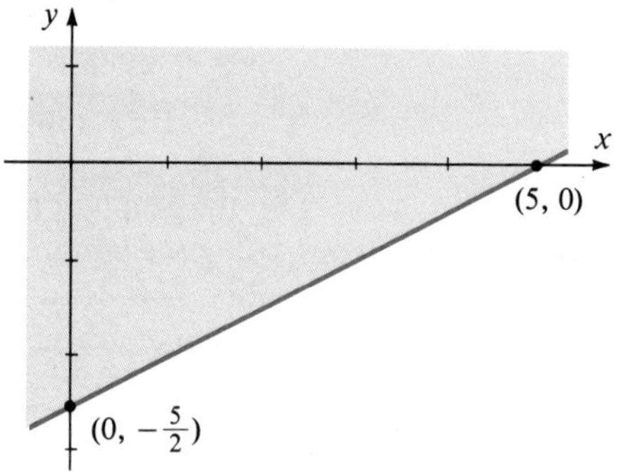

Figure 6.12

■

EXAMPLE 3 Sketch the solution set for the inequality

$$|x| + |y| < 1$$

Solution Because of the absolute values in the expression, it is convenient to consider the representations in each of the four quadrants. By using the definition of the absolute value, we obtain the following inequalities:

in QI: $x + y < 1$
in QII: $-x + y < 1$
in QIII: $-x - y < 1$
in QIV: $x - y < 1$

Each of these inequalities is sketched in Figure 6.13. The total solution set is the union of these individual solution sets, represented in Figure 6.13 by the shaded region.

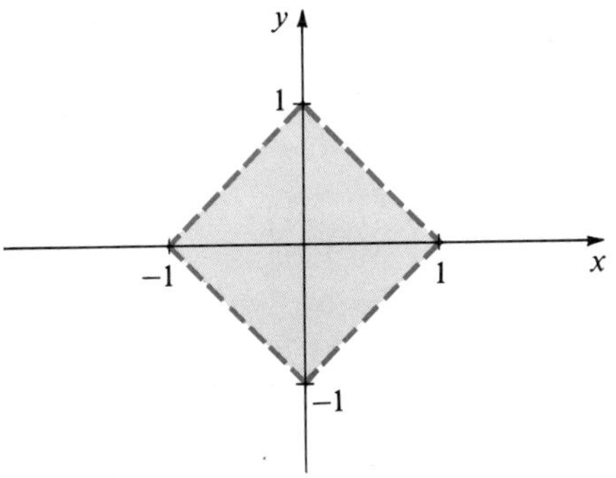

Figure 6.13 ■

EXAMPLE 4 A warehouse has 10,000 sq ft of usable storage space in which to store refrigerators and air conditioners. If each refrigerator requires 6 sq ft and each air conditioner requires 4 sq ft, write an inequality describing the number of each that can be stored in the warehouse. Draw the graph.

Solution The total area needed to store x refrigerators is $6x$ sq ft and that for y air conditioners is $4y$ sq ft. Therefore, the sum $6x + 4y$ must be less than or equal to 10,000 sq ft; that is,

$$6x + 4y \leq 10{,}000$$

Figure 6.14 shows the graph of the line $6x + 4y = 10{,}000$. The desired half-plane lies below this line, as indicated by the shading. Notice that there are some implied restrictions on this problem owing to its physical nature. Since the number of both refrigerators and air conditioners must be greater than zero, the solution is restricted to the triangular region indicated by the dark shading.

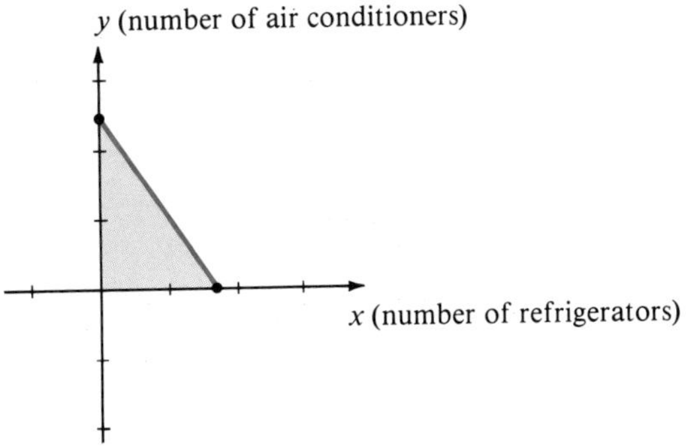

Figure 6.14 ■

Exercises Section 6.8

Graph the solution sets for the inequalities in Exercises 1–16.

1. $x > y$
2. $x \leq y$
3. $3x - y + 7 \leq 0$
4. $y < x + 4$
5. $x + y > x - y$
6. $y - x \geq y + x$
7. $2x - y - 8 > x - 2y + 8$
8. $6x - 2 < y + 1$
9. $3(x - 1) + 4x \geq 7x + y + 2(x - y)$
10. $3x + y + 2x - 3y \leq 2$
11. $|y| < 3$
12. $|x| < 1$
13. $|x| < y$
14. $x \leq |y|$
15. $|x| < 1 - |y|$
16. $|x| + |y| > 1$
17. The formula relating Fahrenheit degrees to degrees Celsius is $F = (\frac{9}{5})C + 32$. For what values of C is $F < 0$?
18. The current in amperes in a certain electrical network is given by $i = 25 - 0.5t$, where t is the elapsed time in milliseconds. For what time t is $i \geq 0$?
19. A retailer wishes to purchase two types of football shoes: a premium brand for \$35 a pair and lesser-quality pair for \$15. Make a sketch showing the possibilities if the capital outlay is limited to \$1000.
20. In designing lighting for a given outdoor area, you are given two different kinds of light bulbs, one 100 w and the other 200 w. The lights will normally be on an average of 6 hr per night. Make a sketch showing the possible combinations of the two different kinds of light bulbs if you are limited to a cost of \$1.00 per night and the cost per kilowatt hour is \$0.05.

6.9 Systems of Linear Inequalities (Optional)

Recall that the graph of a linear inequality in two variables is a half-plane that consists of the region on one side of a straight line. To solve a system of two or more inequalities, graph each inequality on the same plane. The solution set is then the region common to all of the given inequalities.

EXAMPLE 1 Solve the system

$$6x + 3y < 12$$
$$x + 2y \leq 2$$

Solution The shaded area in Figure 6.15 represents the solution set.

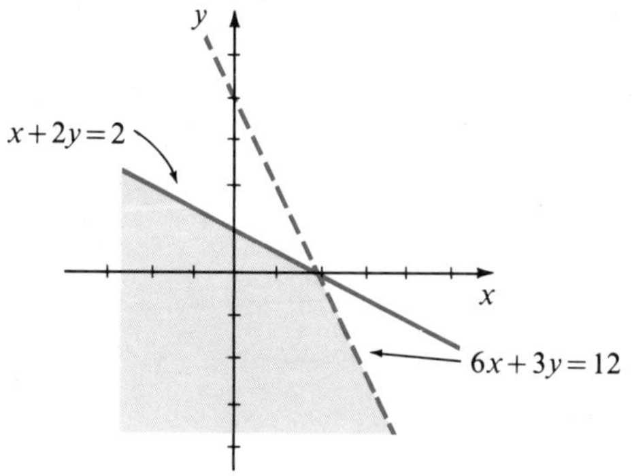

Figure 6.15

■

EXAMPLE 2 Solve the system

$$6x + y \le 24$$
$$2x + 3y \le 24$$
$$x \ge 0$$
$$y \ge 0$$

Solution In Figure 6.16, each of the four indicated half-planes are drawn and their intersection is the shaded area.

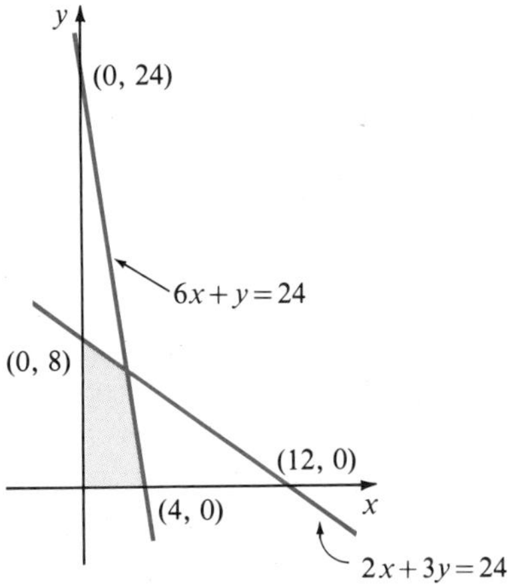

Figure 6.16

■

6.10 Linear Programming (Optional)

In the 1940s, mathematicians developed several techniques to facilitate decision-making in fields such as business and economics when certain limitations, or constraints, are known to exist. One of these methods is called **linear programming.**

In the context of linear programming, the term *programming* refers to the allocation of some usually limited resources to optimize some quantity such as cost, profit, or distance. (Thus, the word programming in this sense is *not* synonymous with its meaning in computer programming.) These allocation problems are linear in the sense that the equations and inequalities describing the constraints and the function to be optimized are linear. Thus, linear programming is a method for optimizing some linear function, called the **objective function,** subject to constraints given in linear form.

For example, a typical objective function might be $P = 3x - 2y$, and some typical constraints are $x \ge 0$, $y \ge 0$, and $x + y \le 2$. Any pair of numbers that satisfies the linear constraints is called a **feasible solution.** Thus, $x = 1$, $y = 1$ is a feasible pair for the example given. If a feasible solution gives the maximum value for P, it is said to be **optimal.** For the objective function $P = 3x - 2y$, $P(1, 1) = 1$. For the feasible point $(2, 0)$, $P(2, 0) = 6$. How do we know when a feasible point will give the maximum value for P? Certain linear-programming problems in two variables can be solved graphically. The technique is explained in the context of Example 1.

EXAMPLE 1 Determine the maximum solution for $P = 3x - 2y$, given the constraints

$$x \geq 0, y \geq 0, x + y \leq 2$$

Solution We begin by graphing the set of feasible solutions as shown in Figure 6.17(a). From this we want to obtain a point for which P is maximum. Observe that for any particular value P_0, of P, $3x - 2y = P_0$ is a straight line with slope $\frac{3}{2}$ and y-intercept $-P_0/2$, as in Figure 6.17(b). Thus, P will be maximum when the y-intercept of the line $y = (3/2)x - P/2$ has the smallest value.

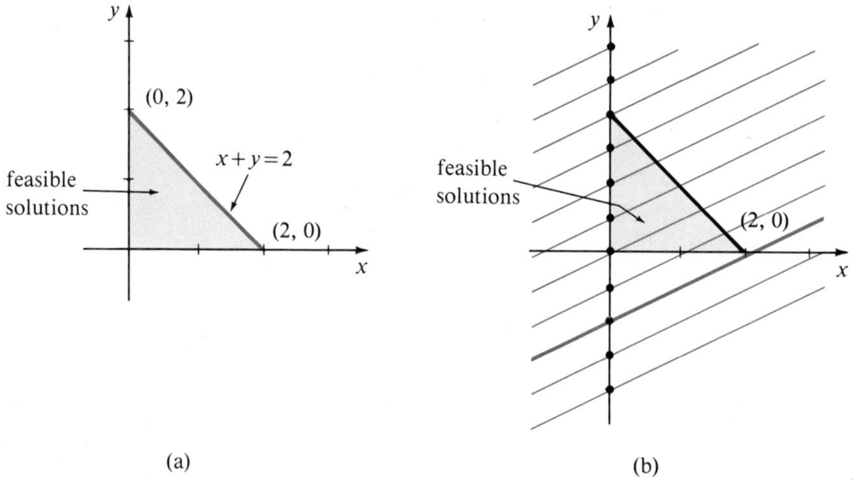

Figure 6.17

(We need the smallest value since the intercept is the *negative* of $P/2$.) Since our optimal solution must be feasible, the line $y = (3/2)x - (1/2)P$ must intersect the feasible region. Hence, we need only select the line from the family of parallel lines with slope $\frac{3}{2}$ that has the smallest y-intercept *and* intersects the feasible region. This is shown in Figure 6.17(b) to be the line with x-intercept (2, 0). Thus the optimal feasible solution is (2, 0) and the maximum value is 6. ■

The solution to Example 1 was a corner point of the feasible region. This is no accident, for there is a theorem proven in most elementary linear-programming texts that states:

> **The optimal solution, if there is one, is found at a corner point of the graph of the set of feasible solutions.**

In summary, the graphical method of solving a linear-programming problem in two variables is:

1. Find the solution set to the set of linear-inequality constraints. This is the set of feasible solutions to the problem.
2. Determine the coordinates of all corner points.
3. Evaluate the given objective function at all corner points to find the solution.

EXAMPLE 2 Minimize $K = y + 5x$ subject to $2x + 3y \geq 12$, $3x + y \geq 11$, $x \geq 0$, $y \geq 0$.

Solution Figure 6.18 shows the feasible region obtained by graphing $2x + 3y = 12$, $3x + y = 11$ and determining the point of intersection of those two lines by simultaneous solution of the two equations.

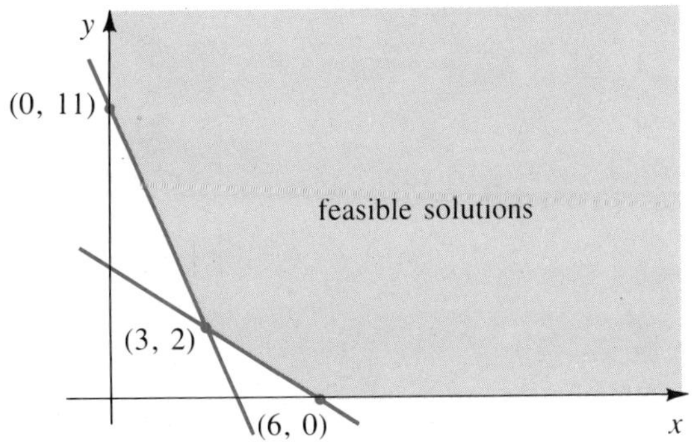

Figure 6.18

The constraint region is unbounded, but the key to the solution is still the vertices of the region. We evaluate K at the vertices:

at (6, 0), $K = 0 + 5(6) = 30$

at (3, 2), $K = 2 + 5(3) = 17$

at (0, 11) $K = 11 + 5(0) = 11$

Thus, K is minimized at (0, 11) and the minimum value is 11 ■

The practical applications of simple linear-programming problems are numerous. Establishing the constraint inequalities is usually the most difficult task.

EXAMPLE 3 A small company produces two styles of the same book, paperback and hardback. Producing the paperback yields a profit of \$400 per day while the hardback yields \$700 per day. The company can employ only one printing crew, which will work only five days a week. Paper limitations demand that the paperback be produced no more than three days per week, whereas the hardback production is limited to four days or less per week. If you owned the company, how would you assign the printing crew?

Solution First, establish the constraints in mathematical terms. Let x equal the number of days the paperback is printed and let y equal the number of days the hardback is printed. Then we want to maximize the profit given by $P = 400x + 700y$. The constraints are

$x + y \leq 5$	(restriction to 5-day week)
$x \leq 3$	(restriction on paperback supplies)
$y \leq 4$	(restriction on hardback supplies)
$x \geq 0, \quad y \geq 0$	(number of days must be positive or zero in either case)

Figure 6.19 displays the graph of the constraint inequalities. The corner points are (0, 4), (1, 4), (3, 2), (3, 0), and (0, 0). The value of the profit at each of these points is

at (0, 4), $P = 2800$

at (1, 4), $P = 3200$

at (3, 2), $P = 2600$
at (3, 0), $P = 1200$
at (0, 0), $P = 0$

Hence the crew should devote one day to paperbacks and four to hardbacks to realize the greatest profit, \$3200.

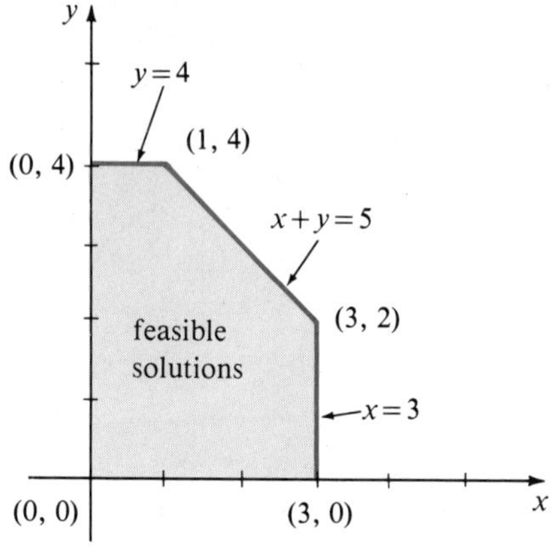

Figure 6.19

■

EXAMPLE 4 A small shop makes both drum brakes and disk brakes. Both types require a lathe and a grinder in production. Drum brakes require 2 hr on the lathe and 4 hr on the grinder, and disk brakes require 3 hr on the lathe and 2 hr on the grinder. The company makes \$14 profit on drum brakes and \$18 on disk brakes. Assuming that the company has one lathe and one grinder and that both machines are used 16 hr per day, how many of each should the company make in order to make the largest profit?

Solution List the required times in a table.

	Lathe	Grinder
Drum brake	2 hr	4 hr
Disk brake	3 hr	2 hr

Let x equal the number of drum brakes produced and y equal the number of disk brakes. Then we want to maximize the profit, $P = 14x + 18y$. The constraints are

$2x + 3y \leq 16$ (restriction of lathe to 16-hour day)
$4x + 2y \leq 16$ (restriction of grinder to 16-hour day)
$x \geq 0, y \geq 0$ (number of pieces made must be positive or zero)

Figure 6.20 pictures the graph of the constraint inequalities. We leave it for you to show that the corner point, (2, 4), gives the maximum profit. Hence, the company makes the maximum profit by producing two drum brakes and four disk brakes. What is the maximum profit?

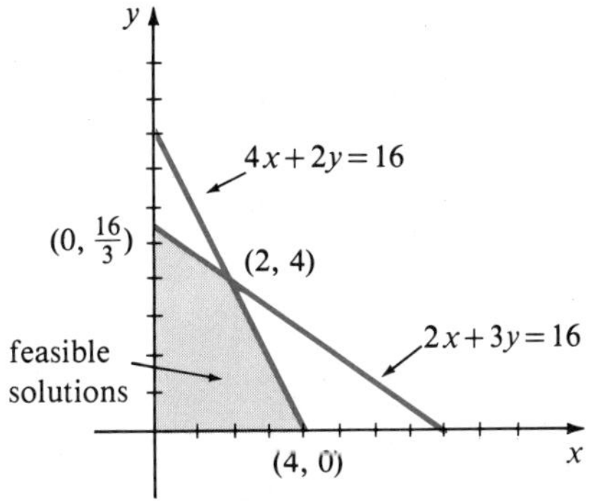

Figure 6.20

Exercises Sections 6.9 and 6.10

In Exercises 1–15, use a graphical method to solve the given system of inequalities.

1. $x \le 2$
   $y > 6$
2. $x > -1$
   $x + y > 0$
3. $x \le 0$
   $y \le x$
4. $x - 4y \le 2$
   $-2x + y \ge -4$
5. $2x + 5y > -4$
   $4x + 3y \le 6$
6. $x + y < 4$
   $x - y > 2$
7. $x \ge 0$
   $y \ge 0$
   $2x + 3y \le 6$
8. $x \ge 0$
   $y \ge 0$
   $2x + y \ge 2$
9. $y \ge 0$
   $x - 3y \ge -3$
   $-2x + y \ge -4$
10. $x > 2$
    $x < 5$
    $y > -1$
11. $x + y < 4$
    $2x + y < 8$
    $x - y > 2$
12. $4x + 3y \le 6$
    $2x + 5y \ge -4$
    $-2x + y \le 2$
13. $x > 0, y > 0$
    $x + y < 2$
    $2x + y > 1$
14. $2x - y > 1$
    $x - y < 1$
    $x > 0, y > 0$
15. $x + 2y > 2$
    $x - y < 1$
    $x > 0, y > 0$

In Exercises 16–30, solve the indicated linear-programming problems.

16. Given $x \ge 0$, $y \ge 0$, $x \le 10$, $x + y \le 15$, maximize $P = 3x + 2y$.
17. Given $x \ge 0$, $y \ge 0$, $y \le 2$, $x + 2y \le 8$, maximize $P = x + 3y$.
18. Given $x \ge 0$, $y \ge 0$, $x + y \le 2$, $x + 3y \le 4$, maximize $P = 2x + 5y$.
19. Given $x \ge 0$, $y \ge 0$, $x + y \le 5$, $x + 2y \le 8$, maximize $P = 5x + y$.
20. Given $x \ge 0$, $y \ge 0$, $3x + 5y \le 30$, $2x + y \le 8$, maximize (a) $P = 3x + 2y$; (b) $P = x + 5y$.
21. Given $x \ge 0$, $y \ge 0$, $x + 3y \le 8$, $2x + y \le 6$, maximize (a) $P = 2x + 3y$; (b) $P = 3x + y$.
22. Given $x \ge 0$, $y \ge 0$, $x + y \ge 5$, $x + 2y \ge 8$, minimize $P = 7x + 2y$.
23. Given $x \ge 0$, $y \ge 0$, $x \le 2$, $x + 2y \ge 3$, $x + 3y \ge 4$, minimize $P = 5x + 3y$.
24. Given $x \ge 0$, $y \ge 0$, $x + 2y \le 10$, $3x + y \le 9$, maximize $P = 2x + y$.
25. Given $x \ge 0$, $y \ge 0$, $2x + y \le 5$, $x + 2y \le 4$, maximize $P = 3x + y$.
26. A businessman finds that his profit equation is $P = 5x + 2y$, where x is the number of desks and y is the number of book cabinets he sells. How many of each should he sell each day to maximize his profit if

$$x \ge 0, \quad y \ge 0, \quad x + \frac{1}{2}y \le 8, \quad \frac{1}{2}x + y \le 7$$

are the constraints on the profit equation?

27. A company makes \$10 on steel castings and \$8 on aluminum castings. If x is the number of steel

castings and y the number of aluminum, the profit equation is $P = 10x + 8y$. Company engineers have found that they must satisfy the following constraints for each day's production:

$$x \geq 0, \quad y \geq 0, \quad 2x + 3y \leq 120, \quad 4x + y \leq 90$$

How many of each kind of casting should the company make each day to maximize its profit?

28. A company produces deluxe and economy model radios. Each economy model yields a profit of \$4, whereas each deluxe model yields \$10 profit. Both models require approximately the same amount of material to build, and the supply allows for a total of 500 radios per day. The sales force reports that the demand for the economy model does not exceed 350 per day but the deluxe radio can be sold as fast as it is made. The deluxe model requires twice as much time to build as the economy, and if only the economy model were built, there would be enough time to produce 700 radios per day. How many economy models and deluxe models should the company construct to maximize its profit?

29. A woman wishes to invest \$20,000, part at 7% and part at 8.5%. The amount she invests at 8.5% cannot be more than twice the amount she invests at 7%. How much should she deposit at each rate to maximize total income? Only multiples of \$100 will be invested.

30. A company produces two kinds of vacuum cleaners, with profits of \$5 and \$8, respectively, on the economy and the deluxe models. No more than 1000 of the economy model can be made per day, and the deluxe model takes three times as long to make. If only the economy model were made, time would allow for production of 1300 per day. Find the number of each that should be built to maximize the profit, and find the maximum profit.

Review Exercises Chapter 6

In Exercises 1–10, solve each of the systems by a method of elimination of a variable.

1. $x + 3y = 5$
$2x - 3y = 1$

2. $3a - b = 5$
$5a + 3b = 13$

3. $2s + 5t = -4$
$6s + 8t = 10$

4. $2x + 3y = 2$
$5x - 4y + 1 = 0$

5. $5x + 6z + 3 = 0$
$7x + 4z - 9 = 0$

6. $4a + 5c = 10$
$7a - 3c = 41$

7. $x + y + z = 1$
$x + y - z = 2$
$x - y + z = 3$

8. $x + y + z = 2$
$3x - y - 2z = 4$
$5x - 2y + 3z = -6$

9. $a + 2b - 3c = 1$
$b - c - 4 = 0$
$b + c - a = 5$

10. $2r + s + 2t = 5$
$4r - s - 3t = 1$
$8r + s - t = 5$

In Exercises 11–16, solve each system using matrix notation.

11. $3x + 5y - 13 = 0$
$-x + 3y - 5 = 0$

12. $4x + y = 11$
$5x + 3y = 5$

13. $x - 2y = 1$
$x + 2y = 3$

14. $3a - 4b = 8$
$9a - 12b = 24$

15. $a - 2b + 3c = 4$
$-3a + 4b - c = -2$
$2a + b - 4c = 3$

16. $3r - 2s + t = 1$
$r + s + t = 0$
$s - 2t = 2$

In Exercises 17–20, solve each nonlinear system.

17. $y + x = -6$
$y + x^2 = 0$

18. $x^2 + 2y = 0$
$4y + 3x = 0$

19. $x^2 + y^2 = 6$
$x^2 - y^2 = 2$

20. $x^2 + 4y^2 = 4$
$2x^2 + y^2 = 8$

In Exercises 21–24, find $A + B$, or tell why the operation cannot be done.

21. $A = \begin{bmatrix} 3 & 5 \\ -1 & 2 \end{bmatrix}, \quad B = \begin{bmatrix} -2 & 4 & 6 \\ 0 & 1 & 5 \end{bmatrix}$

22. $A = \begin{bmatrix} 2 & 1 \\ -3 & 4 \\ 1 & 1 \end{bmatrix}, \quad B = \begin{bmatrix} 0 & 7 \\ 3 & -5 \\ 2 & -2 \end{bmatrix}$

23. $A = \begin{bmatrix} 1 & 1 & 2 \\ 2 & 3 & 2 \\ 0 & 4 & -1 \end{bmatrix}, \quad B = \begin{bmatrix} -3 & 7 & 6 \\ 0 & -2 & 3 \\ -2 & 7 & 1 \end{bmatrix}$

24. $A = \begin{bmatrix} 2 & 2 & 3 \\ -1 & 4 & 3 \end{bmatrix}, \quad B = \begin{bmatrix} 5 & 2 & 8 \\ 3 & -2 & -6 \end{bmatrix}$

In Exercises 25–30, find AB and BA, or tell why the operation cannot be done.

25. $A = \begin{bmatrix} 2 & 3 & -1 \end{bmatrix}, \quad B = \begin{bmatrix} -1 \\ 2 \\ 4 \end{bmatrix}$

26. $A = \begin{bmatrix} 1 & 2 \\ 3 & -2 \end{bmatrix}$, $B = \begin{bmatrix} 2 & 3 & 1 \\ -3 & 0 & 5 \end{bmatrix}$

27. $A = \begin{bmatrix} 2 & -1 \\ 3 & 0 \end{bmatrix}$, $B = \begin{bmatrix} 5 & -3 \\ 1 & 7 \end{bmatrix}$

28. $A = \begin{bmatrix} 0 & 1 \\ 1 & -1 \end{bmatrix}$, $B = \begin{bmatrix} 1 & 0 \\ 0 & 0 \end{bmatrix}$

29. $A = \begin{bmatrix} 2 & 1 & -1 \\ 4 & 0 & 1 \end{bmatrix}$, $B = \begin{bmatrix} 2 & -3 \\ 1 & 2 \\ 4 & 8 \end{bmatrix}$

30. $A = \begin{bmatrix} 2 & 4 \\ 1 & 0 \\ -1 & 1 \end{bmatrix}$, $B = \begin{bmatrix} 2 & 1 & 4 \\ -3 & 2 & 8 \end{bmatrix}$

In Exercises 31–36, find the inverse of each matrix.

31. $\begin{bmatrix} 1 & 2 \\ 3 & 2 \end{bmatrix}$

32. $\begin{bmatrix} -1 & 3 \\ 4 & -2 \end{bmatrix}$

33. $\begin{bmatrix} -1 & 4 \\ 3 & 5 \end{bmatrix}$

34. $\begin{bmatrix} 5 & 3 \\ 2 & 1 \end{bmatrix}$

35. $\begin{bmatrix} 1 & 1 & -1 \\ 2 & 0 & 1 \\ 0 & -2 & 3 \end{bmatrix}$

36. $\begin{bmatrix} -2 & 2 & 0 \\ 1 & 3 & 1 \\ 3 & 1 & 1 \end{bmatrix}$

In Exercises 37–42, solve each system of equations by using the method of matrix inversion.

37. $3x + 5y - 13 = 0$
$-x + 3y - 5 = 0$

38. $4x + y = 11$
$5x + 3y = 5$

39. $x - 2y = 1$
$x + 2y = 3$

40. $3a - 4b = 8$
$9a - 12b = 24$

41. $a - 2b + 3c = 4$
$-3a + 4b - c = -2$
$2a + b - 4c = 3$

42. $3r - 2s + t = 1$
$r + s + t = 0$
$s - 2t = 2$

Evaluate each of the determinants in Exercises 43–52.

43. $\begin{vmatrix} 2 & -1 \\ 3 & 2 \end{vmatrix}$

44. $\begin{vmatrix} 0 & 5 \\ -2 & 7 \end{vmatrix}$

45. $\begin{vmatrix} -8 & 6 \\ 5 & -2 \end{vmatrix}$

46. $\begin{vmatrix} -5 & -7 \\ 3 & -4 \end{vmatrix}$

47. $\begin{vmatrix} 7 & -3 & 2 \\ 4 & -5 & 12 \\ -21 & 9 & -6 \end{vmatrix}$

48. $\begin{vmatrix} 2 & 0 & -2 \\ -3 & 1 & 0 \\ 1 & 2 & -1 \end{vmatrix}$

49. $\begin{vmatrix} 1 & 5 & 4 \\ -2 & 3 & -1 \\ 2 & -1 & 5 \end{vmatrix}$

50. $\begin{vmatrix} -1 & 4 & -5 \\ 6 & 1 & 0 \\ 9 & -7 & 3 \end{vmatrix}$

51. $\begin{vmatrix} 2 & 2 & -1 & 1 \\ 0 & 1 & 3 & 2 \\ -1 & 0 & 1 & 1 \\ 0 & 2 & -2 & 1 \end{vmatrix}$

52. $\begin{vmatrix} 1 & -1 & 1 & -1 \\ 2 & 0 & -1 & 0 \\ 1 & -2 & 3 & 2 \\ 0 & 1 & 3 & 3 \end{vmatrix}$

53. Solve the equation $\begin{vmatrix} 2 & 5 \\ x & 1 \end{vmatrix} = 0.$

54. Solve the equation $\begin{vmatrix} x & 4 \\ 1 & x \end{vmatrix} = 0.$

Use the method of determinants (Cramer's rule) to solve each system of equations in Exercises 55–60.

55. $5x = 2y + 8$
$4x = 3y + 19$

56. $-2x + 5y = -11$
$x + 2y = 1$

57. $-b + 3c = 1$
$a - 2c = 3$
$2a + 5c = 0$

58. $3x + y + 2z = 1$
$-2x - 4y + 2z = 3$
$x + 2y - z = 1$

59. $3r - s - t = 4$
$r + 3s - 2t = 2$
$2r + 6s - 4t = 4$

60. $x + 2y - z = -5$
$x - \frac{1}{2}y + z = 4$
$3x + 3y + 4z = 5$

61. Two angles are complementary and one angle is 3° larger than the other. Find the two angles.

62. The discharge rate of two pipes together is 50 cu ft/sec. If the difference of the rates of the two pipes is 4 cu ft/sec, what is the discharge rate of each?

63. To finance a capital improvement to its plant, a company borrows \$750,000, part at 9% and part at 11%. If the interest on the two loans amounts to \$80,000, what is the amount of each loan?

64. A boat has enough fuel to cruise 7 mph for 5 hr. How far upstream can the boat go and be able to return to the starting point if the current is 2 mph?

65. A solar heating system requires 250 gal of a fluid that is 40% antifreeze. Solutions are available for mixing that are 10%, 30%, and 50% antifreeze. If it is desired to use twice as much of the 50% solution as the 30% solution, how much of each of the three solutions should be used?

66. Three electric currents total 25 A. The largest is 3 A greater than the next largest, and 5 A greater than the smallest. Find the three currents.

In Exercises 67–70, solve graphically the systems of inequalities.

67. $x + y < 1$
$2x - y < 5$

68. $3x - 4y \leq 5$
$x + 2y > 2$

69. $2x + 3y \geq 6$
$x - 2y < 8$

70. $x - 5y \leq 10$
$3x + 5y \leq 15$

In Exercises 71–74, solve the indicated linear programming problems.

71. Given $x \geq 0$, $y \geq 0$, $x \leq 8$, $x + y \leq 12$, maximize $P = x + 2y$.

72. Given $x \geq 0$, $y \geq 0$, $x + y \leq 3$, $x + 2y \leq 4$, maximize $P = 5x + 2y$.

73. Given $x \geq 0$, $y \geq 0$, $x + y \geq 4$, $x + 2y \geq 6$, minimize $P = 3x + 5y$.

74. Given $x \geq 0$, $y \geq 0$, $2x + y \geq 4$, $2x + 3y \geq 6$, minimize $P = \frac{1}{2}x + y$.

Test 1 Chapter 6

Answer True or False to Exercises 1–10.

1. The solution set to a system of two linear equations in two unknowns is empty if the graphs of the two equations do not intersect.
2. Cramer's rule gives the solution to a system of linear equations in terms of determinants.
3. If A and B are square matrices and if $AB = BA = I$ (the identity matrix), then B is the inverse of A.
4. A square matrix will always have an inverse.
5. Equivalent systems of equations have the same solution set.
6. The determinant of a matrix is always positive or zero.
7. A minor of a 2×2 matrix is an element of the matrix.
8. If every element in one row of a square matrix A is 0, then $\det A = 0$.
9. If every element in one row of a square matrix A is 1, then $\det A = 0$.
10. Solutions to a system of equations in two unknowns are displayed graphically as the points at which the graphs of the equations cross the x-axis.
11. Let $A = \begin{bmatrix} 2 & 1 \\ 3 & -1 \end{bmatrix}$ and $B = \begin{bmatrix} 0 & 1 & -1 \\ 2 & 2 & 4 \end{bmatrix}$.

    Find AB and BA, or explain why the operation cannot be done.
12. Solve the following system by using matrix notation.

$$x + y + z = 2$$
$$3x - y - 2z = 4$$
$$5x - 2y + 3z = -6$$

13. Solve the following system by using Cramer's rule.

$$x - 5y = 7$$
$$3x + 2y = 4$$

14. Solve the following system.

$$x^2 + y^2 = 9$$
$$x^2 - y^2 = 1$$

15. Graphically solve the following system.

$$x + y > 1$$
$$2x - y \leq 5$$

16. Find the inverse matrix for $\begin{bmatrix} 3 & 1 & 1 \\ -1 & 2 & 0 \\ 0 & 0 & 5 \end{bmatrix}$.

Test 2 Chapter 6

1. Solve the following system graphically.

$$2x + 3y = 2$$
$$5x - 4y = -1$$

2. Solve the system in Problem 1 by the method of elimination.
3. Let $A = [\,-1 \quad 4 \quad 2\,]$ and $B = \begin{bmatrix} 3 \\ -2 \end{bmatrix}$. Find

AB and BA, or explain why the operation cannot be done.

4. Find the inverse for $\begin{bmatrix} -1 & 0 & 2 \\ 0 & 1 & 3 \\ 3 & 2 & 1 \end{bmatrix}$.

5. Evaluate the following using expansion by minors.

$$\begin{vmatrix} 3 & 2 & -1 \\ 5 & 8 & 2 \\ -4 & 1 & 0 \end{vmatrix}$$

6. Solve the following system by using matrix notation.

$$2r + s + 2t = 5$$
$$4r - s - 3t = 1$$
$$8r + s - t = 5$$

7. Use Cramer's rule to solve the following system.

$$3x - 4y = 5$$
$$-2x + y = -3$$

8. Use Cramer's rule to solve the following system.

$$x + z = 5$$
$$y - x = 0$$
$$z - y = -1$$

9. Graphically solve the following system of inequalities.

$$3x - 4y \leq 5$$
$$x + 2y > 2$$

10. Maximize the function $P = 3x + 4y$, subject to the constraints $x \geq 0$, $y \geq 0$, $x + 3y \leq 6$, $2x + y \leq 7$.

7

Vectors and Complex Numbers*

7.1 Vectors in the Plane

Some physical quantities such as temperature, length, or volume can be described by a single number. These are examples of **scalar** quantities. Other quantities such as velocity, acceleration, or force can only be described by giving both a magnitude and a direction. For example, a velocity of 70 mph to the north is quite different from 70 mph to the south.

To describe quantities that have a magnitude and an associated direction, we use geometric **vectors.** Usually an arrow represents a vector quantity. Its length corresponds to the magnitude of the quantity and the direction of the arrowhead gives its direction. Thus, in Figure 7.1, one arrow represents a velocity of 100 mph north and the other a velocity of 200 mph northeast.

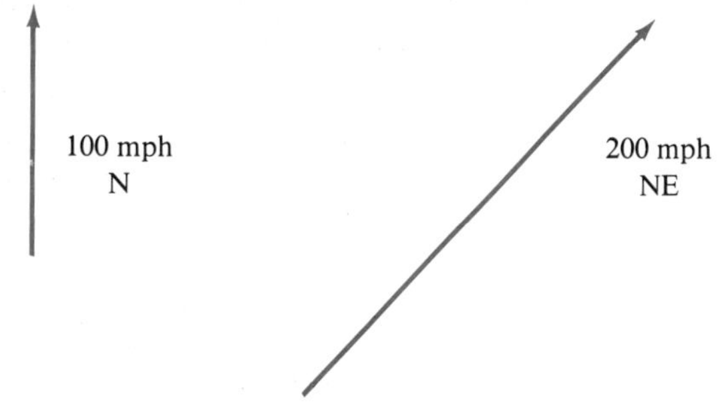

Figure 7.1

Vectors are given in boldface to distinguish them from scalars. The length of a vector **F** is denoted by $|\mathbf{F}|$ and is always a positive quantity. For the sake of completeness, we shall on occasion need to consider a vector with zero length. Such a vector, called the **zero vector,** is denoted by **0** and has an undefined direction.

For mathematical purposes, two vectors are considered the same if they have the same direction and length, regardless of the location of the initial point of the vector. Thus, in Figure 7.2 all the vectors are mathematically equivalent.

* This chapter requires a rudimentary understanding of elementary trigonometry. See the appendix for the basic definitions.

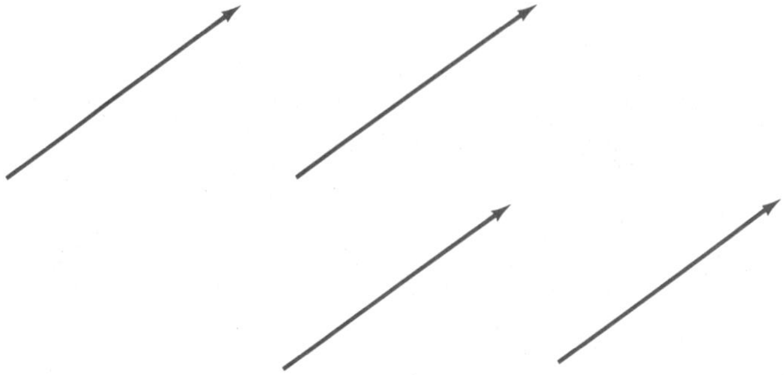

Figure 7.2

Note that this type of vector equality may not always be the kind you need. For example, in Figure 7.3, if **F** is a 10-lb force pointing down, it does make a difference as to which place it is applied. Vectors for which you may ignore the actual point of application are said to be *free*. The physical situation shown in Figure 11.3 cannot be described using free vectors.

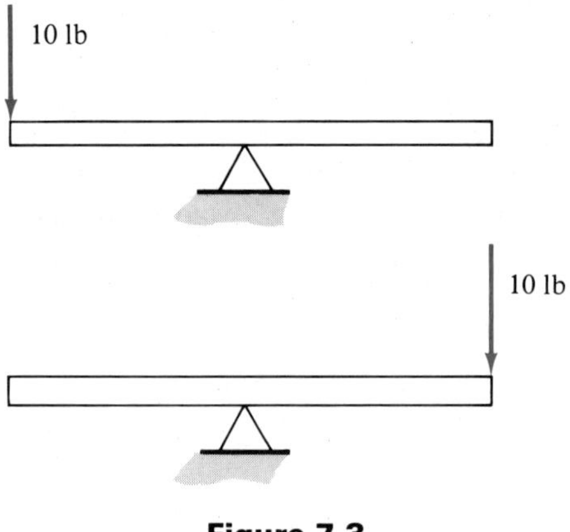

Figure 7.3

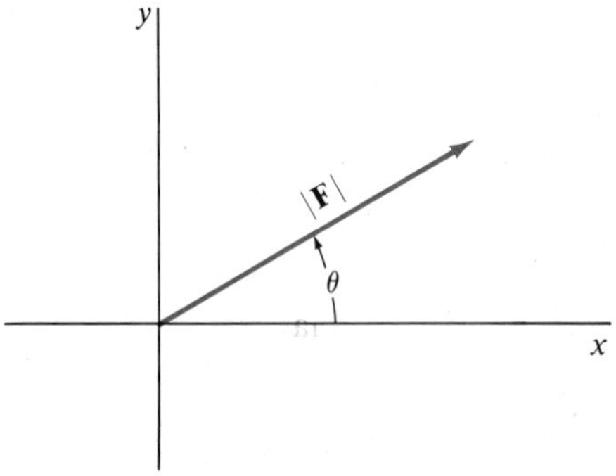

Figure 7.4

By first placing a coordinate system on the plane, we may move all the vectors in this plane so their initial points are at the origin. See Figure 7.4. Such vectors are said to be in **standard position.** In effect, a vector at the origin represents all other vectors with the same direction and length.

If a vector is placed in standard position, its length can be found from the Pythagorean theorem. The direction of the vector is the angle it makes with the positive x-axis.

EXAMPLE 1 Find the magnitude and direction of the vector **F** in standard position whose terminal point is at (2, 1).

Solution Figure 7.5 shows the length of the vector to be

$$|\mathbf{F}| = \sqrt{2^2 + 1^2} = \sqrt{5}$$

and the angle θ that **F** makes with the positive x-axis

$$\theta = \text{Arctan}\ (0.5) = 26.6^\circ$$

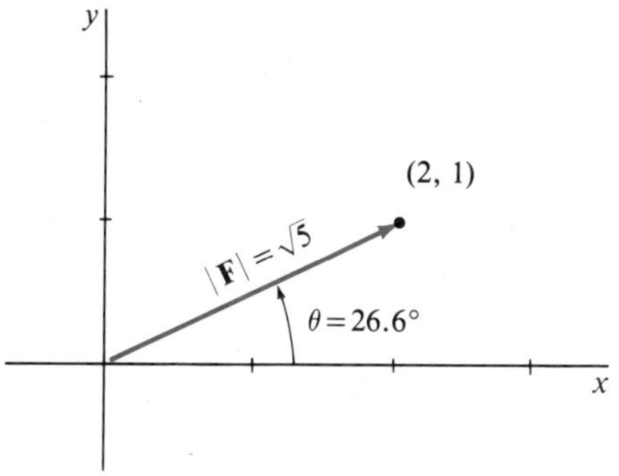

Figure 7.5 ■

The perpendicular projections of the vector onto the x- and y-axes are called the **components** of the vector. We say that a vector is resolved into its x and y components, called the **horizontal** and **vertical components of F**, respectively. Resolving a vector into its x and y components is a simple problem of trigonometry.

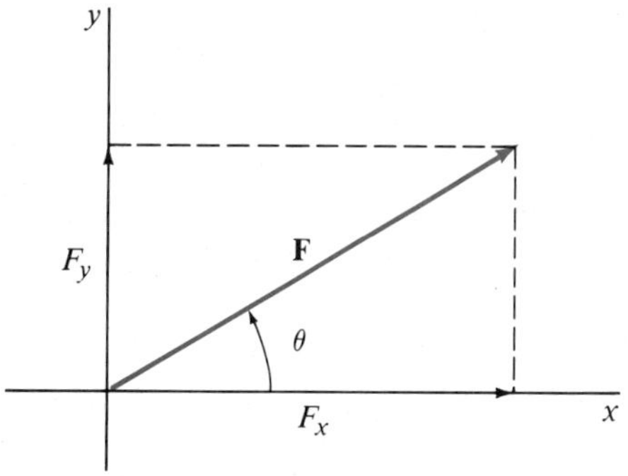

Figure 7.6

From Figure 7.6,

$$F_x = |\mathbf{F}| \cos \theta$$
$$F_y = |\mathbf{F}| \sin \theta$$
$$F_x^2 + F_y^2 = |\mathbf{F}|^2$$

EXAMPLE 2 Find the horizontal and vertical components of a force vector of magnitude 15 lb acting at an angle of 30° to the horizontal.

Solution $F_x = |\mathbf{F}| \cos 30^\circ = (15)(0.866) = 13 \text{ lb}$

$F_y = |\mathbf{F}| \sin 30^\circ = (15)(0.5) = 7.5 \text{ lb}$ ■

EXAMPLE 3 Find the magnitude and the direction of the vector whose components are shown in Figure 7.7.

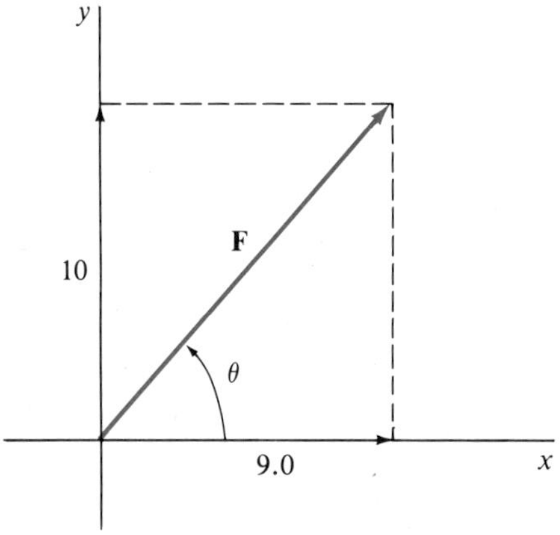

Figure 7.7

Solution The magnitude is

$$|\mathbf{F}| = \sqrt{10^2 + 9^2} = \sqrt{181} = 13.5$$

The angle that the vector makes with the horizontal is determined from

$$\tan \theta = \frac{10}{9.0} = 1.111$$
$$\theta = 48^\circ$$ ■

EXAMPLE 4 A boat that can travel at the rate of 3.5 km/hr in still water is pointed directly across a stream having a current of 4.8 km/hr. What will be the actual speed of the boat relative to the shore and in which direction will the boat go? See Figure 7.8.

Solution In still water, the boat would go at right angles to the bank at the rate of 3.5 km/hr. But the current carries it downstream 4.8 units for every 3.5 units that it goes across. Thus, 4.8 is the X component of velocity and 3.5 is the Y component. Hence, by the Pythagorean theorem, the

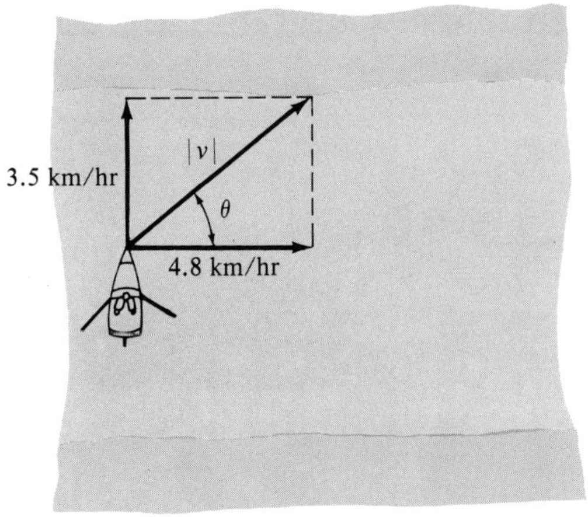

Figure 7.8

magnitude of the velocity is

$$|v| = \sqrt{(3.5)^2 + (4.8)^2} = 5.9$$

Let θ be the angle that the velocity vector makes with the bank. Then,

$$\tan \theta = \frac{3.5}{4.8} = 0.7292$$

$$\theta = 36^\circ$$

The boat will travel at 5.9 km/hr at an angle of 36° with the bank. ■

Comment: Two vectors in the plane are given a special notation. Figure 7.9 shows these two vectors in standard position, one ending at (1, 0), called the **i** vector, and the other ending at (0, 1), called the **j** vector. Every other vector in the plane can be expressed in terms of these two.

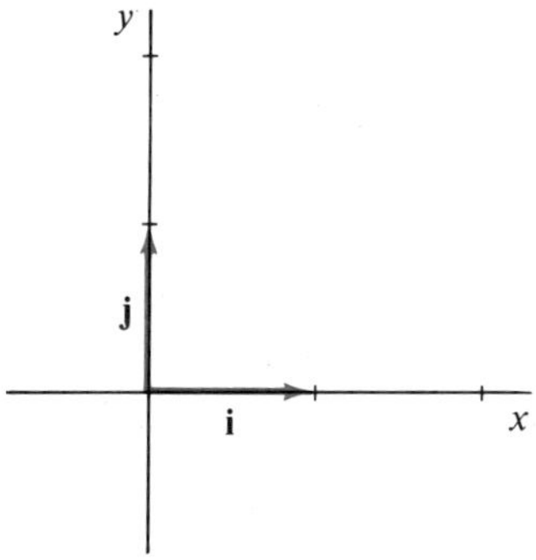

Figure 7.9

Exercises Section 7.1

Draw the vectors in Exercises 1–10 whose initial point is at the origin and whose terminal point is at the indicated point. Calculate the magnitude and direction of each vector.

1. $(1, 2)$ **2.** $(-3, 2)$ **3.** $(\sqrt{2}, \sqrt{7})$

4. $(1, -1)$ **5.** $(-4, -4)$ **6.** $(5, 8)$

7. $(4, -3)$ **8.** $(-3, -7)$ **9.** $(-\sqrt{3}, 6)$

10. $(\sqrt{5}, 3)$

Find the horizontal and vertical components of the vectors in Exercises 11–20.

11. $|\mathbf{F}| = 10, \quad \theta = 50°$ **12.** $|\mathbf{F}| = 25, \quad \theta = 75°$

13. $|\mathbf{F}| = 13.7, \quad \theta = 34°10'$

14. $|\mathbf{F}| = 0.751, \quad \theta = 56°30'$

15. $|\mathbf{F}| = 158, \quad \theta = 125°$

16. $|\mathbf{F}| = 875, \quad \theta = 145°$

17. $|\mathbf{F}| = 43.5, \quad \theta = 220°$

18. $|\mathbf{F}| = 9.41, \quad \theta = 195°$

19. $|\mathbf{F}| = 10.4, \quad \theta = 335°$

20. $|\mathbf{F}| = 0.05, \quad \theta = 280°$

In Exercises 21–30, find the magnitude and direction of the vector whose components are given.

21. $F_x = 20.0, \quad F_y = 15.0$

22. $F_x = 56.0, \quad F_y = 13.0$

23. $F_x = 17.5, \quad F_y = 69.3$

24. $F_x = 0.012, \quad F_y = 0.200$

25. $F_x = 0.130, \quad F_y = 0.080$

26. $F_x = 1930, \quad F_y = 565$

27. $F_x = 8, \quad F_y = -7$

28. $F_x = -3, \quad F_y = 5$

29. $F_x = -2, \quad F_y = -7$

30. $F_x = 7.1, \quad F_y = -9.2$

31. Find the vertical and horizontal components of the force in the following figure.

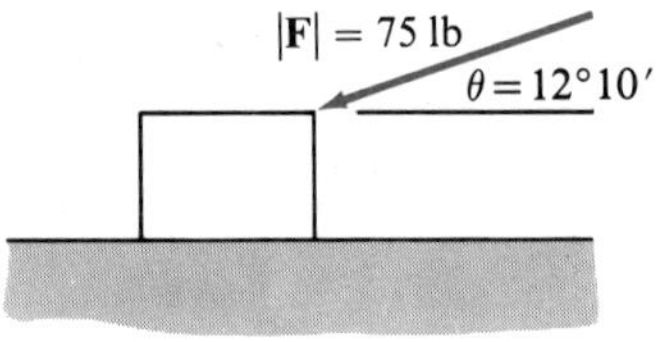

32. Find the vertical and horizontal components in the figure in Exercise 31, if $|\mathbf{F}| = 250$ lb and $\theta = 21.7°$.

33. The north and west components of the velocity of an aircraft are 300 mph and 900 mph, respectively. What is the magnitude of the velocity?

34. A balloon rises at the rate of 20 ft/sec and is being carried horizontally by a wind that has a velocity of 25 mph. Find its actual velocity and the angle that its path makes with the vertical (60 mph = 88 fps).

35. A boat travels at the rate of 5 mph in still water and points directly across a stream having a current of 3 mph. What is the actual speed of the boat and in which direction will the boat go?

36. An airplane having a speed of 190 knots starts to climb at an angle of 13° above the horizontal. How fast is the airplane rising vertically?

7.2 Operations on Vectors

Scalar Multiplication

Given any vector **A**, we may obtain other vectors in the same (or opposite) direction as that of **A** by multiplying **A** by a real number c. The resulting vector, denoted by $c\mathbf{A}$, is a vector that points in the same direction as **A** if $c > 0$ and opposite to that of **A** if $c < 0$. The magnitude of $c\mathbf{A}$ is $|c|\,|\mathbf{A}|$; that is, it is larger than $|\mathbf{A}|$ if $|c| > 1$ and smaller than $|\mathbf{A}|$ if $|c| < 1$. The vector $c\mathbf{A}$ is called a **scalar** multiple of the vector **A**. Figure 7.10 shows some scalar multiples of a given vector **A**.

The particular scalar multiple of a vector obtained by multiplying a vector **A** by the reciprocal of its magnitude leads to a vector in the direction of **A** whose length

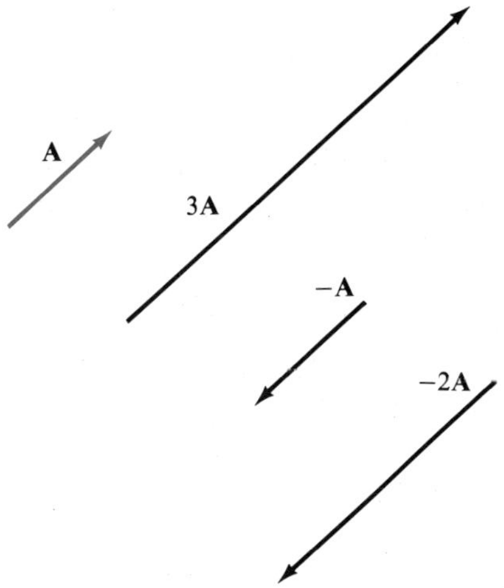

Figure 7.10

is 1. This is the **unit vector** in the direction of **A**, denoted by $\mathbf{u}_A$. Thus,

$$\mathbf{u}_A = \frac{\mathbf{A}}{|\mathbf{A}|} \tag{7.1}$$

Two important examples of unit vectors are the **i** and **j** vectors in the directions of the x- and y-axes.

Vector Addition

Two vectors are added by a rule called the **parallelogram rule.**

Rule

> To add two vectors **A** and **B**, place both with their initial points together. Then form a parallelogram with these vectors as sides. The vector from the initial point, which is the diagonal of the parallelogram, is called the *sum* of **A** and **B**. The term **resultant** is often used instead of sum. Figure 7.11 depicts the resultant of two vectors.

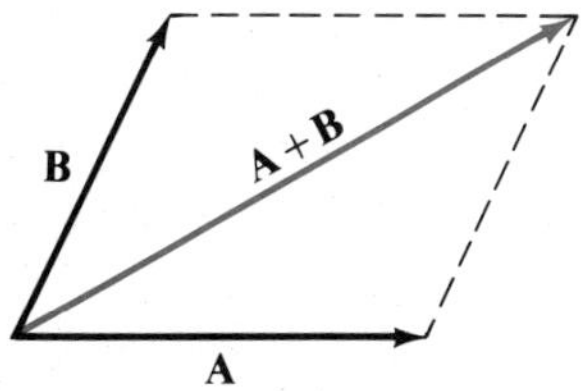

Figure 7.11

EXAMPLE 1 Find the magnitude and direction of the sum of vectors **A** and **B** where $|\mathbf{A}| = 3.0$, $|\mathbf{B}| = 4.0$, $\theta_A = 45°$, and $\theta_B = 60°$.

Solution Figure 7.12 shows the two vectors and the resultant. The resultant **A** + **B** is obtained using the parallelogram rule. Note that the angle θ_{AB} is 165°. To find the length of **A** + **B**, we use the law of cosines:

$$\begin{aligned}|\mathbf{A} + \mathbf{B}| &= \sqrt{|\mathbf{A}|^2 + |\mathbf{B}|^2 - 2|\mathbf{A}||\mathbf{B}| \cos \theta_{AB}} \\ &= \sqrt{3^2 + 4^2 - 2(3)(4) \cos 165°} \\ &= 6.94\end{aligned}$$

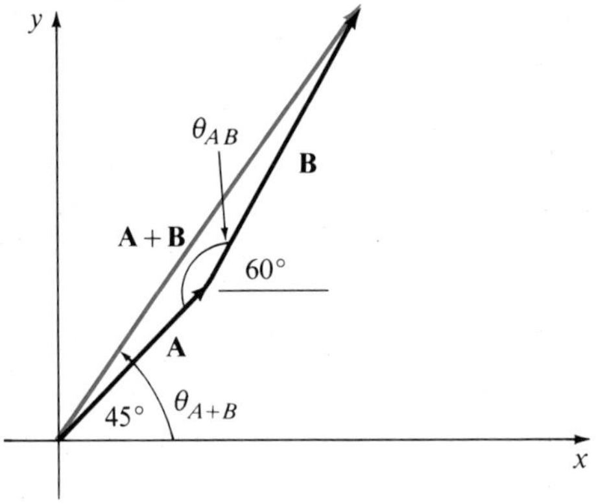

Figure 7.12

To compute the angle that the resultant makes with the x-axis, we compute the angle θ between **A** and **A** + **B** from the law of sines:

$$\frac{\sin \theta}{4} = \frac{\sin 165°}{6.94}$$

Solving for θ, we obtain

$$\theta = 8.6°$$

Hence, the angle that the resultant makes with the x-axis is

$$\begin{aligned}\theta_{A+B} &= \theta_A + \theta \\ &= 45° + 8.6° \\ &= 53.6°\end{aligned}$$

■

Comment: A vector **A** with horizontal component A_x and vertical component A_y may be expressed in the form $A_x\mathbf{i} + A_y\mathbf{j}$, where **i** is the unit vector in the direction of the x-axis and **j** is the unit vector in the direction of the y-axis.

Addition of vectors may be removed from a geometric setting as the directed diagonal of a parallelogram by using the component method of representation. To see this, note that

$$\mathbf{A} = A_x\mathbf{i} + A_y\mathbf{j}$$
$$\mathbf{B} = B_x\mathbf{i} + B_y\mathbf{j}$$

The components A_x, A_y, B_x, and B_y are shown in Figure 7.13. From the figure we see that the horizontal component of $\mathbf{A} + \mathbf{B}$ is $A_x + B_x$ and the vertical component is $A_y + B_y$. Thus,

$$\mathbf{A} + \mathbf{B} = (A_x + B_x)\mathbf{i} + (A_y + B_y)\mathbf{j}$$

In words, the horizontal component of the sum of two vectors is the sum of the individual horizontal components, and the vertical component of the sum is the sum of the individual vertical components.

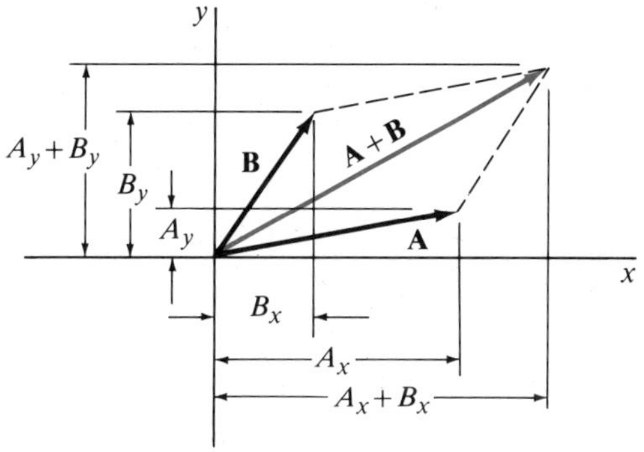

Figure 7.13

EXAMPLE 2 Add the vectors $\mathbf{A} = \mathbf{i} - 3\mathbf{j}$ and $\mathbf{B} = 5\mathbf{i} + \mathbf{j}$. (See Figure 7.14.)

Solution $\mathbf{A} + \mathbf{B} = (\mathbf{i} - 3\mathbf{j}) + (5\mathbf{i} + \mathbf{j}) = 6\mathbf{i} - 2\mathbf{j}$

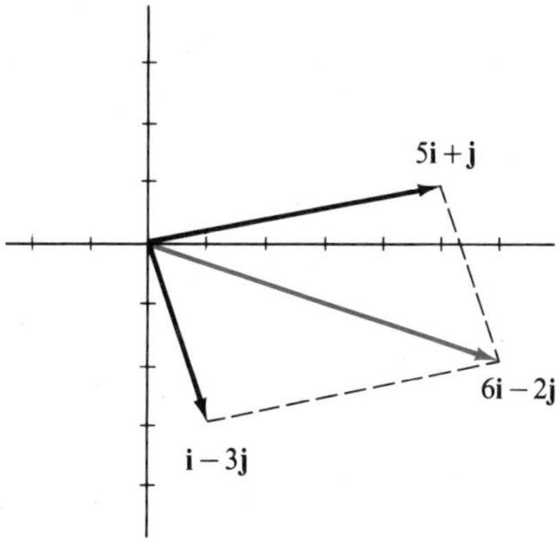

Figure 7.14

■

EXAMPLE 3 Use the method of component addition to perform the vector addition of Example 1.

Solution We first find A_x, A_y, B_x, and B_y.

$$A_x = |\mathbf{A}| \cos \theta_A = 3.0 \cos 45^\circ = 2.12$$
$$A_y = |\mathbf{A}| \sin \theta_A = 3.0 \sin 45^\circ = 2.12$$
$$B_x = |\mathbf{B}| \cos \theta_B = 4.0 \cos 60^\circ = 2.0$$
$$B_y = |\mathbf{B}| \sin \theta_B = 4.0 \sin 60^\circ = 3.46$$

Thus,

$$(A + B)_x = A_x + B_x = 2.12 + 2 = 4.12$$
$$(A + B)_y = A_y + B_y = 2.12 + 3.46 = 5.58$$

Hence,

$$|\mathbf{A} + \mathbf{B}| = \sqrt{(A + B)_x^2 + (A + B)_y^2}$$
$$= \sqrt{4.12^2 + 5.58^2} = 6.94$$

Further,

$$\theta_{A+B} = \text{Tan}^{-1} \frac{(A + B)_y}{(A + B)_x}$$
$$= \text{Tan}^{-1} \frac{5.58}{4.12} = 53.6^\circ$$

which agrees with Example 1. ■

EXAMPLE 4 Find the sum of the two vectors given in Figure 7.15, **A** of magnitude 100 and direction 63° and **B** of magnitude 40 and direction −35°.

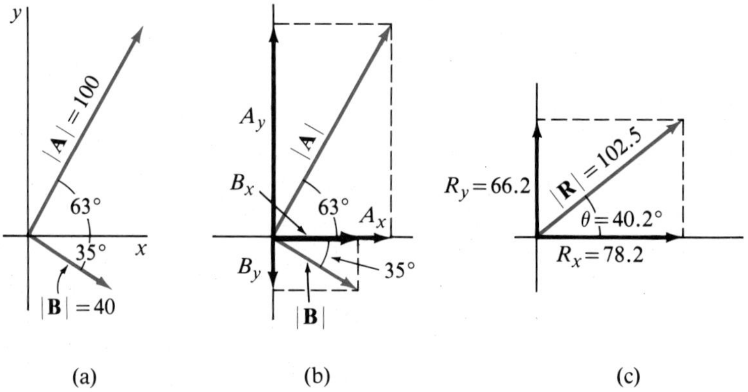

Figure 7.15

Solution

$$A_x = 100 \cos 63^\circ = 45.4$$
$$A_y = 100 \sin 63^\circ = 89.1$$
$$B_x = 40 \cos(-35^\circ) = 32.8$$
$$B_y = 40 \sin(-35^\circ) = -22.9$$

Let **A** + **B** = **R**. Then,

$$R_x = A_x + B_x = 45.4 + 32.8 = 78.2$$
$$R_y = A_y + B_y = 89.1 - 22.9 = 66.2$$

Finally,

$$|\mathbf{R}| = \sqrt{R_x^2 + R_y^2} = \sqrt{78.2^2 + 66.2^2} = \sqrt{10498} = 102.5$$
$$\tan\theta = \frac{R_y}{R_x} = \frac{66.2}{78.2} = .8465$$
$$\theta = 40.2^\circ$$

Comment: There is an alternate, and sometimes illuminating, definition for the addition of two vectors. Place the initial point of the second arrow at the terminal point of the first. Then the resultant, or sum, is the arrow whose initial point is at the initial point of the first arrow and whose terminal point is at the terminal point of the second, as in Figure 7.16(a). Note that this definition of a sum yields the same vector as the first definition.

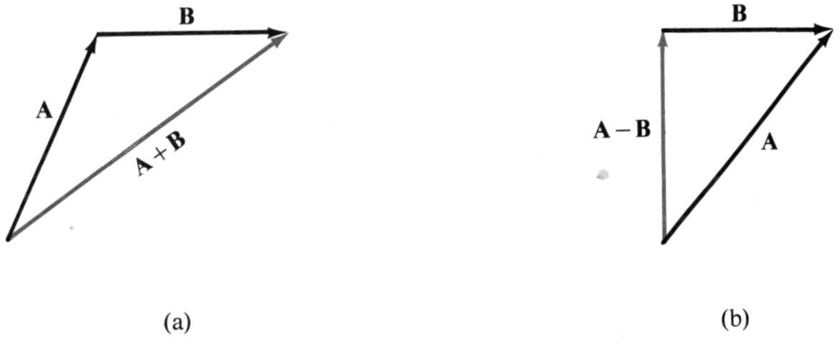

Figure 7.16

For vector subtraction, first reverse the direction of **B** by placing the terminal point of **B** at the terminal point of **A**. Then **A** − **B** is drawn from the initial point of **A** to the initial point of **B**. See Figure 7.16(b).

Exercises Section 7.2

In Exercises 1–9, find the sum of **A** and **B** by adding the respective vertical and horizontal components. Draw each vector and show the sum graphically.

1. **A** = 2**i** + 2**j**
B = 3**i** − **j**

2. **A** = **i** − **j**
B = 5**i** + 3**j**

3. **A** = −2**i** + 3**j**
B = −4**i** − 5**j**

4. **A** = 7**i** + 8**j**
B = 6**i** − 2**j**

5. **A** = −**i** − **j**
B = 2**i** − 2**j**

6. **A** = 6**i** + 6**j**
B = 3**i** − 6**j**

7. **A** = −4**i** − 6**j**
B = 4**i** + 2**j**

8. **A** = 9**i** + 5**j**
B = −7**i** + **j**

9. **A** = 5**i** − 5**j**
B = **i** − 2**j**

The vectors in Exercises 10–17 are defined in terms of a magnitude and a direction. Find the sum of the given vectors by addition of components.

10. $|\mathbf{A}| = 20,\ \theta_A = 15^\circ$
$|\mathbf{B}| = 25,\ \theta_B = 50^\circ$

11. $|\mathbf{A}| = 16,\ \theta_A = 25^\circ$
$|\mathbf{B}| = 22,\ \theta_B = 70^\circ$

12. $|\mathbf{A}| = 15, \quad \theta_A = 0°$
$|\mathbf{B}| = 26, \quad \theta_B = 60°$

13. $|\mathbf{A}| = 9.5, \quad \theta_A = 90°$
$|\mathbf{B}| = 5.1, \quad \theta_B = 40°$

14. $|\mathbf{A}| = 2.5, \quad \theta_A = 35°$
$|\mathbf{B}| = 3.0, \quad \theta_B = 120°$

15. $|\mathbf{A}| = 29.2, \quad \theta_A = 15.6°$
$|\mathbf{B}| = 82.6, \quad \theta_B = 150°$

16. $|\mathbf{A}| = 125, \quad \theta_A = 145°$
$|\mathbf{B}| = 92, \quad \theta_B = 215°$

17. $|\mathbf{A}| = 550, \quad \theta_A = 140°$
$|\mathbf{B}| = 925, \quad \theta_B = 310°$

18. What are the horizontal and vertical components of the velocity of a ball thrown 100 ft/sec at an angle of 40° with respect to the horizontal?

19. A plane is headed due north at 300 mph. If the wind is from the east at 50 mph, what is the velocity of the plane?

20. Both a vertical force of 50 lb and a horizontal force of 75 lb act through the center of gravity of an object. What single force could replace the two given forces?

21. An object is acted upon by a force of 200 lb at an angle of 35° to the horizontal. What is the horizontal component of the force?

22. An object is thrown vertically downward with a speed of 50 ft/sec from a plane moving horizontally with a speed of 250 ft/sec. What is the velocity of the object as it leaves the plane?

23. A force of 60 lb acts horizontally on an object. Another force of 75 lb acts on the object at an angle of 55° with the horizontal. What is the resultant of these forces?

24. A plane flies due west with an air speed of 150 mph. If the wind is from the southwest at 35 mph, what is the resultant speed of the plane? In what direction is it traveling?

25. A bullet is fired from a plane at an angle of 20° below the horizontal and in the direction the plane is moving. If the bullet leaves the muzzle of the gun with a speed of 1200 ft/sec and the plane is flying 500 ft/sec, what is the resultant speed of the bullet?

26. An object weighing 120 lb hangs at the end of a rope. The object is pulled sideways by a horizontal force of 30 lb. What angle does the rope make with the vertical? (*Hint:* Weight is a vector that is always considered to be acting vertically downward.)

7.3 The Dot Product of Two Vectors

The **dot product** of two vectors **A** and **B** (denoted by placing a dot between the factors) is defined by

$$\mathbf{A} \cdot \mathbf{B} = |\mathbf{A}|\,|\mathbf{B}| \cos \theta \tag{7.2}$$

where θ is the angle between the two vectors ($0 \leq \theta \leq \pi$). Notice that a dot product is a scalar quantity since it involves the product of scalars. If **A** and **B** are perpendicular, $\cos \theta$ is zero, and

$$\mathbf{A} \cdot \mathbf{B} = 0$$

Conversely, if the dot product is zero, the vectors are perpendicular or else one of the vectors is the zero vector.

If **A** and **B** have the same direction, $\cos \theta$ is equal to 1, and

$$\mathbf{A} \cdot \mathbf{B} = |\mathbf{A}|\,|\mathbf{B}|$$

In particular,

$$\mathbf{A} \cdot \mathbf{A} = |\mathbf{A}||\mathbf{A}| = |\mathbf{A}|^2$$

Also, since **i** and **j** are perpendicular unit vectors, it follows that

$$\mathbf{i} \cdot \mathbf{i} = 1$$
$$\mathbf{i} \cdot \mathbf{j} = 0$$
$$\mathbf{j} \cdot \mathbf{j} = 1$$

The dot product is distributive over addition, which means that for any three vectors, **A**, **B**, and **C**,

$$\mathbf{A} \cdot (\mathbf{B} + \mathbf{C}) = \mathbf{A} \cdot \mathbf{B} + \mathbf{A} \cdot \mathbf{C}$$

The distributive law allows for the derivation of a convenient formula for determining the value of the dot product in terms of its components. Let

$$\mathbf{A} = A_x\mathbf{i} + A_y\mathbf{j}$$
$$\mathbf{B} = B_x\mathbf{i} + B_y\mathbf{j}$$

Then

$$\begin{aligned}\mathbf{A} \cdot \mathbf{B} &= (A_x\mathbf{i} + A_y\mathbf{j}) \cdot (B_x\mathbf{i} + B_y\mathbf{j}) \\ &= A_xB_x(\mathbf{i} \cdot \mathbf{i}) + A_xB_y(\mathbf{i} \cdot \mathbf{j}) + A_yB_x(\mathbf{j} \cdot \mathbf{i}) + A_yB_y(\mathbf{j} \cdot \mathbf{j})\end{aligned}$$

Because $\mathbf{i} \cdot \mathbf{i} = \mathbf{j} \cdot \mathbf{j} = 1$ and $\mathbf{i} \cdot \mathbf{j} = 0$ we have

$$\mathbf{A} \cdot \mathbf{B} = A_xB_x + A_yB_y \tag{7.3}$$

EXAMPLE 1 Find $\mathbf{A} \cdot \mathbf{B}$ if $\mathbf{A} = 4\mathbf{i} - 3\mathbf{j}$ and $\mathbf{B} = 2\mathbf{i} + \mathbf{j}$. Find the angle between the vectors.

Solution By Equation 7.3,

$$\mathbf{A} \cdot \mathbf{B} = (4)(2) + (-3)(1) = 8 - 3 = 5$$

The cosine of the angle between two nonzero vectors may be calculated from Equation 7.2 if the dot product is known. Thus,

$$\cos\theta = \frac{\mathbf{A} \cdot \mathbf{B}}{|\mathbf{A}||\mathbf{B}|} = \frac{5}{\sqrt{25}\sqrt{5}} = \frac{1}{\sqrt{5}} = 0.447$$

From this result the approximate value of θ is Arccos $0.447 = 63.4°$. ■

One use of the dot product is in the computation of the perpendicular projection of a vector in a specified direction. This quantity, called the **component of the vector** in that direction, is shown in Figure 7.17. Thus, the value of the component of **B** in the direction of **A** is given by $|\mathbf{B}| \cos\theta$. Note that

$$|\mathbf{B}| \cos\theta = |\mathbf{B}|\frac{|\mathbf{A}|}{|\mathbf{A}|}\cos\theta = \frac{|\mathbf{B}||\mathbf{A}|\cos\theta}{|\mathbf{A}|}$$

$$|\mathbf{B}| \cos\theta = \frac{\mathbf{B} \cdot \mathbf{A}}{|\mathbf{A}|} \tag{7.4}$$

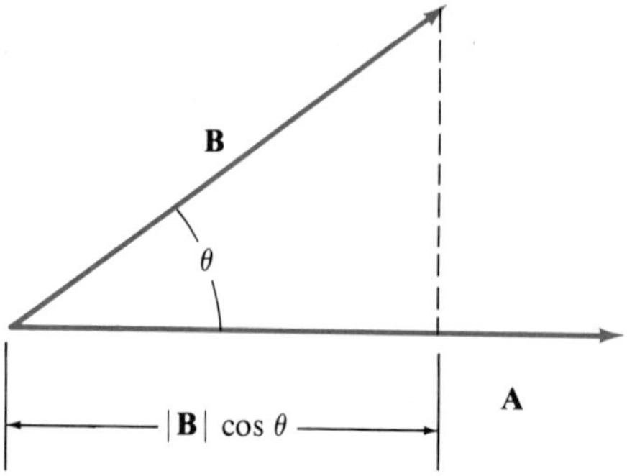

Figure 7.17

EXAMPLE 2 Find the component of $2\mathbf{i} + \mathbf{j}$ in the direction of the vector $\mathbf{i} + 3\mathbf{j}$.

Solution Using Equation 7.4, we find that the component of $2\mathbf{i} + \mathbf{j}$ in the direction of $\mathbf{i} + 3\mathbf{j}$ is

$$\frac{(2\mathbf{i} + \mathbf{j}) \cdot (\mathbf{i} + 3\mathbf{j})}{|\mathbf{i} + 3\mathbf{j}|} = \frac{2 + 3}{\sqrt{10}} = \frac{5}{\sqrt{10}}$$

■

EXAMPLE 3 A physics lab experiment on components of forces is shown schematically in Figure 7.18(a). Calculate the component of the force parallel to the plane.

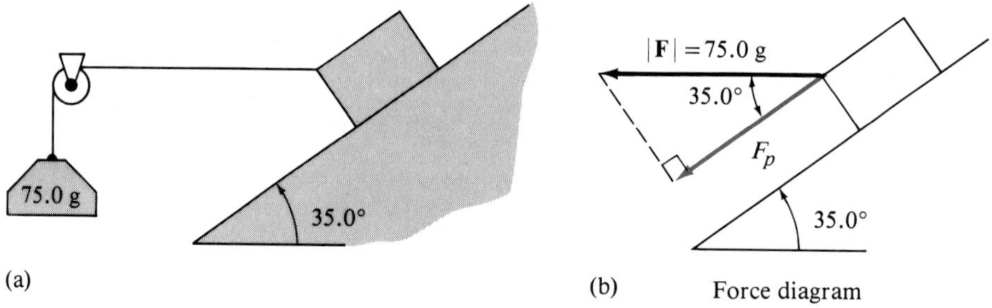

Figure 7.18

Solution The unit vector parallel to the plane is $-\cos 35°\mathbf{i} - \sin 35°\mathbf{j}$. The force vector is $-75\mathbf{i}$. Thus, the component of force parallel to the plane is

$$\begin{aligned} F_p &= (-75\mathbf{i}) \cdot (-\cos 35°\mathbf{i} - \sin 35°\mathbf{j}) \\ &= 75 \cos 35° \\ &= 61.4 \text{ g} \end{aligned}$$

■

EXAMPLE 4 Show that vectors **A** and **B** are perpendicular if

$$\mathbf{A} = \mathbf{i} - 2\mathbf{j} \quad \text{and} \quad \mathbf{B} = 2\mathbf{i} + \mathbf{j}$$

(See Figure 7.19.)

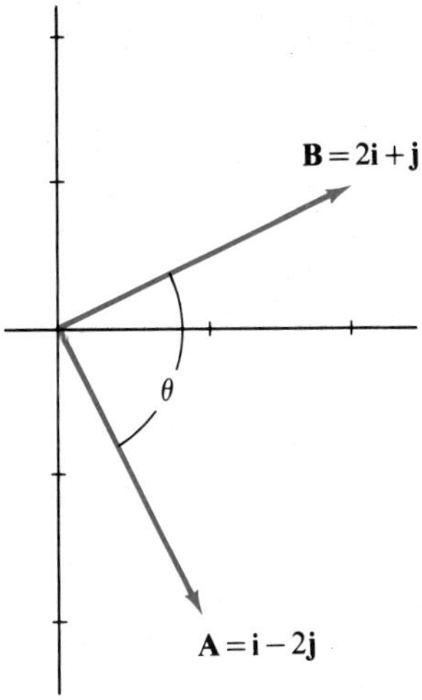

Figure 7.19

Solution Here $\mathbf{A} \cdot \mathbf{B} = 2 - 2 = 0$, from which we conclude that $\cos \theta = 0$ and hence $\theta = 90°$. ■

The dot product is used to express the quantity of mechanical work. When a force **F** experiences a displacement (represented in magnitude and direction by the vector **S** in Figure 7.20), the work done by the force is defined as the product of the displacement by the component of force in the direction of the displacement. Thus,

$$\text{work} = |\mathbf{S}||\mathbf{F}| \cos \theta = \mathbf{F} \cdot \mathbf{S}$$

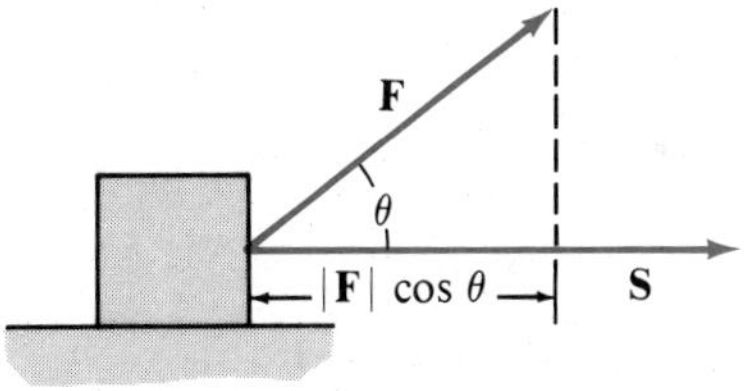

Figure 7.20

As a further result, if $\mathbf{F}_1$ and $\mathbf{F}_2$ are two forces acting at the same point, then the work done by the resultant $\mathbf{F} = \mathbf{F}_1 + \mathbf{F}_2$ is

$$\mathbf{F} \cdot \mathbf{S} = (\mathbf{F}_1 + \mathbf{F}_2) \cdot \mathbf{S} = \mathbf{F}_1 \cdot \mathbf{S} + \mathbf{F}_2 \cdot \mathbf{S}$$

That is, the work of the resultant is equal to the sum of the work done by the separate forces. This is just a restatement of the distributive property of the dot product over addition.

Exercises Section 7.3

Find the dot product for each pair of vectors in Exercises 1–12.

1. $\mathbf{A} = \mathbf{i} + \mathbf{j}$
   $\mathbf{B} = 2\mathbf{i} - \mathbf{j}$
2. $\mathbf{A} = 2\mathbf{i} - 3\mathbf{j}$
   $\mathbf{B} = 3\mathbf{i} + 2\mathbf{j}$
3. $\mathbf{A} = 6\mathbf{i} + \mathbf{j}$
   $\mathbf{B} = 7\mathbf{i} - \mathbf{j}$
4. $\mathbf{A} = 6\mathbf{i} + 2\mathbf{j}$
   $\mathbf{B} = 6\mathbf{i} + 2\mathbf{j}$
5. $\mathbf{A} = \mathbf{i}$
   $\mathbf{B} = \mathbf{i} + 3\mathbf{j}$
6. $\mathbf{A} = 2\mathbf{i} - 3\mathbf{j}$
   $\mathbf{B} = 2\mathbf{j}$
7. $|\mathbf{A}| = 25, \quad \theta_A = 27°$
   $|\mathbf{B}| = 40, \quad \theta_B = 85°$
8. $|\mathbf{A}| = 9.3, \quad \theta_A = 46°$
   $|\mathbf{B}| = 6.5, \quad \theta_B = 105°$
9. $|\mathbf{A}| = 190, \quad \theta_A = 100°$
   $|\mathbf{B}| = 75, \quad \theta_B = 205°$
10. $|\mathbf{A}| = 0.6, \quad \theta_A = 75°$
    $|\mathbf{B}| = 1.3, \quad \theta_B = 180°$
11. $|\mathbf{A}| = 24.3, \quad \theta_A = 245°$
    $|\mathbf{B}| = 16.2, \quad \theta_B = 276°$
12. $|\mathbf{A}| = 975, \quad \theta_A = 135°$
    $|\mathbf{B}| = 562, \quad \theta_B = 300°$

Find the angle between the vectors in Exercises 13–16 by using the definition of the dot product.

13. $\mathbf{A} = 5\mathbf{i} + \mathbf{j}$
    $\mathbf{B} = 2\mathbf{i} - \mathbf{j}$
14. $\mathbf{A} = \mathbf{i} - \mathbf{j}$
    $\mathbf{B} = \mathbf{i} + \mathbf{j}$
15. $\mathbf{A} = -3\mathbf{i} + 4\mathbf{j}$
    $\mathbf{B} = 2\mathbf{i} - 3\mathbf{j}$
16. $\mathbf{A} = 2\mathbf{i} + 4\mathbf{j}$
    $\mathbf{B} = -3\mathbf{i} - 3\mathbf{j}$
17. A large bookcase is pulled a distance of 20 ft along a level floor by a 30-lb force acting 28° above the horizontal. How much work is done on the bookcase?
18. How much work is done in moving a block of wood a distance of 100 ft if a 75-lb force acting 10° above the horizontal is needed to move it?
19. A horizontal force of 100 lb is applied to a block resting on a plane inclined at 30° to the horizontal. How much work is done in moving the block 5 ft up the incline?
20. What work is done in pulling a sled 50 ft horizontally when a 15-lb force is applied through a rope making an angle of 35° with the ground?

7.4 Complex Numbers

Complex numbers were defined in Chapter 2 and have been used as needed in this book when they arose as roots of certain quadratic equations. For instance, in solving the equation $x^2 + 1 = 0$, we wrote the solution as $x = \pm i$. Thus,

$$i^2 = -1 \quad \text{or} \quad i = \sqrt{-1}$$

Numbers of the form bi, where b is a real number, make up the set of **imaginary numbers.**

EXAMPLE 1

$$\sqrt{-4} = \sqrt{(4)(-1)} = \sqrt{4}\sqrt{-1} = 2i$$
$$\sqrt{-25} = \sqrt{25}\sqrt{-1} = 5i$$
$$\sqrt{-a} = i\sqrt{a}, \quad \text{where } a > 0$$

■

The powers of i form an interesting cycle of numbers. Note that $i^2 = -1$, $i^3 = -i$, and $i^4 = i^2 i^2 = (-1)(-1) = 1$. This cycle of $i, -1, -i, 1$ is repeated every fourth integer. To determine the value of i^m, merely divide m by 4 and note the remainder.

EXAMPLE 2

$$i^7 = i^3 \quad \text{(The remainder when dividing 7 by 4 is 3.)}$$
$$= -i$$
$$i^{10} = i^2 = -1, \quad i^{33} = i, \quad i^{100} = 1$$

■

EXAMPLE 3 Solve the equation $x^2 + 9 = 0$.

Solution

$$x^2 + 9 = 0$$
$$x^2 = -9$$
$$x = \pm\sqrt{-9} = \pm 3i$$

■

In solving an equation such as $x^2 - 2x + 5 = 0$, we found the solution from the quadratic formula to be

$$x = \frac{2 \pm \sqrt{4 - 20}}{2} = \frac{2 \pm i\sqrt{16}}{2} = 1 \pm 2i$$

which is a combination of a real and an imaginary number, called a **complex number.** For convenience, we reiterate and highlight the definition of a complex number originally given in Chapter 2.

Definition

> A **complex number** z is any number of the form $z = a + bi$, where a and b are real numbers and $i = \sqrt{-1}$.

The real number a is called the *real part* of z, whereas the real number b is called the *imaginary part* of z. By convention, if $b = 1$, the number is written $a + i$. Further, if $b = 0$, the imaginary part is customarily omitted and the number is said to be *pure real.* If $a = 0$ and $b \neq 0$, the real part is omitted and the number is said to be *pure imaginary.*

Two complex numbers are equal if, and only if, their real parts are equal and their imaginary parts are equal. Thus, $a + bi$ and $c + di$ are equal if, and only if, $a = c$ and $b = d$.

EXAMPLE 4 For which values of x and y is $2x + iy - y + 2xi + 3$ equal to $x - 3iy + ix + y - i + 2$?

Solution The first expression can be written as $(2x - y + 3) + i(y + 2x)$ and the second as $(x + y + 2) + i(-3y + x - 1)$. Equating the real parts, we have

$$2x - y + 3 = x + y + 2$$

Equating imaginary parts, we have

$$y + 2x = -3y + x - 1$$

These two equations can be written

$$x - 2y = -1$$
$$x + 4y = -1$$

The solution is $x = -1$, $y = 0$. ■

By changing the sign of the imaginary part of a complex number, we obtain its **conjugate.** Thus, the conjugate of $a + bi$ is $a - bi$. To indicate a conjugate, a bar is placed over the number.

EXAMPLE 5 a. $\overline{2 - 3i} = 2 + 3i$ b. $\overline{i - 1} = -i - 1$ ■

Complex numbers obey the same algebraic rules as real numbers. Thus, the sum, the difference, the product, or the quotient of two complex numbers is found in the same manner as the sum, the difference, the product, or the quotient of two real binomials—bearing in mind that $i^2 = -1$.

EXAMPLE 6 Find the sum and difference of $3 + 5i$ and $-9 + 2i$.

Solution a. $(3 + 5i) + (-9 + 2i) = (3 - 9) + (5 + 2)i = -6 + 7i$
b. $(3 + 5i) - (-9 + 2i) = (3 + 9) + (5 - 2)i = 12 + 3i$ ■

EXAMPLE 7 Find the product $(3 - 2i)(4 + i)$.

Solution
$$\begin{aligned}(3 - 2i)(4 + i) &= 12 + 3i - 8i - 2i^2 \\ &= 12 - 5i + 2 \\ &= 14 - 5i\end{aligned}$$
■

To find the quotient of two complex numbers, we use the following scheme: *multiply the numerator and the denominator of the given quotient by the conjugate of the denominator*. Example 8 illustrates this technique. Notice that this is the same technique we use when rationalizing a denominator.

EXAMPLE 8 Find the quotient $(2 + 3i)/(4 - 5i)$.

Solution
$$\begin{aligned}\frac{2 + 3i}{4 - 5i} &= \frac{(2 + 3i)(4 + 5i)}{(4 - 5i)(4 + 5i)} \\ &= \frac{8 + (12 + 10)i + 15i^2}{16 - 25i^2} \\ &= \frac{-7 + 22i}{16 + 25} \\ &= \frac{-7 + 22i}{41}\end{aligned}$$
■

The absolute value of a complex number $z = a + bi$, called the **modulus** or **magnitude**, is denoted $|z| = |a + bi|$ and defined by

$$|z| = |a + bi| = \sqrt{a^2 + b^2} \tag{7.5}$$

Notice that if $b = 0$, Equation 7.5 reduces to $|a| = \sqrt{a^2}$, which agrees with our definition of absolute value for real numbers.

EXAMPLE 9 The modulus of $3 - 2i$ is

$$|z| = |3 - 2i| = \sqrt{3^2 + 2^2} = \sqrt{13}$$
■

Exercises Section 7.4

Express each of Exercises 1–5 as a pure imaginary number.

1. $\sqrt{-36}$ 2. $\sqrt{-5}$ 3. $\sqrt{-144}$
4. $\sqrt{-0.01}$ 5. $\sqrt{-\frac{3}{2}}$

Simplify Exercises 6–10.

6. i^9 7. i^{101} 8. i^{20}
9. i^{402} 10. $-i^{10}$

Find the conjugate of the complex numbers in Exercises 11–15. Also, find $|a + bi|$.

11. 2 12. $-9i$ 13. $4 + i$
14. $3 - 2i$ 15. $i - 1$

Find values of x and y for which the complex expressions in Exercises 16–20 are equal.

16. $x - 3y = y - 1 + xi + 2i$
17. $x^2 + iy = 9 - 3i$
18. $y - 1 + (x^2 - 4)i = 3 + 12i$
19. $3x - y + 7 + i(x + y - 1) = 0$
20. $x - y + 2 + i(3x - 2y) = 0$

Perform the indicated operations in Exercises 21–44, expressing all answers in the form $a + bi$.

21. $(3 + 2i) + (4 + 3i)$ 22. $(6 + 3i) + (5 - i)$
23. $(5 - 2i) + (-7 + 5i)$ 24. $(-1 + i) + (2 - i)$
25. $(1 + i) + (3 - i)$ 26. $7 - (5 + 3i)$
27. $(3 + 5i) - 4i$ 28. $(3 + 2i) + (3 - 2i)$
29. $(2 + 3i)(4 + 5i)$ 30. $(7 + 2i)(-1 - i)$
31. $(5 - i)(5 + i)$ 32. $(6 - 3i)(6 + 3i)$
33. $(4 + \sqrt{3}i)^2$ 34. $(5 - 2i)^2$
35. $6i(4 - 3i)$ 36. $3i(-2 - i)$
37. $\dfrac{3 + 2i}{1 + i}$ 38. $\dfrac{4i}{2 + i}$
39. $\dfrac{3}{2 - 3i}$ 40. $\dfrac{7 - 2i}{6 - 5i}$
41. $\dfrac{1}{5i}$ 42. $\dfrac{-3 + i}{-2 - i}$
43. $\dfrac{-1 - 3i}{4 - \sqrt{2}i}$ 44. $\dfrac{i}{2 + \sqrt{5}i}$
45. Show that the sum of a complex number and its conjugate is a real number.
46. Show that the product of a complex number and its conjugate is a real number.
47. For what numbers a and b is $a + bi = \overline{a + bi}$?
48. A certain force may be represented by the complex expression

$$t^2 - 2t + i(3t - 5)$$

where the parameter t is time.
   a. When is the force pure real (that is, directed along the x-axis)?
   b. When is the force pure imaginary (that is, directed along the y-axis)?
   c. Is the force ever 0?
   d. When is the force directed along the line $y = x$?
49. Given that $z = x + iy$, show that $x = (z + \bar{z})/2$, and $y = (z - \bar{z})/2i$.

7.5 Graphical Representation of Complex Numbers and Polar Notation

Since complex numbers may be regarded as ordered pairs of real numbers, a two-dimensional configuration can be used to represent them graphically. The Cartesian coordinate system is often used for this purpose, in which case it is called the **complex plane.** The x-axis is used to represent the real part of the complex number, and the y-axis to represent the imaginary part. Hence, the axes are called **real** and **imaginary,** respectively. Thus, the complex number $a + bi$ is represented by the point whose coordinates are (a, b), as shown in Figure 7.21. For this reason, the complex number $z = a + bi$ is said to be written in **rectangular form.**

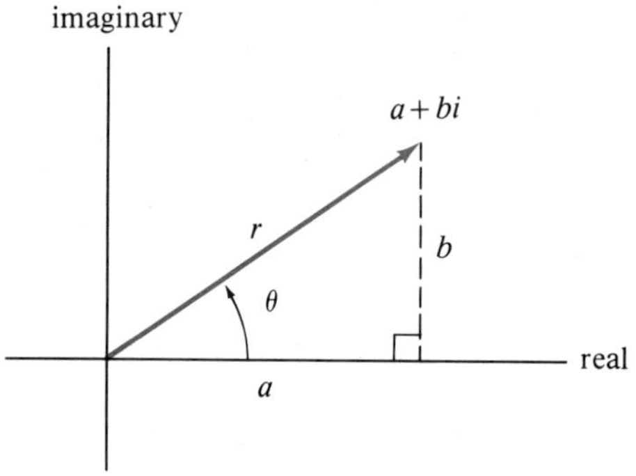

Figure 7.21

Comment: It is often convenient to think of a complex number $a + bi$ as representing a vector. With reference to Figure 7.21, the complex number $a + bi$ can be represented by the vector drawn from the origin to the point $a + bi$ with coordinates (a, b).

EXAMPLE 1 Represent $5 + 3i$, $-2 + 4i$, $-1 - 3i$, and $5 - i$ in the complex plane. (See Figure 7.22.)

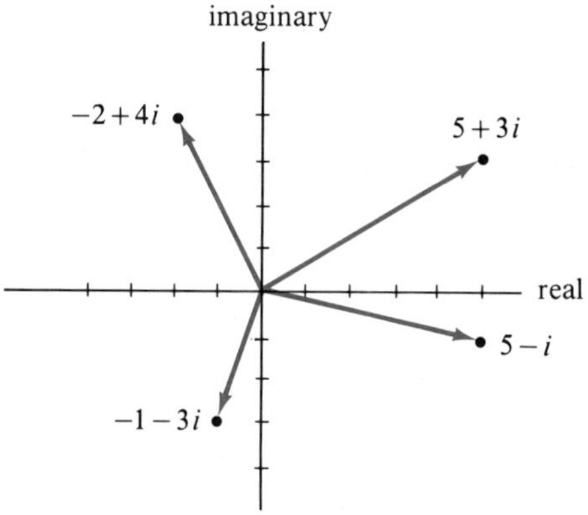

Figure 7.22

■

Comment: The distance from the origin to the point corresponding to $a + bi$ is given by the Pythagorean theorem to be $\sqrt{a^2 + b^2}$, which is also the value of $|a + bi|$. Hence, we interpret the absolute value of a complex number as the distance from the origin to the point corresponding to the number.

It is instructive to show the graphical representation of the sum of two complex numbers. Recalling that the sum of $a + bi$ and $c + di$ is given by

$$(a + bi) + (c + di) = (a + c) + (b + d)i$$

we have represented $a + bi$, $c + di$, and $(a + c) + (b + d)i$ in Figure 7.23. The result is the same as if we had applied the parallelogram law to the vectors representing

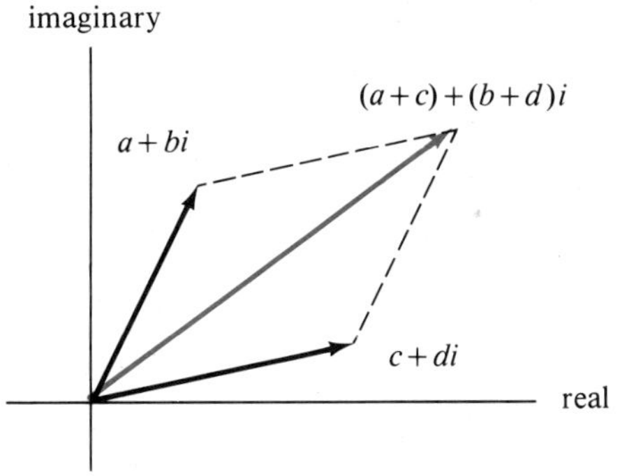

Figure 7.23 Addition of complex numbers

$a + bi$ and $c + di$. Note that $c + di$ is subtracted from $a + bi$ by plotting $a + bi$ and $-c - di$ and then using the parallelogram law.

Polar Representation of Complex Numbers

The geometric representation of complex numbers suggests an alternate method for describing complex numbers. Referring to Figure 7.24, we see that the complex

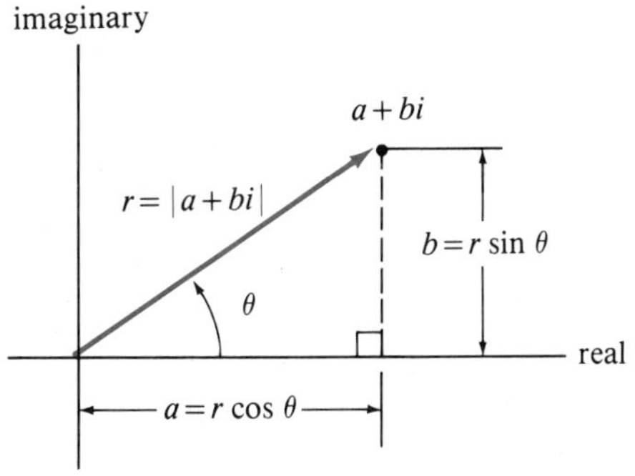

Figure 7.24 Polar form

number $a + bi$ can also be located by giving the length of the vector for $a + bi$ and the angle that it makes with the positive x-axis. Then, from trigonometry we have

$$a = r\cos\theta$$

and

$$b = r\sin\theta$$

Substituting these values yields

$$a + bi = r\cos\theta + ir\sin\theta$$

This is written in the form

$$z = a + bi = r(\cos\theta + i\sin\theta) \tag{7.6}$$

The right-hand side of Equation 7.6 is called the **trigonometric,** or **polar,** form of the complex number $a + bi$. The quantity $(\cos\theta + i\sin\theta)$ is sometimes written cis θ, in which case we write

$$z = r \text{ cis } \theta \tag{7.7}$$

as the polar form of the complex number z. The number r is the **modulus,** or **magnitude,** of the complex number z and is given by

$$r = \sqrt{a^2 + b^2}$$

The angle θ is called the **argument** of the complex number. Since $\tan\theta = b/a$ in Figure 7.24, it follows that θ is an angle whose tangent is b/a; that is,

$$\tan\theta = \frac{b}{a}$$

Warning: Note that a given complex number has many arguments, all differing by multiples of 2π. Sometimes we limit the argument to some interval of length 2π and thus obtain a *principal value.* In this book, unless we say otherwise, the principal values will be between $-\pi$ and π; that is, between $-180°$ and $180°$.

EXAMPLE 2 Represent $z = 1 + \sqrt{3}\,i$ in polar form. (See Figure 7.25.)

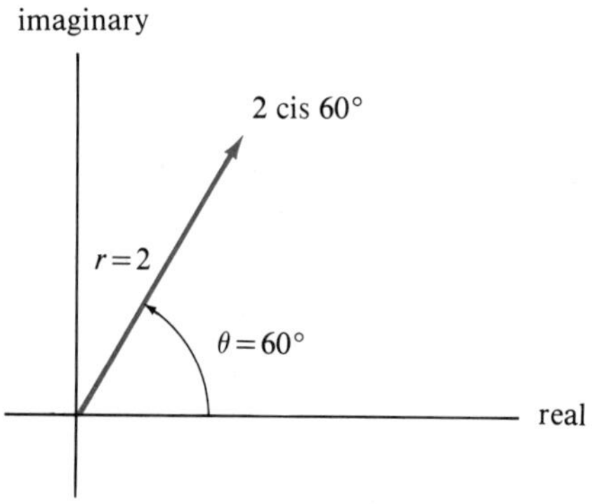

Figure 7.25

Solution The modulus is

$$r = \sqrt{1^2 + (\sqrt{3})^2} = \sqrt{4} = 2$$

and, since the real and imaginary parts of z are both positive,

$$\theta = \text{Arctan}\,\sqrt{3} = 60°$$

Finally, using Equation 7.7, we have

$$1 + \sqrt{3}\,i = 2(\cos 60° + i\sin 60°) = 2 \text{ cis } 60°$$ ■

EXAMPLE 3 Express $z = 6(\cos 120^\circ + i \sin 120^\circ)$ in rectangular form. (See Figure 7.26.)

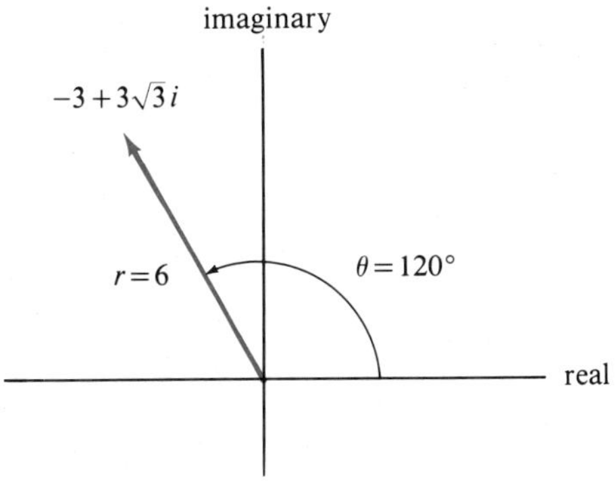

Figure 7.26

Solution Using the fact that $a = r\cos\theta$ and $b = r\sin\theta$, we have

$$a = 6\cos 120^\circ = 6\left(-\frac{1}{2}\right) = -3$$

$$b = 6\sin 120^\circ = 6\left(\frac{\sqrt{3}}{2}\right) = 3\sqrt{3}$$

Therefore,

$$z = a + bi = -3 + 3\sqrt{3}\,i$$

■

The polar form of complex numbers makes it easy to give a geometric interpretation to the product of two complex numbers. Thus, if $z_1 = r_1 \operatorname{cis} \theta_1$ and $z_2 = r_2 \operatorname{cis} \theta_2$, the product $z_1 z_2$ may be written

$$\begin{aligned} z_1 z_2 &= r_1(\cos\theta_1 + i\sin\theta_1)\cdot r_2(\cos\theta_2 + i\sin\theta_2) \\ &= r_1 r_2[\cos\theta_1\cos\theta_2 + i\cos\theta_1\sin\theta_2 \\ &\quad + i\sin\theta_1\cos\theta_2 + i^2\sin\theta_1\sin\theta_2] \\ &= r_1 r_2[(\cos\theta_1\cos\theta_2 - \sin\theta_1\sin\theta_2) \\ &\quad + i(\cos\theta_1\sin\theta_2 + \sin\theta_1\cos\theta_2)] \end{aligned}$$

Now, by using the identities for the sine and cosine of the sum of two angles, we have

$$z_1 z_2 = r_1 r_2[\cos(\theta_1 + \theta_2) + i\sin(\theta_1 + \theta_2)] = r_1 r_2 \operatorname{cis}(\theta_1 + \theta_2) \tag{7.8}$$

Therefore, the modulus of the product of two complex numbers is the product of the individual moduli, and the argument of the product is the sum of the individual arguments. Graphically, multiplication of z_1 by z_2 results in a rotation of the vector through z_1 by an angle equal to the argument of z_2 and an expansion or a contraction of the modulus depending on whether $|z_2| > 1$ or $|z_2| < 1$. (See Figure 7.27.)

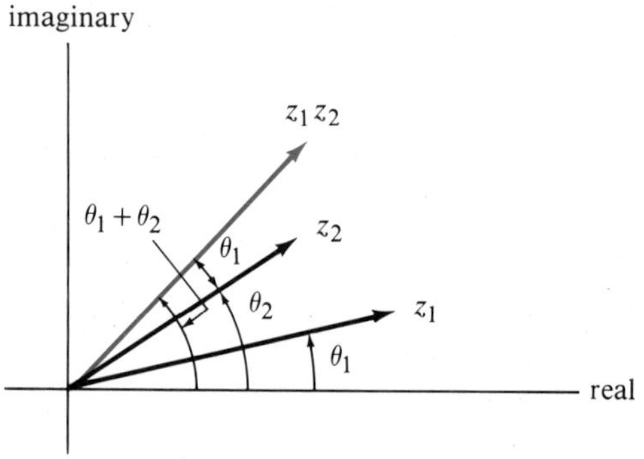

Figure 7.27 Multiplication of complex numbers

EXAMPLE 4 Multiply $z_1 = -1 + \sqrt{3}\,i$ and $z_2 = 1 + i$, using the polar form of each.

Solution Computing the modulus and argument of each complex number yields

$$r_1 = \sqrt{(-1)^2 + (\sqrt{3})^2} = 2, \qquad \tan\theta_1 = \frac{\sqrt{3}}{-1}, \qquad \theta_1 = 120^\circ \qquad (z_1 \text{ in QII})$$

$$r_2 = \sqrt{1^2 + 1^2} = \sqrt{2}, \qquad \theta_2 = \text{Arctan}\,\frac{1}{1} = 45^\circ \qquad (z_2 \text{ in QI})$$

Therefore,

$$\begin{aligned} z_1 z_2 &= (2 \text{ cis } 120^\circ)(\sqrt{2} \text{ cis } 45^\circ) = 2\sqrt{2} \text{ cis } (120^\circ + 45^\circ) \\ &= 2\sqrt{2} \text{ cis } 165^\circ \end{aligned}$$

■

In the same manner as in the above discussion, we may show that if $z_1 = r_1 \text{ cis } \theta_1$ and $z_2 = r_2 \text{ cis } \theta_2$, then

$$\frac{z_1}{z_2} = \frac{r_1}{r_2} \cos(\theta_1 - \theta_2) + i \sin(\theta_1 - \theta_2) = \frac{r_1}{r_2} \text{ cis } (\theta_1 - \theta_2) \tag{7.9}$$

That is, the modulus of the quotient of two complex numbers is the quotient of the individual moduli, and the argument is the difference of the individual arguments.

EXAMPLE 5 Divide $z_1 = 2 \text{ cis } 120^\circ$ by $z_2 = \sqrt{2} \text{ cis } 45^\circ$.

Solution $$\frac{z_1}{z_2} = \frac{2 \text{ cis } 120^\circ}{\sqrt{2} \text{ cis } 45^\circ} = \frac{2}{\sqrt{2}} \text{ cis } (120^\circ - 45^\circ) = \sqrt{2} \text{ cis } 75^\circ$$

■

Exercises Section 7.5

Perform the indicated operations in Exercises 1–14 graphically and check the results algebraically.

1. $(4 + i) + (3 + 5i)$

2. $(3 + 2i) + (1 - 3i)$

3. $(4 + 3i) + (-2 + i)$

4. $(-5 - 7i) + (-1 + 3i)$

5. $(2 - 4i) + (-3 + i)$

6. $i + (3 + 4i)$

7. $(5 + 3i) - 6$

8. $(3 + 2i) + (3 - 2i)$

9. $(5 - 3i) + (5 + 3i)$

10. $(6 + 4i) - 2i$

11. $(1 + 3i) - (2 - 5i)$

12. $(2 - i) - i$

13. $(2 + \sqrt{3}\,i) - (-1 - i)$

14. $(\sqrt{5} - i) - (\sqrt{5} + 3i)$

In Exercises 15–20, plot the number, its negative, and its conjugate on the same coordinate system.

15. $-3 + 2i$

16. $4 - 3i$

17. $-2i$

18. $5 + i$

19. $-1 - i$

20. $3 + 5i$

Plot the complex numbers in Exercises 21–30 and then express them in polar form.

21. $1 - \sqrt{3}\,i$

22. $3 + 4i$

23. $\sqrt{5} + 2i$

24. $\sqrt{3} - i$

25. 9

26. $5i$

27. $3 - 4i$

28. $-1 + i$

29. $5 - 6i$

30. $-3 - 4i$

Plot the complex numbers in Exercises 31–40 and then express them in rectangular form.

31. $2 \text{ cis } 30°$

32. $4 \text{ cis } 60°$

33. $5 \text{ cis } 135°$

34. $10 \text{ cis } 90°$

35. $\sqrt{3} \text{ cis } 210°$

36. $\sqrt{5} \text{ cis } 180°$

37. $3 \text{ cis } 300°$

38. $7 \text{ cis } 0°$

39. $10 \text{ cis } 20°$

40. $2 \text{ cis } 100°$

Perform the indicated operations in Exercises 41–56. If the complex numbers are not already in polar form, put them in that form before proceeding.

41. $(4 \text{ cis } 30°)(3 \text{ cis } 60°)$

42. $(2 \text{ cis } 120°)(\sqrt{5} \text{ cis } 180°)$

43. $(\sqrt{2} \text{ cis } 90°)(\sqrt{2} \text{ cis } 240°)$

44. $(5 \text{ cis } 180°)(3 \text{ cis } 90°)$

45. $(10 \text{ cis } 35°)(2 \text{ cis } 100°)$

46. $(3 \text{ cis } 45°)(2 \text{ cis } 120°)$

47. $(3 + 4i)(\sqrt{3} - i)$

48. $3i(2 - i)$

49. $\dfrac{10 \text{ cis } 30°}{2 \text{ cis } 90°}$

50. $\dfrac{5 \text{ cis } 29°}{3 \text{ cis } 4°}$

51. $\dfrac{4 \text{ cis } 26°40'}{2 \text{ cis } 19°10'}$

52. $\dfrac{12 \text{ cis } 100°}{3 \text{ cis } 23°}$

53. $\dfrac{1 - i}{\sqrt{3} + i}$

54. $\dfrac{\sqrt{3} + i}{\sqrt{3} - i}$

55. $\dfrac{4i}{-1 + i}$

56. $\dfrac{5}{1 + i}$

57. Prove Euler's identities:
$\cos\theta = \frac{1}{2}[\text{cis } \theta + \text{cis } (-\theta)]$ and
$\sin\theta = (1/2i)[\text{cis } \theta - \text{cis } (-\theta)]$

7.6 DeMoivre's Theorem

The square of the complex number $z = r \text{ cis } \theta$ is given by

$$\begin{aligned} z^2 &= (r \text{ cis } \theta)(r \text{ cis } \theta) \\ &= r^2 \text{ cis } 2\theta \end{aligned}$$

Likewise,

$$\begin{aligned} z^3 = z^2 \cdot z &= (r^2 \text{ cis } 2\theta) \cdot (r \text{ cis } \theta) \\ &= r^3 \text{ cis } 3\theta \end{aligned}$$

The pattern shown for z^2 and z^3 applies as well to z^4, z^5, z^6, and so forth. As a matter of fact, if $z = r \text{ cis } \theta$, then we have **DeMoivre's theorem:**

Theorem

$$z^n = r^n \text{ cis } n\theta \qquad (7.10)$$

for all real values of n.

EXAMPLE 1 Use DeMoivre's theorem to find $(-2+2i)^4$.

Solution Here we have

$$r = \sqrt{2^2 + (-2)^2} = \sqrt{8} \qquad \tan\theta = -1 \qquad \theta = 135^\circ \qquad (-2+2i \text{ in QII})$$

Therefore,

$$\begin{aligned}(-2+2i)^4 &= [\sqrt{8}(\cos 135^\circ + i \sin 135^\circ)]^4 \\ &= (\sqrt{8})^4[\cos 4(135^\circ) + i \sin 4(135^\circ)] \\ &= 64[\cos 540^\circ + i \sin 540^\circ] \\ &= 64[\cos 180^\circ + i \sin 180^\circ] \\ &= -64\end{aligned}$$

■

In the system of real numbers there is no square root of -1, no fourth root of -81, and so on. However, if we use complex numbers, we can find the nth root of any number by using DeMoivre's theorem.

Recalling that DeMoivre's theorem is valid for all real n, it is possible to evaluate $[r \text{ cis } \theta]^{1/n}$ as

$$[r \text{ cis } \theta]^{1/n} = r^{1/n} \text{ cis } \frac{\theta}{n} = \sqrt[n]{r} \text{ cis } \frac{\theta}{n} \tag{7.11}$$

Since $\cos\theta$ and $\sin\theta$ are periodic functions with a period of 360°, we can write $\cos\theta = \cos(\theta + k \cdot 360^\circ)$ and $\sin\theta = \sin(\theta + k \cdot 360^\circ)$, where k is an integer. Hence,

$$[r \text{ cis } \theta]^{1/n} = \sqrt[n]{r} \text{ cis } \left(\frac{\theta + k \cdot 360^\circ}{n}\right). \tag{7.12}$$

For a given number n, the right side of this equation takes on n distinct values corresponding to $k = 0, 1, 2, \ldots, n-1$. For $k > n-1$, the result is a duplication of the first n values.

EXAMPLE 2 Find the square roots of $4i$.

Solution We first express $4i$ in polar form using

$$r = \sqrt{0^2 + 4^2} = 4 \quad \text{and} \quad \theta = 90^\circ$$

Thus, $4i = 4 \text{ cis } 90^\circ$ and the square roots of $4i$ are given by

$$2 \text{ cis } \left(\frac{90^\circ + k \cdot 360^\circ}{2}\right)$$

Therefore, for $k = 0$,

$$2 \text{ cis } 45^\circ = \sqrt{2} + \sqrt{2}\,i$$

and for $k = 1$,

$$2 \text{ cis } 225^\circ = -\sqrt{2} - \sqrt{2}\,i$$

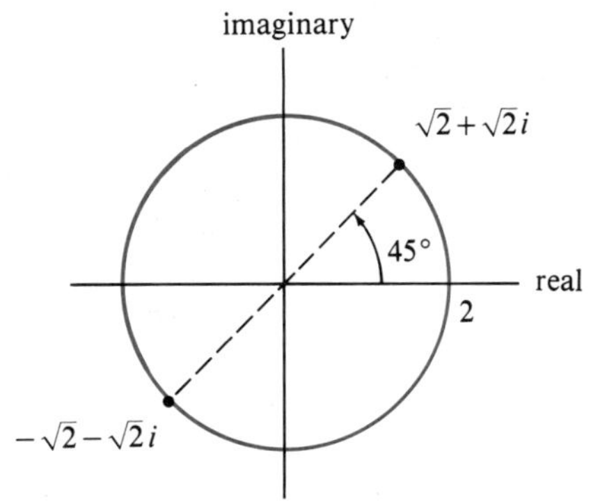

Figure 7.28

It is convenient and informative to plot these values in the complex plane, as shown in Figure 7.28. Notice that both roots are located on a circle of radius 2, but 180° apart. ■

EXAMPLE 3 Find the three cube roots of unity.

Solution In polar form the number 1 may be written 1 cis 0°. Thus,

$$\sqrt[3]{1 \text{ cis } 0^\circ} = 1 \text{ cis}\left(\frac{0^\circ + k \cdot 360^\circ}{3}\right)$$

$$\text{for} \quad k = 0, \quad 1 \text{ cis } 0^\circ = 1$$

$$\text{for} \quad k = 1, \quad 1 \text{ cis } 120^\circ = \frac{-1 + \sqrt{3}i}{2}$$

$$\text{for} \quad k = 2, \quad 1 \text{ cis } 240^\circ = \frac{-1 - \sqrt{3}i}{2}$$

Figure 7.29 displays these roots. Notice that they are located on a circle of radius 1 at equally spaced intervals of 120°.

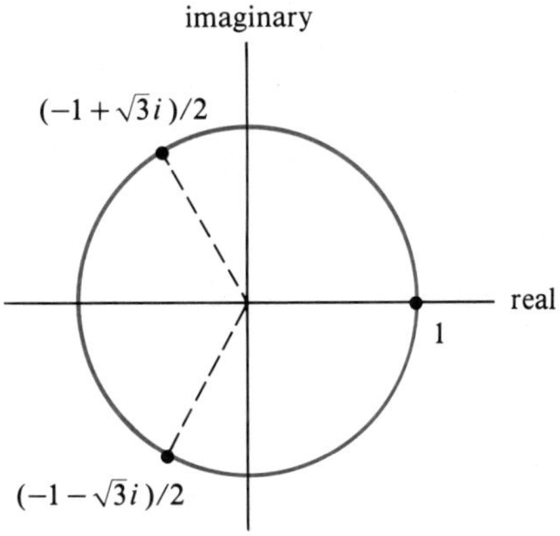

Figure 7.29 ■

EXAMPLE 4 Find the fourth roots of $-1 + \sqrt{3}i$.

Solution Writing $-1 + \sqrt{3}i$ in polar form, we get

$$-1 + \sqrt{3}i = 2 \text{ cis } 120°$$

Therefore,

$$[-1 + \sqrt{3}i]^{1/4} = \sqrt[4]{2} \text{ cis } \frac{120° + k \cdot 360°}{4}$$

The four roots correspond to $k = 0, 1, 2, 3$; that is,

$$\text{for } k = 0, \quad \sqrt[4]{2} \text{ cis } 30° = \sqrt[4]{2}\left(\frac{\sqrt{3}}{2} + \frac{1}{2}i\right)$$

$$\text{for } k = 1, \quad \sqrt[4]{2} \text{ cis } 120° = \sqrt[4]{2}\left(-\frac{1}{2} + \frac{\sqrt{3}}{2}i\right)$$

$$\text{for } k = 2, \quad \sqrt[4]{2} \text{ cis } 210° = \sqrt[4]{2}\left(-\frac{\sqrt{3}}{2} - \frac{1}{2}i\right)$$

$$\text{for } k = 3, \quad \sqrt[4]{2} \text{ cis } 300° = \sqrt[4]{2}\left(\frac{1}{2} - \frac{\sqrt{3}}{2}i\right)$$ ■

Exercises Section 7.6

Use DeMoivre's theorem to evaluate powers in Exercises 1–10. Leave the answer in polar form.

1. $(-1 + \sqrt{3}i)^3$ **2.** $(1 + i)^4$

3. $(\sqrt{3} \text{ cis } 60°)^4$ **4.** $(\sqrt{3} - i)^6$

5. $(-2 + 2i)^5$ **6.** $(-1 + 3i)^3$

7. $(-\sqrt{3} + i)^7$ **8.** $(2 \text{ cis } 20°)^5$

9. $(2 + 5i)^4$ **10.** $(3 + 2i)^{10}$

Find the indicated roots in Exercises 11–20 and sketch their location in the complex plane.

11. Fifth roots of 1 **12.** Cube roots of 64

13. Fourth roots of i **14.** Fourth roots of -16

15. Square roots of $1 + i$

16. Fifth roots of $\sqrt{3} + i$

17. Sixth roots of $-\sqrt{3} + i$

18. Cube roots of $-1 + i$

19. Fourth roots of $-1 + \sqrt{3}i$

20. Sixth roots of $-i$

21. Obtain an expression for $\cos 2\theta$ and $\sin 2\theta$ in terms of trigonometric functions of θ by making use of DeMoivre's theorem.

22. Find all roots of the equation $x^4 + 81 = 0$.

23. Find all roots of $x^3 + 64 = 0$.

Review Exercises Chapter 7

In Exercises 1–5, calculate the magnitude and direction of vectors whose initial point is at the origin and with the given terminal point.

1. $(-3, 5)$ **2.** $(\sqrt{5}, -\sqrt{3})$

3. $(\pi, -5.4)$ **4.** $(1, -6)$

5. $(\sqrt{2}, -\sqrt{\pi})$

Find the x- and y-coordinates of the terminal point of the vectors in standard position in Exercises 6–10.

6. magnitude $= 100$, $\theta = 46°$

7. magnitude $= 15.6$, $\theta = -134°$

8. magnitude $= 85$, $\theta = 60°$

9. magnitude $= 1000$, $\theta = 2.65$ radians

10. magnitude $= 0.001$, $\theta = -45.6$ radians

Find the sum of the pairs of vectors in Exercises 11–20.

11. $\mathbf{A} = 8\mathbf{i} + 4\mathbf{j}, \mathbf{B} = -2\mathbf{i} + \mathbf{j}$

12. $\mathbf{A} = 3\mathbf{i} - 2\mathbf{j}, \mathbf{B} = 4\mathbf{i} - \mathbf{j}$

13. $\mathbf{A} = \mathbf{i} - 3\mathbf{j}, \mathbf{B} = 2\mathbf{i} + 3\mathbf{j}$

14. $\mathbf{A} = \mathbf{i} + \mathbf{j}, \mathbf{B} = \mathbf{i} - \mathbf{j}$

15. $\mathbf{A} = -\mathbf{i} - 2\mathbf{j}, \mathbf{B} = \mathbf{i} - 2\mathbf{j}$

16. $|\mathbf{A}| = 25, \quad \theta_A = 43^\circ$
$|\mathbf{B}| = 16, \quad \theta_B = 27^\circ$

17. $|\mathbf{A}| = 100, \quad \theta_A = 30^\circ$
$|\mathbf{B}| = 83.2, \quad \theta_B = 41.5^\circ$

18. $|\mathbf{A}| = 50, \quad \theta_A = 0.17$ radians
$|\mathbf{B}| = 46, \quad \theta_B = 1.2$ radians

19. $|\mathbf{A}| = 0.5, \quad \theta_A = -0.34$ radians
$|\mathbf{B}| = 1.3, \quad \theta_B = 1.6$ radians

20. $|\mathbf{A}| = 5, \quad \theta_A = 2.45$ radians
$|\mathbf{B}| = 8, \quad \theta_B = -4.36$ radians

21–30. Find the dot product of each pair of vectors given in Exercises 11–20. Also find the angle between the vectors.

In Exercises 31–50, perform the indicated operations with complex numbers. Express answers in the form $a + bi$ and $r \text{ cis } \theta$.

31. $(3 + 4i) - (5 - 2i)$

32. $(2 - i) - (8 + 5i)$

33. $(6 + 3i) - \overline{(6 + 3i)}$

34. $(2 - i) + \overline{(2 - i)}$

35. $(2 + i)(i - 1)$

36. $(-2 - i)(-7 + 2i)$

37. $(2 + 3i)(4 + i)$

38. $(2 + i)(6 - \sqrt{2}i)$

39. $\text{cis}\,(0.45) + 2 \text{ cis}\,(-0.95)$

40. $3 \text{ cis}\,(-4.5) - 5 \text{ cis}\,(4.5)$

41. $\dfrac{4 \text{ cis}\,(4.6)}{\text{cis}\,(-2.9)}$

42. $4 \text{ cis } 86^\circ / 8 \text{ cis } 26^\circ$

43. $\dfrac{2 + 3i}{4 + i}$

44. $\dfrac{-2 - i}{-7 + 2i}$

45. $(\sqrt{5} \text{ cis } 120^\circ)(7 \text{ cis } 80^\circ)$

46. $-5 \text{ cis}\,(-1.5) + 4 \text{ cis}\,(\pi/2)$

47. $100[\text{cis}\,(-120\pi) + \text{cis } 120\pi]$

48. $[\sqrt{3} \text{ cis}\,(120\pi)][2 \text{ cis}\,(120\pi)]$

49. $\dfrac{3.4 + 4i}{3.4 - 4i}$

50. $\dfrac{-2.1 + i}{2.1 + i}$

Find the cube roots of the complex numbers given in Exercises 51–55.

51. -1

52. $-1 + i$

53. i

54. $2 - 3i$

55. $i - 1$

56. Find all the roots of $x^5 + 32 = 0$.

57. Use DeMoivre's theorem to find $(1 + 3i)^5$.

58. A result that relates four important numbers in science is $\text{cis } \pi - 1 = 0$. Verify this result.

59. A force is represented by the complex number $3.4 - 2.5i$. Find the magnitude and direction of this force.

60. Two forces are operating on a body and are represented vectorially by $2\mathbf{i} - 3\mathbf{j}$ and $\mathbf{i} + 3\mathbf{j}$. Find the sum of these two vectors. Give the magnitude and direction of the resultant.

61. Two forces are represented by complex numbers $5 - 3i$ and $-1 + 3i$. Represent these same forces vectorially and find the angle between them.

62. The resistance in a circuit is given by 40 and the inductance by $25i$. The sum of these two is the impedance. Find the impedance and express it in rectangular form.

63. A force that varies with time is given by the complex expression $(t^2 - 3t + 2) - i(t^2 + t - 6)$.
a. Find the times for which the force is horizontal.
b. Find the times for which the force is vertical.
c. Find the time (if any) for which the force is zero.

64. In the study of the high-frequency operation of transistors, the expression $a = 5/(1 + 0.8i)$ occurs. Express a in rectangular form.

65. In an electric circuit, the impedance is the quotient of the voltage and the current. Find the impedance in a circuit in which the voltage is $5 - 4i$ and the current is $3 - i$.

Test 1 Chapter 7

Answer True or False to Exercises 1–10.

1. Vectors that point in the same direction may be added merely by adding their lengths.

2. Two vectors are equal if they have the same length and if they originate from the same point.

3. Ordered pairs of real numbers can describe vectors in the plane.

4. The scalar multiple of a vector **A** always points in the same direction as **A**.

5. To add two vectors, add their magnitudes and their reference angles.

6. The resultant of two vectors is their dot product.
7. The dot product of two vectors is a scalar.
8. The sum of two complex numbers is complex.
9. To multiply two complex numbers, multiply their magnitudes and add their arguments.
10. Complex numbers are added by adding the real part of one to the real part of the other and the imaginary part of one to the imaginary part of the other.
11. Find the x and y components of the vector $\mathbf{V}$ in standard position if $|\mathbf{V}| = 8$ and $\theta = 35°$.
12. Find the angle between the vectors $\mathbf{A} = 2\mathbf{i} + \mathbf{j}$ and $\mathbf{B} = \mathbf{i} - \mathbf{j}$.
13. Find the quotient of the complex numbers $(2 + 3i)/(4 + i)$ and express it in the form $a + bi$.
14. Find $(2 + i) \cdot (6 - \sqrt{2}i)$ by first expressing the given numbers in polar form.
15. Use DeMoivre's theorem to find $(1 + 3i)^5$.
16. Find the three cube roots of -1.

Test 2 Chapter 7

1. Find the x- and y-components of the vector $\mathbf{V}$ for which $|\mathbf{V}| = 25$, $\theta = 15°28'$.
2. Find the sum $\mathbf{A} + \mathbf{B}$ if $\mathbf{A} = 7\mathbf{i} + 8\mathbf{j}$ and $\mathbf{B} = -3\mathbf{i} + \mathbf{j}$.
3. Find the sum $\mathbf{A} + \mathbf{B}$ if $|\mathbf{A}| = 5.6$, $\theta_A = 19°10'$ and $|\mathbf{B}| = 0.9$, $\theta_B = 95°30'$.
4. Find the dot product $\mathbf{A} \cdot \mathbf{B}$ if $|\mathbf{A}| = 0.5$, $\theta_A = 18°50'$, $|\mathbf{B}| = 0.4$, $\theta_B = 2°20'$.
5. Evaluate (a) $(3 + 4i) - (5 - 2i)$ and (b) $(-2 - i)(-7 + 2i)$.
6. Plot $2 - \sqrt{3}i$ and then express it in polar form.
7. Plot $7 \text{ cis } 315°$ and then express it in rectangular form.
8. Evaluate $(\sqrt{5} \text{ cis } 120°)(7 \text{ cis } 80°)$.
9. Find the three cube roots of $-1 + i$.
10. Find all the roots of $x^5 + 32 = 0$.

8 The Algebra of Polynomials

8.1 Polynomials

A polynomial function is a function that can be written in the form

$$P(x) = a_n x^n + a_{n-1} x^{n-1} + \cdots + a_1 x + a_0$$

where n is a nonnegative integer, called the degree of the polynomial, and the coefficients $a_n, a_{n-1}, \ldots, a_1, a_0$ are constants. The "leading" coefficient, a_n, is understood to be nonzero (otherwise the degree of the polynomial would not be n) while some or all of the other coefficients may be zero. Zero coefficients are ordinarily not written. For example,

$$P(x) = 4x^3 + 0x^2 + 7x + 0$$

is written as

$$P(x) = 4x^3 + 7x$$

In general, the coefficients of a polynomial can be real numbers or complex numbers. A polynomial having only real number coefficients is called a **real polynomial;** otherwise it is called a **complex polynomial.** Examples of real polynomials are

$$3x^5 + 3x - 4 \quad \text{and} \quad x^{15} - 24x^9 + 11x$$

Examples of complex polynomials are

$$2x^5 + ix^2 - (4 + i)x - 1 \quad \text{and} \quad (3 - 2i)x^2 + 2x - 32$$

For simplicity, we will discuss only real polynomials. In particular, we explain some of the theory concerned with finding zeros of real polynomials (or, equivalently, the roots of real polynomial equations). The zeros of a real polynomial function can be either real numbers or complex numbers, so *the permissible values for real polynomial functions are the complex numbers.*

EXAMPLE 1

a. The zeros of $x^2 + 4$ are $\pm 2i$.

b. The zeros of $2x^3 + x^2 + 5x - 3$ are $\frac{1}{2}$ and $\frac{1}{2}(-1 \pm i\sqrt{11})$. Later in the chapter, we will explain how to find these zeros. ■

When we discuss polynomials, we use the degree of a polynomial for its name. For instance, $P(x) = 4x^2 - 5x + 4$ is called a second-degree or quadratic polynomial. Other common names are listed in Table 8.1.

TABLE 8.1

Degree	Name	General form
0	constant	$P(x) = a_0$
1	linear	$P(x) = a_1x + a_0$
2	quadratic	$P(x) = a_2x^2 + a_1x + a_0$
3	cubic	$P(x) = a_3x^3 + a_2x^2 + a_1x + a_0$
4	quartic	$P(x) = a_4x^4 + a_3x^3 + a_2x^2 + a_1x + a_0$

Polynomial functions may be combined with other polynomials by the operations of addition, subtraction, multiplication, or division. If $p_1(x)$ and $p_2(x)$ are two polynomials of lesser degree than $P(x)$ and if $p_1(x)p_2(x) = P(x)$, then $P(x)$ is said to be **factorable** and $p_1(x)$ and $p_2(x)$ are called **factors** of $P(x)$. The factors are called real or complex as the coefficients are real or complex numbers. Any polynomial factor of degree one is called a **linear factor.**

EXAMPLE 2

a. $x^3 - 2x + 3$ is a cubic polynomial.
b. $(x^2 + 2x + 3)$ and $(x^3 + x - 2)$ are factors of the fifth-degree polynomial $x^5 + 2x^4 + 4x^3 - x - 6$.
c. $(x - 1)$ is a real linear factor of $x^3 - 1$.
d. $(x - 2i)$ is a complex linear factor of $x^2 + 4$. ■

Division of Polynomials

The division of one polynomial by another yields a quotient and a remainder. We proceed as follows:

1. Arrange both the dividend and the divisor in descending powers of the variable. Leave space between given terms for missing powers of x.
2. Divide the first term of the dividend by the first term of the divisor. This gives the first term of the quotient.
3. Multiply the divisor by the first term of the quotient and subtract the product from the dividend.
4. Divide the first term of this difference by the first term of the divisor. This gives the second term of the quotient; it is multiplied by the divisor and subtracted from the first difference.
5. Repeat these steps until the remainder is either zero or of lower degree than the divisor. If the remainder is zero, the divisor is a factor of the dividend.

EXAMPLE 3 Divide $4x^3 + 5x - 9$ by $2x - 3$.

Solution

1. Since both dividend and divisor are already in descending powers of x, there is nothing to do in this step.
2. The first term of the dividend is $4x^3$ and the first term of the given divisor is $2x$. Since $4x^3 \div 2x = 2x^2$, the term $2x^2$ is the first term of the quotient.

3. Each term of the divisor is multiplied by $2x^2$:

$$2x^2(2x-3) = 2x^2(2x) + 2x^2(-3) = 4x^3 - 6x^2$$

This last expression is subtracted from the dividend:

$$\begin{aligned}(4x^3 + 5x - 9) - (4x^3 - 6x^2) &= 4x^3 + 5x - 9 - 4x^3 + 6x^2 \\ &= 6x^2 + 5x - 9\end{aligned}$$

4. The first term of this expression, $6x^2$, is divided by $2x$ to obtain $3x$, the second term of the quotient. The divisor is multiplied by the second term of the quotient to get $6x^2 - 9x$, and this is subtracted from the $6x^2 + 5x - 9$ to obtain $14x - 9$.
5. Finally, $14x$ divided by $2x$ is 7, which gives the third term of the quotient. Multiplying 7 by the divisor and subtracting from $14x - 9$, we get $+12$. Since this is of lower degree than the divisor, $+12$ is the remainder.

We arrange the above work in the following compact format:

$$\begin{array}{r l}
 & 2x^2 + 3x + 7 \quad = \textit{Quotient} \\
\textit{Divisor} = \underline{2x-3} & \overline{)\,4x^3 \qquad\quad + 5x - 9} = \textit{Dividend} \\
 & \underline{4x^3 - 6x^2} \\
 & 6x^2 + 5x - 9 \\
 & \underline{6x^2 - 9x} \\
 & 14x - 9 \\
 & \underline{14x - 21} \\
 & +12 = \textit{Remainder}
\end{array}$$

(*Note:* A space is left for the missing x^2 term.) ■

EXAMPLE 4 Divide $x^3 + 3x^4 - 2 + x^2 + x^5$ by $3 - x + x^2$.

Solution We first arrange the dividend and divisor in descending powers of x. Restated, the problem is:

Divide $x^5 + 3x^4 + x^3 + x^2 - 2$ by $x^2 - x + 3$

Then the division is carried out as follows:

$$\begin{array}{r l}
 & x^3 + 4x^2 + 2x - 9 \qquad\qquad = \textit{Quotient} \\
\textit{Divisor} = \underline{x^2 - x + 3} & \overline{)\,x^5 + 3x^4 + x^3 + x^2 \qquad\qquad - 2} = \textit{Dividend} \\
 & \underline{x^5 - x^4 + 3x^3} \\
 & 4x^4 - 2x^3 + x^2 \\
 & \underline{4x^4 - 4x^3 + 12x^2} \\
 & 2x^3 - 11x^2 \\
 & \underline{2x^3 - 2x^2 + 6x} \\
 & -9x^2 - 6x - 2 \\
 & \underline{-9x^2 + 9x - 27} \\
 & -15x + 25 = \textit{Remainder}
\end{array}$$

■

8.2 The Remainder and Factor Theorems

In this section we restrict our discussion to the division of polynomials by linear factors of the form $(x - r)$, where r is a real or a complex number. Consider the division of $P(x) = 2x^3 - 3x^2 - 4x - 17$ by the linear expression $x - 3$. By the division process, we have

$$\begin{array}{r|l} & 2x^2 + 3x \quad + 5 \\ x - 3 & 2x^3 - 3x^2 - 4x - 17 \\ & \underline{2x^3 - 6x^2} \\ & \qquad 3x^2 - 4x \\ & \qquad \underline{3x^2 - 9x} \\ & \qquad\qquad 5x - 17 \\ & \qquad\qquad \underline{5x - 15} \\ & \qquad\qquad\quad -2 \quad \text{Remainder} \end{array}$$

There is an interesting and useful observation that we can make about the remainder obtained in the preceding division problem. If we evaluate the function $P(x)$ at $x = 3$, we get

$$\begin{aligned} P(3) &= 2(3)^3 - 3(3)^2 - 4(3) - 17 \\ &= 54 - 27 - 12 - 17 \\ &= -2 \end{aligned}$$

which is the same number as the remainder obtained by dividing $P(x)$ by $x - 3$. This observation motivates the following theorem, known as the **remainder theorem** (Theorem 1).

Theorem 1

> If $P(x)$ is divided by the linear expression $(x - r)$ until a constant remainder R is obtained, then $P(r) = R$; that is, the remainder is always a constant equal to the value of the function evaluated at $x = r$.

Proof By the definition of division,

$$\frac{P(x)}{x - r} = q(x) + \frac{R}{x - r}$$

Therefore,

$$P(x) = (x - r)q(x) + R \tag{8.1}$$

Letting $x = r$, we have

$$P(r) = (r - r)q(r) + R = R$$

EXAMPLE 1 What is the remainder when $x^5 + x^4 + 6$ is divided by $x + 2$?

Solution In this case, $P(x) = x^5 + x^4 + 6$ and $r = -2$. Thus,

$$R = P(-2) = (-2)^5 + (-2)^4 + 6 = -32 + 16 + 6 = -10$$

■

EXAMPLE 2 Find the remainder when $P(x) = x^4 - 1$ is divided by $x + i$.

Solution Here $r = -i$, so $R = P(-i) = (-i)^4 - 1 = 1 - 1 = 0$. ■

The remainder theorem leads directly to another important theorem known as the **factor theorem** (Theorem 2). If, in particular, r is a zero of $P(x)$, then $P(r) = R = 0$. Thus, from Equation 8.1,

$$P(x) = (x - r)q(x)$$

which means that $(x - r)$ is a factor of $P(x)$.

Theorem 2

> The polynomial $P(x)$ has a zero $x = r$ if and only if $(x - r)$ is a factor of the polynomial.

Comment: More generally, $x = r$ is a zero of *multiplicity* k if and only if $(x - r)^k$ is a factor of the polynomial.

EXAMPLE 3 Show that $x - 2$ is a factor of $P(x) = x^3 + 2x^2 - 5x - 6$.

Solution Here $r = 2$ and $P(2) = 2^3 + 2(2)^2 - 5(2) - 6 = 0$. Hence, by the factor theorem, $(x - 2)$ is a factor. ■

EXAMPLE 4 Use the factor theorem to determine whether $2x - 1$ is a factor of $P(x) = 4x^3 - 5x + 2$.

Solution First, note that $2x - 1$ is not of the form $x - r$ and, therefore, we may not use the value of $P(1)$ to determine if $2x - 1$ is a factor. However, $2x - 1 = 2(x - \frac{1}{2})$, which means that if $x - \frac{1}{2}$ is a factor, so is $2x - 1$. Thus, we evaluate $P(\frac{1}{2})$ to find that

$$P\left(\frac{1}{2}\right) = 4\left(\frac{1}{2}\right)^3 - 5\left(\frac{1}{2}\right) + 2 = 0$$

which shows that $2x - 1$ is a factor of $4x^3 - 5x + 2$. ■

If the zeros and their multiplicities are known, the polynomial itself is completely determined except for a multiplicative constant.

EXAMPLE 5 Find the fourth-degree polynomial with zeros at -2, -2, 1, and 3 and y-intercept 2. (Repeating -2 twice is the usual way of indicating that -2 is a zero of multiplicity 2.)

Solution Since each of the zeros gives a factor,

$$P(x) = a(x + 2)^2(x - 1)(x - 3)$$

To evaluate the constant, note that the graph must pass through (0, 2). Substituting these values for x and $P(x)$,

$$12a = 2 \quad \text{or} \quad a = \frac{1}{6}$$

Hence, $P(x) = \frac{1}{6}(x + 2)^2(x - 1)(x - 3)$ is the desired polynomial. ■

Exercises Sections 8.1 and 8.2

Perform the divisions in Exercises 1–15. Check the remainder using the remainder theorem.

1. $(x^2 - 6x + 2) \div (x - 1)$
2. $(3x^2 + 5x - 7) \div (x + 2)$
3. $(x^3 + 2x^2 - 3x + 4) \div (x + 1)$
4. $(x^3 - 2x^2 + 3x - 1) \div (x - 2)$
5. $(2x^3 - 4x^2 + x - 1) \div (x + 2)$
6. $(x^3 - 3x + 9) \div (x + 3)$
7. $(3x^4 - 3x^3 + 2x^2 - 8x + 1) \div (x + 1)$
8. $(2x^3 - 4x^2 + 6x - 2) \div (x + 3)$
9. $(x^4 - 2x^2 + 3x - 2) \div (x + 2)$
10. $(x^5 - 32) \div (x - 2)$
11. $(2x^3 - 9x^2 + 11x - 6) \div (x - 3)$
12. $(x^2 - 5x + 3) \div (x + 4)$
13. $(3x^2 - x^3 + 2x - 7) \div (x + 1)$
14. $(x^3 + 3x - 4) \div (x + 3)$
15. $(3x^3 + 19x^2 + 16x - 20) \div (3x - 2)$

Perform the divisions in Exercises 16–20. (*Note:* the remainder theorem does not apply to these problems.)

16. $(3x^3 - 5x^2 - 3x - 1) \div (x^2 - x - 1)$
17. $(3x^4 - 7x^2 + 1) \div (x^2 + 1)$
18. $(x^5 + 2x^4 - 5x^2 - 3) \div (x^2 + x + 1)$
19. $(2x^3 - 7x^2 + 9x - 3) \div (x^2 - 3x + 3)$
20. $(8x + 2x^3 - 3x^2 - 2) \div (x^2 - x + 2)$

Use the factor theorem to determine whether or not the second expression is a factor of the first in Exercises 21–36.

21. $x^2 - 5x + 4, \quad x - 4$
22. $x^2 + 7x + 12, \quad x - 3$
23. $x^3 - 1, \quad x + 1$
24. $x^4 - x^3 + 2x^2 - 72, \quad x - 3$
25. $4x^3 + x^2 - 16x - 4, \quad x - 2$
26. $2x^4 - 7x^3 - x^2 + 8, \quad x - 5$
27. $3x^5 + 7x - 8, \quad x - 2$
28. $x^3 + 27, \quad x + 3$
29. $x^4 + 2x^3 - 15x^2 - 32x - 16, \quad x - 4$
30. $x^4 - 8x^3 + 6x^2 + 40x - 56, \quad x - 2$
31. $3x^3 + 2x^2 - 4x + 1, \quad 3x - 1$
32. $3x^3 - 20x^2 + 23x + 10, \quad 3x + 1$
33. $x^4 - 16, \quad x + 2i$
34. $x^6 + 1, \quad x - i$
35. $x^3 - 2x^2 + 4x - 8, \quad x - 2i$
36. $x^3 + 3x - 5, \quad x + 3i$

Write expressions for the polynomials in Exercises 37–42 with the indicated properties.

37. Third-degree polynomial with zeros at 1, -1, and 2. Has y-intercept of -2.
38. Fifth-degree polynomial with zeros of -3, 0, 0, 2, and 1. Passes through $(3, -1)$.
39. Fourth-degree polynomial with zeros of 1, 1, 2, and 2. Has y-intercept of 3.
40. Sixth-degree polynomial with zeros of $-2, -1, 0, 1$, i, and $-i$. Passes through (2, 1).
41. Third-degree polynomial with zeros of $(2 - i)$, $(2 + i)$, and $\sqrt{2}$. Has y-intercept of 2.
42. Fourth-degree polynomial with zeros of $(1 \pm \sqrt{2})$, $\sqrt{3}$, and π. Has y-intercept of $1/\pi$.
43. In a linear algebra treatment of the differential equations used to solve a specified electric circuit, the following determinant must be evaluated:

$$\begin{vmatrix} -\lambda & -\frac{3}{5} & 0 \\ \frac{5}{3} & -\lambda & -\frac{5}{3} \\ 0 & 6 & -(\lambda + 6) \end{vmatrix}$$

Show that the value of this determinant is a cubic function of λ and that $(\lambda + 1)$ is one of its factors.

8.3 Synthetic Division

As the degree of a polynomial function $P(x)$ increases, the problem of evaluating $P(r)$ becomes tedious because we must find and combine high powers of r. A shorthand technique of dividing a polynomial by a linear factor, called **synthetic**

division, when combined with the remainder theorem, facilitates finding $P(r)$. The method, which is related to long division, is developed in this context in the next example.

EXAMPLE 1 a. Divide $3x^3 - 7x^2 - x - 2$ by $x - 3$.

b. Use this problem to develop the method of synthetic division.

Solution a. Using long division, we have

$$\begin{array}{r|l}
 & 3x^2 + 2x \;\; + 5 \\ \hline
x - 3 & 3x^3 - 7x^2 - \;x - \;2 \\
 & 3x^3 - 9x^2 \\ \cline{2-2}
 & \qquad\;\; 2x^2 - \;x \\
 & \qquad\;\; 2x^2 - 6x \\ \cline{2-2}
 & \qquad\qquad\quad 5x - \;2 \\
 & \qquad\qquad\quad 5x - 15 \\ \cline{2-2}
 & \qquad\qquad\qquad\;\; 13
\end{array}$$

b. The method of synthetic division is the method of long division with all redundancy removed; that is, all unnecessary symbols stripped away. First, observe that in long division the coefficients are the only important quantities. Since the powers of x are not needed, we omit them and write the indicated division as

$$\begin{array}{r|rrrr}
 & 3 & 2 & 5 & \\ \hline
-3 & \textcircled{3} & -7 & -1 & -2 \\
 & 3 & -9 & & \\ \cline{2-3}
 & & \textcircled{2} & -1 & \\
 & & 2 & -6 & \\ \cline{3-4}
 & & & \textcircled{5} & -2 \\
 & & & 5 & -15 \\ \cline{4-5}
 & & & & 13
\end{array}$$

Next, since the three circled coefficients are identical to those of the quotient, we eliminate the quotient and other identical terms.

$$\begin{array}{r|rrrr}
-3 & \textcircled{3} & -7 & -1 & -2 \\
 & & -9 & & \\ \cline{2-3}
 & & \textcircled{2} & & \\
 & & & -6 & \\ \cline{3-4}
 & & & \textcircled{5} & \\
 & & & & -15 \\ \cline{5-5}
 & & & & 13
\end{array}$$

Now the numbers below the dividend may be written on two lines as

$$\begin{array}{r|rrrr}
-3 & \textcircled{3} & -7 & -1 & -2 \\
 & & -9 & -6 & -15 \\ \hline
 & & \textcircled{2} & \textcircled{5} & 13
\end{array}$$

All coefficients of the quotient appear below the line except the first. Therefore, we write this one below the line. It is always the same as the first coefficient of the dividend.

$$\begin{array}{r|rrrr} -3 & 3 & -7 & -1 & -2 \\ & & -9 & -6 & -15 \\ \hline & & \nearrow & \nearrow & \nearrow \\ & 3 & 2 & 5 & 13 \end{array}$$

After bringing down the first coefficient, notice that $3(-3) = -9$; subtracting -9 from -7 yields 2. Next, $2(-3) = -6$; subtracting -6 from -1 yields 5. Finally, $5(-3) = -15$; subtracting -15 from -2 the remainder is 13. In each of these operations we subtracted the second line from the first. By changing the sign of the divisor, we can add the terms instead of subtracting them; hence, the entire outline takes on a false, or *synthetic*, appearance. The original division problem can now be performed and written as

$$\begin{array}{r|rrrr} 3 & 3 & -7 & -1 & -2 \\ & & 9 & 6 & 15 \\ \hline & & \nearrow & \nearrow & \nearrow \\ & 3 & 2 & 5 & 13 \end{array}$$

The meaning of the various coefficients relative to the original problem is indicated next.

$$\begin{array}{r|rrrrl} \underbrace{x - 3} & \multicolumn{4}{c}{\underbrace{3x^3 - 7x^2 - x - 2}} & \\ 3 & 3 & -7 & -1 & -2 & \\ & & 9 & 6 & 15 & \\ \hline & 3 & 2 & 5 & 13 & = \textit{Remainder} \end{array}$$

$$\textit{Quotient} = 3x^2 + 2x + 5$$

■

The preceding example illustrates the method of synthetic division. To divide a polynomial $P(x)$ by $x - r$ using this method, proceed as follows:

1. Arrange the coefficients of $P(x)$ in order of descending powers of x, remembering that missing terms have a coefficient of zero.
2. Replace $x - r$ by r.
3. Bring down the coefficient of the highest power of x, multiply it by r, and add the result to the coefficient of the next highest power of x. Multiply this sum by r and add to the next coefficient. Continue this process until there is a product added to the constant term.
4. The last number in the bottom row is the remainder. The numbers to the left of the remainder are the respective coefficients of the quotient. Notice that the degree of the quotient is one less than that of $P(x)$.

EXAMPLE 2 Divide $5x^4 - 18x^2 - 6x + 3$ by $x + 2$ using synthetic division.

Solution Since the divisor is $x + 2$, $r = -2$. Thus,

$$\begin{array}{r|rrrrr} -2 & 5 & 0 & -18 & -6 & 3 \\ & & -10 & 20 & -4 & 20 \\ \hline & 5 & -10 & 2 & -10 & 23 \end{array}$$

The quotient is $5x^3 - 10x^2 + 2x - 10$ with a remainder of 23. ■

EXAMPLE 3 Given $P(x) = 8x^5 - x^3 + 2$, find $P(\frac{1}{2})$ by using synthetic division and the remainder theorem.

Solution

$\frac{1}{2}$	8	0	−1	0	0	2
		4	2	$\frac{1}{2}$	$\frac{1}{4}$	$\frac{1}{8}$
	8	4	1	$\frac{1}{2}$	$\frac{1}{4}$	$\frac{17}{8}$

The remainder is $\frac{17}{8}$. Therefore, by the remainder theorem, $P(\frac{1}{2}) = \frac{17}{8}$. ■

EXAMPLE 4 Show that $x + 2i$ is a factor of $x^3 - 5x^2 + 4x - 20$.

Solution We use synthetic division with $r = -2i$.

$-2i$	1	-5	4	-20
		$-2i$	$-4 + 10i$	20
	1	$-5 - 2i$	$10i$	0

Since the remainder is zero, we conclude that $x + 2i$ is a factor. ■

The Nested Multiplication Algorithm (Optional)

Closely related to the use of synthetic division and the remainder theorem to evaluate a polynomial, $P(x)$, at x_0 is an algorithmic approach especially suitable for hand calculators (or better still, computers). This technique is called the method of **nested multiplications,** for the polynomial is put into a form whereby its evaluation consists of simple multiplications and additions. The technique is based on the recognition of the following pattern.

1. First-degree polynomials: $P(x) = a_1x + a_0$

   $P(x_0)$ can be found in two steps:

   $$S_1 = a_1 \cdot x_0$$
   $$S_2 = S_1 + a_0 = P(x_0)$$

2. Second-degree polynomials: $P(x) = a_2x^2 + a_1x + a_0 = (a_2x + a_1)x + a_0$

   $P(x_0)$ can be found in four steps:

   $$S_1 = a_2 \cdot x_0$$
   $$S_2 = S_1 + a_1$$
   $$S_3 = S_2 \cdot x_0$$
   $$S_4 = S_3 + a_0 = P(x_0)$$

3. Third-degree polynomials: $P(x) = a_3x^3 + a_2x^2 + a_1x + a_0$

   $$= [(a_3x + a_2)x + a_1]x + a_0$$

   $P(x_0)$ can be found in six steps:

   $$S_1 = a_3 \cdot x_0$$
   $$S_2 = S_1 + a_2$$
   $$S_3 = S_2 \cdot x_0$$
   $$S_4 = S_3 + a_1$$
   $$S_5 = S_4 \cdot x_0$$
   $$S_6 = S_5 + a_0 = P(x_0)$$

We note that the general nth-degree polynomial can be evaluated in $2n$ steps by multiplying alternately the previous quantity by x_0 and then adding the next coefficient. The algorithm permits the computation of any polynomial without specifically using the exponent.

EXAMPLE 5 Use the nested multiplication algorithm to evaluate

$$P(x) = 2x^5 + 3x^4 - 5x^2 + x - 6 \text{ at } x_0 = 3$$

Solution Let $a_5 = 2$, $a_4 = 3$, $a_3 = 0$, $a_2 = -5$, $a_1 = 1$, and $a_0 = -6$. Using the method of nested multiplications, proceed as follows to evaluate $P(3)$.

$$S_1 = a_5 \cdot x_0 = 2 \cdot 3 = 6$$
$$S_2 = S_1 + a_4 = 6 + 3 = 9$$
$$S_3 = S_2 \cdot x_0 = 9 \cdot 3 = 27$$
$$S_4 = S_3 + a_3 = 27 + 0 = 27$$

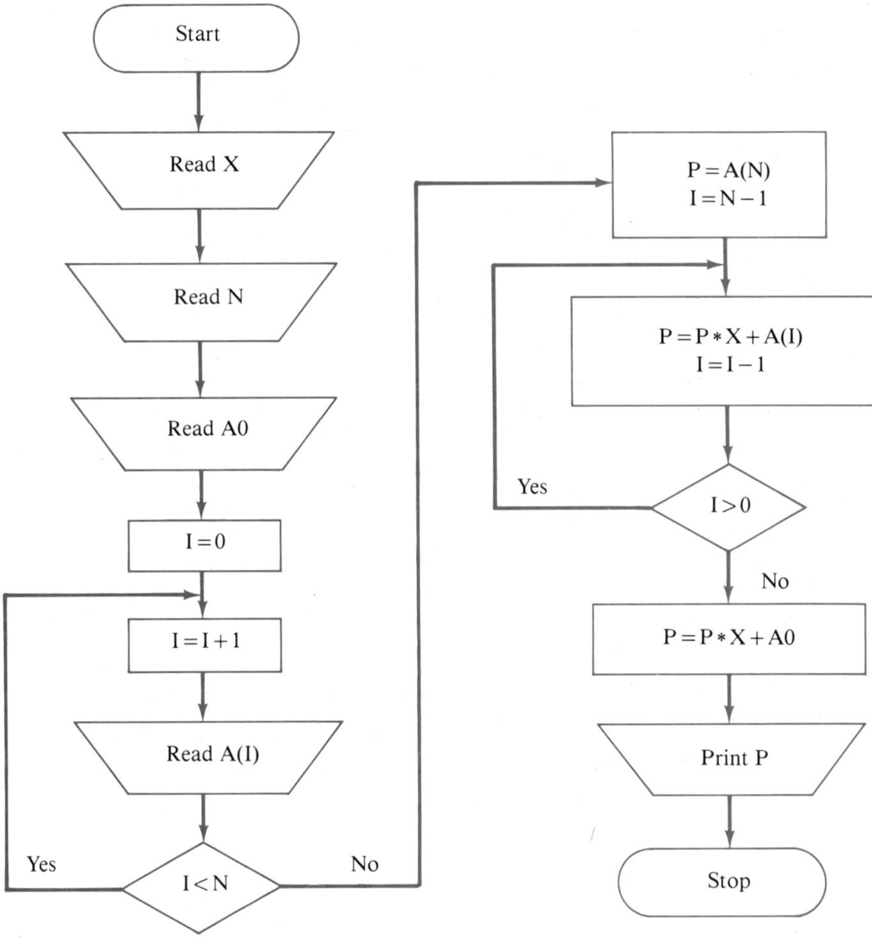

Figure 8.1

$$S_5 = S_4 \cdot x_0 = 27 \cdot 3 = 81$$
$$S_6 = S_5 + a_2 = 81 - 5 = 76$$
$$S_7 = S_6 \cdot x_0 = 76 \cdot 3 = 228$$
$$S_8 = S_7 + a_1 = 228 + 1 = 229$$
$$S_9 = S_8 \cdot x_0 = 229 \cdot 3 = 687$$
$$S_{10} = S_9 + a_0 = 687 - 6 = 681$$

Hence, $P(3) = 681$. ■

The flow diagram of Figure 8.1 illustrates the simplicity of the method of nested multiplications for computer applications. You may want to write this program and use the computer to solve Exercises 27–32 in the exercise set.

Exercises Section 8.3

Perform the divisions in Exercises 1–12 by using synthetic division.

1. $(x^2 - 5x + 4) \div (x - 4)$
2. $(x^2 + 7x + 12) \div (x - 3)$
3. $(x^3 - 2x^2 + 3x - 1) \div (x - 2)$
4. $(x^3 + 2x^2 - 3x + 4) \div (x + 1)$
5. $(x^3 - 3x + 9) \div (x + \frac{1}{2})$
6. $(x^3 - 1) \div (x + 1)$
7. $(x^4 - x^3 + 2x^2 - 72) \div (x - 3)$
8. $(2x^3 - 4x^2 + x - 1) \div (x + 2)$
9. $(8 + 7x - 3x^5) \div (x - 2)$
10. $(4x^3 + x^2 - 16x - 4) \div (x + 1)$
11. $(3x^3 - 20x^2 + 23x + 10) \div (x + \frac{1}{3})$
12. $(3x^3 + 2x^2 - 4x + 1) \div (x - \frac{1}{3})$

Use the remainder theorem and synthetic division to find the functional values in Exercises 13–22.

13. $P(3)$ for $P(x) = x^3 + 2x - 5$
14. $P(-4)$ for $P(x) = x^4 + 3x^3 - x^2 - 2x + 6$
15. $P(\frac{1}{2})$ for $P(x) = 3x^3 + 2x^2 - 4x + 1$
16. $P(-\frac{1}{2})$ for $P(x) = 3x^3 + 2x^2 - 4x + 1$
17. $P(0.1)$ for $P(x) = -6x^4 + 5x^2 - 2$
18. $P(0.2)$ for $P(x) = 3 + x - 4x^2 - 7x^3$
19. $P(3i)$ for $P(x) = x^2 - 2x - 1$
20. $P(-i)$ for $P(x) = x^3 + 1$
21. $P(-2 + i)$ for $P(x) = x^3 + 5x^2 + 9x + 5$
22. $P(-1 + i)$ for $P(x) = x^2 + 2x + 2$

In Exercises 23–26, determine k such that

23. $x - 1$ is a factor of $x^3 - 2x^2 + 3kx - 3$
24. $x + i$ is a factor of $x^4 - 3x^2 + kx - 2$
25. $x - \sqrt{2}$ is a factor of $x^3 - 2kx + 5$
26. $x + \pi$ is a factor of $kx^2 - 2x + 5$

Use the nested multiplication algorithm to evaluate the functional values in Exercises 27–32.

27. $P(2)$ for $P(x) = x^3 + 8x + 12$
28. $P(5)$ for $P(x) = x^6 + 9x^3 + x^2 + 5$
29. $P(-3)$ for $P(x) = 3x^7 - 2x^4 + 7x^2 - 5$
30. $P(10)$ for $P(x) = 5x^4 - x^3 + 6x^2 + x + 6$
31. $P(2.4)$ for $P(x) = 2x^4 - 3x^3 + 5x + 25$
32. $P(1.6)$ for $P(x) = 1.2x^3 + 5.7x^2 + 0.4x + 17.9$
33. Round-off error is reduced considerably by using the nested multiplication algorithm for evaluating polynomial functions. Evaluate

$$P(x) = 3x^5 - 4x^3 + 5x^2 - 7x + 2$$

for $x = 23.89$ both directly and using the algorithm. Compare your results.

8.4 The Zeros of a Polynomial Function

The factor theorem is useful only if we know something about the zeros of the polynomial. The following theorem tells us that even the most complicated-looking polynomial has a zero, although not necessarily a real zero, and therefore may be factored. The theorem is called the **fundamental theorem of algebra.**

Theorem 3

> Every nonconstant polynomial function has at least one zero.

While not giving us a clue as to how to find it, Theorem 3 does assure us that the polynomial

$$P(x) = 49x^9 - \sqrt{2}x^6 + \pi^2x^4 + (2 + \pi)x^3 - 6.235x^2 + 10^5$$

has at least one zero.

If $P(x)$ is a polynomial of degree n, $n > 0$, there must be at least one zero: say $x = r_1$. By the factor theorem we write

$$P(x) = P_1(x)(x - r_1)$$

where $P_1(x)$ is the polynomial found by dividing $P(x)$ by $x - r_1$. The degree of $P_1(x)$ is one less than the degree of $P(x)$. If the degree of $P_1(x)$ is greater than 0, then it must have at least one zero; say $x = r_2$. Therefore, $x - r_2$ is a factor of $P_1(x)$ and we can write

$$P(x) = (x - r_1)(x - r_2)P_2(x)$$

Similarly, if the degree of $P_2(x)$ is greater than 0, it must have at least one zero. Continuing this reasoning for n steps, we will obtain a zero, r_n, and hence a factor $(x - r_n)$. When we divide $P_{n-1}(x)$ by $x - r_n$, we obtain a constant c. Thus,

$$P(x) = c(x - r_1)(x - r_2)(x - r_3) \cdot \cdots \cdot (x - r_n)$$

In words, we have Theorem 4.

Theorem 4

> If $P(x)$ is a polynomial of degree n, then there are n numbers $r_1, r_2, \ldots, r_n$, not necessarily distinct, such that
>
> $$P(x) = a_n(x - r_1)(x - r_2) \cdot \cdots \cdot (x - r_n)$$
>
> where a_n is a constant.

As an immediate corollary we have Theorem 5.

Theorem 5

> A polynomial of degree n has exactly n zeros.

Warning: Theorem 5 must be given the proper interpretation. The theorem does not say that there are n *distinct* zeros, but rather that the total number of zeros, counting multiple zeros, is equal to the degree of the polynomial. Since the zeros of a polynomial $P(x)$ correspond to the roots of the equation $P(x) = 0$, the theorems on zeros are applicable to polynomial equations.

EXAMPLE 1 Given that $x = -4.7$ is a root of $P(x) = x^3 + 0.4x^2 - 16.49x + 17.484 = 0$, determine the other roots.

Solution Since $x = -4.7$ is a root, $x + 4.7$ is a factor of $P(x)$. By dividing $P(x)$ by $x + 4.7$, we obtain $P_1(x) = x^2 - 4.3x + 3.72$. The roots to this quadratic are obtained using the quadratic formula.

$$x = \frac{4.3 \pm \sqrt{(4.3)^2 - 4(3.72)}}{2} = \frac{4.3 \pm 1.9}{2}$$

$$x = 3.1, 1.2$$

Thus, the three roots of the given cubic equation are -4.7, 3.1, and 1.2. ■

Complex zeros of real polynomials must occur in complex conjugate pairs of the form $a \pm bi$; that is, a real polynomial cannot have an odd number of complex zeros. Complex zeros arise from linear factors of the form $x - (a + bi)$ and $x - (a - bi)$ or, equivalently, from the real quadratic factor $x^2 - 2ax + (a^2 + b^2)$. To verify this statement, note that

$$\begin{aligned}[x - (a - bi)][x - (a + bi)] &= x^2 - (a + bi)x - (a - bi)x \\ &\quad + (a - bi)(a + bi) \\ &= x^2 - 2ax + (a^2 + b^2)\end{aligned}$$

Real quadratic polynomials that cannot be factored into the product of real linear factors are said to be **irreducible.**

Theorem 6

> A real polynomial can be written as a product of a constant and real linear and irreducible quadratic factors.

Comment: Since irreducible quadratic polynomials can be factored into a product of complex linear factors, every real polynomial can be written as a product of real and complex linear factors.

EXAMPLE 2 The polynomial $x^4 - 1$ can be written as

$$\begin{aligned}x^4 - 1 &= (x^2 - 1)(x^2 + 1) \\ &= (x - 1)(x + 1)(x + i)(x - i)\end{aligned}$$

■

Rational Zeros

You have learned that an nth degree polynomial has n zeros, but so far no hint has been given as to how these zeros can be found. Of course, for degree two, the quadratic formula may be used. There are similar procedures using radicals for finding the zeros for third- and fourth-degree polynomials, but the formulas are hard to memorize and, consequently, are seldom used. For polynomials of degree greater than four, no general method to find zeros exists, although there are a number of good numerical approximation methods. Numerical methods usually require the use of a computer to be of any real practical value. Aside from these more advanced numerical methods, we frequently resort to methods of trial and error. These trial-and-error methods, however, should not be pure guesswork. For example, do not expect a positive zero for the polynomial $y = x^3 + 2x^2 + x + 2$. Why not? The following theorem tells how to find the rational zeros of a polynomial.

Theorem 7

> If the coefficients of $P(x) = a_nx^n + a_{n-1}x^{n-1} + \cdots + a_1x + a_0$ are integers, then any rational zero must be of the form of a factor of a_0 divided by a factor of a_n.

This theorem may also be applied to polynomials with rational coefficients. To obtain an equivalent polynomial with integer coefficients, multiply the entire polynomial by the greatest common multiple of the denominators of the coefficients. Thus, if

$$P(x) = \frac{3}{4}x^2 + \frac{2}{3}x - \frac{1}{6}$$

we may consider, instead, the polynomial

$$P_1(x) = 12P(x) = 9x^2 + 8x - 2$$

which has integer coefficients and the same zeros as $P(x)$.

Theorem 7 limits the number of trials that must be made to determine the rational roots of a polynomial equation. For example, you need not try $x = 2$ as a possible root of the equation $x^4 - 7x^3 + 3x^2 + 2x + 15 = 0$ because 2 is not a factor of 15.

EXAMPLE 3 The possible rational roots of $2x^3 - 5x + 6 = 0$ are

$$\pm\frac{1}{2}, \pm\frac{3}{2}, \pm 1, \pm 2, \pm 3, \pm 6$$

■

EXAMPLE 4 Find the rational zeros of $f(x) = x^3 + x^2 - 8x - 12$.

Solution Since the coefficient of the x^3-term is 1, any rational zero of $f(x)$ must be a factor of 12. Thus, the possible rational zeros are $\pm 1, \pm 2, \pm 3, \pm 4, \pm 6, \pm 12$. By synthetic division, we find that $x = -2$ is a zero.

$$\begin{array}{r|rrrr} -2 & 1 & 1 & -8 & -12 \\ & & -2 & 2 & 12 \\ \hline & 1 & -1 & -6 & 0 \end{array} \leftarrow x^2 - x - 6$$

Using the results of the synthetic division, we can express $f(x)$ as follows:

$$f(x) = (x + 2)(x^2 - x - 6)$$

Since $x^2 - x - 6$ is a factorable quadratic, we have $x^2 - x - 6 = (x + 2)(x - 3)$. The other zeros are then -2 and 3. Therefore, the three zeros are $-2, -2, 3$. ■

EXAMPLE 5 Find the roots of the equation $f(x) = 3x^4 + 11x^3 + 3x^2 - 20x - 12 = 0$.

Solution The possible rational roots are obtained by dividing the factors of 12 by the factors of 3; that is,

$$\pm 1, \pm 2, \pm 3, \pm 4, \pm 6, \pm 12, \pm \tfrac{1}{3}, \pm \tfrac{2}{3}, \pm \tfrac{4}{3}$$

The following synthetic division shows that $x = -2$ is a root.

$$\begin{array}{r|rrrrr} -2 & 3 & 11 & 3 & -20 & -12 \\ & & -6 & -10 & 14 & 12 \\ \hline & 3 & 5 & -7 & -6 & 0 \end{array} \leftarrow 3x^3 + 5x^2 - 7x - 6$$

The polynomial can then be written in the form

$$f(x) = (x + 2)(3x^3 + 5x^2 - 7x - 6)$$

Any rational root of this cubic factor must be a factor of 6 divided by a factor of 3; that is, ± 1, ± 2, ± 3, ± 6, $\pm \frac{1}{3}$, $\pm \frac{2}{3}$. By synthetic division,

$$\begin{array}{r|rrrr} -\frac{2}{3} & 3 & 5 & -7 & -6 \\ & & -2 & -2 & 6 \\ \hline & 3 & 3 & -9 & 0 \end{array} \leftarrow 3x^2 + 3x - 9$$

Hence, $x = -\frac{2}{3}$ is a root and we write $f(x)$ as

$$f(x) = 3(x + 2)\left(x + \frac{2}{3}\right)(x^2 + x - 3) = 0$$

Since this expression has a quadratic factor, we immediately use the quadratic formula to obtain

$$x = \frac{-1 \pm \sqrt{1 + 12}}{2}$$

Therefore, the desired roots are -2, $-\frac{2}{3}$, $(-1 + \sqrt{13})/2$, and $(-1 - \sqrt{13})/2$. ■

Exercises Section 8.4

Find all the roots of the equations in Exercises 1–17.

1. $x^3 + 2x^2 - x - 2 = 0$
2. $x^3 - 4x^2 + x + 6 = 0$
3. $y^3 + 2y^2 + y + 2 = 0$
4. $m^3 - 3m^2 - 4m + 12 = 0$
5. $2x^3 + x^2 - 18x - 20 = 0$
6. $x^3 - 9x^2 + 23x - 15 = 0$
7. $z^4 - 2z^3 - 7z^2 + 8z + 12 = 0$
8. $2r^4 - 9r^3 + 15r^2 - 11r + 3 = 0$
9. $3p^3 - 10p^2 + 12p - 3 = 0$
10. $y^4 + 2y^3 - 4y^2 - 5y + 6 = 0$
11. $x^4 - 6x^2 - 8x - 3 = 0$
12. $x^3 + 8 = 0$
13. $9w^3 - w + 2 = 0$
14. $16x^4 - 150x^3 + 381x^2 - 262x - 39 = 0$
15. $2x^3 - 3x^2 + 5x = 2$
16. $12x^3 + 4x^2 - 3x = 1$
17. $x^5 - x^3 - 8x^2 + 8 = 0$

In Exercises 18–23, factor the given polynomials into real and complex linear factors.

18. $x^3 - x^2 + 2$
19. $x^3 + 6x^2 + 2x - 3$
20. $2x^3 + 5x^2 + x - 2$
21. $4x^3 + 8x^2 + 9x + 3$
22. $4x^4 + 2x^3 - 24x^2 + 3x - 45$
23. $4x^4 - 4x^3 - 57x^2 + 81x$

Solve the systems of equations in Exercises 24–27. Find both real and complex solutions.

24. $y = x^3$
$y = 4x - 3$

25. $y = x^4$
$y = 2x - x^3$

26. $x^2y = 9$
$y = (x - 1)^2$

27. $x^2 - xy = y + 1$
$xy + x = 4y^2$

28. A psychologist finds that the response to a certain stimulus varies with age group according to $R = x^3 - 4x^2 - 19x - 10$, where R is response in milliseconds and x is age group in years. For what age group is the response equal to 4 msec? (Ignore negative solutions.)

29. In analyzing trends in a public opinion poll, a researcher found that the percentage P of people favoring a particular issue varied with age according to $P = x^3 - 21x^2 - 45x - 8$, where x is age in years. In what age group did 15% of the people indicate a favorable opinion? (Ignore negative solutions.)

30. A box without a top is to be constructed from a 10 in. by 16 in. metal sheet. The box is formed by cutting equal squares from each corner of the sheet and then bending up the sides. What size square should be cut to give a box with a volume of 144 cu in.?

8.5 The Real Zeros of a Polynomial by Graphing

In Section 8.4 you learned how to locate the rational zeros of a polynomial, but that technique was restricted to polynomials that have integral (or rational) coefficients. Thus, the zeros of polynomials such as $P(x) = \sqrt{2}x^3 - x^2 + x - \pi$ or even the nonrational zeros of a polynomial with integer coefficients cannot be found from Theorem 7.

Since the real zeros of the polynomial correspond to the x-intercepts of the graph, the accuracy of the estimates depends on the scale chosen and the care taken in drawing the graph.

EXAMPLE 1 Find the real roots of the equation $x^3 - 4x + 1 = 0$.

Solution The graph of $f(x) = x^3 - 4x + 1$ is shown in Figure 8.2.

x	$f(x)$
3	16
2	1
1	−2
0	1
−1	4
−2	1
−3	−14

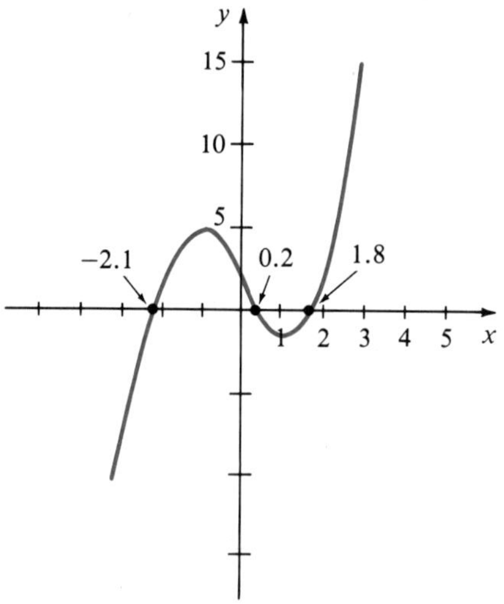

Figure 8.2

From the graph we estimate the roots of the equation to be $x_1 = -2.1$, $x_2 = 0.2$, $x_3 = 1.8$. ■

EXAMPLE 2 Find the real zeros of $y = 3x^4 - 4x^3 + 1$.

Solution The graph is shown in Figure 8.3 with the accompanying table of values.

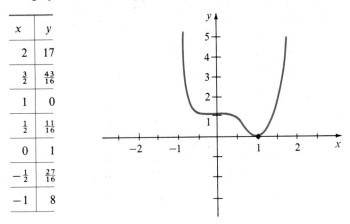

x	y
2	17
$\frac{3}{2}$	$\frac{43}{16}$
1	0
$\frac{1}{2}$	$\frac{11}{16}$
0	1
$-\frac{1}{2}$	$\frac{27}{16}$
-1	8

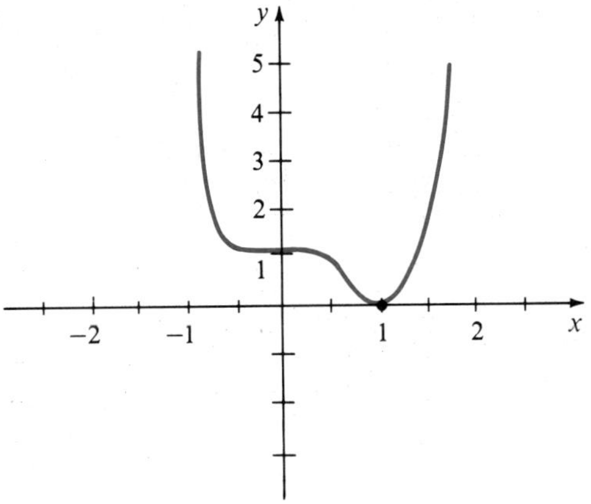

Figure 8.3

The graph and the table verify that $x = 1$ is a zero. To show that it is a double zero, divide $3x^4 - 4x^3 + 1$ by $(x - 1)^2$ to obtain $3x^2 + 2x + 1$. This latter quadratic is irreducible, and hence, the only real zero is at $x = 1$. ■

In general, if $P(a)$ is negative and $P(b)$ is positive, the graph of $P(x)$ must cross the x-axis somewhere between $x = a$ and $x = b$. This fact is represented graphically in Figure 8.4 and motivates Theorem 8, called the **intermediate value theorem for polynomials.**

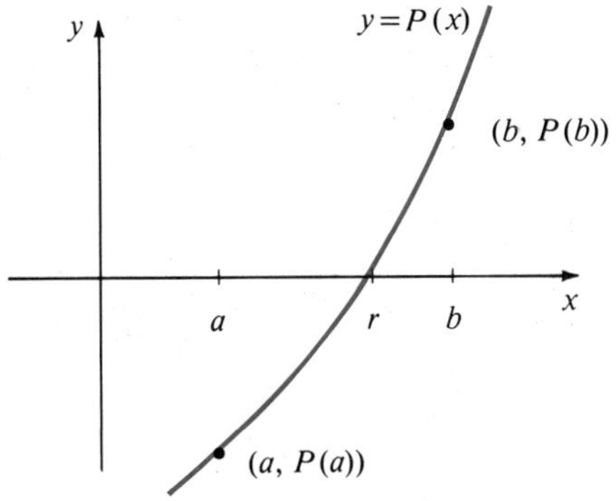

Figure 8.4

Theorem 8

If $P(x)$ is a polynomial with real coefficients and $a < b$, then if $P(a)$ and $P(b)$ are of opposite sign, there is a number r between $x = a$ and $x = b$ such that $P(r) = 0$.

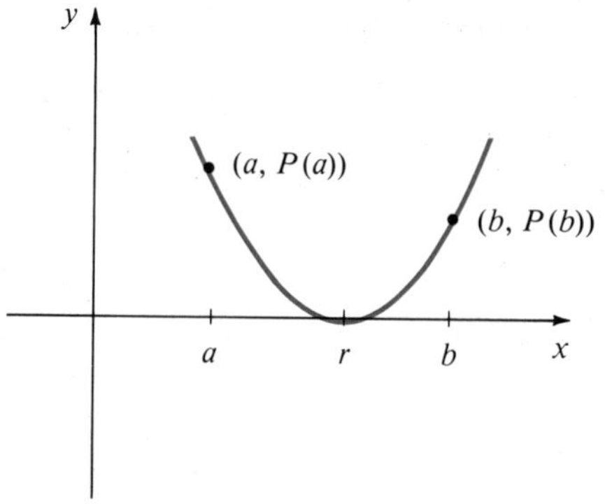

Figure 8.5

Warning: The theorem assures us that there will be at least one zero between $x = a$ and $x = b$ if $P(a)$ and $P(b)$ have opposite signs; it does not say there are no zeros between $x = a$ and $x = b$ if $P(a)$ and $P(b)$ have the same sign. Figure 8.5 shows why. Further, you should be aware that there may be more than one zero between $x = a$ and $x = b$ if $P(a)$ and $P(b)$ have opposite signs. That is, as Figure 8.6 shows, there may be multiple crossings between $x = a$ and $x = b$.

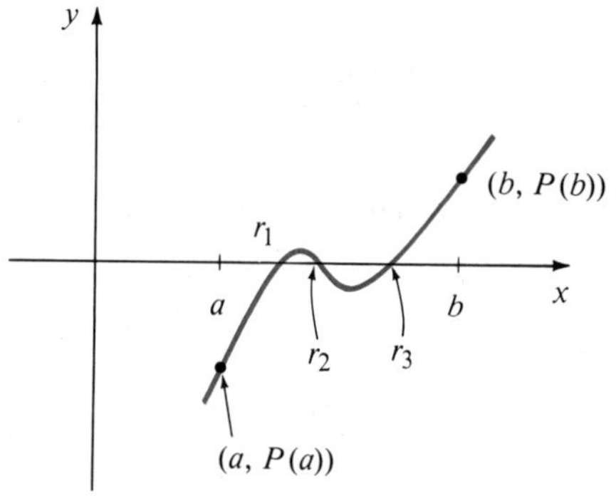

Figure 8.6

EXAMPLE 3 Show that the polynomial $P(x) = x^3 + x^2 + x - 4$ has a real zero between $x = 1$ and $x = 2$ and estimate its value to the nearest hundredth.

Solution Since $P(1) = -1$ and $P(2) = 10$, we know from Theorem 8 that there is at least one zero between 1 and 2. We can refine the location of the zero by evaluating $P(x)$ at 1.1, 1.2, 1.3, and so on. Thus,

$$P(1.0) = -1.0$$
$$\left.\begin{aligned} P(1.1) &= -0.359 \\ P(1.2) &= 0.368 \end{aligned}\right\} \text{a zero occurs within this interval}$$

To refine this estimate of the zero, we evaluate $P(x)$ at 1.11, 1.12, 1.13, and so on. Thus,

$$P(1.10) = -0.359$$

$$\left.\begin{aligned} P(1.15) &= -0.00663 \\ P(1.16) &= 0.0665 \end{aligned}\right\} \text{a zero occurs within this interval}$$

Finally, to decide whether the zero is 1.15 or 1.16 (the nearest hundredth), we evaluate $P(x)$ at 1.151, 1.152, and so on. Thus,

$$\left.\begin{aligned} P(1.150) &= -0.00663 \\ P(1.151) &= 0.00065 \end{aligned}\right\} \text{a zero occurs within this interval}$$

Since the zero occurs between 1.150 and 1.151, we can be sure that $x = 1.15$ is accurate to the nearest hundredth. ■

Another approach, called **linear interpolation,** avoids much of the laborious computations. The assumption in this technique is that the points $(a, P(a))$ and $(b, P(b))$ are connected by a straight line. Figure 8.7 shows the difference between the actual zero and the one obtained by linear interpolation. Analytically, the equation of the straight line connecting these two points is given by

$$\frac{y - P(a)}{x - a} = \frac{P(b) - P(a)}{b - a}$$

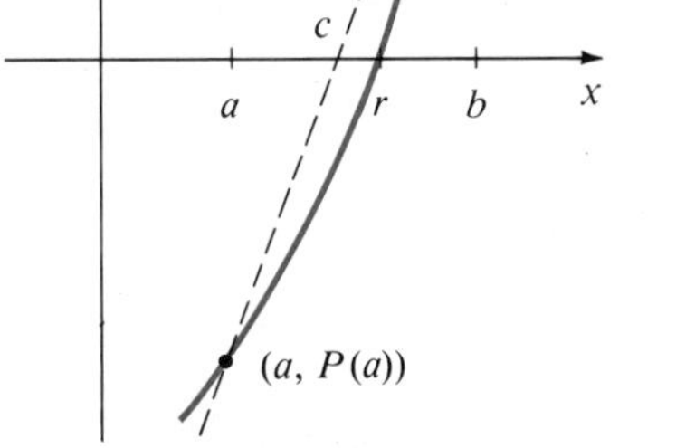

Figure 8.7

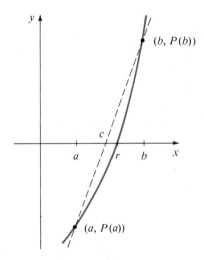

The x-intercept of this line is $(c, 0)$. Substituting $x = c$ and $y = 0$ in the preceding equation of the line, we have

$$\frac{-P(a)}{c - a} = \frac{P(b) - P(a)}{b - a}$$

Solving for c, we get

$$c = \frac{aP(b) - bP(a)}{P(b) - P(a)}$$

This value of c is used to approximate r between $x = a$ and $x = b$.

EXAMPLE 4 Approximate the zero of the polynomial of the previous example to the nearest tenth.

Solution Using the preceding formula with $b = 2$, $a = 1$, $P(2) = 10$, $P(1) = -1$, we have

$$r \approx c = \frac{10 - 2(-1)}{10 - (-1)} = \frac{12}{11} = 1.1$$ ■

To conclude this section, we discuss a method of estimating the total number of real zeros of a real polynomial. The method is called **Descartes' rule of signs** (Theorem 9) and is based on the concept of a *variation in sign* between the terms of a polynomial.

Definition

Let $P(x)$ be a polynomial arranged in decreasing powers of x. Then, there is a **variation in sign** whenever two successive terms differ in sign.

Note that terms with zero coefficients are disregarded when considering variation in sign.

EXAMPLE 5 There are three variations in sign in the polynomial

$$P(x) = 2x^5 - x^4 + x^2 + 3x - 2$$

The variations in sign are indicated by the arrows. ■

Descartes' rule of signs is given in Theorem 9.

Theorem 9

The number of positive zeros of a real polynomial is less than or equal to the variations in sign of $P(x)$. The number of negative zeros is less than or equal to the variations in sign of $P(-x)$. In both cases, the number of zeros is less than the number of variations in sign by an even number.

If $P(x)$ has five variations in sign, then by Theorem 9, $P(x)$ has five, three, or one positive zero (never four or two). Observe that the theorem allows us to conclude that there is *at least one* positive real zero of such a polynomial. Notice also that a polynomial with precisely one change in sign will have precisely one positive real zero.

EXAMPLE 6 Consider the polynomial

$$P(x) = x^5 - x^3 - 2$$

a. Determine the number of zeros.
b. Estimate the number of real positive and negative zeros.
c. Estimate the number of complex zeros.

Solution a. There are (counting multiplicities) five zeros since the degree of $P(x)$ is 5.
b. Since $P(x)$ has one change in sign, there is precisely one positive real zero. Since $P(-x) = -x^5 + x^3 - 2$, $P(-x)$ has two variations in sign. Thus, $P(x)$ has zero or two negative zeros.
c. Because of item b, there are either one or three real zeros. Hence, there are two or four complex zeros. ■

Exercises Section 8.5

In Exercises 1–10, use Theorem 9 (Descartes' rule of signs) to determine the possible number of positive and negative real roots and the possible number of complex roots.

1. $x^3 + 3x + 2 = 0$
2. $4x^3 - x^2 - 5 = 0$
3. $x^4 + 13x^2 - 7 = 0$
4. $2x^3 + 5x - 6 = 0$
5. $2x^3 - 7x^2 - 3x - 1 = 0$
6. $x^4 + x^3 - x^2 + x - 1 = 0$
7. $-2x^5 + 8x^3 - 7x + 15 = 0$
8. $4x^5 - 2x^4 + x - 10 = 0$
9. $3x^6 + x^4 - 8x^2 + 16 = 0$
10. $x^7 - x^3 + x^2 - 5x + 7 = 0$

In Exercises 11–22, use Theorem 8 to show that the given polynomial equation has a real root between the indicated points. (Use linear interpolation to estimate the root.)

11. $x^3 + 2x^2 + 8x - 3 = 0$ ($x = 0$ and $x = 1$)
12. $x^3 - 5x^2 + 3x + 4 = 0$ ($x = 1$ and $x = 2$)
13. $x^3 - 3x + 1 = 0$ ($x = 1$ and $x = 2$)
14. $x^3 + 2x + 20 = 0$ ($x = -3$ and $x = -2$)
15. $2x^3 - 3x^2 - 12x + 6 = 0$ ($x = 3$ and $x = 4$)
16. $x^3 - 6x^2 + 16 = 0$ ($x = 5$ and $x = 6$)
17. $x^4 - x^3 - 5x^2 + 3x + 2 = 0$ ($x = -1$ and $x = 0$)
18. $2x^4 - x^3 - 5x^2 - 3x - 3 = 0$ ($x = -2$ and $x = -1$)
19. $x^4 - x^3 - 2x^2 - x - 3 = 0$ ($x = 2$ and $x = 3$)
20. $4.3x^3 - 1.4x + 5.6 = 0$ ($x = -2$ and $x = -1$)
21. $2.1x^3 + 3.4x^2 - 1.8x + 5.3 = 0$ ($x = -3$ and $x = -2$)
22. $6.3x^4 - 2.5x^2 - 6.3 = 0$ ($x = 1$ and $x = 2$)

In Exercises 23–30, estimate the real roots of the equations by graphing the polynomial functions.

23. $x^3 - 4x^2 + 3x + 1 = 0$
24. $x^3 - 3x^2 + 4x - 5 = 0$
25. $2x^4 - 3x^3 - 6x^2 + 2x - 15 = 0$
26. $5x^3 + 6x^2 + 6x + 1 = 0$
27. $x^3 - 3x + 1 = 0$
28. $x^3 - 6x^2 + 16 = 0$
29. $x^4 - x^3 - 5x^2 + 3x + 2 = 0$
30. $2x^4 - 3x^3 - 6x^2 + 2x - 15 = 0$

8.6 Decomposition of Rational Functions into Partial Fractions (Optional)

A **rational function** is one that can be expressed as the ratio of polynomials. In this section we show how to express rational functions in terms of simpler functions. If the degree of the polynomial in the numerator is less than the degree of the polynomial in the denominator, then the rational function is said to be **proper;**

otherwise it is said to be **improper.** Any improper function can be reduced to a form consisting of a sum of a polynomial and a proper rational function. The process is a matter of dividing the numerator by the denominator. For example, to express the rational function

$$\frac{6x^4 + 7x^3 + 6x^2 + 32x - 7}{3x^2 + 5x - 2}$$

as a sum of a polynomial and a proper rational function, we divide the numerator by the denominator to obtain

$$2x^2 - x + 5 + \frac{5x + 3}{3x^2 + 5x - 2}$$

A proper rational function can frequently be written or decomposed into a sum of functions, each of which has but one factor in the denominator. This sum is often called the **partial fraction decomposition** of the rational function. It is literally the reverse of what we learned in Chapter 1. That is, we learned there that

$$\frac{2}{x - 3} - \frac{1}{x + 1} = \frac{x + 5}{x^2 - 2x - 3}$$

Now we will show how to "recover" the elements of the sum making up the proper rational function

$$\frac{x + 5}{x^2 - 2x - 3}$$

Recall that every real polynomial can be factored into real linear and irreducible quadratic factors of the form $ax + b$ and $ax^2 + bx + c$. These factors are the basis of decomposition. The following rules govern the form of the partial fraction decomposition of a given rational function. In each case, it is the factors of the denominator of the rational function that are being considered.

Rule 1

If the denominator has an unrepeated linear factor of the form $ax + b$, a fraction of the form

$$\frac{A}{ax + b}$$

must be included in the partial fraction decomposition.

Rule 2

If the denominator has a linear factor $(ax + b)$ that is repeated n times, a sum of fractions of the form

$$\frac{A}{ax + b} + \frac{A_2}{(ax + b)^2} + \cdots + \frac{A_n}{(ax + b)^n}$$

must be included in the partial fraction decomposition.

Rule 3

> If the denominator has an unrepeated quadratic factor $ax^2 + bx + c$, a fraction of the form
>
> $$\frac{Ax + B}{ax^2 + bx + c}$$
>
> must be included in the partial fraction decomposition.

EXAMPLE 1 Find the partial fraction decomposition of $\dfrac{x - 11}{2x^2 + 5x - 3}$.

Solution The factors of the denominator are $x + 3$ and $2x - 1$. Hence, the given fraction can be expressed as the sum of the partial fractions

$$\frac{A}{x + 3} \quad \text{and} \quad \frac{B}{2x - 1}$$

where A and B are constants to be determined. Thus, we write

$$\frac{x - 11}{(x + 3)(2x - 1)} = \frac{A}{x + 3} + \frac{B}{2x - 1}$$

To solve for A and B, clear the fractions from the equation to get

$$x - 11 = A(2x - 1) + B(x + 3)$$

$$x - 11 = 2Ax - A + Bx + 3B \qquad \text{Expanding}$$

$$x - 11 = (2A + B)x + (3B - A) \qquad \text{Collecting like terms}$$

For the two polynomials to be equal, the coefficients of corresponding powers of x must be equal. Thus,

$$2A + B = 1 \quad \text{and} \quad 3B - A = -11$$

Solving these equations simultaneously, we get $A = 2$ and $B = -3$. Hence,

$$\frac{x - 11}{(x + 3)(2x - 1)} = \frac{2}{x + 3} - \frac{3}{2x - 1}$$

■

EXAMPLE 2 Find the partial fraction decomposition of $\dfrac{x^2}{(x + 1)^3}$.

Solution Assume that the partial fractions may be written

$$\frac{x^2}{(x + 1)^3} = \frac{A}{x + 1} + \frac{B}{(x + 1)^2} + \frac{C}{(x + 1)^3}$$

$$x^2 = A(x + 1)^2 + B(x + 1) + C \qquad \text{Clearing fractions}$$

$$x^2 = Ax^2 + 2Ax + A + Bx + B + C \qquad \text{Expanding}$$

$$x^2 = Ax^2 + (2A + B)x + (A + B + C) \qquad \text{Collecting like terms}$$

$$\left.\begin{aligned} A &= 1 \\ 2A + B &= 0 \\ A + B + C &= 0 \end{aligned}\right\} \quad \text{Equating the coefficients of like powers of } x$$

These equations yield the values $A = 1$, $B = -2$, and $C = 1$. Making these substitutions, we have

$$\frac{x^2}{(x+1)^3} = \frac{1}{x+1} - \frac{2}{(x+1)^2} + \frac{1}{(x+1)^3}$$ ■

EXAMPLE 3 Find the partial fraction decomposition of the rational function $\dfrac{2x+8}{x(x+2)^2}$.

Solution The factors of the denominator are x and $(x+2)^2$. Therefore, the partial fractions are

$$\frac{2x+8}{x(x+2)^2} = \frac{A}{x} + \frac{B}{x+2} + \frac{C}{(x+2)^2}$$

$$2x + 8 = A(x+2)^2 + Bx(x+2) + Cx \qquad \text{Clearing fractions}$$

$$2x + 8 = Ax^2 + 4Ax + 4A + Bx^2 + 2Bx + Cx \qquad \text{Expanding}$$

$$2x + 8 = (A+B)x^2 + (4A + 2B + C)x + 4A \qquad \text{Collecting like terms}$$

$$\left.\begin{aligned} A + B &= 0 \\ 4A + 2B + C &= 2 \\ 4A &= 8 \end{aligned}\right\} \quad \text{Equating coefficients of like powers of } x$$

The solution of these equations yields $A = 2$, $B = -2$, and $C = -2$. The desired decomposition is

$$\frac{2x+8}{x(x+2)^2} = \frac{2}{x} - \frac{2}{x+2} - \frac{2}{(x+2)^2}$$ ■

EXAMPLE 4 Decompose $\dfrac{9x+14}{(x-2)(x^2+4)}$ into its partial fractions.

Solution The denominator is composed of a linear factor $(x - 2)$ and an irreducible quadratic factor $(x^2 + 4)$. Therefore, the required partial fractions are

$$\frac{9x+14}{(x-2)(x^2+4)} = \frac{A}{x-2} + \frac{Bx+C}{x^2+4}$$

$$9x + 14 = A(x^2+4) + (Bx+C)(x-2) \qquad \text{Clearing fractions}$$

$$9x + 14 = Ax^2 + 4A + Bx^2 - 2Bx + Cx - 2C \qquad \text{Expanding}$$

$$9x + 14 = (A+B)x^2 + (C - 2B)x + (4A - 2C) \qquad \text{Collecting terms}$$

$$\left.\begin{aligned} A + B &= 0 \\ C - 2B &= 9 \\ 4A - 2C &= 14 \end{aligned}\right\} \quad \text{Equating coefficients of corresponding powers of } x$$

from which $A = 4$, $B = -4$, and $C = 1$. Substituting these values in the partial fractions, we obtain

$$\frac{9x+14}{(x-2)(x^2+4)} = \frac{4}{x-2} - \frac{4x-1}{x^2+4}$$ ■

Exercises Section 8.6

In Exercises 1–21, find the partial fraction expansion for the given rational function.

1. $\dfrac{x+1}{x^2+4x-5}$

2. $\dfrac{x-2}{x^2-x-6}$

3. $\dfrac{1}{x^2+x}$

4. $\dfrac{2}{x^3-4x}$

5. $\dfrac{2x^2+5x+5}{x(x+5)(x+2)}$

6. $\dfrac{2x^2-11x-9}{x^3-2x^2-3x}$

7. $\dfrac{x+3}{x^2+6x+5}$

8. $\dfrac{1}{(2x+3)^3}$

9. $\dfrac{x^2+3x-6}{x(x-1)^2}$

10. $\dfrac{x+1}{x^3-x^2}$

11. $\dfrac{1}{x^3+2x^2+x}$

12. $\dfrac{-x^2+11x-6}{(x+2)(x-2)^2}$

13. $\dfrac{x^2-3x+6}{(x^2-1)(3-2x)}$

14. $\dfrac{x^2}{(x+1)^3}$

15. $\dfrac{2x-1}{(x-1)^2}$

16. $\dfrac{2(x^2+1)}{x^3+2x}$

17. $\dfrac{x^2+x+2}{x^3+2x}$

18. $\dfrac{9x+14}{(x+2)(x^2+4)}$

19. $\dfrac{x^2+1}{(2x+3)(x^2+2x+4)}$

20. $\dfrac{x^3+x^2-x+1}{(x-1)^2(x^2+1)}$

21. $\dfrac{x^3-3x^2+7x-5}{(x^2+2x+3)(x^2+5)}$

22. Partial fraction decompositions are used in calculus to simplify certain integrals. Find the partial fraction decomposition of

$$\frac{3x^2+8x-15}{(x^2+3)(x-4)}$$

Review Exercises Chapter 8

Divide the polynomials in Exercises 1–10 by the given linear factors. Check your remainder by using the remainder theorem.

1. x^2-3x+4 by $x-1$
2. $2x^2-x-5$ by $x+2$
3. $3x^2-x+4$ by $x-2$
4. x^4-x^2+1 by $x-\frac{1}{3}$
5. $2x^3-x+1$ by $x-\frac{1}{2}$
6. $2x^5-x^3+x^2-3$ by $2x-1$
7. $x^4+3x^5-x+x^2-2$ by $1+x$
8. x^6-1 by x
9. $2x^4-1+x$ by $-1+3x$
10. $5x^2-x^3+2x^4-x+5$ by $2x+3$

In Exercises 11–16, use the factor theorem to determine if the given linear factor is a factor of the polynomial.

11. $x^2-3x+2,\ x-3$
12. $x^3-x^2-2x+2,\ x-1$
13. $x^4-16,\ x-2$
14. $2x^5-3x-x^2-4,\ x+1$
15. $2x^3-x^2+x-1,\ 2x+1$
16. $3x^4-4x^2-x-30,\ x-2$

In Exercises 17–19, write expressions for polynomials with the properties given.

17. $P(x)$, a fifth-degree real polynomial with zeros 2, $2+i$, and i. (*Hint:* You should be able to determine the remaining zeros.) Assume that $P(0)=1$.
18. $P(x)$, a third-degree polynomial that has zeros 0, 1, and -1. Assume that $P(2)=6$.
19. $P(x)$, a fourth-degree real polynomial with zeros i and $2i$. Assume that $P(1)=20$.
20. Write the most general expression for a third-degree polynomial with zeros, 3, -2, and 1.
21. The graph of a fifth-degree polynomial is shown in the accompanying figure. Write the expression for the polynomial.

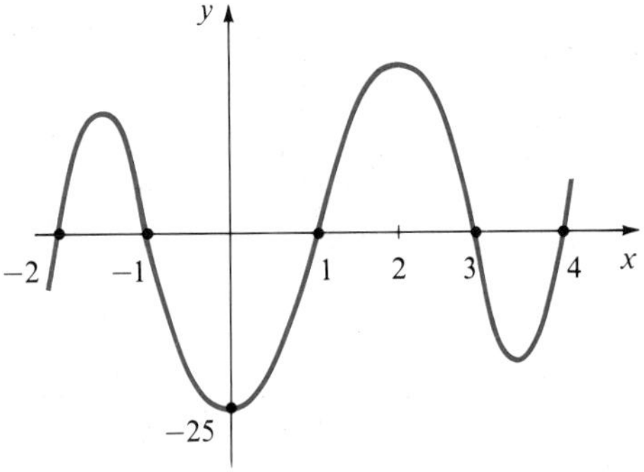

22. Determine the value of k so that $(x - 3)$ is a factor of $x^3 - 5x^2 + kx + 6$.

In Exercises 23–30, find all the roots of the given equations.

23. $x^4 + x^3 - x^2 + x - 2 = 0$
24. $x^3 - 6x^2 + 12x - 8 = 0$
25. $x^4 + x^3 - 3x^2 - x + 2 = 0$
26. $x^5 - 2x^4 + x^3 - x^2 + 2x - 1 = 0$
27. $x^3 - 7x^2 + 5x + 1 = 0$
28. $6x^4 - 11x^3 + 14x^2 - 44x - 40 = 0$
29. $2x^3 - 3x^2 + 2x + 2 = 0$
30. $x^6 + 9x^4 + 24x^2 + 16 = 0$

In Exercises 31–35, estimate the possible number of positive and negative zeros of the given polynomial. Use linear interpolation and graphing to estimate the values of the real zeros.

31. $P(x) = x^4 - x - 3$
32. $P(x) = x^3 - 3x^2 + 2$
33. $P(x) = x^5 - 1.1$
34. $P(x) = x^3 - 2x^2 + x - 1$
35. $P(x) = 2.3x^3 - 7x + 1.8$

In Exercises 36–40, determine the partial fraction decomposition.

36. $\dfrac{2x - 3}{(x - 4)(x + 3)}$
37. $\dfrac{8x + 7}{(x - 1)(x^2 + 4)}$
38. $\dfrac{3x - 5}{(x - 1)(x - 2)(x + 2)}$
39. $\dfrac{x^2 + 3x - 9}{x^3 - x^2 + 4x - 4}$
40. $\dfrac{x - 2}{x^3 - 1}$

41. For small intervals, polynomials are used to approximate other functions. For example, if $|x|$ is small, we can use $P(x) = x - \frac{1}{3}x^3$ to approximate $\sin x$. Show how good this approximation is by evaluating both $P(x)$ and $\sin x$ for $x = 0.01, 0.1, 0.2,$ and 0.5. (*Caution:* Your calculator must be in the radian mode when you are evaluating $\sin x$.)

42. The polynomial $1 - \frac{1}{2}x^2$ is used to approximate $\cos x$ for small values of $|x|$. Evaluate and compare $P(x)$ and $\cos x$ for $x = 0, 0.1, 0.2,$ and 0.5.

43. The equivalent resistance, R, of three resistances, R_1, R_2 and R_3, connected in parallel is given by

$$\frac{1}{R} = \frac{1}{R_1} + \frac{1}{R_2} + \frac{1}{R_3}$$

What is R_1 if $R_1 = R_2 - 1$, $R_3 = R_2 + 1$, and R is measured at 2 ohms.

44. In calculus, the difference quotient is a very important quantity and is particularly easy to compute for polynomials. Find the difference quotient

$$\frac{P(2 + h) - P(2)}{h}$$

for the polynomial $P(x) = 2x^3 - x^2 - x - 3$.

45. If the radius of a particular sphere is increased by 1 cm, its volume is increased by 15 cm^3. Find the radius of the original sphere.

Test 1 Chapter 8

Answer True or False to Exercises 1–10.

1. Quadratic functions are polynomials.
2. A polynomial is any algebraic expression with two or more terms.
3. The only possible rational roots of $x^9 + x - 10 = 0$ are ± 10, ± 5, ± 2, and ± 1.
4. The real zeros of a polynomial are the x-intercepts of the graph of the polynomial.
5. Polynomials with real coefficients have only real zeros.
6. Rational functions are zero only where the numerator is zero.
7. When a polynomial $f(x)$ is divided by $x + a$, the remainder is $f(a)$.
8. An nth degree polynomial has n distinct zeros.
9. If $x = a$ is a zero of a polynomial, then $x - a$ is a factor of that polynomial.
10. A real cubic polynomial has at least one real zero.
11. Determine the value of k so that $x - 3$ is a factor of $x^3 - 5x^2 + kx + 6$.
12. Use the remainder theorem to find the remainder when dividing $x^5 - x^3 + x^2 + 5$ by $x - 1$.
13. Write an expression for a third-degree polynomial with roots 2 and $1 \pm 2i$.

14. The graph of a fourth-degree polynomial has intercepts on the x-axis at $x = -2, 1, 4$, and 6. The y-intercept is (0, 12). Write the expression for the polynomial.

15. Estimate the number of positive and negative zeros of the polynomial $P(x) = x^4 - x - 3$. Use linear interpolation and graphing to estimate the values of the positive zeros.

16. Determine the partial fraction decomposition of

$$\frac{2x - 3}{(x^2 - 4)(x + 3)}$$

Test 2 Chapter 8

1. Answer True or False to the following statements.
   a. $f(x) = x^2 + x^{-2}$ is a polynomial.
   b. $(x + 2)$ is a factor of $(x^{15} + 2^{15})$.
   c. A fifth-degree polynomial has five distinct zeros.
   d. The nonreal zeros of any polynomial with real number coefficients occur in complex conjugate pairs.
   e. $x = -\frac{3}{2}$ is a potential rational root of $2x^3 + 4x^2 - x + 6 = 0$.

2. Show that $x - 2$ is a factor of $3x^4 - 4x^2 - x - 30$.

3. Use synthetic division to find the quotient and remainder of

$$\frac{2x^4 + 2x^3 - 5x^2 - x + 3}{2x - 4}$$

4. Find all the roots of the equation $x^4 + x^3 - x^2 + x - 2 = 0$.

5. Find the partial fraction expansion of

$$\frac{8x + 7}{(x - 1)(x^2 + 4)}$$

6. If you know that a fifth-degree real polynomial has the zeros $\sqrt{2}$, i, and $2 + i$, find the remaining zeros and write the polynomial in real form.

7. Write the third-degree polynomial with zeros at 0, 2, and 3, and passing through (4, 5).

8. Use a graphical method to estimate the real zeros of $y = x^3 - 3x^2 + 2$.

9

Sequences, Probability, and Mathematical Induction

9.1 Sequences in General

A **sequence** is a set of numbers in a prescribed order. Each number is called a **term** of the sequence, and we denote the *general term* by a_n. Using this notation, we write the entire sequence of numbers as $\{a_n\}$, where n is a positive integer.

The ordering arrangement allows us to designate the first term a_1, the second term a_2, the third term a_3, and so on, where the subscript indicates the position of each term. Thus, a sequence is often written $a_1, a_2, a_3, \ldots$, which is read "a sub 1, a sub 2, a sub 3, and so forth."

EXAMPLE 1 For the sequence of terms 5, 9, 13, 17, we write

$$a_1 = 5, a_2 = 9, a_3 = 13, a_4 = 17$$ ■

If, as in Example 1, a sequence has a finite number of terms, it is called a **finite sequence;** otherwise it is an **infinite sequence.** For finite sequences, it is at least theoretically possible to list every term. For infinite sequences (and for some finite ones), the terms are often designated by a formula that gives the value of a_n for each positive integer n for which the sequence is defined.

EXAMPLE 2 The formula $a_n = 2n + 1$ defines the sequence whose first few terms are

$$a_1 = 3, a_2 = 5, a_3 = 7, a_4 = 9, a_5 = 11, \ldots$$ ■

Another method of giving the terms of a sequence is in a **recursive** (or inductive) manner. We give the first term of the sequence, followed by a recursive formula from which any term (after the first) can be determined from the preceding one.

EXAMPLE 3 The formula $a_n = a_{n-1} + 2$, along with $a_1 = 3$, recursively defines the sequence whose first few terms are

$$3, 5, 7, 9, \ldots$$ ■

Whether defined by listing the terms, by giving an explicit formula for the nth term, or by supplying a recursive formula, a sequence may be considered a function whose domain is some subset of the positive integers. In fact, a sequence is sometimes called a **sequence function.** The range values are the terms of the sequence.

EXAMPLE 4 What is the range of the sequence function defined by the following formula?

$$a_n = (-1)^n$$

Solution Since $a_1 = -1$, $a_2 = 1$, $a_3 = -1$, and so on, the range values are 1 and -1. ■

Sometimes you are asked to find a formula for the nth term of a sequence when several consecutive terms are known. Example 5 illustrates the technique.

EXAMPLE 5 Find a formula for the general term of the sequence

$$5, 9, 13, 17, \ldots$$

Solution Notice that the rule is "add 4 to each term." Therefore, the general term can be written

$$a_n = 5 + 4(n - 1) = 4n + 1$$ ■

In this chapter, we examine a few of the important sequences. The following sequences are included for reference with no other details given.

- The sequence of natural numbers: $1, 2, 3, 4, 5, \ldots, n, \ldots$
- The sequence of positive even numbers: $2, 4, 6, 8, \ldots, 2n, \ldots$
- The sequence of positive odd numbers: $1, 3, 5, 7, 9, \ldots, 2n - 1, \ldots$
- The sequence of squares: $1, 4, 9, 16, 25, \ldots, n^2, \ldots$
- The sequence of cubes: $1, 8, 27, 64, \ldots, n^3, \ldots$
- The sequence of k-powers: $1^k, 2^k, 3^k, 4^k, \ldots, n^k, \ldots$
- The sequence of reciprocals: $1, \frac{1}{2}, \frac{1}{3}, \frac{1}{4}, \frac{1}{5}, \ldots, \frac{1}{n}, \ldots$

Exercises Section 9.1

Write the first five terms of the sequences in Exercises 1–15.

1. $a_n = n + 1$

2. $a_n = 2^n$

3. $a_n = 1 - (-1)^n$

4. $a_n = \sin n\pi$

5. $a_n = \cos n\pi$

6. $a_n = \log n$

7. $a_n = \dfrac{n+2}{n+1}$

8. $a_n = n - \dfrac{1}{n}$

9. $a_n = n^2$

10. $a_n = n(n + 1)$

11. $a_n = 2n + 1$

12. $a_n = \dfrac{1}{n}$

13. $a_n = \dfrac{1}{n^2}$

14. $a_n = (-1)^{2n+1}$

15. $a_n = 5(\frac{1}{2})^n$

Find the first five terms of the sequences in Exercises 16–20, given the following recursive information.

16. $a_1 = 2, a_n = a_{n-1} + 2$

17. $a_1 = 3, a_n = a_{n-1}^2$

18. $a_1 = -1, a_n = 5a_{n-1}$

19. $a_1 = 10, a_n = 5 - a_{n-1}$

20. $a_1 = 1, a_2 = 1, a_n = a_{n-1} + a_{n-2}$

Find a formula for the general term of the sequences in Exercises 21–26.

21. $2, 4, 6, 8, \ldots$

22. $1, 3, 7, 15, 31, \ldots$

23. $1, 4, 7, 10, 13, \ldots$

24. $\frac{1}{2}, \frac{2}{3}, \frac{3}{4}, \frac{4}{5}, \ldots$

25. $1, 4, 9, 16, 25, \ldots$

26. $1, 8, 27, 64, \ldots$

27. Suppose that in a year's time an automobile loses one fourth of the value it had at the beginning of the year. If a new car costs $4000, what is its value at the end of four years?

28. A certain yeast plant matures in one hour; each hour thereafter it buds off one new plant, which also matures in one hour and starts to produce new plants, and so on. Write the terms of the sequence that describe the total number of plants at any time. This is an example of a *Fibonacci sequence*. Can you write a recursive formula for this sequence? (*Hint:* See Exercise 20.)

9.2 Sequences of Partial Sums

Corresponding to each sequence $\{a_n\}$ another sequence $\{S_n\}$ can be written by forming sums of the first n terms of $\{a_n\}$. Thus, if $a_1, a_2, a_3, \ldots, a_n, \ldots$ are the terms of a sequence, then

$$S_1 = a_1$$
$$S_2 = a_1 + a_2$$
$$S_3 = a_1 + a_2 + a_3$$

$$S_n = a_1 + a_2 + a_3 + \cdots + a_n$$

The sequence $\{S_n\}$ is called the **corresponding sequence of partial sums of $\{a_n\}$.**

A compact notation often used to express terms of the sequence of sums is called the sigma, or summation, notation. The Greek letter Σ (sigma) means to form the sum of the indicated terms.

Definition

> By $\sum_{k=1}^{n} a_k$ is meant the sum
>
> $$a_1 + a_2 + a_3 + \cdots + a_n$$

The subscript k, called the **index of summation,** is often called a "dummy" variable since its only purpose is to indicate the steps in the summation process. The choice of the letter k for the index is arbitrary—any other symbol would serve as well.

The 1 and the n indicate the range of the index. In the definition, k begins at 1 and increases in steps of 1 until it becomes equal to n.

EXAMPLE 1 The sum of the first 100 integers may be written $\sum_{k=1}^{100} k$. ■

Writing a sum such as $\sum_{k=2}^{5} k^2$ in the form $4 + 9 + 16 + 25$ is called *expanding* the summation, or writing it in *expanded form.*

EXAMPLE 2 Write $\sum_{k=2}^{4} x^k$ in expanded form.

Solution $\sum_{k=2}^{4} x^k = x^2 + x^3 + x^4$ ■

EXAMPLE 3 Write $\sum_{i=1}^{10} (-1)^{i-1}$ in expanded form and simplify.

Solution $\sum_{i=1}^{10} (-1)^{i-1} = (-1)^0 + (-1)^1 + (-1)^2 + \cdots + (-1)^9 = 0$ ■

Two basic rules govern the use of the summation symbol. The first allows us to factor out a constant coefficient, and the second allows us to compute the sum of sums on a term-by-term basis. Together these two properties are called the **linearity properties.**

Property 1 $$\sum_{k=1}^{n} ca_k = c \sum_{k=1}^{n} a_k$$

Property 2 $$\sum_{k=1}^{n} (a_k + b_k) = \sum_{k=1}^{n} a_k + \sum_{k=1}^{n} b_k$$

As an example of the use of these properties, the sum

$$\sum_{k=1}^{3} k(5k + 1) = 1(6) + 2(11) + 3(16) = 76$$

can also be written

$$\sum_{k=1}^{3} (5k^2 + k) = 5 \sum_{k=1}^{3} k^2 + \sum_{k=1}^{3} k = 5(1 + 4 + 9) + (1 + 2 + 3) = 76$$

Either way the value is the same.

You should also be aware that a sum may be represented by more than one summation expression. One such instance is given in the following example.

EXAMPLE 4 $\sum_{k=1}^{n} \frac{1}{k} = \sum_{k=0}^{n-1} \frac{1}{k+1}$

Showing that these two sums are equal is merely a matter of writing them both in expanded form. The index on the left summation ranges from 1 to n, and on the right it ranges from 0 to $n - 1$. The second sum is said to be obtained by a **shift of index.** ■

EXAMPLE 5 Write the summation $\sum_{k=0}^{n} a_k(k - 1)x^k$ as a summation whose index begins at 2.

Solution Proceeding in a formal manner, let $k = t - 2$. Then when $k = 0$, $t = 2$, and when $k = n$, $t = n + 2$, so that the summation becomes

$$\sum_{t=2}^{n+2} a_{t-2}(t - 3)x^{t-2}$$

Letting $k = t$, we find that this last sum becomes

$$\sum_{k=2}^{n+2} a_{k-2}(k-3)x^{k-2}$$ ■

EXAMPLE 6 The sum of the first six terms of the sequence of reciprocals is $1 + \frac{1}{2} + \frac{1}{3} + \frac{1}{4} + \frac{1}{5} + \frac{1}{6}$. The first term can be written as $\frac{1}{1}$ and since the denominator varies from 1 to 6 in steps of 1, the sum can be written in summation notation as

$$\sum_{n=1}^{6} \frac{1}{n}$$ ■

Exercises Section 9.2

Write Exercises 1–10 in expanded form and evaluate.

1. $\displaystyle\sum_{m=1}^{5} \frac{1}{m+2}$
2. $\displaystyle\sum_{k=2}^{3} \frac{1-k}{1+k}$
3. $\displaystyle\sum_{n=0}^{5} n^2$
4. $\displaystyle\sum_{k=0}^{3} \left(-\frac{1}{2}\right)^k$
5. $\displaystyle\sum_{j=1}^{5} 3j$
6. $\displaystyle\sum_{k=0}^{5} (-1)^k$
7. $\displaystyle\sum_{k=1}^{5} (1+k)$
8. $\displaystyle\sum_{k=0}^{5} [2 + 3(k-1)]$
9. $\displaystyle\sum_{n=-2}^{2} n^2$
10. $\displaystyle\sum_{k=-1}^{2} (3k-1)$

Write the terms of the summation in Exercises 11 and 12.

11. $\displaystyle\sum_{k=1}^{5} x_k$
12. $\displaystyle\sum_{k=1}^{5} x^k$

Represent the summations in Exercises 13–17 by using the sigma notation.

13. $1 + 2 + 3 + 4$
14. $\frac{1}{2} + \frac{1}{4} + \frac{1}{8}$
15. $1 + 4 + 9 + 16$
16. $x_0 + x_1 + x_2 + x_3 + x_4$
17. $2x + 4x + 8x + 16x + 32x$

Which of the statements in Exercises 18–23 are true?

18. $\displaystyle\sum_{k=1}^{n} ax_k = a \sum_{k=1}^{n} x_k$
19. $\displaystyle\sum_{i=1}^{n} (x_i + d) = nd + \sum_{i=1}^{n} x_i$
20. $\displaystyle\sum_{k=1}^{n} d = nd$
21. $\displaystyle\sum_{k=2}^{5} a_{k-2} = \sum_{k=0}^{3} a_k$
22. $\displaystyle\sum_{n=1}^{4} n^2 = \sum_{n=2}^{5} n^2$
23. $\displaystyle\sum_{n=1}^{3} x^n = \sum_{t=2}^{4} x^{t-1}$

Find the sequence whose sequence of sums is given by the formulas in Exercises 24–27.

24. $S_n = \dfrac{n}{n+1}$
25. $S_n = 2$
26. $S_n = n$
27. $S_n = (-1)^n$
28. Find the sum of the first six terms of the Fibonacci sequence defined by $a_1 = 2$, $a_2 = 3$ and by $a_n = a_{n-2} + a_{n-1}$.

9.3 Arithmetic Sequences

A sequence of n equally spaced numbers is called an **arithmetic sequence.** To put it another way, an arithmetic sequence is one in which each term differs from the preceding term by the same constant amount. This constant number is called the **common difference** and is usually denoted by the letter d. Thus, an arithmetic sequence is defined by the following recursive relationship:

$$a_1 = a; \qquad a_n = a_{n-1} + d$$

Like all sequences, arithmetic sequences can be finite or infinite; unless stated otherwise, assume it to be infinite. Perhaps the simplest arithmetic sequence is the sequence of counting numbers, 1, 2, 3, 4, . . . , whose general term is $a_n = n$.

EXAMPLE 1 Find the first few terms of the arithmetic sequence with

$$a_1 = 7 \quad \text{and} \quad d = -3$$

Solution $a_1 = 7, \quad a_2 = 7 - 3 = 4, \quad a_3 = 4 - 3 = 1, \quad a_4 = 1 - 3 = -2,$
$a_5 = -2 - 3 = -5, \ldots$ ■

EXAMPLE 2 When a parachutist jumps from an airplane, the distances, in feet, he falls in successive seconds before pulling the rip cord are

$$16, 48, 80, 112, 144, \ldots$$

These numbers form an arithmetic sequence whose common difference is 32. ■

To find the general term of any arithmetic sequence with first term a_1 and common difference d, we note that the succeeding terms are $a_2 = a_1 + d$, $a_3 = a_1 + 2d$, $a_4 = a_1 + 3d, \ldots$. Therefore, the general term of an arithmetic sequence is

$$\boldsymbol{a_n = a_1 + (n - 1)d}$$

EXAMPLE 3 Find the hundredth term of the arithmetic sequence whose first term is 3 and whose common difference is 2.

Solution Using the formula for the general term with $a_1 = 3$, $d = 2$, and $n = 100$, we get

$$a_{100} = 3 + (99)(2) = 201$$ ■

The sequence of partial sums corresponding to an arithmetic sequence is a_1, $a_1 + a_2 = 2a_1 + d$, $a_1 + a_2 + a_3 = 3a_1 + 3d$, and so on. The formula for the nth term of the sequence of sums is derived by a method attributed to Karl Gauss* for computing the sum of the first 100 integers. Gauss recognized the simple but significant fact that the sum is the same regardless of the order in which the terms are written. Thus, for the sum of the first 100 positive integers,

$$S_{100} = 1 + 2 + 3 + \cdots + 98 + 99 + 100$$

and, in reverse order,

$$S_{100} = 100 + 99 + 98 + \cdots + 3 + 2 + 1$$

Adding these two equalities, we have

$$\begin{aligned} 2S_{100} &= 101 + 101 + 101 + \cdots + 101 + 101 + 101 \\ 2S_{100} &= (100)(101) \\ S_{100} &= 5050 \end{aligned}$$

This technique can be used to derive a formula for the nth term of the sequence of sums corresponding to *any* arithmetic sequence. We proceed as follows:

* Karl Friedrich Gauss (1777–1855) is often ranked, with Archimedes and Isaac Newton, as one of the three greatest mathematicians of all time.

$$\begin{array}{rl} S_n = a_1 & + (a_1 + d) + (a_1 + 2d) + \cdots + (a_n - 2d) + (a_n - d) + a_n \\ S_n = a_n & + (a_n - d) + (a_n - 2d) + \cdots + (a_1 + 2d) + (a_1 + d) + a_1 \\ \hline 2S_n = (a_1 + a_n) & + (a_1 + a_n) + (a_1 + a_n) + \cdots + (a_1 + a_n) + (a_1 + a_n) + (a_1 + a_n) \end{array}$$

$$S_n = \frac{n(a_1 + a_n)}{2}$$

Thus, the sum of n terms of an arithmetic sequence is the average of the first and last terms times the number of terms. Since $a_n = a_1 + (n - 1)d$, we may express this formula in terms of a_1 and d.

$$S_n = \frac{n(a_1 + a_1 + (n - 1)d)}{2} = a_1 \cdot n + \frac{n(n - 1)}{2} d$$

EXAMPLE 4 Find the sum of the first 50 terms of the arithmetic sequence whose first term is 2 and whose common difference is -3.

Solution Here $a_{50} = 2 + (49)(-3) = 2 - 147 = -145$. Hence,

$$S_{50} = 50\frac{(2 - 145)}{2} = 25(-143) = -3575$$

■

EXAMPLE 5 Find $\sum_{k=1}^{25} (5k - 3)$.

Solution This sum can be identified with the sum of the first 25 terms of an arithmetic sequence whose first term is 2 and whose common difference is 5. Thus, the sum is equal to

$$2(25) + \frac{25 \cdot 24}{2} \cdot (5) = 1550$$

■

The concepts of an arithmetic sequence and a linear function are closely related. To see this, we sketch the points $(1, a_1)$, $(2, a_2)$, $(3, a_3)$, and so on, in Figure 9.1, and join them by a straight line as if the domain were all real numbers. The equation of the line is

$$\frac{y - a_1}{x - 1} = \frac{a_2 - a_1}{2 - 1} = d$$

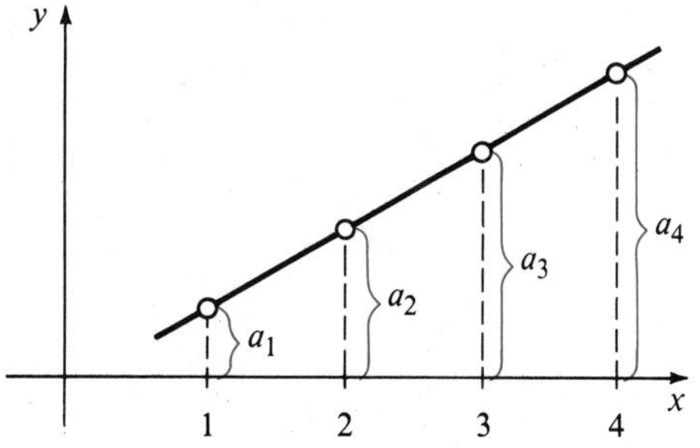

Figure 9.1

Thus,

$$y = a_1 + (x - 1)d$$

which is the arithmetic sequence rule with n replaced by x. In this manner, every arithmetic sequence determines a linear function. Conversely, given a linear function $f(x)$, the terms $f(1)$, $f(2)$, $f(3)$, and so on determine an arithmetic sequence with common difference $f(2) - f(1)$. Thus, an arithmetic sequence is a linear function whose domain is restricted to the positive integers. Note that the common difference, d, is the slope of the line.

Exercises Section 9.3

Determine which of the sequences in Exercises 1–10 are arithmetic and which are not. For those that are, give the common difference.

1. $1, 2, 3, 4, 5, \ldots$

2. $2, 5, 8, 11, \ldots$

3. $2, 4, 6, 8, 10, \ldots$

4. $3, 9, 27, 81, \ldots$

5. $3, 6, 9, 12, \ldots$

6. $1, \frac{1}{2}, 0, -\frac{1}{2}, \ldots$

7. $1, \frac{1}{2}, \frac{1}{4}, \frac{1}{8}, \ldots$

8. $1, -1, 1, 3, 1, 3, 5, 3, \ldots$

9. $\frac{1}{2}, \frac{1}{3}, \frac{1}{4}, \frac{1}{5}, \frac{1}{6}, \ldots$

10. $4, 14, 24, 34, 44, \ldots$

For Exercises 11–16, suppose that $\{a_n\}$ is an arithmetic sequence.

11. If $a_1 = 2$ and $d = 3$, find the general term.

12. If $a_1 = 3$ and $a_7 = 23$, find the common difference.

13. If $a_1 = 2$ and $S_7 = 35$, find the common difference.

14. If $a_1 = -1$ and $d = 3$, find S_8.

15. If $a_2 = 5$ and $d = -4$, find S_{10}.

16. If $d = 3$ and $S_6 = 57$, find a_1.

Find the value of the sums in Exercises 17–22.

17. $\sum_{k=1}^{8} (2k - 3)$

18. $\sum_{k=2}^{7} (k + 4)$

19. $\sum_{k=0}^{4} (7k - 4)$

20. $\sum_{n=1}^{5} \left(\frac{1}{2}n + 3\right)$

21. $\sum_{k=0}^{4} 7(k - 4)$

22. $\sum_{k=1}^{5} (2k + 1)$

23. Find a formula for the sum of the first n positive odd integers.

24. Find a formula for the sum of the first n positive even integers.

25. Show that the technique for finding the sum of an arithmetic sequence does not work for the sequence of squares.

26. A gasoline company runs a contest in which it sends the winner some money every day for a month. The amounts are \$50 the first day, \$100 the second day, \$150 the third day, and so on. In a 30-day month, how much will the winner collect?

Find the first five terms of the arithmetic sequence determined by the linear functions in Exercises 27–32.

27. $f(x) = x + 2$

28. $f(x) = 2x + 1$

29. $f(x) = -x + 2$

30. $f(x) = x$

31. $f(x) = 2x + 5$

32. $f(x) = -2x + 4$

What linear function is defined by the arithmetic sequences in Exercises 33–38?

33. $3, 6, 9, 12, \ldots$

34. $a_n = 2n + 3$

35. $a_1 = 4, d = 3$

36. $a_1 = 2, d = -1$

37. $a_1 = 5, a_8 = 26$

38. $a_1 = 1, d = 2$

9.4 Geometric Sequences

A number sequence constructed by successively multiplying by the same number is called a **geometric sequence.** The constant multiplier is called the **common ratio** and is usually denoted by r. The recursive definition of a geometric sequence is

$$a_1 = a_1$$

$$a_n = ra_{n-1}$$

The sequence giving the number of your direct ancestors in the preceding generations is 2, 4, 8, 16, . . . and is obviously a geometric sequence with common ratio 2.

A geometric sequence is completely determined by its first term a_1 and the common ratio r. To determine the general term, we note that

$$\begin{aligned} a_1 &= a_1 \\ a_2 &= a_1 r \\ a_3 &= a_2 r = a_1 r^2 \\ a_4 &= a_3 r = a_1 r^3 \\ &\vdots \\ a_n &= a_{n-1} r = a_1 r^{n-1} \end{aligned}$$

EXAMPLE 1 What is the tenth term of a geometric sequence whose first term is 1 and whose common ratio is 0.1? Write an expression for the general term.

Solution Using the formula for the nth term, we have

$$a_{10} = (1)(0.1)^9 = 10^{-9}$$

The general term for this sequence can be written

$$a_n = (1)(0.1)^{n-1} = 10^{1-n}$$

■

EXAMPLE 2 Find the recursive form for the geometric sequence whose general formula is

$$a_n = 5\left(\frac{1}{3}\right)^{n-3}$$

Solution From the given formula for a_n,

$$a_1 = 5\left(\frac{1}{3}\right)^{-2} = 45$$

Also,

$$r = \frac{a_n}{a_{n-1}} = \frac{5(\frac{1}{3})^{n-3}}{5(\frac{1}{3})^{n-4}} = \frac{1}{3}$$

Therefore, we have the recursive definition

$$a_1 = 45, a_n = \frac{1}{3}a_{n-1}$$

■

To find the sequence of partial sums corresponding to the geometric sequence, we proceed as follows. Let

$$S_n = a_1 + a_1 r + \cdots + a_1 r^{n-1}$$

Multiplying both sides of this equation by the common ratio r yields

$$rS_n = a_1 r + a_1 r^2 + \cdots + a_1 r^n$$

Subtracting the left-hand side of the second equation from the first equation and equating it to the difference of the right-hand sides of the two equations, we obtain

$$S_n(1 - r) = a_1(1 - r^n)$$

from which, if $r \neq 1$,

$$S_n = \frac{1 - r^n}{1 - r} a_1$$

EXAMPLE 3 Find $\sum_{k=1}^{10} (0.1)^k$.

Solution This sum can be written as the sum of the first ten terms of a geometric sequence whose first term is 0.1 and whose common ratio is 0.1. Thus,

$$S_{10} = \frac{1 - (0.1)^{10}}{1 - 0.1}(0.1) = (1.111111111)(0.1)$$
$$= 0.1111111111$$

■

Exponential functions of the type $f(x) = ca^x$ can be closely identified with geometric sequences of the type $a_n = ca^n$ in a manner analogous to the identification of arithmetic sequences and linear functions. The sequence is obtained from the function by restricting the domain of the function to the positive integers. Conversely, by sketching terms of the geometric sequence ca^n and connecting the points by a smooth curve, we obtain an exponential curve whose equation is $f(x) = ca^x$. (See Figure 9.2.)

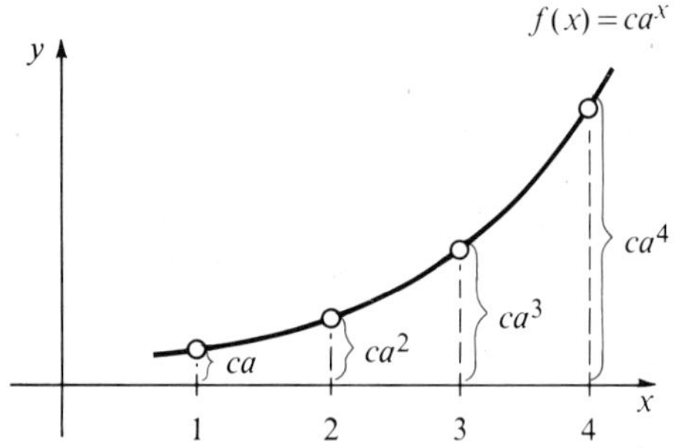

Figure 9.2

Geometric sequences are used in computing accumulated interest. Recall that money paid for the use of another person's money is called **interest.** If the interest is computed on the original principal only, it is called **simple interest.** In contrast, if the interest is permitted to accumulate and is paid not only on the original principal but on the accumulated interest as well, the investment is said to earn **compound interest.** The formula for compound interest is

$$A = A_0(1 + i)^n$$

where A_0 is the amount invested, i is the interest rate per period, and n is the number of payment periods. The justification of this formula follows the same reasoning as that used in the solution to Example 4.

EXAMPLE 4 A principal of \$2000 is invested at 8% interest for ten years. Find the accumulated interest if it is compounded (a) annually and (b) semiannually.

Solution a. In the case of the annual compounding, at the end of the first year the accumulated total amount is $A_1 = 2000 + .08(2000) = 2000(1.08)$. At the end of the second year, $A_2 = A_1 + .08A_1 = 2000(1.08)^2$. Continuing in this manner, we find that the accumulated amount at the end of ten years is given by $A_{10} = 2000(1.08)^{10} = 2000(2.1589) = \$4318$.

b. For the case of semiannual compounding, the reasoning is similar. Note that the interest rate per period is 4%. The accumulated amount at the end of 20 payment periods is

$$B_{20} = 2000(1.04)^{20} = \$4382$$

Thus, in the annual compounding case, the accumulated interest is \$2318 and in the semiannual case, \$2382. ■

Geometric sequences are also used to predict population growth. If a population P_0 increases $r\%$ each year, then the population at the end of the first year is $P_1 = P_0(1 + r)$, at the end of the second year it is $P_2 = P_1(1 + r) = P_0(1 + r)^2$, and so on. Hence, the population at the end of n years is

$$P_n = P_0(1 + r)^n$$

EXAMPLE 5 The world population in 1978 was approximately 4 billion. If the population is increasing at 2% each year, (a) what will the world population be in 2000? and (b) what is the doubling period of the population?

Solution a. Letting $P_0 = 4 \times 10^9$, $r = 0.02$, and $n = 22$, we have

$$P = 4 \times 10^9(1.02)^{22} = 6.18 \times 10^9$$

b. The doubling period is the time that it takes the population to double in size. Although we could use a specific population for P_0, we note that the doubling period depends only on the rate of growth, r. Therefore, we let $P_n = 2P_0$ and $r = 0.02$ and solve the population equation for n. Thus,

$$2P_0 = P_0(1.02)^n$$
$$2 = (1.02)^n$$

Taking the logarithm of both sides, we get

$$\log 2 = \log (1.02)^n$$
$$= n \log (1.02)$$

Solving for n, we get

$$n = \frac{\log 2}{\log (1.02)} = 35.00278878 = 35.0$$

Therefore, the doubling period for $r = 2\%$ is 35 years. Based on this period, the world population will be approximately 8 billion in 2013 (1978 + 35) and 16 billion in 2048. ■

Exercises Section 9.4

Determine which of the sequences defined in Exercises 1–8 are geometric sequences and for those that are, give the value of the common ratio. For each of the geometric sequences, find the general term.

1. 4, 12, 36, 108, . . .

2. 1, −3, 7, −11, . . .

3. 3, 6, 9, 12, . . .

4. 2, 4, 16, 256, . . .

5. $\frac{1}{3}, \frac{-2}{3}, \frac{4}{3}, -\frac{8}{3}, \ldots$

6. 1, −1, 1, −1, . . .

7. $\frac{1}{2}, \frac{1}{4}, \frac{1}{8}, \frac{1}{16}, \frac{1}{32}, \ldots$

8. $6, -6, 6, -6, 6, \ldots$

In Exercises 9–14 assume that $\{a_n\}$ is a geometric sequence.

9. If $a_1 = 3$ and $r = 5$, find a_4 and S_4.

10. If $a_2 = 2$ and $r = 2$, find S_{10}.

11. If $a_1 = 5$ and $a_5 = 80$, find all possible real values of r and S_5.

12. If $a_3 = \frac{1}{2}$ and $a_7 = \frac{1}{32}$, find a_{20}.

13. If $a_1 = -2$ and $r = \frac{2}{3}$, find a_{10}.

14. If $a_4 = 4$ and $a_7 = 32$, find a_1 and r.

Find the value of the sums in Exercises 15–21.

15. $\sum_{n=1}^{5} 2(3)^n$

16. $\sum_{k=2}^{6} (3^k + 2k)$

17. $\sum_{k=1}^{10} \left[\left(\frac{1}{2}\right)^k + \left(\frac{3}{2}\right)^k\right]$

18. $\sum_{n=1}^{10} 2^n$

19. $\sum_{k=1}^{6} 5\left(\frac{1}{2}\right)^k$

20. $\sum_{n=1}^{3} \left(\frac{2}{3}\right)^n$

21. $\sum_{n=1}^{3} \left(\frac{1}{4}\right)^n$

22. A certain ball, when dropped from a height, rebounds to three fourths of the original height. At what bounce will the ball fail to reach one fourth of the original height?

23. With each stroke a vacuum pump removes one fifth of the air in a container. After how many strokes will it remove three fourths of the original air?

Find the exponential functions defined by the geometric sequences in Exercises 24–26.

24. $a_1 = 2, r = \frac{2}{3}$

25. $a_3 = 4, a_4 = 8$

26. $a_1 = 1, r = 3$

Give the first five terms of the geometric sequences defined by the given exponential functions in Exercises 27–29.

27. $f(x) = 3^x$

28. $f(x) = 2(10)^x$

29. $f(x) = (\frac{1}{2})^x$

30. What is the formula for the sum of n terms of a geometric sequence if $r = 1$?

31. The speed of a chemical reaction approximately doubles each time the temperature increases by 10° C. Write a geometric sequence to show how many times faster paper will burn if the temperature rises by 10°, 20°, 30°, and 40° C.

32. Find the amount of an investment of $5,500 at the end of three years invested at 8% compounded quarterly.

33. What rate of interest, compounded annually, does an investment earn if the principal of $8000 amounts to $12,000 at the end of six years?

34. What principal should be invested to amount to $10,000 at the end of 20 years with interest at 8% compounded semiannually?

35. A particular substance decays in such a way that it loses half its weight each day. What is its half-life? In how many days will it have lost 90% of its initial weight?

36. A binary sequence is defined by the formula $a_n = 2^{n-1}$. Find the formula for the sum of the first n terms of a binary sequence.

9.5 The General Power of a Binomial

In Section 1.4 we showed that the expanded product of two binomials follows a special pattern. In particular, you were asked to memorize the expansions of the special products of $(x + y)^2$ and $(x + y)^3$ since they are so frequently used. Now we want to show that the general expansion of $(x + y)^n$ follows a recognizable and important pattern that will allow the easy expansion of any binomial as well as the determination of any particular term within that expansion.

By actually performing the multiplications for $n = 1$ through 5, we find

$$(x + y)^1 = x + y$$
$$(x + y)^2 = x^2 + 2xy + y^2$$
$$(x + y)^3 = x^3 + 3x^2y + 3xy^2 + y^3$$
$$(x + y)^4 = x^4 + 4x^3y + 6x^2y^2 + 4xy^3 + y^4$$
$$(x + y)^5 = x^5 + 5x^4y + 10x^3y^2 + 10x^2y^3 + 5xy^4 + y^5$$

Here are some pertinent observations:

1. There are always $(n + 1)$ terms, the first being $x^n y^0$ and the last, $x^0 y^n$.
2. Each intermediate term contains a product of $x^j y^k$, where the sum of j and k in every term is n. Thus, the product is of the form $x^{n-k}y^k$.
3. The exponents of x decrease by 1 from one term to the next, whereas the exponent associated with y increases by 1.
4. The coefficients follow a symmetric pattern; that is, by starting at either end of the expansion, the coefficients match those obtained by starting at the other end and proceeding in the reverse direction.
5. The actual formula for the coefficients is more difficult to guess with such limited information. However, note that the coefficient of the second term is $n/1$, the coefficient of the third term is $n(n - 1)/2$, the coefficient of the fourth term is $n(n - 1)(n - 2)/1 \cdot 2 \cdot 3$.

It can be shown in general that the coefficient of $x^{n-k}y^k$ in the expansion of $(x + y)^n$ is given by

$$\begin{aligned} C_{n,k} &= \frac{n(n-1)(n-2)\cdots(n-k+1)}{1\cdot 2\cdot 3\cdot 4\cdots k} \qquad &&\text{if } k \neq 0 \\ &= 1 &&\text{if } k = 0 \end{aligned} \tag{9.1}$$

Equation 9.1 is known as the **binomial coefficient.** It depends not only on the order of the expansion n, but also on the number of the term within that expansion, $(k + 1)$. Thus, the general expansion of a binomial consists of terms of the form $C_{n,k}x^{n-k}y^k$, where $k = 0, 1, 2, \ldots, n$.

EXAMPLE 1 Expand $(x^{1/4} - y^{1/3})^3$.

Solution Using the binomial expansion formula, we have

$$\begin{aligned} (x^{1/4} - y^{1/3})^3 &= (x^{1/4})^3 - 3(x^{1/4})^2 y^{1/3} + 3x^{1/4}(y^{1/3})^2 - (y^{1/3})^3 \\ &= x^{3/4} - 3x^{1/2}y^{1/3} + 3x^{1/4}y^{2/3} - y \end{aligned}$$

Note that the coefficient of the second term is $m/1 = 3$, the coefficient of the third term is $m(m - 1)/2 = 3(2)/2 = 3$, and the coefficient of the fourth term is $m(m - 1)(m - 2)/3 \cdot 2 = 3(2)(1)/3 \cdot 2 = 1$. ■

The binomial coefficient $C_{n,k}$ may be considerably shortened and thereby made easier to learn with use of **factorial notation,** a mathematical abbreviation for the product of integers 1 through n. The symbol $n!$ is read "n factorial" and is defined as

$$n! = n(n-1)(n-2)(n-3)\cdots 3\cdot 2\cdot 1 \tag{9.2}$$

The number 0! does not quite fit into this definition, but in order to make some mathematical formulas make sense, we define 0! as 1. Note also that $(n + 1)! = (n + 1)n!$.

EXAMPLE 2 $5! = 5 \cdot 4 \cdot 3 \cdot 2 \cdot 1 = 120$

$10! = 10 \cdot 9 \cdot 8 \cdot 7 \cdot 6 \cdot 5! = 30{,}240 \cdot 120 = 3{,}628{,}800$

$$\frac{10!}{5!} = 30{,}240$$

$$8! = 8 \cdot 7 \cdot 6 \cdot 5 \cdot 4 \cdot 3 \cdot 2 \cdot 1 = 8(7 \cdot 6 \cdot 5 \cdot 4 \cdot 3 \cdot 2 \cdot 1) = 8(7!)$$ ■

Most calculators can rapidly compute the product given by a factorial. For example, using a calculator, you can obtain $60! = 8.321 \times 10^{81}$ *(approximately).*

The factorial symbol simplifies the formula for $C_{n,k}$. Note that the numerator, which is the product of integers that begin at n and end at $(n - k + 1)$, may be written as $n!/(n - k)!$. The denominator is the product of integers from k to 1 and, hence, is simply $k!$ Thus, the binomial coefficient is given by

$$C_{n,k} = \frac{n!}{(n-k)!k!} \tag{9.3}$$

The $(k + 1)$th term of the expansion of $(x + y)^n$ is then

$$\frac{n!}{(n-k)!k!}x^{n-k}y^k, \qquad k = 0, 1, \ldots, n$$

Notice that the numerator is the factorial of the power of the binomial and the denominator is the product of the factorials of each of the exponents of the $(k + 1)$th term of the expansion. Thus, the sixth term (that is, $k = 5$) of the binomial $(x + y)^9$ is

$$\frac{9!}{4!5!}x^4y^5 = 126x^4y^5$$

EXAMPLE 3 Find the coefficient of x^9y^7 in the expansion of $(2x^3 - y)^{10}$.

Solution Let A be the desired coefficient of x^9y^7. The term of the expansion is of the form

$$Ax^9y^7 = C_{10,k}(2x^3)^{10-k}(-y)^k$$

Thus, $k = 7$, and

$$A = C_{10,7}2^3(-1)^7 = \frac{10!}{7!3!} \cdot 8 \cdot (-1)$$

$$= -960$$ ■

The binomial coefficients $C_{n,k}$ have many interesting properties. Perhaps the best device for memorizing the pattern of the coefficients is through a triangular display called **Pascal's* triangle.** Write $C_{n,k}$ for $k = 0, 1, 2, 3, \ldots$ on successive lines to obtain

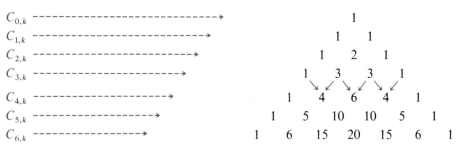

$C_{0,k}$ --------→ 1

$C_{1,k}$ --------→ 1 1

$C_{2,k}$ --------→ 1 2 1

$C_{3,k}$ --------→ 1 3 3 1

↘ ↙ ↘ ↙ ↘ ↙

$C_{4,k}$ --------→ 1 4 6 4 1

$C_{5,k}$ --------→ 1 5 10 10 5 1

$C_{6,k}$ --------→ 1 6 15 20 15 6 1

* Blaise Pascal (1623–1662) was a prominent French mathematician and physicist.

Each number *within* the triangle is found by adding the pair of numbers directly above it. For example, look at the interior numbers in the fifth row ($C_{n,4}$): $4 = 1 + 3$, $6 = 3 + 3$, and $4 = 3 + 1$. This observation suggests the following formula:

$$C_{n+1,k+1} = C_{n,k+1} + C_{n,k}$$

which is easily proven using the formula for $C_{n,k}$ directly.

The first two terms of a binomial expansion are often used to give a rough approximation to powers of numbers.

EXAMPLE 4 By using the first two terms of the binomial expansion, approximate the value of $(1.01)^{50}$.

Solution Letting $x = 1$ and $y = .01$ in the binomial, we have

$$\begin{aligned}(1.01)^{50} = (1 + .01)^{50} &\approx 1^{50} + 50(1^{49})(.01)\\ &= 1 + 50(.01) = 1.5\end{aligned}$$

■

The **binomial theorem** can be generalized to include expansions of $(1 + x)^n$ where n is not an integer if $|x| < 1$. When you are using the generalized form of the binomial theorem, you cannot compute the binomial coefficient from Equation 9.3 since we have not defined the factorial of a fraction. In this case, use Equation 9.1.

EXAMPLE 5 By using the first three terms of the generalized binomial expansion, approximate the value of $\sqrt[3]{5}$.

Solution $$\sqrt[3]{5} = (5)^{1/3} = (8 - 3)^{1/3} = 8^{1/3}\left(1 - \frac{3}{8}\right)^{1/3} = 2\left(1 - \frac{3}{8}\right)^{1/3} = 2(1 - .375)^{1/3}$$

Using the first three terms of the generalized binomial expansion for $(1 - .375)^{1/3}$, we have

$$\begin{aligned}\sqrt[3]{5} = 2(1 - .375)^{1/3} &\approx 2\left[1 + \frac{1}{3}(-.375) + \frac{(\frac{1}{3})(-\frac{2}{3})}{1 \cdot 2}(-.375)^2\right]\\ &\approx 2[1 - .125 - .015625]\\ &\approx 1.7188\end{aligned}$$

■

Exercises Section 9.5

Expand and simplify Exercises 1–16 by using the binomial formula.

1. $(x - y)^6$

2. $(x + 7y)^4$

3. $(3x - y)^5$

4. $(x - .1)^5$

5. $(x + (1/x))^5$

6. $(x + (1/3x^2))^4$

7. $(y^2 + 3x)^3$

8. $(\sqrt{x} + x)^5$

9. $(\sqrt{x} + \sqrt{y})^6$

10. $(yx^2 + (2/y))^4$

11. $(x^{1/3} + x^{-3/4})^4$

12. $(2y^{1/5} - 3z^{1/3})^4$

13. $(2 + .1)^4$

14. $(x^{-1} + y^{-1})^5$

15. $(x^{-3/4} - x^{3/4})^3$

16. $(2x^5 + 5y^{-3})^4$

17. Find the 4th term in the expansion of $(\sqrt{x} + \sqrt{y})^{10}$.

18. Find the 8th term in the expansion of $(1 + .1)^{20}$.

19. Find the 12th term in the expansion of $(3x^3 - 7y^{1/3})^{20}$.

20. Find the 15th term in the expansion of $(2y^3 - 3x^4)^{20}$.

21. Find the coefficient of $x^{12}y^2$ in the expansion of $(x^3 - 2y^2)^5$.

22. Find the coefficient of $(x/y)^5$ in the expansion of $(2x + 3y^{-1})^{10}$.

23. Find the coefficient of the constant term in the expansion of $[x + (1/3x)]^8$.

24. Find the coefficient of the x term in the expansion of $(2x^{1/3} - 7)^9$.

By using the first two terms of an appropriate binomial expansion, approximate the numbers given in Exercises 25–30.

25. $(2.3)^6$ **26.** $(1.99)^5$ **27.** $(3.99)^3$

28. $(.99)^{100}$ **29.** $(1.01)^{500}$ **30.** 99^4

By using the first three terms of the generalized binomial expansion, approximate the numbers given in Exercises 31–40.

31. $\sqrt{24}$ **32.** $\sqrt{13}$ **33.** $\sqrt[3]{7}$

34. $\sqrt{66}$ **35.** $\sqrt[3]{30}$ **36.** $\sqrt{5}$

37. $\sqrt[4]{80}$ **38.** $\sqrt[5]{31}$ **39.** $\sqrt{98}$

40. $\sqrt[3]{120}$

Use a calculator to compute Exercises 41–44.

41. $40!/30!$ **42.** $50!$

43. $(35 - 5)!$ **44.** $54!$

45. Using the formula for $C_{n,k}$, show that $\sum_{k=0}^{n} C_{n,k} = 2^n$. Notice that this formula represents the sum of the numbers in the nth row of Pascal's triangle.

46. Using the formula for $C_{n,k}$, show that $C_{n+1,k+1} = C_{n,k+1} + C_{n,k}$.

9.6 Permutations and Combinations (Optional)

Some applications of mathematics, particularly those involving statistics, require some systematic approach to counting. Typically, the things we count are called objects, or **decisions.** We attempt to simplify the counting process by considering independent successive decisions by using the following principle.

> **The Fundamental Principle of Counting**
>
> To find the number of ways of making several decisions in succession, multiply the number of choices that can be made in each of the individual decisions.

EXAMPLE 1 In how many different patterns can you answer a true-false test consisting of ten questions?

Solution Assuming each answer to be independent of the others, there are two possible choices for each answer. Hence, the total is

$$2 \cdot 2 \cdot 2 \cdot 2 \cdot 2 \cdot 2 \cdot 2 \cdot 2 \cdot 2 \cdot 2 = 2^{10} = 1024$$

■

EXAMPLE 2 How many different numbers can be written with the digits 1, 3, 5, 7, and 9 if none is to be repeated?

Solution There are five successive independent decisions. The first can be made in five ways, after which four digits remain. Hence, the second choice can be made in one of four ways. Continuing in this manner, we see that the total number of ways is

$$5 \cdot 4 \cdot 3 \cdot 2 \cdot 1 = 5! = 120$$

■

This last example is an application of the fundamental counting principle, which is important enough to analyze more generally. The question to answer is, "Given n distinct objects, in how many ways can we arrange them in a definite order?" Each such ordered arrangement is called a **permutation.**

To determine the number of permutations of n objects, apply the fundamental principle, noting that there are n choices for the first object, $(n - 1)$ for the second, $(n - 2)$ for the third, and so forth. Therefore, the total number is given by the product $n(n - 1)(n - 2) \cdots 3 \cdot 2 \cdot 1 = n!$

There are $n!$ permutations of n objects.

Often we wish to choose only a part of the set to make the arrangements. The next example illustrates the point.

EXAMPLE 3 If nine horses enter a race, in how many ways can the first three places be won?

Solution Note that the answer is *not* 9! since we are not concerned with the total number of possible finishes of all nine horses. There are nine possible winning horses, after which eight possible horses could finish in second place and finally seven who could finish third. Using the fundamental counting principle, there would be

$$9 \cdot 8 \cdot 7 = 504$$

possible ways for the top three to finish. ■

The foregoing example is typical of picking k objects at a time from n objects. The totality of these possible choices for fixed k and n is called **permutations of n objects taken k at a time** and is denoted by $P_{n,k}$. To find the value of $P_{n,k}$, note that the first may be chosen in n ways, the second in $(n - 1)$ ways, and so on for the k choices. Thus,

$$P_{n,k} = \underbrace{n(n-1)\cdots(n-k+2)(n-k+1)}_{k \text{ numbers}}$$

In factorial notation, the number of permutations of n objects taken k at a time is

$$P_{n,k} = \frac{n!}{(n-k)!}$$

EXAMPLE 4 The number of ways to deal five cards from a pack of 52 cards is

$$\frac{52!}{(52-5)!} = 52 \cdot 51 \cdot 50 \cdot 49 \cdot 48 = 311{,}875{,}200$$

Note that this number is *not* the number of distinct poker hands because a poker player holding a hand of five cards ordinarily disregards the order. ■

The distinction between an ordered arrangement as in the previous example and one for which order is immaterial leads to the idea of choosing a **combination** of k objects from n objects. Instead of deriving directly the formula for the number N of combinations, we will see how this number is related to $P_{n,k}$.

An ordered selection of k objects taken from n objects may be thought of as the following two-step procedure:

1. Choose k objects from the n. (We let N denote the number of ways of choosing these objects.)
2. Permute these k objects. ($P_{k,k} = k!$)

By the fundamental counting principle, $P_{n,k}$ is the product of N and $k!$ Thus,

$$P_{n,k} = N \cdot k!$$

and

$$N = \frac{P_{n,k}}{k!} = \frac{n!}{(n-k)!k!}$$

which we recognize as the binomial coefficient, $C_{n,k}$. Thus, the number of combinations of n objects taken k at a time is

$$C_{n,k} = \frac{n!}{k!(n-k)!}$$

EXAMPLE 5 a. The number of combinations taken five at a time from a set of ten is $C_{10,5} = 10!/(5!)(5!) = 252$.
b. The number of possible single bridge hands consisting of 13 cards is $C_{52,13} = 52!/(13!)(39!)$. ■

EXAMPLE 6 A baseball team has three catchers, nine pitchers, six infielders, and seven outfielders. In how many ways can a team of nine be chosen?

Solution The number of ways of choosing a catcher = 3.
The number of ways of choosing a pitcher = 9.
The number of ways of choosing the infielders = $C_{6,4} = 15$.
The number of ways of choosing the outfielders = $C_{7,3} = 35$.
Hence, by the fundamental counting principle, the total number of distinct teams = $3 \cdot 9 \cdot 15 \cdot 35 = 14{,}175$. ■

Exercises Section 9.6

1. Find the value of $P_{7,4}$, of $C_{7,4}$.
2. Given that $P_{n,2} = 56$, find n.
3. Given that $P_{n,3} = 9P_{n,2}$, find n.
4. Show that $P_{20,2} = 19P_{5,2}$.
5. Show that $\sum_{k=1}^{4} P_{4,k} = 4^3$.
6. Show that $\sum_{k=1}^{4} (C_{4,k})^2 = C_{8,4} - 1$.
7. From a committee of eight people, how many subcommittees of three people are possible?
8. In how many ways can ten people line up at a box office?
9. In how many ways can four candidates for public office be listed on the ballot?
10. How many ways are there of arranging the letters of the word MATH?
11. In how many ways can you arrange the digits in a seven-digit number, assuming there are no zeros and no repetitions?
12. In poker in how many ways can you get a flush (all of the same suit)?
13. In poker in how many ways can you get a full house (three of a kind and a pair)?
14. Four persons enter a room in which there are seven chairs. In how many ways can they select their chairs?
15. How many four-letter "words" ending in a vowel can be constructed from the word VOWEL?
16. A building has five entrances. In how many ways can you enter the building and leave by a different entrance?
17. How many committees of four women can be selected from ten women if two certain women refuse to serve on a committee together?

9.7 Probability (Optional)

When a coin is flipped into the air, we can state with certainty that the coin will fall. The outcome of this event can be predicted with certainty because of gravitational attraction, which is known to hold for all objects in the universe. On the other hand, we cannot state with certainty that the coin will land heads up. We know that "heads" or "tails" is a matter of chance and not something that can be predicted with certainty. Thus, when we flip a coin, we can only be certain that it will fall and that it will land in one of two ways, "heads" or "tails." We say there is a "50–50 chance" that a coin will land heads up. The systematic study of chance events, such as flipping a coin, is called **probability.**

The probability of an event A is a number we denote by $P(A)$. To determine $P(A)$, you must know not only the number of ways that the event A can occur as the outcome of some operation, but also the number of ways in which the event A does not occur. The occurrences of A are called *successes* and the nonoccurrences of A are called *failures.* If s is the number of successful outcomes and f is the number of failures, then $s + f = n$ is the total number of outcomes of the operation. The probability of the occurrence of an event A is defined by

$$P(A) = \frac{s}{n} \tag{9.4}$$

Thus, to determine the probability of an event A,

1. Determine the total number of ways for the outcomes to occur.
2. Determine the number of ways for a successful outcome to happen.
3. Use these numbers in Equation 9.4.

EXAMPLE 1

a. The operation of tossing a coin has two possible outcomes. The event "heads" is one of the two outcomes. Thus,

$$P(\text{heads}) = \frac{1}{2}$$

b. The operation of throwing a die has six possible outcomes. The event "number less than three" can occur in two ways. Thus,

$$P(\text{number less than 3}) = \frac{2}{6} = \frac{1}{3}$$

c. The operation of drawing a card from a deck has 52 possible outcomes. The event "ace" can occur in four different ways. Thus,

$$P(\text{ace}) = \frac{4}{52} = \frac{1}{13}$$

■

EXAMPLE 2 What is the probability of getting three heads in five tosses of a coin?

Solution On each toss the coin can land in two ways, so there are $2 \cdot 2 \cdot 2 \cdot 2 \cdot 2 = 2^5$ ways the coin can land in five tosses. The number of ways we can get three "heads" in five tosses is given by $C_{5,3} = 5!/3!2! = 10$. Hence,

$$P(\text{3 heads}) = \frac{C_{5,3}}{2^5} = \frac{10}{32} = \frac{5}{16}$$

■

EXAMPLE 3 What is the probability that three balls drawn at random from a box of five red balls and seven black balls will all be red?

Solution The number of ways in which three red balls can be drawn from the five red balls in the box is $C_{5,3}$, and the number of ways three balls can be drawn from the 12 in the box is $C_{12,3}$. Therefore, the probability of a red ball is

$$P(\text{red}) = \frac{C_{5,3}}{C_{12,3}} = \frac{\dfrac{5!}{3!2!}}{\dfrac{12!}{3!9!}} = \frac{10}{220} = \frac{1}{22}$$ ■

EXAMPLE 4 What is the probability that five balls drawn at random from the box in the preceding example will consist of two red balls and three black balls?

Solution The number of ways two red balls can be drawn from the five red ones in the box is $C_{5,2}$, and the number of ways three black balls can be drawn from the seven black ones in the box is $C_{7,3}$. Therefore, by the counting principle, the number of ways two red balls and three black balls can be drawn is $C_{5,2} \cdot C_{7,3}$. Finally, the number of ways five balls can be drawn from the 12 balls in the box is $C_{12,5}$. Hence,

$$P(2 \text{ red}, 3 \text{ black}) = \frac{C_{5,2} \cdot C_{7,3}}{C_{12,5}} = \frac{\dfrac{5!}{2!3!}\ \dfrac{7!}{3!4!}}{\dfrac{12!}{5!7!}} = \frac{10 \cdot 35}{792} = \frac{350}{792} = \frac{175}{396}$$ ■

The probability of an event cannot be less than zero or greater than one; that is,

$$0 \leq P(A) \leq 1$$

If $P(A) = 1$, we say the event is *certain* to happen, and if $P(A) = 0$, we say the event cannot happen.

Comment: Note that if the probability of A occurring is $P(A)$, then the probability of A not occurring is $1 - P(A)$.

EXAMPLE 5 a. The probability of *not* getting "heads" is

$$P(\text{tails}) = 1 - P(\text{heads}) = 1 - \frac{1}{2} = \frac{1}{2}$$

b. The probability of *not* throwing a 5 on a roll of a die can be expressed by

$$P(\text{not a 5 on the die}) = 1 - P(\text{5 on the die}) = 1 - \frac{1}{6} = \frac{5}{6}$$

c. The probability of *not* drawing an ace from a deck of 52 cards can be expressed by

$$P(\text{not an ace}) = 1 - P(\text{ace}) = 1 - \frac{1}{13} = \frac{12}{13}$$ ■

The determination of the number of *successful* outcomes can be tricky, particularly when the individual outcomes are not equally probable; that is, each outcome does not have the same chance of occurring. Consider, for example, the outcomes of the roll of two dice. There are 11 possible outcomes (2 through 12) but 36 ways for the dice to land. Hence, each of the sums is not equally probable. The sum of 2 can be obtained with a 1 on the first die and a 1 on the second die. The sum of 3 can be obtained with a 2 on the first die and a 1 on the second or a 2 on the second die and a 1 on the first die. Table 9.1 shows the 36 ways the dice can land, grouped by sums.

TABLE 9.1

Sum	Outcome of pair of dice	Number of ways
2	(1, 1)	1
3	(1, 2), (2, 1)	2
4	(2, 2), (3, 1), (1, 3)	3
5	(2, 3), (3, 2), (4, 1), (1, 4)	4
6	(3, 3), (4, 2), (2, 4), (5, 1), (1, 5)	5
7	(1, 6), (6, 1), (5, 2), (2, 5), (4, 3), (3, 4)	6
8	(4, 4), (5, 3), (3, 5), (6, 2), (2, 6)	5
9	(6, 3), (3, 6), (5, 4), (4, 5)	4
10	(5, 5), (6, 4), (4, 6)	3
11	(6, 5), (5, 6)	2
12	(6, 6)	1

This table can be used to determine the probability of events involving the throwing of two dice.

EXAMPLE 6 What is the probability of throwing other than an 11 on a throw of two dice?

Solution Since $P(11) = \frac{2}{36} = \frac{1}{18}$, it follows that

$$P(\text{not an } 11) = 1 - \frac{1}{18} = \frac{17}{18}$$

■

Exercises Section 9.7

1. What is the probability of drawing a heart from a deck of 52 cards?
2. What is the probability of drawing the king of clubs from a deck of 52 cards?
3. If a box contains three bolts and five nuts, what is the probability of drawing a bolt from the box? What is the probability of drawing a nut?
4. A piggy bank contains 20 dimes and 15 nickels. Assuming each has an equally likely chance to fall out when the bank is shaken, what is the probability that the first coin to fall out will be a dime?
5. What is the probability that an odd number will turn up on one roll of a die?
6. What is the probability of getting a number greater than 4 on one roll of a die?
7. If three pennies are tossed simultaneously, what is the probability that two of them will be "heads"?
8. If girls and boys have an equally likely chance of being born, what is the probability that all three children in a family are girls?
9. A set of three red balls, four white balls, and six yellow balls is mixed together in a box. What is the probability that a ball drawn from the box will not be red?
10. What is the probability of getting five "heads" if seven coins are tossed onto a tabletop?

11. Six coins are tossed and allowed to land on the floor. What is the probability that three of them will be "tails"?

12. Five boys and eight girls place their names in a hat. If seven names are drawn from the hat, what is the probability of getting three boys and four girls?

13. A box contains six quarters, five dimes, and 15 nickels. If two coins are drawn at random from the box, what is the probability that they are both nickels?

14. In the preceding problem, what is the probability that two coins drawn from the box will be the same value?

15. Two letters are chosen at random from the word PROBABILITY. What is the probability that they are both vowels?

16. Three cards are drawn at random from a deck of playing cards. What is the probability of getting two hearts and one spade?

17. What is the probability of rolling a 3 with a pair of dice?

18. What is the probability of rolling a 7 with a pair of dice?

19. What is the probability that a five-card hand from a deck of playing cards will contain two and only two aces?

20. What is the probability that a seven-card hand from a deck of playing cards will contain five and only five of the same suit?

9.8 Mathematical Induction (Optional)

Proving a mathematical generalization from a given set of hypotheses and axioms is called **deduction.** Another way of proving a generalization is to observe a specific event and then assume that these observations are true in general. Scientific laws are for the most part established by this process of **incomplete induction.** While incomplete induction is adequate in the physical sciences, it fails in mathematics. To see why, consider this generalization: $n^2 - n + 41$ is prime if n is a positive integer. For the first 40 integers, this formula yields a prime number. However, $41^2 - 41 + 41$ is obviously not prime. Therefore, we *cannot* generalize in mathematics by using incomplete induction because the "next" case may be the one that fails.

EXAMPLE 1 If we reason by example (experimentally), we might conclude that all integers are less than 1,000,000,000—unless we just happen to use an example greater than 1,000,000,000. ■

We now examine a process called **mathematical induction,** a procedure for proving the validity of a generalization concerning some sequential statements.

EXAMPLE 2 We would use mathematical induction to *prove,* not derive, the formula

$$\sum_{k=1}^{n} k^2 = \frac{1}{6}n(n+1)(2n+1)$$ ■

The method of mathematical induction consists of two parts.

1. **Verification.** The given proposition must be shown to be true for the smallest integral value of n for which the proposition holds. (Ordinarily, this step is carried out for more than just one case, since showing the statement true for several cases will make the given proposition plausible.)

2. **Implication.** Demonstrate that if the proposition is true for $n = k$, then it must hold for $n = k + 1$. The assumption that the proposition is true for $n = k$ is sometimes called the **inductive hypothesis.**

If the conditions of both the verification and implication steps have been met, then the statement is true for all positive integers greater than or equal to the smallest number used in the verification step.

The logic behind mathematical induction is similar to that behind knocking over an infinite row of dominoes by pushing the first one and letting each domino knock over the one immediately following it. (See Figure 9.3.) If the first domino cannot be knocked over or if the dominoes are not close enough (that is, the kth one will not push over the $k + 1$st), then all the dominoes will not fall.

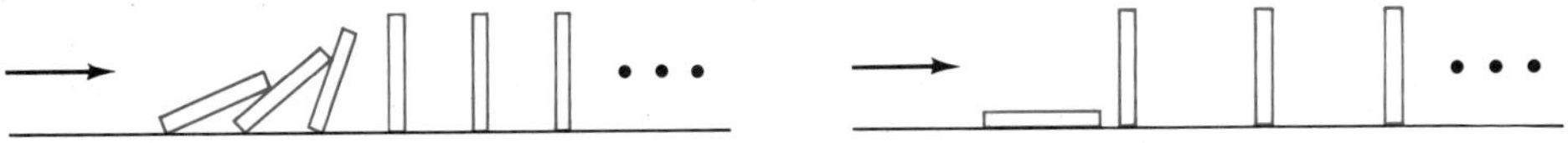

All dominoes will fall in this scheme.

Only one domino will fall in this scheme.

Figure 9.3

EXAMPLE 3 Prove by mathematical induction that the sum of the first n integers is given by the formula $S_n = n(n + 1)/2$.

Solution

1. *Verification.* Verify that when $k = 1$, $S_1 = 1$. Substituting 1 into the proposed formula, we get $S_1 = 1(1 + 1)/2 = 1$.
2. *Implication.* We assume the formula true for $n = k$; that is, $S_k = k(k + 1)/2$. Then we must show that $S_{k+1} = (k + 1)(k + 2)/2$ is true. By definition,

$$S_{k+1} = S_k + (k + 1)$$

Using the inductive hypothesis, we get

$$S_{k+1} = \frac{k(k+1)}{2} + (k + 1) = \frac{k^2 + k + 2k + 2}{2} = \frac{k^2 + 3k + 2}{2}$$
$$= \frac{(k+1)(k+2)}{2}$$

Hence, since both steps have been validated, the given statement is true for all positive integers. ■

Comment: Both parts of the method of mathematical induction are absolutely necessary. The next two examples emphasize this fact.

EXAMPLE 4 Consider the "formula" that the sum of the first n integers is given by

$$A_n = n^2 - n + 1$$

Note that $A_1 = 1$, which verifies the formula for $k = 1$. Assuming that

$$A_k = k^2 - k + 1$$

we must show that $A_{k+1} = (k + 1)^2 - (k + 1) + 1 = k^2 + k + 1$. However, by definition,

$$A_{k+1} = A_k + (k + 1) = (k^2 - k + 1) + (k + 1) = k^2 + 2$$

and since $k^2 + k + 1 \neq k^2 + 2$ (except for $k = 1$), the implication step is unproved. ■

EXAMPLE 5 Suppose we try to show that the sum of the first n integers is given by the formula $n(n + 1)/2 + 1$. Then the implication step is to assume $B_k = k(k + 1)/2 + 1$ and to attempt to show $B_{k+1} = (k + 1)(k + 2)/2 + 1$. By definition,

$$B_{k+1} = B_k + (k + 1) = \frac{k(k + 1)}{2} + 1 + (k + 1)$$
$$= \frac{(k + 1)(k + 2)}{2} + 1$$

which proves this step. However, $B_1 = 2$, which is *not* the first integer. In fact, B_n does not represent the sum for any value of n. This example illustrates the importance of checking both parts of the induction process. ■

EXAMPLE 6 Show that if n is a positive integer and $x \neq y$, then $x^n - y^n$ is always divisible by $x - y$.

Solution Since $x^n - y^n = x - y$ when $n = 1$, the verification step is trivial. Now assume that $x^n - y^n$ is divisible by $x - y$ if $n = k$. Thus, assume that

$$\frac{x^k - y^k}{x - y} = q$$

where the division process yields no remainder. Then,

$$\frac{x^{k+1} - y^{k+1}}{x - y} = \frac{x^{k+1} - xy^k + xy^k - y^{k+1}}{x - y}$$
$$= \frac{x(x^k - y^k) + y^k(x - y)}{x - y}$$
$$= \frac{x(x^k - y^k)}{x - y} + y^k = xq + y^k$$

which means that for $n = k + 1$, the division process does not yield a remainder. Because the verification and implication steps are validated, we conclude that $x^n - y^n$ is divisible by $x - y$ for all n. ■

Exercises Section 9.8

Using mathematical induction, prove the statements in Exercises 1–13 valid for all $n \geq 1$.

1. $\sum_{k=1}^{n} 2k = n(n + 1)$

2. $\sum_{k=1}^{n} 2^k = 2^{n+1} - 2$

3. $\sum_{k=1}^{n} (3k - 2) = \frac{n(3n - 1)}{2}$

4. $\sum_{k=1}^{n} (3k - 1) = \frac{n(3n + 1)}{2}$

5. $\sum_{k=1}^{n} k(k + 1) = \frac{n(n + 1)(n + 2)}{3}$

6. $\sum_{k=1}^{n} (2k - 1) = n^2$

7. $\sum_{k=1}^{n} k^2 = \frac{n(n + 1)(2n + 1)}{6}$

8. $\sum_{k=1}^{n} k^3 = \frac{n^2(n+1)^2}{4}$

9. $\sum_{k=1}^{n} r^{k-1} = \frac{1-r^n}{1-r}, \quad r \neq 1$

10. $\sum_{k=1}^{n} \frac{1}{k(k+1)} = \frac{n}{n+1}$

11. $n(n+1)(n+2)$ is a multiple of 6 for all $n \geq 1$.

12. $x^{2n-1} + y^{2n-1}$ is divisible by $x + y$ for all $n \geq 1$.

13. $\sum_{k=1}^{n+1} \frac{1}{n+k} \leq \frac{5}{6}$

Review Exercises Chapter 9

Find a formula for the general term for each of the sequences in Exercises 1–10.

1. 1, 3, 5, 7, 9, ...
2. 10, 8, 6, 4, 2, ...
3. 3, 9, 15, 21, ...
4. −1, 4, 9, 14, 19, ...
5. 1, 1, 1, 1, 1, ...
6. −1, 1, (−1), 1, ...
7. 2, 4, 8, 16, 32, ...
8. $\frac{2}{3}, \frac{2}{9}, \frac{2}{27}, \ldots$
9. −5, 25, −125, 625, ...
10. 625, −125, 25, −5, ...

11–20. Find the sum of the first 20 terms of each of the sequences of Exercises 1–10.

Write the indicated sums in Exercises 21–26 in expanded form and evaluate.

21. $\sum_{k=1}^{2} 2^k$

22. $\sum_{k=-1}^{4} (-1)^k$

23. $\sum_{i=1}^{4} i(i+2)$

24. $\sum_{k=1}^{20} i^k \quad (i = \sqrt{-1})$

25. $\sum_{k=2}^{10} \left[\frac{1}{k+3} - \frac{1}{k+2}\right]$

26. $\sum_{k=0}^{8} \left[\frac{1}{k+3} - \frac{1}{k+4}\right]$

Which of the statements in Exercises 27–30 are true?

27. $\sum_{k=2}^{10} a_k = \sum_{k=4}^{12} a_{k-2}$

28. $\sum_{k=1}^{3} a_k = \sum_{t=1}^{3} a_t$

29. $\sum_{t=1}^{5} (t^2-1)(t-2) = \sum_{s=-1}^{3} (s^2+1)(s)$

30. $\sum_{r=2}^{5} (r-4)(r-3) = \sum_{t=-2}^{1} t(t+1)$

31. Find the constant term in the expansion of $(x - 1/x)^{10}$.

32. Find and simplify the coefficient of $x^{12}y^6$ in the expansion of $(2x^2 - 3y)^{12}$.

33. Using the binomial theorem, expand $(x - 5y)^4$.

34. Use the first two terms of the binomial expansion to approximate $\sqrt{7}$.

35. Using the first three terms of the binomial expansion, approximate $(1.01)^{100}$.

36. Find the amount of an investment of \$4500 at the end of five years at 9% compounded quarterly.

37. How many ways are there to answer a 20-question true-false test.

38. How many ways can ten people be arranged in teams of three?

39. Calculate $P_{5,2}$ and $P_{100,2}$.

40. Calculate $C_{8,3}$ and $C_{52,5}$.

41. Simplify $\frac{(2n)!}{(2n-3)!}$

42. A business firm wants to hire six men and three women. If ten men and seven women apply for the positions, in how many ways can the selections be made?

43. What is the probability of drawing a jack of hearts from a deck of 52 cards?

44. What is the probability of drawing a king from a deck of 52 cards?

45. What is the probability of getting a number greater than 3 on one roll of a die?

46. What is the probability of getting a 2 or a 5 on one roll of a die?

47. What is the probability of getting four tails if seven coins are tossed onto a tabletop?

48. What is the probability of drawing two dimes from a box containing 25 pennies and 15 dimes?

49. What is the probability of rolling a 5 with a pair of dice?

50. What is the probability that a ten-card hand from a deck of playing cards will contain three aces?

Test 1 Chapter 9

Answer True or False to the statements in Exercises 1–10.

1. No term of the sequence whose nth term is $n/(n+1)$ ever exceeds 1.
2. $\sum_{k=2}^{2} 2^k = 2$
3. If $\sum_{k=1}^{n} a_k = \dfrac{n}{n+1}$, then $a_n = \dfrac{1}{n(n+1)}$.
4. For any sequence $\{a_k\}$, $\sum_{k=1}^{n} a_k < \sum_{k=1}^{n+1} a_k$.
5. $\sum_{k=1}^{20} i^k = 0 \qquad (i = \sqrt{-1})$
6. $(2n)!/n! = 2!$
7. The constant term in the expansion of $[x - (1/x)]^{10}$ is $C_{10,5}$.
8. The number of ways to answer a 20-question, true-false test is 20!
9. The principle of mathematical induction can be used to prove $\sum_{k=1}^{n} k = n(n+1)/2$.
10. $\sum_{k=2}^{10} (k+1)(k+2) = \sum_{k=0}^{8} (k+3)(k+4)$
11. Consider the sequence 3, 9, 15, 21, . . .
    a. Find a formula for the general term.
    b. Find the sum of the first 60 terms.
12. Prove the following formula by mathematical induction:
    $$\sum_{k=1}^{n} (2k+1) = n(n+2)$$
13. By using the first two terms of the generalized binomial expansion, approximate $(1.01)^{100}$.
14. Find and simplify the coefficient of $x^{12}y^6$ in the expansion of $(2x^2 - 3y)^{12}$.
15. Find the amount of an investment of \$4500 at the end of five years at 8% compounded quarterly.
16. A box contains four red balls and nine white balls. If three balls are drawn at random from the box, what is the probability that they are all white?

Test 2 Chapter 9

1. Find a formula for the general term of the sequence 1, 3, 5, 7, 9, ...
2. Write in expanded form and evaluate $\sum_{i=1}^{4} i(i+2)$.
3. Write the general term and find the sum of the first 99 terms of 2, 4, 6, 8, ...
4. Write the general term and write the sum of the first ten terms of $\frac{2}{3}, \frac{2}{9}, \frac{2}{27}, \ldots$.
5. Use the binomial theorem to expand $(x+5)^6$.
6. Use the first two terms of the binomial expansion to approximate $\sqrt{7}$.
7. How many committees of four people can be chosen from a group of 20?
8. Calculate (a) $P_{10,2}$ and (b) $C_{10,3}$.
9. The mathematics department at a major university wants to form a committee consisting of 4 men and 4 women. If the department includes 20 men and 9 women, in how many ways can this committee be selected?
10. Use mathematical induction to prove $4 + 7 + 10 + \cdots + (3n+1) = \frac{1}{2}n(3n+5)$.
11. If four cards are drawn at random from a deck of playing cards, what is the probability of getting two hearts and two spades?

10

The Conic Sections

Curves that can be formed by cutting a right circular cone with a plane are called **conic sections.** Greek mathematicians in 300 B.C. discovered that they could obtain four distinct curves by cutting a right circular cone with a plane: the circle, the ellipse, the hyperbola, and the parabola. The properties of the conics discovered by the Greeks include those that we use as definitions in this chapter.

If two right circular cones are placed vertex to vertex with a common axis, the resulting figure is referred to as a cone with two *nappes.* To see how the four conics can be generated from a cone with two nappes, refer to Figure 10.1.

a. A **circle** is obtained when the cutting plane is perpendicular to the axis, provided it does not pass through the vertex.
b. An **ellipse** is obtained when the cutting plane is inclined so as to cut entirely through one nappe of the cone without cutting the other nappe.
c. A **parabola** is obtained when the cutting plane is parallel to one element in the side of the cone.
d. A **hyperbola** is obtained when the cutting plane is parallel to the axis of the cone so that it cuts through both nappes.

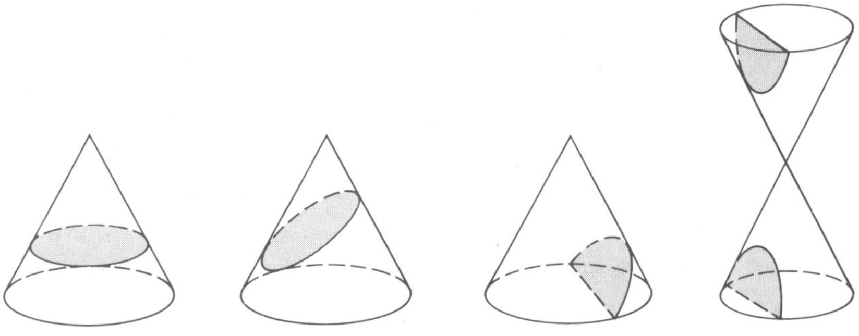

(a) (b) (c) (d)

Figure 10.1

10.1 The Parabola

Recalling that analytic geometry is the study of the relationship between algebra and geometry, we wish to establish the algebraic representation of the four conic sections. In this section we define and discuss the **parabola.**

Definition

> A parabola is the set of all points in a plane that are equidistant from a fixed point and a fixed line.

The fixed point is called the **focus** and the fixed line, the **directrix,** of the parabola. The line through the focus and perpendicular to the directrix is called the **axis** of the parabola. By definition, the midpoint between the focus and the directrix is a point on the parabola and is known as the **vertex.** (Recall from Chapter 4 that the shape of the graph of a quadratic function is a parabola whose axis is vertical.)

Figure 10.2 shows a parabola with vertex located at the origin, focus at $F(a, 0)$, and directrix perpendicular to the x-axis at $D(-a, 0)$. Observe that a is the distance from the vertex to the focus, sometimes referred to as the **focal distance.**

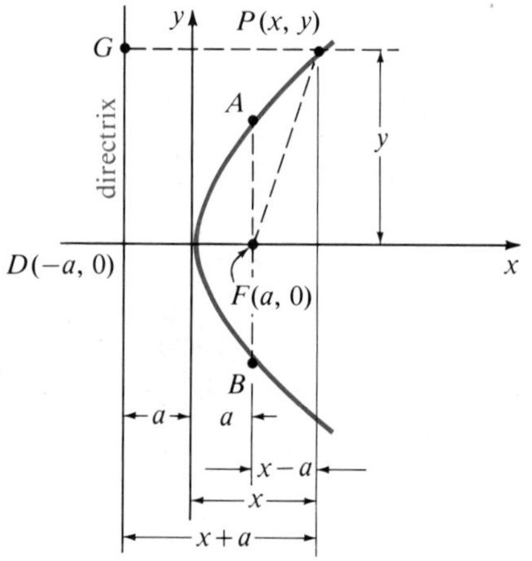

Figure 10.2

To find the algebraic equation of this parabola, consider a point $P(x, y)$ on the parabola. Then, by definition,

$$\overline{GP} = \overline{FP} \tag{10.1}$$

But from Figure 10.2 we see that

$$\overline{GP} = |x + a|$$

and

$$\overline{FP} = \sqrt{(x - a)^2 + y^2}$$

Substituting these expressions in Equation 10.1 yields

$$|x + a| = \sqrt{(x - a)^2 + y^2}$$

or, squaring both sides,

$$(x + a)^2 = (x - a)^2 + y^2$$

Expanding and collecting like terms, the equation of the parabola becomes

$$\mathbf{y^2 = 4ax} \tag{10.2}$$

Equation 10.2 is referred to as the **standard form** of the equation of a parabola with vertex at the origin and focus on the x-axis. It is clearly symmetric about its axis. The focus is at $(a, 0)$ if the coefficient of x is positive. In this case, the parabola opens to the right. If the coefficient of x is negative, the focus is at $(-a, 0)$ and the parabola opens to the left.

The chord AB through the focus and perpendicular to the axis is called the **right chord,** or frequently, the **latus rectum.** The length of the right chord is found by letting $x = a$ in Equation 10.2. Upon making this substitution, we find

$$y^2 = 4a^2$$

from which

$$y = \pm 2a$$

The length of the right chord is, therefore, equal numerically to $4|a|$. This fact is useful because it helps define the shape of the parabola by giving us an idea of the "opening" of the parabola.

The standard form of a parabola with vertex at the origin and focus on the y-axis is

$$\mathbf{x^2 = 4ay} \tag{10.3}$$

The derivation of this formula parallels that of Equation 10.2. The parabola represented by Equation 10.3 is symmetric about the y-axis. It opens upward if the coefficient of y is positive and downward if it is negative.

The equation of a parabola is characterized by one variable being linear and the other being squared. *The linear variable indicates the direction of the axis of the parabola.*

A rough sketch of the parabola can be drawn if the location of the vertex and the extremities of the right chord are known. This information can be obtained from the standard form of the equation.

EXAMPLE 1 Discuss and sketch the graph of the equation $x^2 = 8y$.

Solution This equation has the form of Equation 10.3 with $4a = 8$ or $a = 2$. The y-axis is the axis of the parabola, the focus is at $(0, 2)$, and the directrix is the line $y = -2$. The endpoints of the right chord are then $(-4, 2)$ and $(4, 2)$. Figure 10.3 shows the parabola.

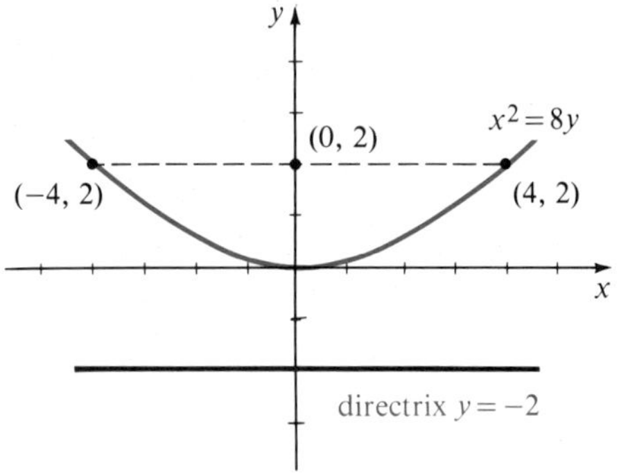

Figure 10.3

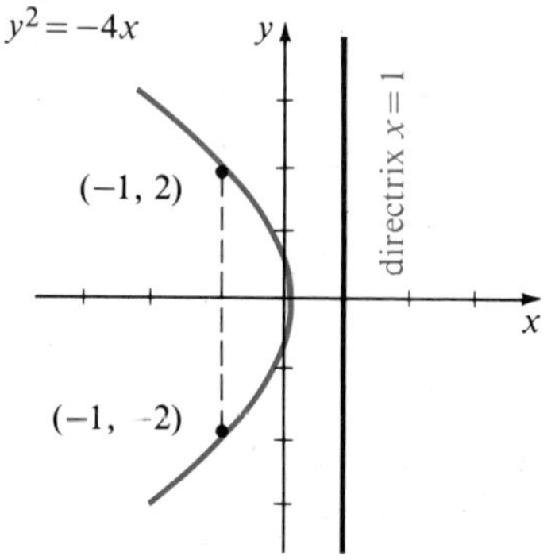

Figure 10.4

EXAMPLE 2 Find the equation of the parabola with focus at $(-1, 0)$ and directrix $x = 1$ and sketch the curve.

Solution The focus lies on the x-axis to the left of the directrix, so the parabola opens to the left. The desired equation is then the form in Equation 10.2 with $a = -1$; that is,

$$y^2 = -4x$$

To sketch the parabola, note that the length of the right chord is $\overline{AB} = 4$. Its extremities are therefore $(-1, 2)$ and $(-1, -2)$. The curve appears in Figure 10.4.

Comment: A unique physical property of the parabola is that it will reflect all rays emitted from the focus such that they travel parallel to the axis of the parabola. This feature makes the parabola a particularly desirable shape for reflectors in spotlights and reflecting telescopes and also for radar antennas. See Figure 10.5.

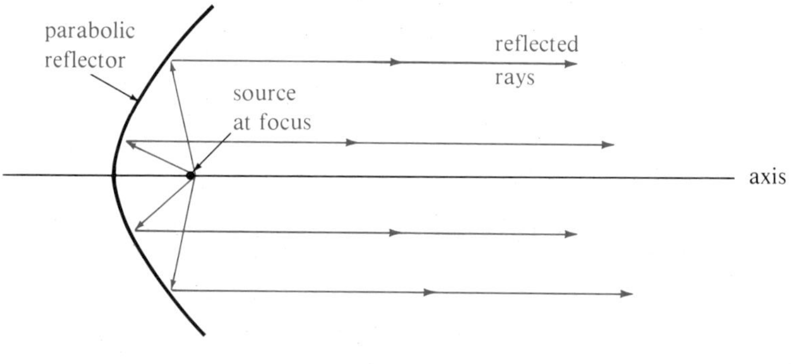

Figure 10.5

EXAMPLE 3 A parabolic reflector is to be built with a focal distance of 2.25 ft. What is the diameter of the reflector if it is to be 1 ft deep at its axis?

Solution To solve this problem, we need the equation of the parabola used to generate the reflector. Referring to Figure 10.6, we see that the vertex of the parabola is located at the origin and the focus on the x-axis.

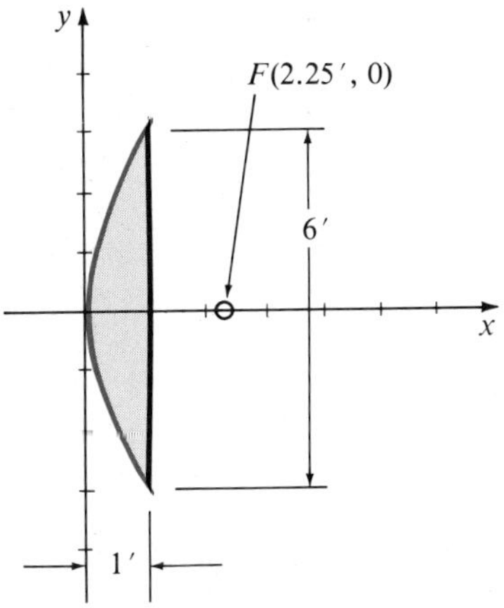

Figure 10.6

(We could have just as well placed the focus on the y-axis.) Then using Equation 10.2 with $a = 2.25$ yields the equation

$$y^2 = 4(2.25)x = 9x$$

The diameter of the reflector can be found by substituting $x = 1$ into this equation. Thus,

$$y^2 = 9 \quad \text{and} \quad y = \pm 3$$

which means that the diameter of the reflector is 6 ft. ■

Exercises Section 10.1

In Exercises 1–10, find the coordinates of the focus, the endpoints of the right chord, and the equation of the directrix of each of the parabolas. Sketch the graph of each parabola.

1. $y^2 = -8x$
2. $x^2 = 12y$
3. $2x^2 = 12y$
4. $x^2 = -24y$
5. $y^2 + 16x = 0$
6. $y + 2x^2 = 0$
7. $y^2 = 3x$
8. $3x^2 = 4y$
9. $y^2 = -2x$
10. $y^2 = 10x$

In Exercises 11–18, find the equation of the parabolas having the given properties. Sketch each curve.

11. Focus at (0, 2), directrix $y = -2$.
12. Focus at $(0, -\frac{1}{2})$, directrix $y = \frac{1}{2}$.
13. Focus at $(\frac{3}{2}, 0)$, directrix $x = -\frac{3}{2}$.
14. Focus at $(-10, 0)$, directrix $x = 10$.
15. Endpoints of right chord $(2, -1)$ and $(-2, -1)$, vertex at (0, 0).
16. Endpoints of right chord (3, 6) and $(3, -6)$, vertex at (0, 0).
17. Vertex at (0, 0), vertical axis, one point of the curve (2, 4).
18. Vertex at (0, 0), horizontal axis, one point of the curve (2, 4).

In Exercises 19–22, solve the given system of equations graphically.

19. $2x + 4y = 0$
$x^2 - 4y = 0$

20. $y = e^x$
$y^2 = -3x$

21. $y^2 = 12x$
$y = \log x$

22. $y = x^3$
$x^2 = 8y$

23. In the accompanying figure, the supporting cable of a suspension bridge hangs in the shape of a parabola.* Find the equation of a cable hanging

* *Free*-hanging cables hang in the shape of a curve called a **catenary.** Supporting cables such as the one described are more closely approximated by a parabola.

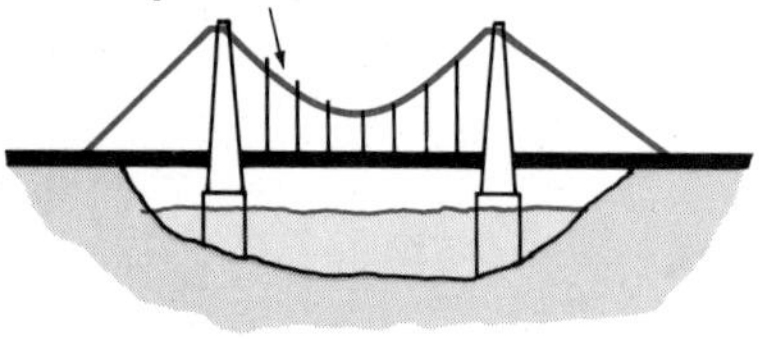

from two 400-ft-high supports that are 1000 ft apart, if the lowest point of the cable is 250 ft below the top of the supports. Choose the origin in the most convenient location.

24. A parabolic antenna is to be constructed by revolving the parabola $y^2 = 24x$. Sketch the cross-section of the antenna if the diameter of the circular front is to be 12 ft. Locate the focus.

10.2 The Ellipse and the Circle

The Ellipse

An ellipse can be constructed from a loop of string in the following way. Place two pins at F and F', as shown in Figure 10.7, and place the loop of string over them. Pull the string taut with the point of a pencil and then move the pencil, keeping the string taut. The figure generated is an ellipse. From this construction observe that the sum of the distances from the two fixed points to the point P is always the same since the loop of string is kept taut. This property characterizes the ellipse.

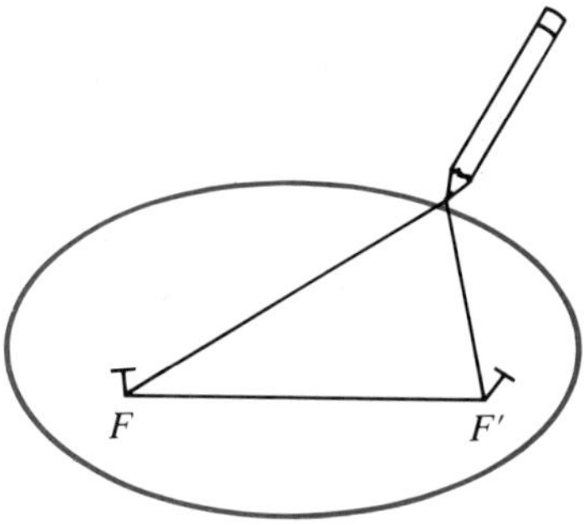

Figure 10.7

Definition

An **ellipse** is the set of all points in a plane the sum of whose distances from two fixed points in the plane is constant.

The fixed points are called the **foci** of the ellipse. The midpoint of a line through the foci is called the **center** of the ellipse. We use the center of the ellipse to locate the ellipse in the plane in the same way we used the vertex to locate the parabola.

To obtain the equation of an ellipse, consider an ellipse with foci located on the x-axis such that the origin is midway between them, as in Figure 10.8. Let the foci be the points $F(c, 0)$ and $F'(-c, 0)$ and let the sum of the distances from a point $P(x, y)$ of the ellipse to the foci be $2a$, where $a > c$. Then

$$PF + PF' = 2a$$

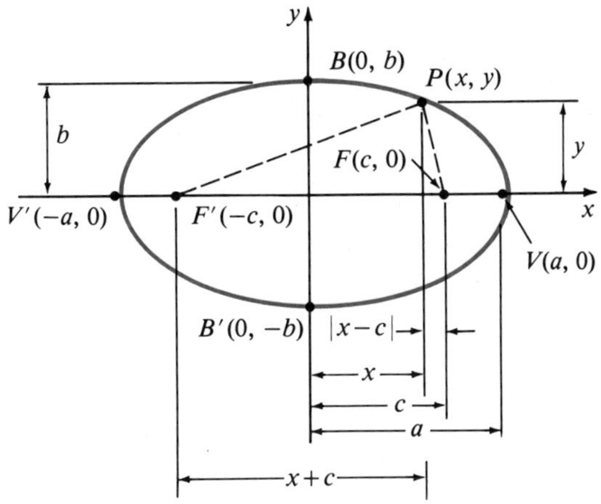

Figure 10.8

From Figure 10.8 it is clear that

$$PF = \sqrt{(x - c)^2 + y^2}$$

and

$$PF' = \sqrt{(x + c)^2 + y^2}$$

so that

$$\sqrt{(x - c)^2 + y^2} + \sqrt{(x + c)^2 + y^2} = 2a$$

Transposing the first radical and squaring, we get

$$(x + c)^2 + y^2 = 4a^2 - 4a\sqrt{(x - c)^2 + y^2} + (x - c)^2 + y^2$$

Expanding and collecting like terms, we have

$$a\sqrt{(x - c)^2 + y^2} = a^2 - cx$$

Squaring again and simplifying, we obtain

$$(a^2 - c^2)x^2 + a^2y^2 = a^2(a^2 - c^2)$$

If we substitute $b^2 = a^2 - c^2$, this equation becomes

$$b^2x^2 + a^2y^2 = a^2b^2$$

Finally, dividing through by the nonzero quantity a^2b^2, we can write the equation of an ellipse with its center at the origin and its foci on the x-axis as

$$\frac{x^2}{a^2} + \frac{y^2}{b^2} = 1 \tag{10.4}$$

The graph of Equation 10.4 is symmetric about both axes and the origin. Letting $y = 0$ in Equation 10.4, we see that the x-intercepts of the ellipse are $(a, 0)$ and $(-a, 0)$. The segment of the line through the foci from $(a, 0)$ to $(-a, 0)$ is called the **major axis** of the ellipse. The length of the major axis is $2a$, which is also the value chosen for the sum of the distances PF and PF'. The endpoints of the major axis are called the **vertices** of the ellipse.

The y-intercepts of the ellipse are found to be $(0, b)$ and $(0, -b)$ by letting $x = 0$ in Equation 10.4. The segment of the line perpendicular to the major axis from $(0, b)$ to $(0, -b)$ is called the **minor axis.** The graph of an ellipse can readily be sketched once the endpoints of the axes are known.

The foci of an ellipse are located by solving the equation $b^2 = a^2 - c^2$ for the focal distance c. Thus, the expression for c is

$$c = \sqrt{a^2 - b^2}$$

A similar derivation will show that

$$\frac{x^2}{b^2} + \frac{y^2}{a^2} = 1 \qquad (10.5)$$

is the equation of an ellipse with its center at the origin and its foci on the y-axis. [Note that the vertices are $(0, a)$ and $(0, -a)$.]

EXAMPLE 1 Find the equation of an ellipse centered at the origin with foci on the x-axis if the major axis is 10 and the minor is 4.

Solution In this case, the major axis is on the x-axis with $a = 5$ and $b = 2$. Substituting these values into Equation 10.4 yields

$$\frac{x^2}{5^2} + \frac{y^2}{2^2} = 1$$

or

$$\frac{x^2}{25} + \frac{y^2}{4} = 1$$

which is the required equation. ■

EXAMPLE 2 Find the equation of the ellipse with vertices at $(0, 5)$ and $(0, -5)$ and foci at $(0, 4)$ and $(0, -4)$.

Solution From the given information we are able to conclude that the foci are on the y-axis, the center of the ellipse is at the origin, and $a = 5$. To find b, use the relation $b^2 = a^2 - c^2$. Thus, $b = \sqrt{25 - 16} = \sqrt{9} = 3$. Substituting $a = 5$ and $b = 3$ into Equation 10.5 yields

$$\frac{x^2}{9} + \frac{y^2}{25} = 1$$

The ellipse is sketched in Figure 10.9. ■

EXAMPLE 3 Sketch the graph of the ellipse $4x^2 + 16y^2 = 64$.

Solution The given equation divided by 64 can be written in the form

$$\frac{x^2}{16} + \frac{y^2}{4} = 1$$

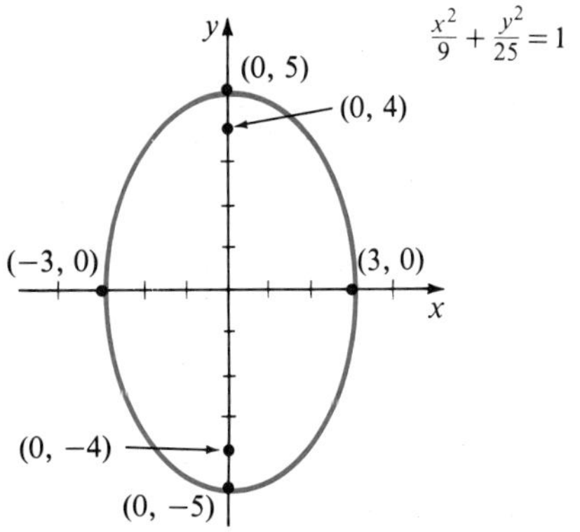

Figure 10.9

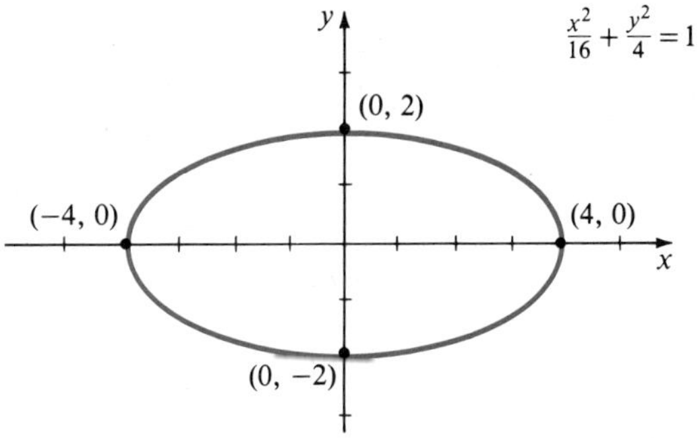

Figure 10.10

The major axis lies along the x-axis since the denominator of the x term in the equation is larger than the denominator of the y term. Consequently, $a = 4$ and $b = 2$. The vertices are then (4, 0) and (−4, 0) and the endpoints of the minor axis are (0, 2) and (0, −2). The ellipse is sketched in Figure 10.10. ■

Comment: One of the first scientific applications of the ellipse was in astronomy. The astronomer Johannes Kepler (c. 1600) discovered that the planets moved in elliptical orbits about the sun with the sun at one focus. Artificial satellites also move in elliptical orbits about the earth. Another application is in the design of machines, in which elliptical gears are used to obtain a slow, powerful movement with a quick return. A third application of the ellipse is found in electricity, in which the magnetic field of a single-phase induction motor is elliptical under normal operating conditions.

The Circle

When a plane intersects a cone perpendicular to the axis of the cone, other than at the vertex, a circle is formed. See Figure 10.1(a). If the plane intersects the vertex, the result is a single point.

Definition

> A circle is the set of points in a plane equidistant from a fixed point.

We can obtain the equation of a circle centered at the origin by observing that an ellipse becomes a circle when both foci are located at the origin. When the foci coincide at the origin, the major and minor axes are equal and $a = b$. Replacing a and b in Equation 10.4 with r, we find that the equation of a circle is

$$\frac{x^2}{r^2}+\frac{y^2}{r^2}=1$$

Multiplying both sides of this equation by r^2, we obtain

$$x^2 + y^2 = r^2 \tag{10.6}$$

as the standard form of the equation of a circle with center at the origin and radius equal to r.

EXAMPLE 4 Write the equation of a circle centered at the origin with radius 4.

Solution Substituting $r = 4$ into Equation 10.6, we get the desired equation:

$$x^2 + y^2 = 16$$

See Figure 10.11.

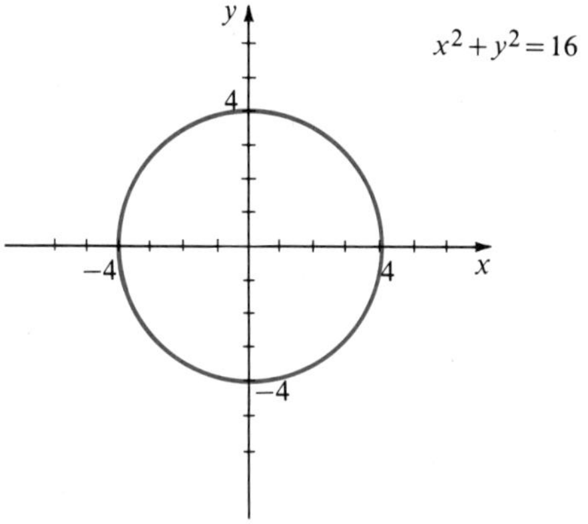

Figure 10.11

Exercises Section 10.2

In Exercises 1–10, discuss each of the given equations and sketch their graphs.

1. $5x^2 + y^2 = 25$
2. $4x^2 + 9y^2 = 36$
3. $16x^2 + 4y^2 = 16$
4. $3x^2 + 9y^2 = 27$
5. $x^2 + y^2 = 9$
6. $25x^2 + 4y^2 = 100$
7. $2x^2 + 3y^2 - 24 = 0$
8. $5x^2 + 20y^2 = 20$
9. $9x^2 + 4y^2 = 4$
10. $4x^2 + y^2 = 25$

In Exercises 11–20, find the equation of the ellipses having the given properties. Sketch each curve.

11. Vertices at $(\pm 4, 0)$, minor axis 6.
12. Vertices at $(0, \pm 1)$, minor axis 1.
13. Vertices at $(0, \pm 5)$, minor axis 3.
14. Vertices at $(\pm 6, 0)$, minor axis 4.
15. Major axis 10, foci at $(\pm 4, 0)$.
16. Major axis 10, foci at $(0, \pm 3)$.
17. Foci at $(\pm 1, 0)$, major axis 8.
18. Vertices at $(0, \pm 7)$, foci at $(0, \pm\sqrt{28})$.
19. Vertices at $(\pm\frac{5}{2}, 0)$, one point of the curve at $(1, 1)$.
20. Vertices at $(\pm 3, 0)$, one point of the curve at $(\sqrt{3}, 2)$.

In Exercises 21–24, solve the given system of equations graphically.

21. $\dfrac{x^2}{4} + y^2 = 4$, $2y + 3x = 0$
22. $\dfrac{x^2}{9} + \dfrac{y^2}{9} = 1$, $y = e^{x+2}$
23. $y = x^2$, $x^2 + 4y^2 = 4$
24. $y^2 - 12x = 0$, $y^2 + 9x^2 = 9$
25. An elliptical cam with a horizontal major axis of 10 in. and a minor axis of 3 in. is to be machined by a numerically controlled vertical mill (see the figure).

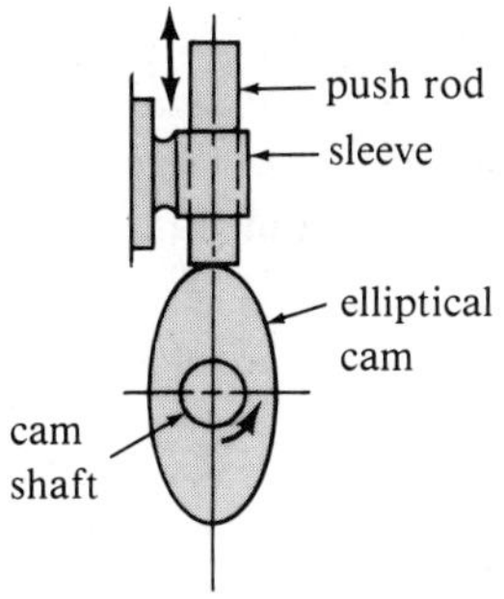

Find the equation of the ellipse to be used in programming the control device.

26. An elliptical cam having the equation $9x^2 + y^2 = 81$ revolves against a push rod. What is the maximum travel of the push rod? Assume the cam revolves about its center.

27. The magnetic field curves of a single-phase induction motor are given by the set of ellipses $x^2 + 4y^2 = c^2$. Sketch some of the curves.

28. A "ripple" tank is a tank of water in the form of an ellipse. When water is disturbed at one focus, ripples radiate outward and, eventually, a drop of water spurts up at the other focus. Suppose such a tank is of the shape given by the equation

$$3.1x^2 + 4.5y^2 = 15.6$$

Determine where to poke your finger into the water and where the water will spurt up.

29. The elliptical orbit of the earth is very nearly circular. In fact, it is much like the ellipse $x^2 + (y/1.1)^2 = 1$. Make a sketch of this ellipse.

10.3 The Hyperbola

The final conic that we consider is the hyperbola.

Definition

> A hyperbola is the set of all points in a plane the difference of whose distances from two fixed points in the plane is constant.

Figure 10.12 shows a hyperbola with foci at $F(c, 0)$ and $F'(-c, 0)$. The origin is then at the midpoint between the foci, which corresponds to the **center** of the hyperbola. The points $V(a, 0)$ and $V'(-a, 0)$ are called the **vertices,** and the segment $\overline{VV'}$ is called the **transverse axis** of the hyperbola. The length of the transverse axis is $2a$.

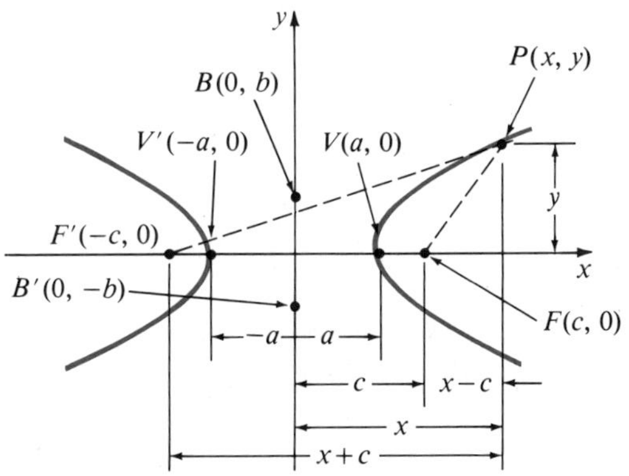

Figure 10.12

The segment BB', which is perpendicular to the transverse axis at the center of the hyperbola, is called the **conjugate axis** and has a length of $2b$. The conjugate axis has an important relation to the curve even though it does not intersect the curve.

To find the algebraic equation of a hyperbola, consider a point $P(x, y)$ on the hyperbola. Then, by definition,

$$\overline{F'P} - \overline{FP} = 2a$$

which in turn can be written

$$\sqrt{(x + c)^2 + y^2} - \sqrt{(x - c)^2 + y^2} = 2a$$

Using the same procedure here that we used for the ellipse, we can reduce the radical equation to

$$\frac{x^2}{a^2} - \frac{y^2}{c^2 - a^2} = 1$$

Or, if we let $b^2 = c^2 - a^2$, the equation of the hyperbola becomes

$$\frac{x^2}{a^2} - \frac{y^2}{b^2} = 1 \qquad \textbf{(10.7)}$$

which, like the ellipse, is symmetric about both axes and the origin. Letting $y = 0$, we find the x-intercepts of the graph of Equation 10.7 to be $x = \pm a$. Additional information on the shape of the hyperbola can be obtained by solving Equation 10.7 for y:

$$y = \pm \frac{b}{a}\sqrt{x^2 - a^2}$$

This equation shows that there are no points on the curve for which $x^2 < a^2$. Consequently, the hyperbola consists of two separate curves, or *branches*—one to the right of $x = a$ and a similar one to the left of $x = -a$.

The shape of the hyperbola is constrained by two straight lines called the **asymptotes** of the hyperbola. The asymptotes of a hyperbola are the extended diagonals of the rectangle formed by drawing lines parallel to the coordinate axes through the endpoints of both the transverse axis and the conjugate axis. Referring to Figure 10.13, we see that the slope of the diagonals of this rectangle are

$$m = \pm \frac{b}{a}$$

Therefore, the asymptotes are given by the lines

$$y = \pm \frac{b}{a} x$$

Now we show that the lines $y = \pm(b/a)x$ are asymptotes of the hyperbola; that is, that the hyperbola approaches arbitrarily close to the lines as x increases without bound. Solving Equation 10.7 for y^2, we can write it in the form

$$y^2 = \frac{b^2x^2}{a^2}\left(1 - \frac{a^2}{x^2}\right)$$

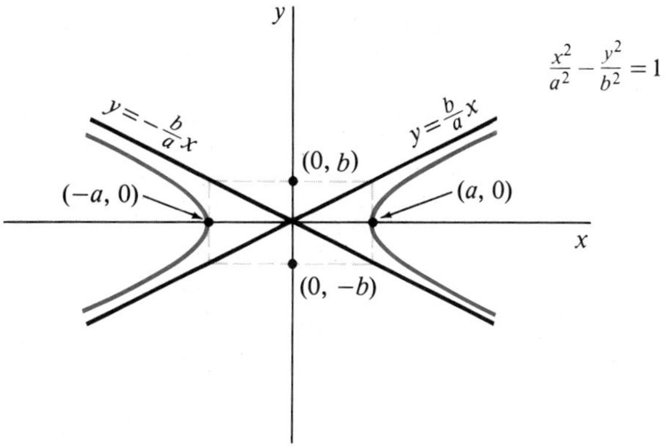

Figure 10.13

or, taking the square root of both sides,

$$y = \pm\frac{b}{a}x\sqrt{1 - \frac{a^2}{x^2}}$$

Now consider the value of the right member as x becomes large. The quantity a^2/x^2 becomes small and, therefore,

$$\pm\frac{b}{a}x\sqrt{1 - \frac{a^2}{x^2}}$$

approaches $\pm(b/a)x$, which means that the hyperbola $(x^2/a^2) - (y^2/b^2) = 1$ is asymptotic to the lines $y = \pm(b/a)x$.

If we begin with the foci of the hyperbola on the y-axis and the center at the origin, the standard form of the equation of a hyperbola becomes

$$\frac{y^2}{a^2} - \frac{x^2}{b^2} = 1 \qquad \textbf{(10.8)}$$

The vertices of this hyperbola are on the y-axis; **the positive term always indicates the direction of the transverse axis.** Notice that the standard form of the hyperbola, like that for the ellipse, demands that the coefficients of x^2 and y^2 be in the denominator and that the number of the right-hand side be 1. In the case of the hyperbola the *sign* of the term, *not the magnitude* of the denominator, determines the transverse axis.

To sketch the hyperbola, draw the rectangle through the extremities of the transverse and conjugate axes and extend the diagonals of the rectangle. Then draw the hyperbola so that it passes through the vertex and comes closer to the extended diagonals as x moves away from the origin.

EXAMPLE 1 Discuss and sketch the graph of $4x^2 - y^2 = 16$.

Solution Dividing by 16, we have

$$\frac{x^2}{4} - \frac{y^2}{16} = 1$$

which is the equation of a hyperbola with center at the origin and foci on the x-axis. It has vertices at $(\pm 2, 0)$, and its conjugate axis extends from (0, 4) to (0, −4). The foci are found from the equation $b^2 = c^2 - a^2$. Thus,

$$c = \sqrt{a^2 + b^2} = \sqrt{4 + 16} = \sqrt{20} = 2\sqrt{5}$$

and the foci are located at $(\pm 2\sqrt{5}, 0)$. Plotting these points and drawing the rectangle and its extended diagonals, we obtain the hyperbola shown in Figure 10.14.

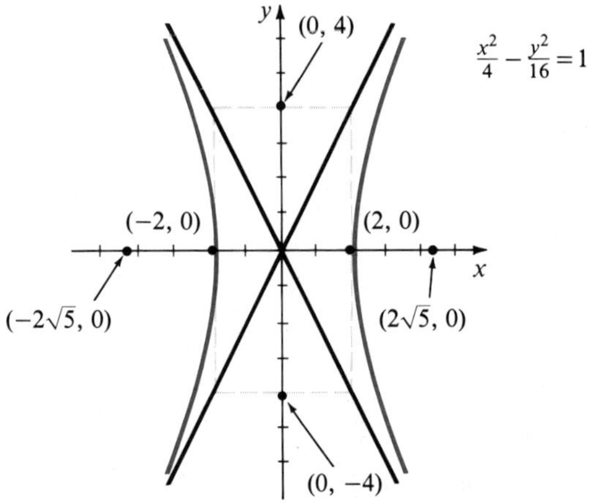

Figure 10.14 ■

EXAMPLE 2 Discuss and sketch the graph of $\frac{y^2}{13} - \frac{x^2}{9} = 1$.

Solution This hyperbola has a vertical transverse axis with vertices at $(0, \sqrt{13})$ and $(0, -\sqrt{13})$. The extremes of the conjugate axis are then (3, 0) and (−3, 0). The foci are located at $(0, \sqrt{22})$ and $(0, -\sqrt{22})$. This information is used to sketch the hyperbola in Figure 10.15.

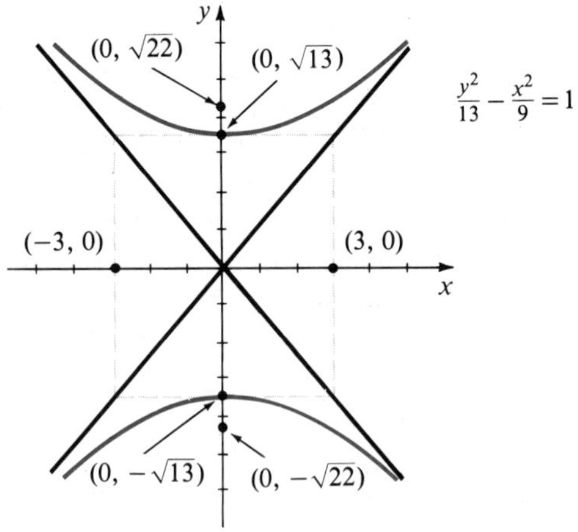

Figure 10.15 ■

EXAMPLE 3 Determine the equation of the hyperbola centered at the origin with foci at $(\pm 6, 0)$ and a transverse axis 8 units long.

Solution Here $a = 4$ and $c = 6$. Since $c^2 = a^2 + b^2$, we have $b^2 = c^2 - a^2 = 36 - 16 = 20$. Substituting $a^2 = 16$ and $b^2 = 20$ into Equation 10.7, we get

$$\frac{x^2}{16} - \frac{y^2}{20} = 1$$

■

Exercises Section 10.3

In Exercises 1–10, discuss the properties of the graph of each of the given equations and then sketch the graph.

1. $x^2 - y^2 = 16$
2. $y^2 - x^2 = 9$
3. $4x^2 - 9y^2 = 36$
4. $9x^2 - y^2 = 9$
5. $4y^2 - 25x^2 = 100$
6. $3x^2 - 3y^2 = 9$
7. $4x^2 - 16y^2 = 25$
8. $4y^2 - x^2 = 9$
9. $y^2 + 1 = x^2$
10. $x^2 - 25 = 5y^2$

In Exercises 11–20, find the equation of the hyperbolas having the given properties. Sketch each curve.

11. Vertices at $(\pm 4, 0)$, foci at $(\pm 5, 0)$.
12. Vertices at $(0, \pm 3)$, foci at $(0, \pm 5)$.
13. Conjugate axis 4, vertices at $(0, \pm 1)$.
14. Conjugate axis 1, vertices at $(\pm 4, 0)$.
15. Transverse axis 6, foci at $(\pm \frac{7}{2}, 0)$.
16. Transverse axis 3, foci at $(\pm 2, 0)$.
17. Vertices at $(0, \pm 4)$, asymptotes $y = \pm(\frac{1}{2})x$.
18. Vertices at $(\pm 3, 0)$, asymptotes $y = \pm 2x$.
19. Vertices at $(0, \pm 3)$, one point of the curve $(2, 7)$.
20. Vertices at $(\pm 3, 0)$, one point of the curve $(7, 2)$.
21. In the study of electrostatic potential with particular boundary conditions, the equipotential curves are found to be

$$\frac{x^2}{\sin^2 c} - \frac{y^2}{\cos^2 c} = 1$$

Show that every member of this family has foci at $(-1, 0)$ and $(1, 0)$.

22. Curves of the form $xy = c$ are hyperbolas, but their foci lie along the lines $y = \pm x$ instead of along the coordinate axes. Make a sketch of the hyperbola $xy = 2$.
23. Any two variables x and y that are related by the equation $xy = c$ are said to vary inversely with each other. Sketch the inverse variation $xy = -1$ and note the hyperbolic shape.
24. Show that the curve defined parametrically by

$$x = \frac{e^t - e^{-t}}{2}, \quad y = \frac{e^t + e^{-t}}{2}$$

is a hyperbola. (*Hint:* Show that x and y satisfy the equation $y^2 - x^2 = 1$. The two given functions are called the **hyperbolic functions** and are denoted respectively by $\sinh t$ and $\cosh t$.)

10.4 Translation of Axes

In the first three sections of this chapter we developed the equations of the conic sections relative to the origin. Now we wish to write the equations of the conics referenced to some point (h, k) in the plane. To see how this is done, consider a point $P(x, y)$ in the xy-plane and an $x'y'$-coordinate system whose origin is at (h, k), as shown in Figure 10.16. Then the coordinates of P may be given with respect either to the xy-plane or to the $x'y'$-plane. From Figure 10.16, we see that the relationship between (x, y) and (x', y') is given by the equations

$$\mathbf{x = x' + h \qquad y = y' + k}$$

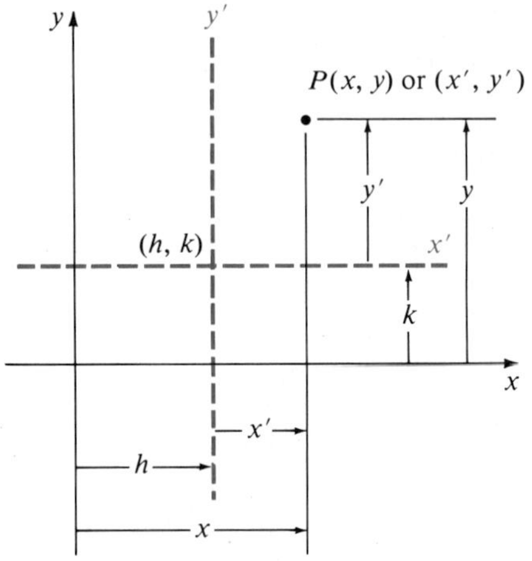

Figure 10.16

or

$$x' = x - h \qquad y' = y - k$$

These equations are called **translation equations.**

To discover the equation of a circle with its center at (h, k), we note that since (h, k) is the origin of the $x'y'$-coordinate system, the equation of the circle may be written as

$$(x')^2 + (y')^2 = r^2$$

The translation equations $x' = x - h$ and $y' = y - k$ are then used to give

$$(x - h)^2 + (y - k)^2 = r^2 \tag{10.9}$$

as the standard form of a circle with center at (h, k) and radius r. Similarly, the equation of a parabola with vertex at (h, k) is

$$(x - h)^2 = 4a(y - k) \tag{10.10}$$

if the axis of symmetry is parallel to the y-axis and

$$(y - k)^2 = 4a(x - h) \tag{10.11}$$

if the axis of symmetry is parallel to the x-axis. By a similar procedure, if $a > b$ the standard equations of an ellipse centered at a point (h, k) are seen to be

$$\frac{(x - h)^2}{a^2} + \frac{(y - k)^2}{b^2} = 1 \tag{10.12}$$

if the major axis is parallel to the x-axis and

$$\frac{(x - h)^2}{b^2} + \frac{(y - k)^2}{a^2} = 1 \tag{10.13}$$

if it is parallel to the y-axis. Finally, the standard equations of the hyperbola centered at a point (h, k) are seen to be

$$\frac{(x-h)^2}{a^2} - \frac{(y-k)^2}{b^2} = 1 \tag{10.14}$$

if the transverse axis is parallel to the x-axis and

$$\frac{(y-k)^2}{a^2} - \frac{(x-h)^2}{b^2} = 1 \tag{10.15}$$

if it is parallel to the y-axis.

EXAMPLE 1 Write the equation of the ellipse centered at $(2, -3)$ with horizontal axis 10 units and vertical axis 4 units. (See Figure 10.17.)

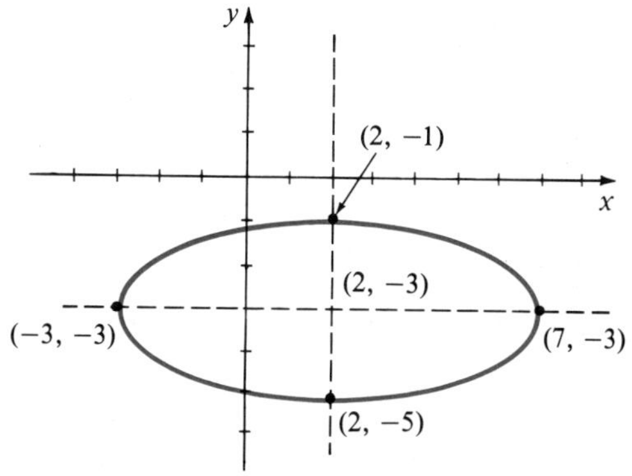

Figure 10.17

Solution Since the longer of the two axes is the horizontal axis, use Equation 10.12 with $a = 5$ and $b = 2$. Also, $h = 2$ and $k = -3$. Making these substitutions, we have

$$\frac{(x-2)^2}{25} + \frac{(y+3)^2}{4} = 1$$

as the equation of the ellipse. ■

EXAMPLE 2 Write the equation of the parabola whose directrix is the line $y = -2$ and whose vertex is located at $(3, 1)$. (See Figure 10.18.)

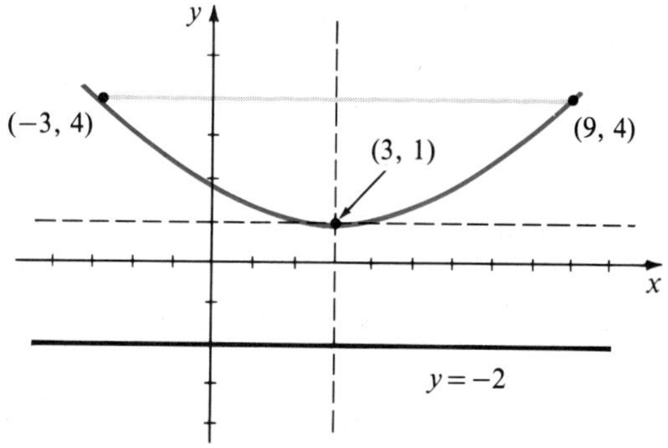

Figure 10.18

Solution This parabola has a vertical axis and opens upward because the directrix is horizontal and lies below the vertex. The vertex lies midway between the focus and the directrix so that $a = 3$. If we let $h = 3$, $k = 1$, and $a = 3$ in Equation 10.10, the equation of the parabola is

$$(x - 3)^2 = 12(y - 1)$$

■

EXAMPLE 3 Discuss and sketch the graph of the hyperbola

$$\frac{(x + 5)^2}{16} - \frac{(y - 2)^2}{9} = 1$$

Solution The hyperbola is centered at $(-5, 2)$. By Equation 10.14, it has a horizontal transverse axis with vertices at $(-9, 2)$ and $(-1, 2)$. The endpoints of the conjugate axis are located at $(-5, 5)$ and $(-5, -1)$. Also, the foci are at $(-10, 2)$ and $(0, 2)$ since $c = \sqrt{9 + 16} = 5$. The graph appears in Figure 10.19.

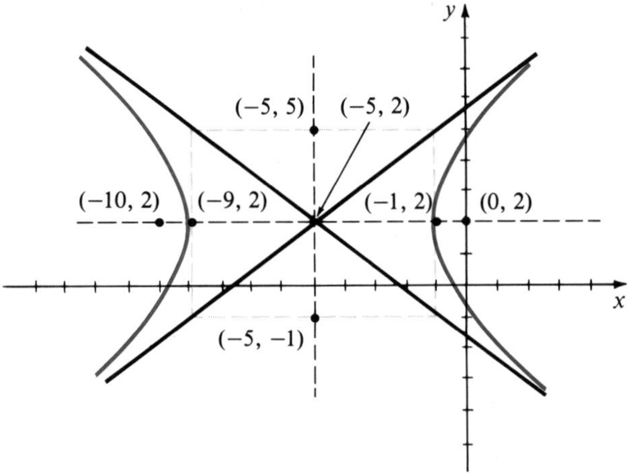

Figure 10.19

■

Exercises Section 10.4

In Exercises 1–6, write the equations of the *parabolas* having the given properties. Sketch each graph.

1. Vertex at (3, 1), focus at (5, 1).
2. Vertex at $(-2, 3)$, focus at $(-2, 0)$.
3. Directrix $y = 2$, vertex at $(1, -1)$.
4. Directrix at $x = -1$, vertex at (0, 4).
5. Endpoints of right chord (2, 4) and (2, 0), opening to the right.
6. Endpoints of right chord $(-1, -1)$ and $(5, -1)$, opening upward.

In Exercises 7–12, write the equations of the *ellipses* having the given properties. Sketch each graph.

7. Major axis 8, foci at (5, 1) and $(-1, 1)$.
8. Minor axis 6, vertices at $(2, -1)$ and $(10, -1)$.
9. Minor axis 2, vertices at $(\frac{1}{2}, 0)$ and $(\frac{1}{2}, -8)$.
10. Major axis 3, foci at (1, 1) and $(1, -1)$.
11. Vertices at $(-6, 3)$ and $(-2, 3)$, foci at $(-5, 3)$ and $(-3, 3)$.
12. Center at $(1, -3)$, major axis 10, minor axis 6, vertical axis.

In Exercises 13–18, write the equations of the *hyperbolas* having the given properties. Sketch each graph.

13. Center at $(-1, 2)$, transverse axis 7, conjugate axis 8, vertical axis.

14. Center at (3, 0), transverse axis 6, conjugate axis 2, horizontal axis.

15. Vertices at (5, 1) and (−1, 1), foci at (6, 1) and (−2, 1).

16. Vertices at (2, ±4), conjugate axis 2.

17. Vertices at (−4, −2) and (0, −2), slope of the asymptotes $m = \pm\frac{1}{2}$.

18. Vertices at (3, 3) and (5, 3), slope of asymptotes $m = \pm 3$.

Write the equation of the family of curves indicated in Exercises 19–24.

19. Circles with center on the x-axis.

20. Parabolas with vertical axis and vertex on the x-axis.

21. Parabolas with vertex and focus on the x-axis.

22. Ellipses with center on the y-axis and horizontal major axis.

23. Circles passing through the origin with center on the x-axis.

24. Circles tangent to the x-axis.

25. The path of a projectile is given by $y = 20x - \frac{1}{10}x^2$, where y is the vertical distance and x the horizontal distance away from the initial point. Locate the vertex and sketch the path.

10.5 Rotation of Axes (Optional)*

In the previous section we saw how an analytic representation of a curve can be considerably simplified by moving the origin of the Cartesian coordinate system. This section shows how to rotate the axes to yield a new rectangular system of coordinates.

Figure 10.20 shows two rectangular coordinate systems with the $x'y'$-axes at an angle θ with the xy-axes. We say that the coordinates of a point (x, y) are **transformed** into the coordinates (x', y') by rotating the axes through an angle θ.

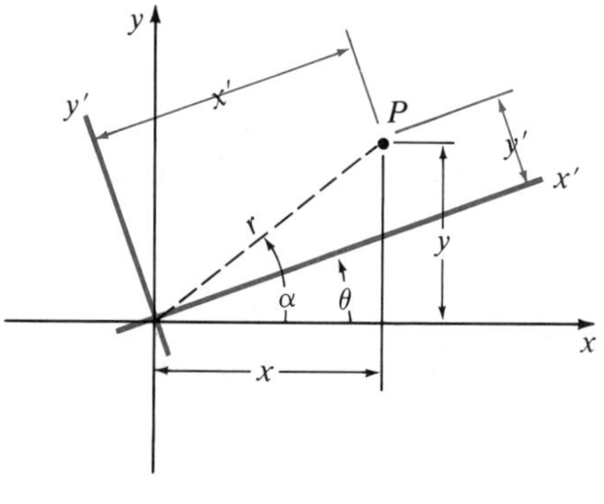

Figure 10.20

The equations of rotation are obtained by expressing (x', y') in terms of (x, y) and the rotation angle θ. From Figure 10.20,

$$\begin{aligned} x' &= r\cos(\alpha - \theta) \\ y' &= r\sin(\alpha - \theta) \end{aligned} \tag{10.16}$$

where α is the angle made by the x-axis and the line drawn from the origin to the point P. Using the trigonometric identities for the cosine and sine of the difference of

* Sections 10.5–10.7 require a rudimentary understanding of elementary trigonometry. See the appendix for the basic definitions.

two angles, we may write Equations 10.16 as

$$x' = r \cos \alpha \cos \theta + r \sin \alpha \sin \theta$$
$$y' = r \sin \alpha \cos \theta - r \cos \alpha \sin \theta \tag{10.17}$$

From Figure 10.20, $x = r \cos \alpha$ and $y = r \sin \alpha$; hence, the required relationship between the two coordinate systems is given by

$$\mathbf{x' = x \cos \theta + y \sin \theta}$$
$$\mathbf{y' = -x \sin \theta + y \cos \theta} \tag{10.18}$$

Solving these equations for x and y in terms of x', y', and θ, we obtain the **equations of the inverse transformation.**

$$\mathbf{x = x' \cos \theta - y' \sin \theta}$$
$$\mathbf{y = x' \sin \theta + y' \cos \theta} \tag{10.19}$$

You can use Equations 10.18 to find the coordinates of any point in the rotated system if you know the coordinates in the original system.

EXAMPLE 1 If the coordinates of a point in a coordinate system are $x = 4$, $y = 3$, find the coordinates of the same point in a rectangular system whose axes are rotated at 30° to the original.

Solution Using the equations of rotation, we get

$$x' = 4 \cos 30^\circ + 3 \sin 30^\circ$$
$$y' = -4 \sin 30^\circ + 3 \cos 30^\circ$$

from which $x' = 2\sqrt{3} + \frac{3}{2}$ and $y' = -2 + (3\sqrt{3})/2$. ■

To express an equation of a curve given in xy-coordinates in terms of $x'y'$-coordinates, merely use the rotation equations in Equations 10.19 to substitute for x and y in terms of x', y', and θ.

EXAMPLE 2 Find the equation of the straight line $x + y = 1$ in $x'y'$-coordinates if the prime coordinate system is rotated 45° to the xy-system.

Solution From Equations 10.19 the expressions for x and y in terms of x' and y' are

$$x = x'\frac{\sqrt{2}}{2} - y'\frac{\sqrt{2}}{2}$$
$$y = x'\frac{\sqrt{2}}{2} + y'\frac{\sqrt{2}}{2}$$

Hence, the equation $x + y = 1$ becomes

$$\frac{\sqrt{2}}{2}(x' - y') + \frac{\sqrt{2}}{2}(x' + y') = 1$$

After simplification, this equation becomes

$$\sqrt{2}x' = 1$$ ■

The foregoing example is typical of the actual use of rotation of coordinates; that is, the resulting equation should be in a simpler form. In the case of Example 2, the straight line is parallel to the y'-coordinate axis, which can be considered a simplification. Sometimes the curve itself becomes recognizable only after rotation. This simplification is done by judiciously choosing the rotation angle.

EXAMPLE 3 Consider the equation $x^2 + xy + y^2 = 1$. Choose a rotated coordinate system in which the "product term" (that is, the product of the coordinates) is not present. Identify and sketch the curve that the equation represents.

Solution Using the equations of rotation in Equations 10.19 and substituting into the given equation, we have

$$(x' \cos\theta - y' \sin\theta)^2 + (x' \cos\theta - y' \sin\theta)(x' \sin\theta + y' \cos\theta) + (x' \sin\theta + y' \cos\theta)^2 = 1$$

Simplifying yields

$$(x')^2(1 + \sin\theta\cos\theta) + (\cos^2\theta - \sin^2\theta)x'y' + (1 - \sin\theta\cos\theta)(y')^2 = 1$$

Note that the coefficient of $x'y'$ vanishes if $\cos^2\theta = \sin^2\theta$, so that we choose $\theta = 45°$, and the equation of the curve becomes

$$\left(1 + \frac{\sqrt{2}}{2}\frac{\sqrt{2}}{2}\right)(x')^2 + \left(1 - \frac{\sqrt{2}}{2}\frac{\sqrt{2}}{2}\right)(y')^2 = 1$$

or

$$\frac{(x')^2}{\frac{2}{3}} + \frac{(y')^2}{2} = 1$$

Hence, the equation represents an ellipse whose axes are at 45° to the xy-axes. Figure 10.21 displays the graph.

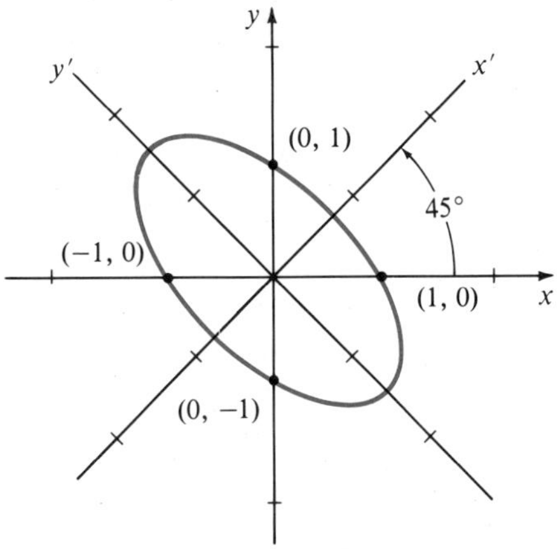

Figure 10.21 ■

Exercises Section 10.5

Find the coordinates of the points in Exercises 1–5 in a coordinate system rotated 30° from the x, y coordinate system.

1. (3, 1) **2.** (−5, 3) **3.** (−1, −1)

4. (2, 1) **5.** (2, −1)

6. Find the equations of rotation for a system rotated first through 30° and then 45°. Compare with the equations obtained by one rotation of 75°.

Find the equations of the curves in Exercises 7–13 after the given rotation.

7. The line $y = 2x$ after a 45° rotation.

8. The line $y = x + 5$ after a 45° rotation.

9. The line $2x + 7y = 3$ after a 60° rotation.

10. The circle $x^2 + y^2 = 4$ after a rotation of any angle θ.

11. The ellipse $x^2 + 4y^2 = 4$ after a rotation of 90°.

12. The parabola $y = x^2$ after a rotation of 30°.

13. The circle $x^2 + 2x + y^2 = 0$ after a rotation of 30°.

14. What is the slope of the line $y = mx$ in a system of coordinates rotated at 45° from the x, y system?

15. Given the transformation equations

$$x' = 0.6x + 0.8y$$
$$y' = -0.8x + 0.6y$$

what is the angle of rotation?

16. Consider the curve $(x - y)^2 - (x + y) = 0$. Rotate the coordinate system 45° and identify the curve.

17. Consider the curve $3x^2 - 2xy + 3y^2 = 2$. Rotate the coordinate system 45° and identify the curve.

Eliminate the product term in Exercises 18–21 by using a proper rotation and then sketch.

18. $xy = 1$ **19.** $x^2 + xy = 1$

20. $y - xy = 1$ **21.** $x^2 - xy + y^2 = 1$

22. What is the form of the equation of the hyperbola whose equation is $x^2 - y^2 = a^2$ in a system rotated 45°?

10.6 The General Second-Degree Equation (Optional)

The general second-degree equation is of the form

$$Ax^2 + Bxy + Cy^2 + Dx + Ey + F = 0 \tag{10.20}$$

where A, B, C, D, E, and F are constants. Each conic described in Sections 10.1 through 10.4 can be expressed in the form of Equation 10.20 with $B = 0$. This is seen by expanding the standard form of each conic. Assuming that $B = 0$, the following statements are easy to show.

- If $A = C$, Equation 10.20 represents a circle.
- If $A \neq C$ and A and C have the same numerical sign, Equation 10.20 represents an ellipse.
- If A and C have different numerical signs, Equation 10.20 represents a hyperbola.
- If A or $C = 0$ (but not both), then Equation 10.20 represents a parabola.
- Special cases such as a single point or no graph may result.

If $B = 0$, the general form of a conic can be reduced to one of the standard forms by completing the square on x and y. Several examples of this technique follow.

EXAMPLE 1 Discuss and sketch the graph of $x^2 - 4y^2 + 6x + 24y - 43 = 0$.

Solution This is the equation of a hyperbola since the coefficients of the x^2 and y^2 terms have unlike signs. To sketch the hyperbola, reduce the given equation to standard form by rearranging the terms and completing the square on the x-terms and the y-terms. Thus,

$$x^2 - 4y^2 + 6x + 24y - 43 = 0$$

may be written

$$(x^2 + 6x) - 4(y^2 - 6y) = 43$$

Completing the square on each variable, we get

$$(x^2 + 6x + 9) - 4(y^2 - 6y + 9) = 43 + 9 - 36$$
$$(x + 3)^2 - 4(y - 3)^2 = 16$$
$$\frac{(x + 3)^2}{16} - \frac{(y - 3)^2}{4} = 1$$

The center of the hyperbola is the point $(-3, 3)$. The transverse axis is horizontal with vertices at $(1, 3)$ and $(-7, 3)$. The endpoints of the conjugate axis are located at $(-3, 5)$ and $(-3, 1)$. Finally, the foci are at $(-3 + 2\sqrt{5}, 3)$ and $(-3 - 2\sqrt{5}, 3)$ since $c = \sqrt{16 + 4} = 2\sqrt{5}$. The graph appears in Figure 10.22.

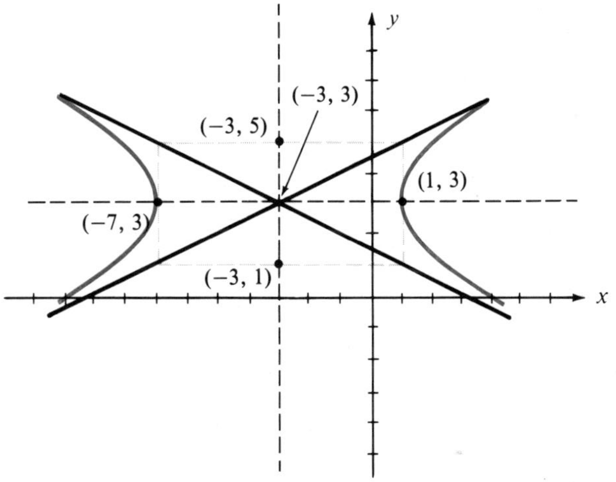

Figure 10.22

EXAMPLE 2 Discuss and sketch the graph of $2y^2 + 3x - 8y + 9 = 0$.

Solution By completing the square on the y-variable, this equation can be reduced to the form of Equation 10.11. Thus,

$$2y^2 + 3x - 8y + 9 = 0$$
$$2(y^2 - 4y) = -3x - 9$$
$$2(y^2 - 4y + 4) = -3x - 9 + 8$$
$$2(y - 2)^2 = -3x - 1$$
$$2(y - 2)^2 = -3\left(x + \frac{1}{3}\right)$$
$$(y - 2)^2 = -\frac{3}{2}\left(x + \frac{1}{3}\right)$$

This is the standard form of the equation of a parabola with horizontal axis and vertex at $(-\frac{1}{3}, 2)$. We see that $4a = -\frac{3}{2}$, so $a = -\frac{3}{8}$. Therefore, the focus is at $(-\frac{17}{24}, 2)$ and the endpoints of the right chord are $(-\frac{17}{24}, \frac{11}{4})$ and $(-\frac{17}{24}, \frac{5}{4})$. The parabola, which opens to the left, is shown in Figure 10.23.

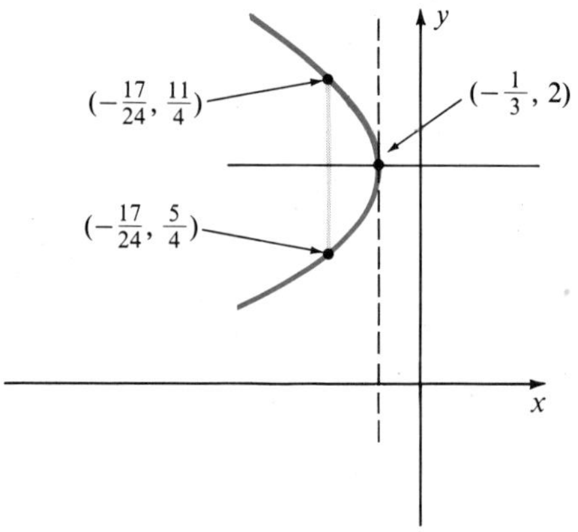

Figure 10.23 ■

If the axis of the conic is not parallel to one of the coordinate axes, then a product term is present, $B \neq 0$, and the nature of the conic is not immediately obvious. By properly choosing θ, we may remove this product in a rotated $x'y'$-system and reduce the problem essentially to the case of $B = 0$.

By substituting the general rotation equations in Equation 10.20, we may show that the product term can be made to vanish if we choose a rotation angle θ so that

$$\cot 2\theta = \frac{A - C}{B}$$

Unfortunately, this formula does not give the angle of rotation directly but requires a little unraveling using familiar trigonometric identities. (See Example 3.)

EXAMPLE 3 Eliminate the xy term in $3x^2 - 4xy = 20$ and sketch the graph.

Solution Here $A = 3$, $B = -4$, and $C = 0$. Hence,

$$\cot 2\theta = \frac{3 - 0}{-4} = -\frac{3}{4}$$

which implies the angle shown in Figure 10.24. Assuming that 2θ lies in the second quadrant and noting that $\sin \theta = \sqrt{(1 - \cos 2\theta)/2}$ and $\cos \theta = \sqrt{(1 + \cos 2\theta)/2}$, we find that

$$\sin \theta = \sqrt{\frac{1 + \frac{3}{5}}{2}} = \frac{2\sqrt{5}}{5}$$

$$\cos \theta = \sqrt{\frac{1 - \frac{3}{5}}{2}} = \frac{\sqrt{5}}{5}$$

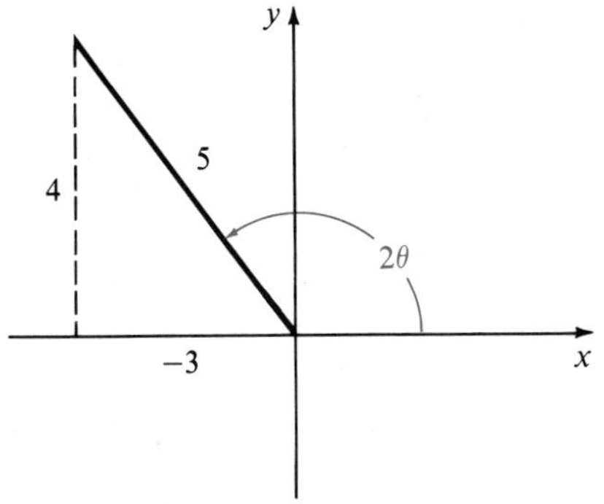

Figure 10.24

Substituting these values into the rotation Equations 10.19, we get

$$x = \frac{\sqrt{5}}{5}x' - \frac{2\sqrt{5}}{5}y'$$

$$y = \frac{2\sqrt{5}}{5}x' + \frac{\sqrt{5}}{5}y'$$

The equation $3x^2 - 4xy = 20$ can then be written

$$3\left(\frac{\sqrt{5}}{5}x' - \frac{2\sqrt{5}}{5}y'\right)^2 - 4\left(\frac{\sqrt{5}}{5}x' - \frac{2\sqrt{5}}{5}y'\right)\left(\frac{2\sqrt{5}}{5}x' + \frac{\sqrt{5}}{5}y'\right) = 20$$

This equation reduces (with some effort) to

$$20y'^2 - 5x'^2 = 100$$

or

$$\frac{y'^2}{5} - \frac{x'^2}{20} = 1$$

which is a hyperbola in standard form with respect to the $x'y'$-coordinate system. (See Figure 10.25.) The rotation angle, θ, is given by

$$\theta = \text{Sin}^{-1}\left(\frac{2\sqrt{5}}{5}\right) = 63.4°$$

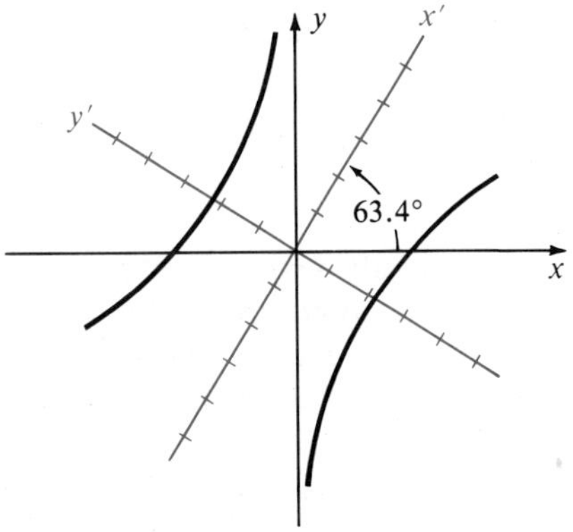

Figure 10.25

The asymptotes are

$$y' = \pm\frac{1}{2}x'$$

or, in terms of the original coordinates,

$$x = 0 \text{ (the } y \text{ axis)} \quad \text{and} \quad y = \frac{3}{4}x$$

■

Exercises Section 10.6

Transform each of the equations in Exercises 1–20 into standard form and sketch their graphs.

1. $x^2 + y^2 + 4x + 6y + 4 = 0$

2. $x^2 - 2x - 8y + 25 = 0$

3. $9x^2 + 4y^2 + 18x + 8y - 23 = 0$

4. $2x^2 + 2y^2 - 4x - 16 = 0$

5. $x^2 - y^2 - 4x - 21 = 0$

6. $y^2 + 4y + 6x - 8 = 0$

7. $x^2 - 6x - 3y = 0$

8. $x^2 + 4y^2 + 8x = 0$

9. $2y^2 - 2y + x - 1 = 0$

10. $3x^2 + 4y^2 - 18x + 8y + 19 = 0$

11. $4x^2 - y^2 + 8x + 2y - 1 = 0$

12. $y^2 - 2x - 4y + 10 = 0$

13. $9x^2 + 4y^2 - 18x + 16y - 11 = 0$

14. $y^2 - 25x^2 + 50x - 50 = 0$

15. $x^2 - 2y^2 + 2y = 0$

16. $y^2 - y - \frac{1}{2}x + \frac{1}{4} = 0$

17. $x(x + 4) = y^2 + 3$

18. $x^2 + y(4 + 2y) = 0$

19. $y = x^2 + 5x + 7$

20. $y = 2x^2 + 10x$

Use rotation of axes to identify and sketch the conics in Exercises 21–24.

21. $5x^2 + 12xy = 9$

22. $5x^2 + 3xy + 5y^2 = 7$

23. $5x^2 + 24xy - 2y^2 = 44$

24. $x^2 + 2xy + y^2 = 1$

25. In the analysis of the heat distribution on a hotplate, the isotherms are found to be included in the family of curves

$$c^2x^2 - 8c^2x + 4y^2 + 12c^2 = 0$$

What type of curve is each of the isotherms? Sketch a few of them for $y > 0$.

26. A space vehicle is scheduled to take off from Earth and follow the curved path given by the equation $y^2 - 4y - x^2 + 2x + 7 = 0$. Assuming that Earth is represented by the vertex in the part of the plane to the right of center of the conic, find the coordinates of Earth. Will the vehicle ever return to the neighborhood of Earth?

27. A garden is dug in the shape of a right triangle so that the hypotenuse is always 5 ft larger than one of the legs. Find the equation relating the legs. What kind of curve does it represent?

28. The outline of a lens of a camera has the approximate equation $2x^2 - 3y - 4x + 2 = 0$. Where is the focus? What kind of curve describes the outline of the lens?

10.7 Polar Equations and Their Graphs (Optional)

The rectangular coordinate system has been used exclusively in this book up to now. Another coordinate system widely used in science and mathematics is the **polar** coordinate system. In this system, the position of a point is determined by specifying a distance from a given point and the direction from a given line. Actually, this concept is not new; we frequently use this system to describe the relative locations of geographic points. When we say that Cincinnati is about 300 miles southeast of Chicago, we are using polar coordinates.

To establish a frame of reference for the polar coordinate system, we begin by choosing a point O and extending a line from this point. The point O is called the **pole,** and the extended line is called the **polar axis.** The position of any point P in the plane can then be determined if we know the distance OP and the angle AOP, as indicated in Figure 10.26. The directed distance OP is called the **radius vector** of P and is denoted by r. The angle AOP is called the **vectorial angle** and is denoted by θ. The coordinates of a point P are then written as the ordered pair (r, θ). Notice that the radius vector is the first element and the vectorial angle is the second.

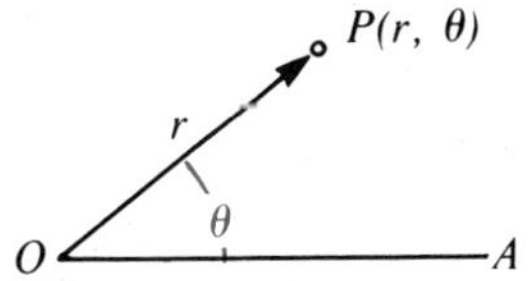

Figure 10.26

Polar coordinates, like rectangular coordinates, are regarded as signed quantities. When stating the polar coordinates of a point, it is customary to use the following sign conventions.

1. The radius vector is positive when measured on the terminal side of the vectorial angle and is negative when measured in the opposite direction.
2. The vectorial angle is positive when generated by a counterclockwise rotation from the polar axis and negative when generated by a clockwise rotation.

The polar coordinates of a point uniquely determine the location of the point. However, the converse is not true, as Figure 10.27 shows. Ignoring vectorial angles that are numerically greater than 360°, we have four pairs of coordinates that yield the same point: $(5, 60°)$, $(5, -300°)$, $(-5, 240°)$, and $(-5, -120°)$.

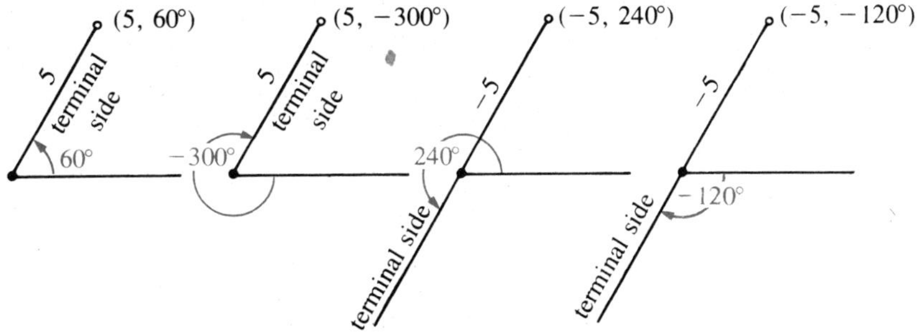

Figure 10.27

The equations $x^2 + y^2 = 25$ and $y^2 = 2x + 1$ are called rectangular equations because x and y represent coordinates in the Cartesian plane. These two equations can be expressed in polar coordinates as $r = 5$ and $r(1 - \cos\theta) = 1$, respectively. The relationship between the rectangular and polar forms of an equation can be found by superimposing the rectangular coordinate system on the polar coordinate system so that the origin corresponds to the pole and the positive x-axis to the polar axis. Under these circumstances, the point P shown

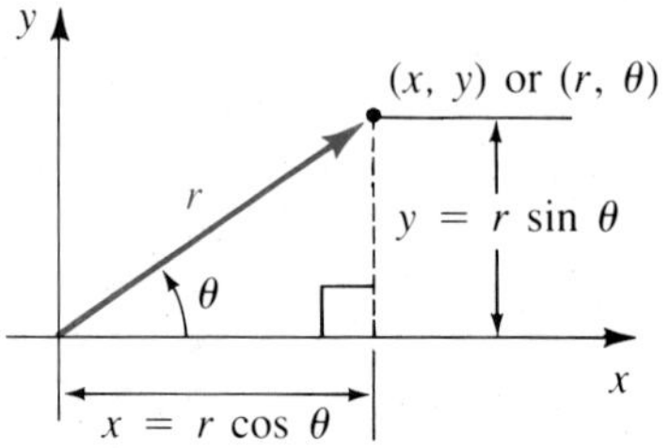

Figure 10.28

in Figure 10.28 has both (x, y) and (r, θ) as coordinates. The desired relationship is then an immediate consequence of the triangle. Hence, the equations

$$x = r\cos\theta \tag{10.21}$$

and

$$y = r\sin\theta \tag{10.22}$$

can be used to transform a rectangular equation into a polar equation.

EXAMPLE 1 Find the polar equation of the circle whose rectangular equation is $x^2 + y^2 = a^2$.

Solution Substituting Equations 10.21 and 10.22 into the given equation, we have

$$\begin{aligned} r^2\cos^2\theta + r^2\sin^2\theta &= a^2 \\ r^2(\cos^2\theta + \sin^2\theta) &= a^2 \\ r^2 &= a^2 \\ r &= a \end{aligned}$$

Hence, $r = a$ is the polar equation of the given circle. ■

To make the transformation from polar coordinates into rectangular coordinates, we use the following equations.

$$r = \sqrt{x^2 + y^2} \tag{10.23}$$

$$\sin\theta = \frac{y}{\sqrt{x^2 + y^2}} \tag{10.24}$$

$$\cos\theta = \frac{x}{\sqrt{x^2 + y^2}} \tag{10.25}$$

$$\tan\theta = \frac{y}{x} \tag{10.26}$$

These equations are derived from Figure 10.28.

EXAMPLE 2 Transform the following polar equation into a rectangular equation:

$$r = 1 - \cos\theta$$

Solution Substituting Equations 10.23 and 10.25 into the given equation, we have

$$\sqrt{x^2 + y^2} = 1 - \frac{x}{\sqrt{x^2 + y^2}}$$

$$x^2 + y^2 = \sqrt{x^2 + y^2} - x$$

Therefore,

$$x^2 + y^2 + x = \sqrt{x^2 + y^2}$$

is the required equation. ■

EXAMPLE 3 Show that

$$r = \frac{1}{1 - \cos \theta}$$

is the polar form of a parabola.

Solution Here our work is simplified if we multiply both sides of the given equation by $1 - \cos \theta$ before making the substitution. Thus,

$$r - r \cos \theta = 1$$

Substituting for r and $\cos \theta$ using Equations 10.23 and 10.25, we get

$$\sqrt{x^2 + y^2} - x = 1$$

Transposing x to the right and squaring both sides of the resulting equation, we get

$$x^2 + y^2 = x^2 + 2x + 1$$

$$y^2 = 2x + 1$$

$$y^2 = 2(x + \tfrac{1}{2})$$

This is the standard form of a parabola having its vertex at $(-\frac{1}{2}, 0)$ and a horizontal axis. ■

A polar equation has a graph in the polar coordinate plane, just as a rectangular equation has a graph in the rectangular coordinate plane. To draw the graph of a polar equation, we start by assigning values to θ and finding the corresponding values of r. The desired graph is then generated by plotting the ordered pairs (r, θ) and connecting them with a smooth curve. Use of polar coordinate paper greatly simplifies graphing a polar equation. Polar coordinate paper is commercially available. As Figure 10.29 shows, this paper consists of

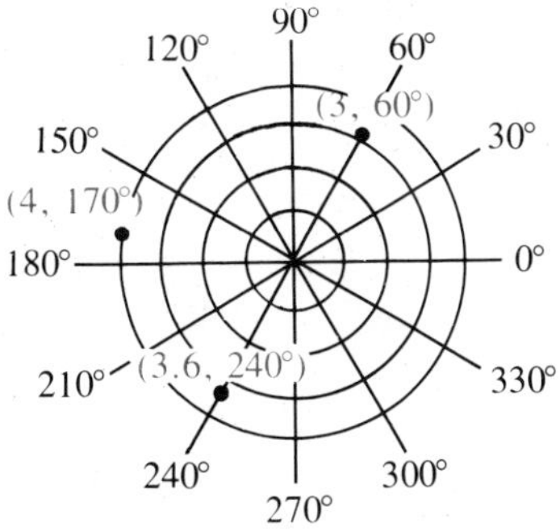

Figure 10.29

equally spaced concentric circles with radial lines extending at equal angles through the pole. Several points are plotted in Figure 10.29 for illustrative purposes.

EXAMPLE 4 Sketch the graph of the equation $r = 1 + \cos\theta$.

Solution Using increments of 45° for θ, we obtain the following table.

θ	0	45°	90°	135°	180°	225°	270°	315°	360°
r	2.00	1.71	1.00	0.29	0.00	0.29	1.00	1.71	2.00

The curve obtained by connecting these points with a smooth curve is called a *cardioid*. (See Figure 10.30.)

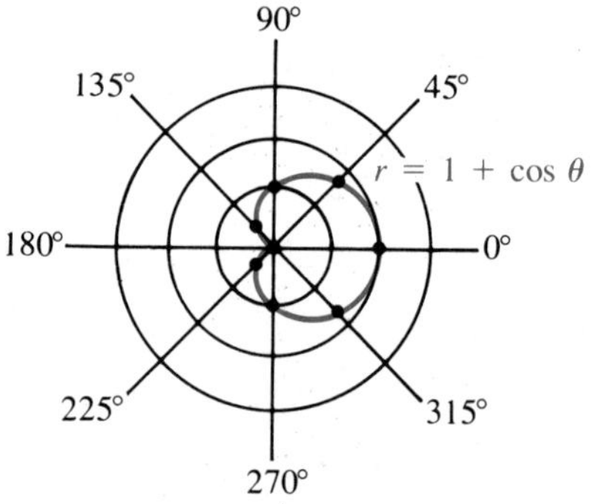

Figure 10.30 ■

EXAMPLE 5 Sketch the graph of the equation $r = 4\sin\theta$.

Solution The table on page 349 gives values of r corresponding to the indicated values of θ. Drawing a smooth curve through the plotted points, we obtain the *circle* shown in Figure 10.31. Notice that θ varies only from 0 to π radians. If we allow θ to vary from 0 to 2π radians, the graph will be traced out twice: once for $0 \le \theta \le \pi$ and again for $\pi < \theta \le 2\pi$. You should demonstrate this by plotting points in the interval $\pi < \theta \le 2\pi$.

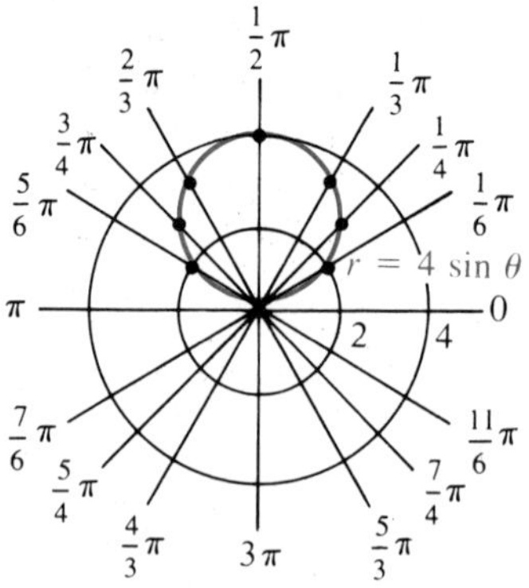

Figure 10.31

θ	0	$\frac{1}{6}\pi$	$\frac{1}{4}\pi$	$\frac{1}{3}\pi$	$\frac{1}{2}\pi$	$\frac{2}{3}\pi$	$\frac{3}{4}\pi$	$\frac{5}{6}\pi$	π
r	0	2	2.8	3.5	4	3.5	2.8	2	0

■

EXAMPLE 6 Sketch the graph of $r = \sin 3\theta$ for $0° \leq \theta \leq 180°$, using increments of 15° for θ.

Solution The following table gives values of r corresponding to the indicated values of θ. Notice that the values of r corresponding to $\theta = 75°$, 90°, and 105° are negative and are plotted accordingly in Figure 10.32. This curve, which is called a *three-leaved rose*, is traced again for $180° \leq \theta \leq 360°$. The arrowheads on the graph are to show how the graph is traced from $\theta = 0$ to $\theta = 180°$.

θ	0	15°	30°	45°	60°	75°	90°	105°	120°	135°	150°	165°	180°
r	0	0.7	1.0	0.7	0	−0.7	−1.0	−0.7	0	0.7	1.0	0.7	0

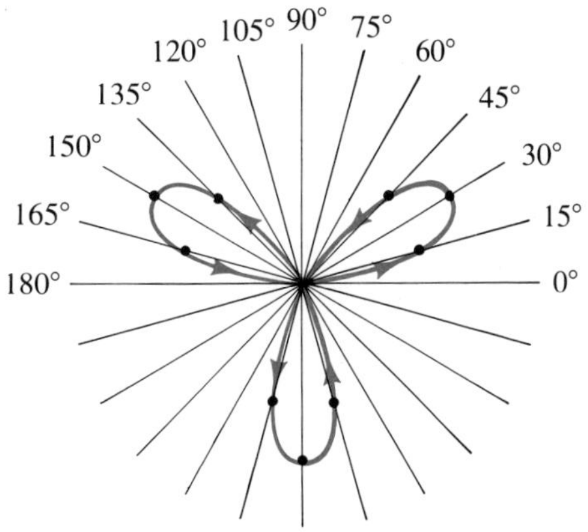

Figure 10.32

■

Exercises Section 10.7

In Exercises 1–10, plot each point on polar coordinate paper.

1. (5, 30°)
2. (3.6, −45°)
3. $(12, \frac{2}{3}\pi)$
4. (0.5, 220°)
5. (−7.1, 14°)
6. $(-2, \frac{7}{3}\pi)$
7. (1.75, −200°)
8. $(\sqrt{2}, -311°)$
9. (−5, −30°)
10. (5, 150°)

In Exercises 11–18, convert each rectangular equation into an equation in polar coordinates.

11. $2x + 3y = 6$
12. $y = x$
13. $x^2 + y^2 - 4x = 0$
14. $x^2 - y^2 = 4$
15. $x^2 + 4y^2 = 4$
16. $xy = 1$
17. $x^2 = 4y$
18. $y^2 = 16x$

In Exercises 19–26, convert each polar equation into an equation in rectangular coordinates.

19. $r = 5$
20. $r = \cos \theta$
21. $r = 10 \sin \theta$
22. $r = 2(\sin \theta - \cos \theta)$
23. $r = 1 + 2 \sin \theta$
24. $r \sin \theta = 10$
25. $r = \dfrac{5}{1 + \cos \theta}$
26. $r(1 - 2 \cos \theta) = 1$

In Exercises 27–40, sketch the graph of the given equation.

27. $r = 5.6$

28. $r = \sqrt{2}$

29. $\theta = \frac{1}{3}\pi$

30. $\theta = 170°$

31. $r = 2 \sin \theta$

32. $r = 0.5 \cos \theta$

33. $r \sin \theta = 1$

34. $r \cos \theta = -10$

35. $r = 1 + \sin \theta$

36. $r = 1 - \cos \theta$

37. $r = \sec \theta$

38. $r = -\sin \theta$

39. $r = 4 \sin 3\theta$

40. $r = \sin 2\theta$

41. The radiation pattern of a particular two-element antenna is a cardioid of form $r = 100(1 + \cos \theta)$. Sketch the radiation pattern of this antenna.

42. The radiation pattern of a certain antenna is given by

$$r = \frac{1}{2 - \cos \theta}$$

Plot this pattern.

43. By transforming the polar equation in Exercise 42 into rectangular coordinates, show that the indicated radiation pattern is elliptical.

44. The feedback diagram of a certain electronic tachometer can be approximated by the curve $r = \frac{1}{2}\theta$. Sketch the feedback diagram of this tachometer from $\theta = 0$ to $\theta = \frac{7}{6}\pi$.

Review Exercises Chapter 10

Sketch the graph of each of the equations given in Exercises 1–10. Identify all important parts.

1. $x^2 = -3y$

2. $x = -y^2 + 2y$

3. $x^2 = -y^2 - 4y + 5$

4. $x^2 - 3y^2 - 4 = 0$

5. $(x + 1)^2 - 2y = y^2$

6. $2x^2 - 3y^2 - x = 4$

7. $x^2 = y^2 - 100$

8. $y = 2x^2 + 3$

9. $y^2 + 2x^2 + 6x = 7$

10. $y^2 - y = x^2$

11. Write the equation of the parabola with vertex at (2, 0) and focus at the origin.

12. Write the equation of the parabola with vertex at (7, −2) and focus at (10, −2).

13. Write the equation of the circle with center at (−1, 2) and radius equal to 8.

14. Write the equation of the circle with center at (1, 3) that passes through (6, 4).

15. Write the equation of the ellipse with center at the origin, focus at (2, 0), and major axis equal to 8.

16. Write the equation of the hyperbola with center at (2, −2), ends of transverse axis at (2, 0) and (2, −4), and one focus at (2, 1).

17. Write the equation of the hyperbola with vertices at (7, 4) and (−1, 4) and whose asymptotes have slope ±2.

18. Show that each ellipse in the family of ellipses

$$\frac{x^2}{\sin^2 c} + \frac{y^2}{\cos^2 c} = 1$$

has its foci at the same two points. What are the foci? Sketch a few ellipses from the family. These ellipses are said to be **confocal.**

19. "Whispering" galleries have cross-sections that are ellipses. In such galleries a whisper at one focus will be heard distinctly at the other focus. Find the two foci in a gallery whose cross-section is a semiellipse with a height of 12 ft and length of 30 ft.

20. Certain navigational systems use the set of hyperbolas

$$\frac{x^2}{e^c - e^{-c}} - \frac{y^2}{e^c + e^{-c}} = 2$$

as references in a coordinate system. Show that each hyperbola pair has the same foci. Sketch a few hyperbolas from this family.

21. Solve the system of equations $2x^2 + x + y^2 + 2y = 1$ and $y + 2x = 1$ graphically.

22. Show graphically that $x^2 - 4y^2 = 4$ and $y = 3x + 2$ do not have any common real solutions.

23. Explain how each of the conic sections may be obtained from a right circular cone.

24. The trajectory of a body projected at an angle θ with the horizontal is shown to be $x = tv_0 \cos \theta$, $y = (v_0 \sin \theta)t - \frac{1}{2}gt^2$. Eliminate the variable t in these two equations and show that the path is parabolic. Make a sketch of the trajectory from the time it leaves the muzzle until it returns to the same level at which it was fired.

In Exercises 25–30, convert each expression to polar coordinates and sketch.

25. $y = 3$

26. $x^2 + y^2 + y = 0$

27. $y = 2x$

28. $y^2 + x^2 - 3x = 1$

29. $4x^2 + y^2 = 1$

30. $x = 4y^2$

In Exercises 31–40, convert each expression to rectangular coordinates and sketch.

31. $r = 2$
32. $r = 2 + 3\cos\theta$
33. $r = 2/(1 + \sin\theta)$
34. $r\cos\theta = 3$
35. $r = 3\cos\theta$
36. $r = \theta$
37. $r = \sin 2\theta$
38. $r^2 = \sin\theta$
39. $r^2 - r = 0$
40. $r^2 - 3r + 2 = 0$

Test 1 Chapter 10

Answer True or False to Exercises 1–10.

1. The coordinates of every point (x, y) on a curve satisfy the equation of the curve.
2. The curve $y = x^2$ is symmetric with respect to the origin.
3. The line $y = x$ and the curve $x^2 - y^2 = 1$ are asymptotic.
4. The graph of $x^2 - y^2 = 0$ is a hyperbola.
5. The circle $x^2 + y^2 = 4$ has radius 2.
6. The ellipse $2x^2 + y^2 = 1$ has a major axis of length $\sqrt{2}$.
7. The equation of an ellipse centered at the origin is of the form $ax^2 + by^2 = 1$ where a and b are both >0.
8. The hyperbola has four branches.
9. The hyperbola $y^2 = 1 + x^2$ has two y-intercepts, ± 1.
10. The curve $y = x^2 - 1$ is above the x-axis between $x = -1$ and $x = 1$.
11. Sketch the graph of $x^2 + y^2 + 4y = 0$.
12. Sketch the graph of $x^2 + 4y^2 = 4$. Locate the foci.
13. Sketch the graph of $2x^2 + x + y^2 + 2y = 1$. Determine the translation that will place the center of the curve at a new origin.
14. Sketch $x^2 - 4y^2 = 4$, being sure to give the oblique asymptotes both graphically and analytically.
15. Convert $y = 3 - 2x$ to polar coordinates.
16. Sketch $r = -2\sin\theta$.

Test 2 Chapter 10

1. Find the equation of the parabola with focus at $(-2, 1)$ and directrix $x = 3$.
2. Find the equation of the ellipse with center at $(0, 5)$, a vertical major axis of 6, and a minor axis of 3.
3. Find the equation of the hyperbola with center at the origin, vertices at $(\pm 3, 0)$, and foci at $(\pm 4, 0)$.
4. Find the equation of the circle with center at $(-2, -3)$ and passing through $(0, 2)$.
5. Explain how each of the conic sections is obtained from a right circular cone.

Discuss and sketch the graphs of the equations in Exercises 6–10.

6. $x^2 + y^2 - y = 0$
7. $y = (x + 3)(x - 2)$
8. $x(x + 8) = y^2$
9. $x^2 + 3y^2 + x - y = 0$
10. $r = 4\cos\theta$

APPENDIX **A**

Approximate Numbers

Significant Digits

If you count each card in a deck of 52 playing cards, you can say there are exactly 52 cards in the deck. However, if, when using a meter stick, you measure the distance between two points to be 3.5 cm, you realize that 3.5 is only an approximation to the precise answer and that the accuracy of the measurement depends on the accuracy of the measuring device. Similarly, most calculations in the physical sciences involve measurements that are accurate only to some specified number of digits. These digits that are known to be accurate are called **significant digits.** The zeros required to locate the decimal point are not significant digits.

EXAMPLE 1

a. 5.793 has four significant digits.
b. 20.781 has five significant digits.
c. 0.000059 has two significant digits.
d. 0.08300 has four significant digits.
e. $\sqrt{2}$, π, and 3 are examples of *exact* numbers. When used in computations, an exact number is considered to have as many significant digits as any other number in the same computation. ■

EXAMPLE 2 How many significant digits does 9480 have?

Solution A number like 9480 is difficult to categorize unless we know something about the number. Thus, it could represent the exact number of cards in a computer program. Or, it could represent a measurement accurate to either three or four significant digits. Sometimes we use scientific notation for numbers like this to avoid confusion. Thus,

$$9.48 \times 10^3$$

is used to indicate three significant digits while

$$9.480 \times 10^3$$

indicates four significant digits. ■

Note that the last significant digit of an approximate number is not completely accurate. For instance, if you measure a length of wire to be 2.56 cm, you realize that the length could be anywhere between 2.555 and 2.565 cm since it has been obtained by estimation.

The two numbers 28,500 and 0.285 are both accurate to three significant digits. However, 0.285 is a more precise measurement than 28,500. **The decimal position of the last significant digit of a number determines its precision.** Both accuracy and precision are important when making computations with approximate numbers.

EXAMPLE 3 a. The measurements 395 cm and 0.0712 cm are both accurate to three significant digits, but 395 cm is precise to the nearest 1 cm and 0.0712 cm is precise to the nearest 0.0001 cm.
b. 497.3 is more accurate than 0.025 but less precise. ■

The process of reducing a given number to a specified number of significant figures is called **rounding off.** There are several ways of rounding off numbers, but the following method is used in many calculators and computers.

Rounding Off

1. If the last digit is less than 5, drop the digit and use the remaining digits. For example, 8.134 rounds off as 8.13 to three significant figures.
2. If the last digit is 5 or greater, drop the digit and increase the last remaining digit by 1. For example, 0.0225 rounds off as 0.023 to two significant figures.

Another method used to reduce the digits in an approximate number is ***truncation.*** *In this scheme, the unwanted digits are simply dropped or truncated. Thus, the numbers* 23.157 *and* 23.154 *both truncate to the four-digit number* 23.15. *Likewise, under the truncation scheme,* $\frac{2}{3}$ *to seven decimal places is carried as* 0.6666666, *not as* 0.6666667. *Check your calculator to see if it rounds off or truncates.*

EXAMPLE 4 Round off each of the following numbers to three significant figures:
a. 18.89 b. 0.0003725 c. 99430 d. 4.996

Solution a. 18.89 becomes 18.9.
b. 0.0003725 becomes 0.000373.
c. 99430 becomes 99400.
d. 4.996 becomes 5.00. ■

Operations with Approximate Numbers

There is a great temptation, especially when you are using a calculator, to write the answer to arithmetic calculations to as many digits as the calculator will display. In doing so, you make the answer seem more accurate or precise than it really is. For instance, writing

$$8.4 \times 12.137 = 101.9508$$

implies that the product is accurate to seven significant figures, when the numbers being multiplied are only accurate to two and five significant figures, respectively. To avoid this problem, we adopt the following convention when performing arithmetic operations on approximate numbers.

- When adding or subtracting approximate numbers, express the result with the precision of the least precise number.
  Example: $0.74 + 0.0515 - 0.3329 = 0.4586$ is rounded off to 0.46.

- When multiplying or dividing approximate numbers, express the result with the accuracy of the least accurate number.
  Example: $1.93(13.77) = 26.5761$ is rounded off to 26.6.

- When finding the root of an approximate number, express the root with the same accuracy as the number.
  Example: $\sqrt{29.14} = 5.398$

EXAMPLE 5 a. The answer to $R = 1.90(63.21) + 4.9072$ should have three significant figures. Thus, $R = 125$.
b. The answer to $Q = 3.005\sqrt{2}$ should have four significant figures. Thus, $Q = 4.250$.
c. The answer to $y = 3 - \sqrt{29}$ where 3 is an exact number can be written to as many significant figures as desired since there are no approximate numbers being used. ■

EXAMPLE 6 The length of a rectangle is measured with a meter stick to be 95.7 cm and the width is measured with a micrometer to be 8.433 cm. What is the area of the rectangle?

Solution The area is given by

$$A = 8.433 \times 95.7 = 807.0381 \text{ cm}^2$$

Since the length has only three significant figures, the area must be rounded off to three significant figures. Therefore, $A = 807 \text{ cm}^2$. ■

Exercises

In Exercises 1–10, indicate the number of significant figures in the given numbers.

1. 3.37 **2.** 2.002 **3.** 812.0
4. 6161 **5.** 0.03 **6.** 0.000215
7. 0.40 **8.** 57.001 **9.** 500.0
10. 0.06180

In Exercises 11–20, round off the given number to three significant figures.

11. 9818 **12.** 72,267 **13.** 54.745
14. 1.002 **15.** 0.06583 **16.** 2435
17. 39.75 **18.** 0.4896 **19.** 0.9997
20. 900,498

In Exercises 21–32, perform the indicated operations and round off the answer to the appropriate number of significant figures.

21. $23.45(0.91669)$ **22.** $4.7(54.75)$
23. $0.5782 + 1.34 + 0.0057$
24. $50.68 + 9.666 - 24.059$
25. $2.9(3.57 + 10.28) + 25.0$
26. $0.20 + 3.86(0.127 - 0.097)$
27. $\sqrt{2.4^2 + 0.9^2}$ **28.** $2.176\sqrt{3}$
29. $\dfrac{25(0.9297)}{0.0102}$ **30.** $\dfrac{5.0887(2.20)}{8813}$
31. $\dfrac{0.9917(771.33)}{\sqrt{30}}$ **32.** $\sqrt{2.14^2 + 3.9^2}$

APPENDIX **B**

Basic Trigonometry

A knowledge of the material in this appendix will expand your algebraic skills to include vectors, complex numbers, rotation of coordinates and polar coordinates.

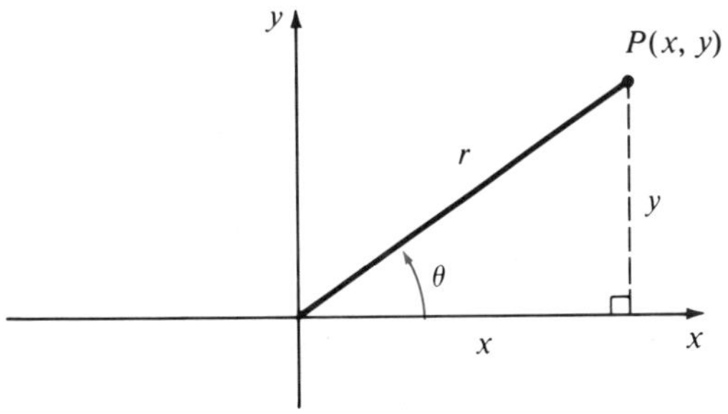

Figure B.1

Figure B.1 shows an angle θ in standard position on the Cartesian coordinate plane. Any point on the terminal side may be chosen with coordinates (x, y) and distance from the origin $r = \sqrt{x^2 + y^2}$. From the numbers x, y, and r we name and define the following ratios:

$$\sin\theta = \frac{y}{r}, \quad \cos\theta = \frac{x}{r}, \quad \tan\theta = \frac{y}{x}$$

EXAMPLE 1 If the terminal side of θ passes through $(1, -2)$, then $r = \sqrt{5}$ and

$$\sin\theta = -\frac{2}{\sqrt{5}}, \quad \cos\theta = \frac{1}{\sqrt{5}}, \quad \text{and} \quad \tan\theta = -\frac{2}{1} = -2$$

■

If θ is restricted to the first quadrant, then we can think of x, y, and r as forming the sides of a right triangle. In that case we say that y is the side **opposite** $\boldsymbol{\theta}$, x is the **side adjacent** $\boldsymbol{\theta}$, and r is the hypotenuse. The definitions then take the form:

$$\sin\theta = \frac{\text{side opposite}}{\text{hypotenuse}}, \quad \cos\theta = \frac{\text{side adjacent}}{\text{hypotenuse}}, \quad \tan\theta = \frac{\text{side opposite}}{\text{side adjacent}}$$

EXAMPLE 2 If θ is an angle of a right triangle with vertical leg 2 and horizontal leg 3, and if θ is the angle opposite the vertical leg as shown in Figure B.1, then the length of the hypotenuse is $\sqrt{2^2 + 3^3} = \sqrt{13}$ and $\sin \theta = 2/\sqrt{13}$, $\cos \theta = 3/\sqrt{13}$, $\tan \theta = 2/3$. ■

We see from Examples 1 and 2 that the trigonometric ratios depend on the size of the angle θ. These ratios are thus called **trigonometric functions.** The values of these functions can be found on calculators that have keys for $\sin \theta$, $\cos \theta$, and $\tan \theta$. Just enter the angle and push the desired key. (For some calculators the order of entry is reversed.)

EXAMPLE 3

a. To find sin 37°, enter 37 and push the [sin] key to obtain 0.60192.

b. To find tan 122°, enter 122 and push the [tan] key to obtain −1.6003. ■

Sometimes we are given the value of the trigonometric function and wish to find the angle. The procedure to use with a calculator varies with the brand but most require that you enter the given number and then push an [inv] or [2nd] button. Other calculators have single buttons labeled [$\sin^{-1}$], [$\cos^{-1}$], or [$\tan^{-1}$] for that purpose.

EXAMPLE 4

a. To find the angle θ for which $\tan \theta = 1.5$, enter 1.5 and then push [inv] [tan] to obtain 56.31°.

b. To find the angle for which $\cos \theta = -0.5369$, we enter -0.5639 and push [inv] [cos] to obtain 122.47°. ■

The trigonometric functions may be used to find the unknown parts of right triangles.

EXAMPLE 5 If the side adjacent to an angle of 27° is 5.9, then we can use trigonometry to obtain either of the other two sides. For example to obtain the side opposite we would use the relation

$$\tan 27^\circ = \frac{\text{side opposite}}{5.9}$$

from which we have

$$\text{side opposite} = 5.9 \tan 27^\circ = 5.9(0.5095) = 3.0$$ ■

The values of the trigonometric functions are interrelated by some interesting formulas called **identities.** The following identities are listed for reference.

$$\tan \theta = \frac{\sin \theta}{\cos \theta}$$

$$\sin^2 \theta + \cos^2 \theta = 1$$

$$\cos(\theta_1 \pm \theta_2) = \cos \theta_1 \cos \theta_2 \mp \sin \theta_1 \sin \theta_2$$

$$\sin(\theta_1 \pm \theta_2) = \sin \theta_1 \cos \theta_2 \pm \sin \theta_2 \cos \theta_1$$

$$\cos 2\theta = \cos^2 \theta - \sin^2 \theta$$

$$\sin 2\theta = 2 \sin \theta \cos \theta$$

Answers to Odd-Numbered Exercises

Section 1.1 (page 7)

1. T **3.** F **5.** T **7.** F **9.** F **11.** $0.\overline{142857}$, nonterminating
13. 0.375, terminating **15.** $1.\overline{2}$, nonterminating **17.** $1.8\overline{3}$, nonterminating
19. $0.\overline{461538}$, nonterminating **21.** 13 **23.** -12 **25.** 28 **27.** -19.4

29.
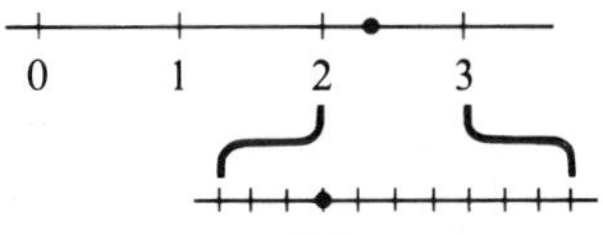

31.
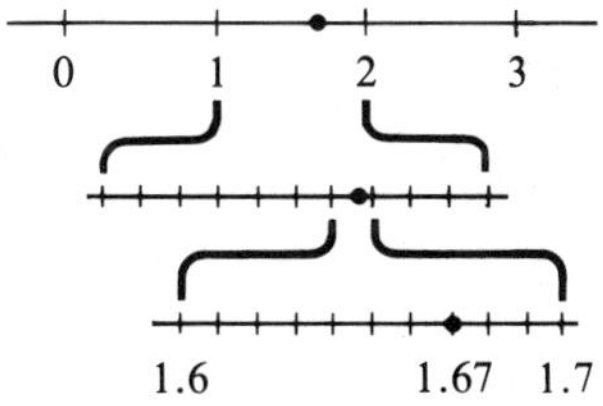

33.
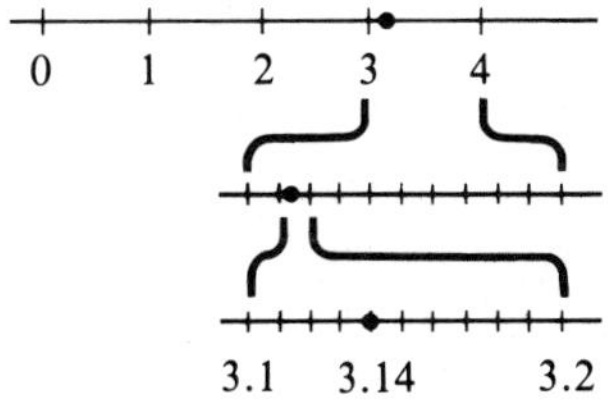

35.
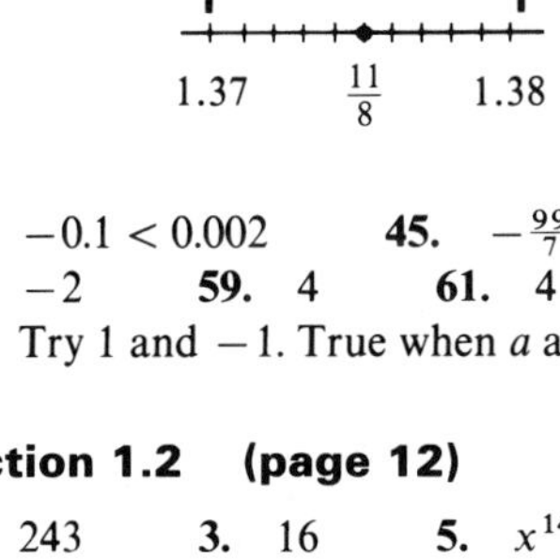

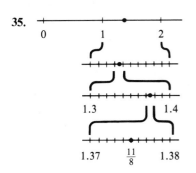

37.
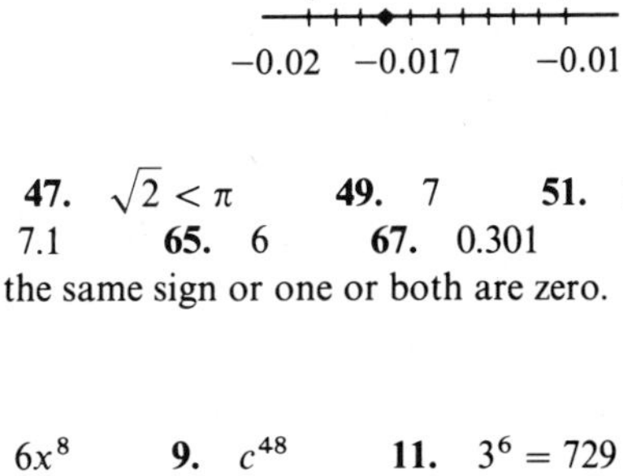

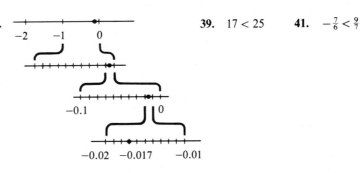

39. $17 < 25$ **41.** $-\frac{7}{6} < \frac{9}{7}$

43. $-0.1 < 0.002$ **45.** $-\frac{99}{7} < \frac{99}{12}$ **47.** $\sqrt{2} < \pi$ **49.** 7 **51.** 3 **53.** 14 **55.** 6
57. -2 **59.** 4 **61.** 4 **63.** 7.1 **65.** 6 **67.** 0.301
69. Try 1 and -1. True when a and b have the same sign or one or both are zero.

Section 1.2 (page 12)

1. 243 **3.** 16 **5.** x^{14} **7.** $6x^8$ **9.** c^{48} **11.** $3^6 = 729$ **13.** x^5y^5
15. $8x^9y^{21}$ **17.** 5 **19.** $\frac{4}{49}$ **21.** $7xy^4/27$ **23.** x^{12}/y^{30} **25.** $\frac{1}{8}$ **27.** $5/x^2$
29. y^{20}/x^8 **31.** $y^3/(8x^3)$ **33.** a^{10}/b^6 **35.** x^8y^4 **37.** $1/(x+y)$ **39.** 2

41. 8.2344×10^9 **43.** 5.2×10^{-11} **45.** 4.6×10^{39} **47.** 3,485,200,000 **49.** 0.0000009385
51. 0.02222 **53.** 3.0×10^{10} **55.** 1,500,000 **57.** False **59.** False

Section 1.3 (page 16)

1. 7 **3.** 5 **5.** -2 **7.** 25 **9.** $45\sqrt{3}$ **11.** a^2b **13.** $3a^2b^4\sqrt{7a}$
15. $z^3\sqrt[4]{2x^3}$ **17.** $2m^3n\sqrt{mn}$ **19.** $\dfrac{x^3\sqrt{x}}{y^2}$ **21.** $\dfrac{2\sqrt{5}}{5}$ **23.** $\dfrac{\sqrt{a}}{a}$ **25.** 10 **27.** $2a$
29. $x^{1/3}$ **31.** $(x/y)^{1/4}$ **33.** $x^{2/3}$ **35.** $x^{5/6}$ **37.** $\sqrt[5]{x^3}$ **39.** $\sqrt[8]{a^3}$ **41.** $\sqrt[3]{a+b}$
43. 8 **45.** 27 **47.** $\frac{1}{8}$ **49.** $x^{7/6}$ **51.** $y^{5/6}$ **53.** $5ab^3$ **55.** $3x^{1/3}$ **57.** $\sqrt[12]{y^7}$
59. $\sqrt[12]{5^4 \cdot 4^3}$ **61.** $\sqrt[6]{x^3(x+y)^2}$ **63.** $\sqrt[5]{x^2}$ **65.** $\sqrt{3}$ **67.** $\sqrt{a+1}$ **69.** $\sqrt{y+2}$
71. 0.00279 **73.** 36.462 **75.** 2.35589 **77.** 0.0011387 **79.** 4.994×10^5 **81.** 5.28, 7.41

Section 1.4 (page 20)

1. $x^5 + 2x^2$ **3.** $x^5 - 5x^4$ **5.** $x^2 - 4y^2$ **7.** $x^4 - 1$ **9.** $x + \sqrt{xy}$ **11.** $x^2y^2 - 1$
13. $x^3 + 3x^2y^2 + 3xy^4 + y^6$ **15.** $x^4 - x^2y^2 - x^2y + y^3$ **17.** $x^2 + y^2 + z^2 + 2xy + 2xz + 2yz$
19. $6x^2 - 12y^2 - xy - 2xz + 3yz$ **21.** $x^2 + 8x + 16$ **23.** $x^2 + 30x + 225$ **25.** $b^2 - 144$
27. $4x^2 + 20x + 25$ **29.** $a - 2\sqrt{ab} + b$ **31.** $16x^2 - 25$ **33.** $x^3 + 6x^2 + 12x + 8$
35. $125a^3 + 75a^2b + 15ab^2 + b^3$ **37.** $8x^3 - 60x^2 + 150x - 125$ **39.** $x^3 + 8$ **41.** $x^3 - 27$
43. $C\sqrt{C} + D\sqrt{D}$ **45.** $x^2 + 14x + 45$ **47.** $6x^2 - 14x - 40$ **49.** $2y^2 + 9y + 10$
51. $2x^2 + 5xy - 12y^2$ **53.** $36x^2 - 111x + 40$ **55.** $h^2 + 6h + 12$ **57.** $10t^2 - 11t + 3$
59. $24T^2 + 44T + 12$

Section 1.5 (page 25)

1. $x(3x^2 - 5x + 15)$ **3.** $y^3(13y^4 - 27)$ **5.** $(z - 12)^2$ **7.** $(3x + 1)^2$ **9.** $(\frac{1}{2}x + 1)^2$
11. $(x + 13)(x - 13)$ **13.** $4(m + 4)(m - 4)$ **15.** $(x - \sqrt{7})(x + \sqrt{7})$ **17.** $(\frac{1}{2}x + \frac{1}{3})(\frac{1}{2}x - \frac{1}{3})$
19. $(3x + 2)^2$ **21.** $\frac{1}{9}(x + 1)^2$ **23.** $(x - 4)(x + 3)$ **25.** $(y + 6)(y + 7)$ **27.** $(x - 9)(x + 6)$
29. $(2x + 1)(x + 3)$ **31.** $(5x - 3)(x - 5)$ **33.** $[6(a + b) - 5][(a + b) - 1]$ **35.** $(3x - 5y)(x + 3y)$
37. $(3x + 2y)(x - 2y)$ **39.** $4(2x - y)(x - 2y)$ **41.** $(x + 4)(x^2 - 4x + 16)$
43. $(2x + 1)(4x^2 - 2x + 1)$ **45.** $(a + \frac{1}{2})(a^2 - \frac{1}{2}a + \frac{1}{4})$ **47.** $(y - 3)^3$ **49.** $(2x + 1)^3$
51. $(1 + ab)(a^2 + b^2)$ **53.** $(z - w)(z + w - 3)$ **55.** $(a - c + d)(a + c - d)$
57. $(x + 2 - \sqrt{3})(x + 2 + \sqrt{3})$ **59.** $(a - 4 - \sqrt{21})(a - 4 + \sqrt{21})$ **61.** $(x + \frac{3}{2} + \sqrt{\frac{3}{2}})(x + \frac{3}{2} - \sqrt{\frac{3}{2}})$
63. $4(y - 1 - \sqrt{3})(y - 1 + \sqrt{3})$ **65.** $[\sqrt{2}(b + \frac{3}{2}) - \sqrt{\frac{15}{2}}][\sqrt{2}(b + \frac{3}{2}) + \sqrt{\frac{15}{2}}]$ **67.** $(x + 2L)(x - L)$
69. $(R - r)(5 + r)$ **71.** $\sqrt{2} + \sqrt{3}$ **73.** $8 - \sqrt{7}$ **75.** $\sqrt{7} + 3$ **77.** $\sqrt{2} + 1$

Section 1.6 (page 31)

1. $\dfrac{5c}{12a^2b^2}$ **3.** $\dfrac{1}{6x^3y^2}$ **5.** $\dfrac{6a^4}{b^2c^2}$ **7.** $\dfrac{x-3}{2}$ **9.** $\dfrac{6y}{5x(2x-3)}$ **11.** $\dfrac{x(x-2)}{y(x-1)}$
13. $\dfrac{2y+1}{y+2}$ **15.** $\dfrac{x(2x+3)}{x+6}$ **17.** $\dfrac{(s+1)^2}{s+3}$ **19.** 1 **21.** $-(2y + 1)(y + 4)$
23. $-\dfrac{(a+100)(a+400)}{2(a+40)}$ **25.** $\dfrac{2ac + ab - 3bc}{abc}$ **27.** $\dfrac{2t - 3s + 1}{3st}$ **29.** $\dfrac{3 + 2y^2 - 3xy}{xy^2}$
31. $\dfrac{5x-7}{(x+1)(x-3)}$ **33.** $\dfrac{x^2 + 5x - 10}{(x-5)(x+3)}$ **35.** $\dfrac{x+5}{x(x+2)}$ **37.** $\dfrac{7a+4}{a(2a+3)}$ **39.** $\dfrac{3x+32}{3x+4}$
41. $\dfrac{p^2 + 5p + 2}{p(p+1)^2}$ **43.** $\dfrac{x-4}{(x+1)(x-2)(x+3)}$ **45.** $\dfrac{5x^2 - x - 3}{(x+3)(x-2)^2}$ **47.** $\dfrac{(2x+1)(x-2)^{1/2}}{x-2}$
49. $\sqrt{2}(\sqrt{5} - \sqrt{3})$ **51.** $\dfrac{x - 2\sqrt{xy} + y}{x - y}$ **53.** $x + 1$ **55.** $\dfrac{a-b}{b}$ **57.** $-\dfrac{x+1}{x}$

59. $\dfrac{c^2+d^2}{c+d}$ 61. $\dfrac{x+2}{x-1}$ 63. $\dfrac{(x+2)(x-3)}{(x-4)(x+1)}$ 65. $\dfrac{x}{y(y-x)}$ 67. $\dfrac{2t^3+3t^2-15}{6t^3}$

69. $\dfrac{5s+9}{s(s+3)(s+1)}$

Section 1.7 (page 33)

1. $(2x)^2 = 4x^2$ 3. $-(2x-1) = -2x+1$ 5. $\dfrac{1}{2}+\dfrac{3}{4}=\dfrac{5}{4}$ 7. $\dfrac{x+2}{x}=1+\dfrac{2}{x}$

9. $(x^{-1}+y^{-1})^{-1}=\left(\dfrac{1}{x}+\dfrac{1}{y}\right)^{-1}=\left(\dfrac{y+x}{xy}\right)^{-1}=\dfrac{xy}{y+x}$ 11. $(x^3+x^2)=x^2(x+1)$

13. $\dfrac{1}{x+y}$ is in simplified form. 15. $(-x)^2=x^2$ 17. $(x^2)^3=x^6$ 19. $x+x=2x$

21. $\dfrac{3(5x+2)}{x^2+5x+2}$ cannot be reduced by cancellation of $5x+2$.

Review Exercises for Chapter 1 (page 34)

1. T 3. T 5. F 7. 2.125 9. $24 > 17$ 11. $-21 < -8$ 13. $145 > -2007$
15. 4 17. 6 19. -61 21. 9 23. 2 25. 3 27. $-a-b+c$
29. $11x+48y$ 31. $5a^3-a^4b^2$ 33. $3x^2+xy-14y^2$ 35. $2xy-6y^2+y+3x+15$
37. x^3-125 39. $8+36y+54y^2+27y^3$ 41. x^2-2 43. $5x(1-3y+x)$ 45. $(x-25)^2$
47. $(2b-13)(2b+13)$ 49. $(2-5x)(4-10x+25x^2)$ 51. $(y+5)^3$ 53. $(5x-2)(3x+4)$
55. $-(2x-1)(x-3)$ 57. $(2a-3b)(a+2b)$ 59. $(b-x)(a-3)$ 61. $\dfrac{1}{6y}$ 63. $\dfrac{a(a+3)}{b(a-b)}$
65. $\dfrac{r(r+1)}{r+2}$ 67. $\dfrac{2b-3a+1}{ab}$ 69. $\dfrac{2x^2+8x-3}{x(x+3)}$ 71. $\dfrac{a^3-10a^2+24a+2}{(a-2)(a-5)^2}$ 73. $-\dfrac{y}{x}$
75. 1 77. $y^2/(x+y^2)$ 79. $\dfrac{x^2y(xy+1)}{3x^2y^2+x^2+y^2}$ 81. $8x^6y^{15}$ 83. $(x+1)/(x-1)$
85. $\dfrac{1+a-a^2}{a(a^2-1)}$ 87. $\sqrt{2}$ 89. $35+\sqrt{3}$ 91. $\sqrt{2}(5-\sqrt{2})/23$ 93. $\sqrt[15]{3}$
95. $(1/cd)\sqrt{2cd^2+c^2}$ 97. $(\sqrt{x}-\sqrt{y})^2/(x-y)$ 99. $a\sqrt[3]{ab^2}/bc$
101. $a^{5/6}+(ab)^{1/2}+ba^{1/3}+b^{3/2}$ 103. $x^{1/2}/(x-1)$ 105. $4/x$
107. $\dfrac{1}{a^{2/3}}[1-4(ab)^{1/3}+4(ab)^{2/3}]$ 109. $a^2x+b^2x^{1/2}+c^2+2abx^{3/4}+2acx^{1/2}+2cbx^{1/4}$
111. $\dfrac{3x^2-2x-24}{(x+1)(x-3)}$ 113. $\dfrac{1}{t+1}$

Section 2.1 (page 40)

1. $-\frac{3}{2}$ 3. $\frac{2}{3}$ 5. 13 7. $\frac{18}{25}$ 9. 7 11. $\frac{1}{2}$ 13. -20 15. $\frac{1}{3}$ 17. 6
19. 2 21. $-\frac{22}{3}$ 23. $\frac{4}{5}$ 25. $\frac{5}{3}$ 27. No solution 29. No solution 31. $\frac{1}{2}$
33. No solution 35. 2 37. $-\frac{9}{2}$, 19

Section 2.2 (page 45)

1. $A=\frac{1}{2}bh$ 3. $P=4s$ 5. $a=v/t$ 7. $x-8$ 9. $5(x+3)$ 11. $0.20(x-12000)$
13. $\frac{1}{3}(x+y+z)$ 15. $I=PR$ 17. $2(x+y)$ 19. $A=6s^2$ 21. $t=\dfrac{v-b}{a}$
23. $b=\dfrac{2A}{h}-a$ 25. $T_1=\dfrac{1}{\alpha}\left(\dfrac{L}{L_0}-1\right)+T_0$ 27. $n=\dfrac{2D}{d-D}$ 29. $R=\dfrac{R_1R_2}{R_1+R_2}$

31. 9 and 11 A **33.** 102, 104, 106 **35.** 0.7 mi **37.** 220 mi **39.** **a.** \$175 **b.** \$400
41. 133 mph **43.** 0.5 hr **45.** 4 touchdowns, 4 extra points, 4 field goals, 2 safeties
47. 8 ft from the 150-lb boy **49.** 1.785 hr

Section 2.3 (page 53)

1. $0, 2$ **3.** $-1, 2$ **5.** $-2, 3$ **7.** $-5, 2$ **9.** $-4, \frac{3}{2}$ **11.** $-\frac{1}{3}, 2$ **13.** $0, \frac{1}{5}$
15. $-2, 5$ **17.** $-\frac{6}{7}, \frac{4}{5}$ **19.** $\frac{2}{3}, -2$ **21.** $-1, \frac{3}{5}$ **23.** $(1 \pm \sqrt{17})/4$ **25.** $(1 \pm \sqrt{33})/4$
27. $(5 \pm \sqrt{5})/2$ **29.** $(-6 \pm \sqrt{6})/5$ **31.** $(1 \pm i\sqrt{5})/3$ **33.** $(1 \pm 3i)/2$
35. $\dfrac{\pi}{6} \pm \dfrac{\sqrt{24 - \pi^2}}{6} i \approx 0.524 \pm 0.627i$ **37.** $-1.66, 0.66$ **39.** $0.091 \pm 0.848i$ **41.** $k = 3/\pi$
43. $k \le \frac{1}{32}$ **45.** $k = 4, -4$, and others **47.** $k = 2$ **49.** $k = -4$

Section 2.4 (page 55)

1. $-3 + \sqrt{2} \approx -1.59$ and $-3 - \sqrt{2} \approx -4.41$ **3.** $10 + 2\sqrt{10} \approx 16.32$ and $10 - 2\sqrt{10} \approx 3.68$
5. $(-15 \pm \sqrt{285})/2$ **7.** $T = 87.4°$ ($T = 12.6°$ is unrealistic since water freezes at 32° F.) **9.** 0.90 km
11. 5 m, 12 m **13.** 25 cm, 75 cm **15.** 56 ft × 42 ft **17.** 2 mph **19.** 40 hr
21. 11, 12, 13, and −11, −12, −13 **23.** 4 ft, 10 ft **25.** 8.4 hr **27.** 27 and 49 both work

Section 2.5 (page 59)

1. ± 2 **3.** $\pm 2\sqrt{2}$ **5.** No real solutions **7.** $-2, \frac{1}{3}$ **9.** $-\frac{3}{2}, \frac{1}{2}$ **11.** $-4, 2$
13. No real solutions **15.** 11/5, 15/7 **17.** ± 1 **19.** ± 5 **21.** $-3, 5$
23. $\dfrac{32 \pm \sqrt{1636}}{34}$ **25.** $\dfrac{7 \pm \sqrt{97}}{2}$ **27.** ± 1.3636 **29.** 10, 15 **31.** 3 **33.** $-5, 5$
35. $-7, 2$ **37.** 3 **39.** 2 **41.** No solution **43.** 18 **45.** 0, 1 **47.** 30 in.
49. $h = \sqrt{s^2 - \pi^2 r^4}/\pi r$ **51.** $t = 2$

Section 2.6 (page 66)

1. 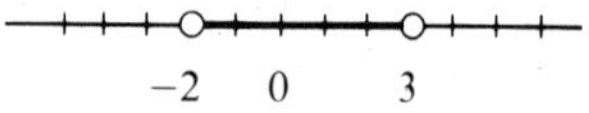

3. 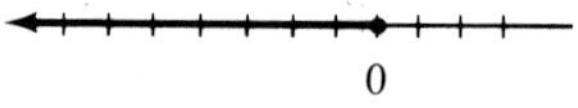

5. 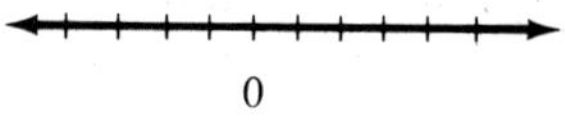

7. 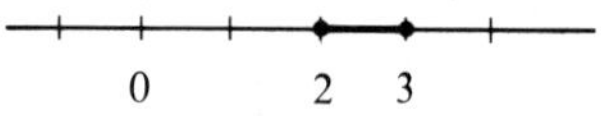

9. 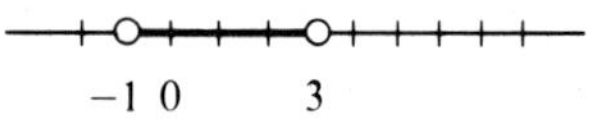

11. 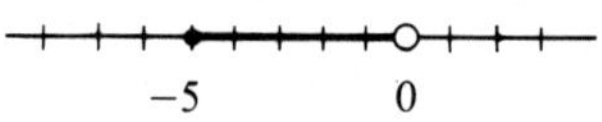

13. No solution **15.** 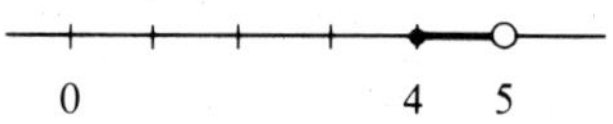

17. $x > -\frac{5}{2}$ **19.** $x \ge (\sqrt{2} - 1)/(1 + \sqrt{3})$

21. $x > \frac{70}{11}$ **23.** $x > -13$ **25.** $x \le -\frac{5}{3}$ **27.** $x > 0$ **29.** $x > \frac{4}{3}$ **31.** $x \ge -\frac{1}{2}$
33. $x > 8$ **35.** $-\frac{1}{5} \le x < \frac{11}{7}$ **37.** $(-1.5, 1.5)$ **39.** $(-\infty, -4] \cup [4, \infty)$ **41.** $(-1, 5)$
43. $(-7, 3)$ **45.** $(-\infty, 4) \cup (6, \infty)$ **47.** $[-4, 16]$ **49.** $[\frac{1}{2}, \frac{5}{2}]$ **51.** $|x| < 5$
53. $|x| > 3$ **55.** $|x - 4| < 2$ **57.** $|x - 3| < 13$ **59.** $|x| > 2$ **61.** $|2x - 9| \le 5$
63. It implies that $-2 > 2$. **65.** $9.99 < M < 10.01$

Section 2.7 (page 70)

1. $x \le -3$ or $x \ge 1$ **3.** $x < -\frac{1}{3}$ or $x > 2$ **5.** $-\frac{3}{2} \le x \le \frac{5}{2}$ **7.** All x
9. $x < (1 - \sqrt{33})/2 \approx -2.37$ or $x > (1 + \sqrt{33})/2 \approx 3.37$ **11.** $x < -5, -4 < x < -1$

13. $x \le -2$ or $x > -\frac{3}{2}$ **15.** $-2 < x \le -1, 1 \le x < 2$

17. All x **19.** $(-1-\sqrt{5})/2 < x < (-1+\sqrt{5})/2$ or $x \ge 2$ **21.** $\left.\begin{array}{l} x \le (1-\sqrt{21})/2 \\ -\sqrt{3} < x < \sqrt{3} \\ x \ge (1+\sqrt{21})/2 \end{array}\right\} \begin{array}{l} x \le -1.79 \\ -1.73 < x < 1.73 \\ x \ge 2.79 \end{array}$

23. $k \ge \sqrt{48}$ or $k \le -\sqrt{48}$ **25.** $0 < t < 5$ **27.** $10 < T < 20$

Review Exercises for Chapter 2 (page 70)

1. $x = 3$ **3.** $x = 60/43$ **5.** $x = 18a/(1+2a)$ **7.** $x = 7/10$ **9.** $y = 23/8$

11. $t = 11/4$ **13.** $-4, 4$ **15.** $-6, 14$ **17.** -2 **19.** $0, 7/3$ **21.** $\pm\sqrt{10}$

23. $1/2, 3$ **25.** $-1, -5$ **27.** $\dfrac{1 \pm 2\sqrt{3}}{2}$ **29.** $\dfrac{6 \pm \sqrt{66}}{2}$ **31.** $2/5, -4/3$ **33.** $2 \pm 2i$

35. $\dfrac{-7 \pm \sqrt{73}}{6}$ **37.** $\pm\sqrt{3}, \pm 2$ **39.** $1/3, 5$ **41.** $4, -5/9$ **43.** $1/4$ **45.** $-2, -1$

47.
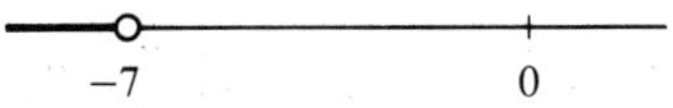

$x < -7$

49.
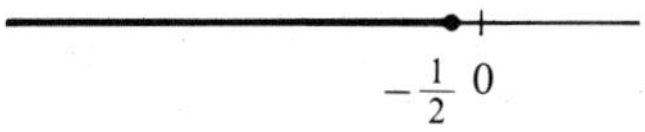

$x \le -\frac{1}{2}$

51.
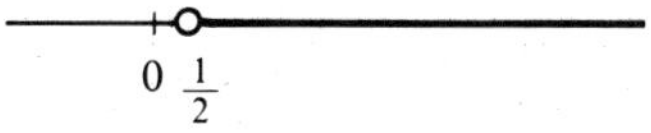

$x > \frac{1}{2}$

53.
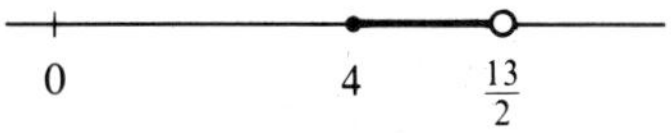

$4 \le x < \frac{13}{2}$

55.

$-1 < x$

57.
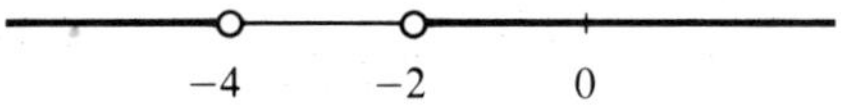

$x < -4, x > -2$

59. $|x - \frac{3}{2}| < \frac{7}{2}$ **61.** $|x-1| \ge 2$ **63.** $-6 \le x \le 1$ **65.** $-2 < x < 1$

67. $3 < x, x \ne 5$ **69.** $\rho = \dfrac{2(P_1 - P_2)}{v_2^2 - v_1^2}$ **71.** $m_0 = \dfrac{c^2 m - E}{c^2}$ **73.** \$196.75, \$590.25

75. 7.5 liters of the 6% solution, 2.5 liters of the 2% solution **77.** $\dfrac{5 + \sqrt{6425}}{32} \approx 2.66$ sec

79. $\dfrac{9 \pm 3\sqrt{5}}{2}$ **81.** $v = c\left(1 - \dfrac{m_0^2}{m^2}\right)^{1/2}$

Section 3.1 (page 79)

1, 3, 5.
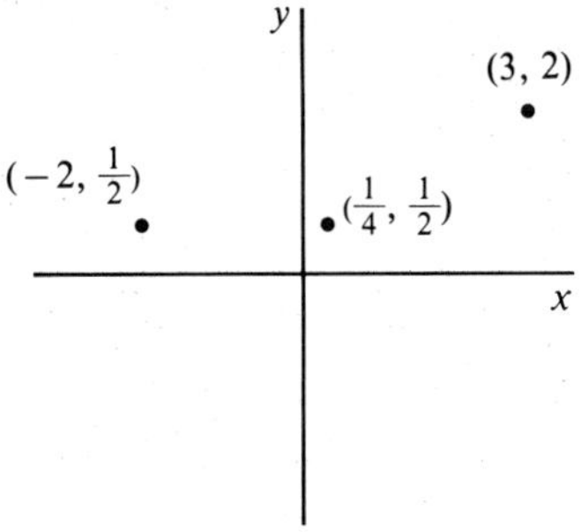

7. I, IV **9.** III **11.** 0

13.
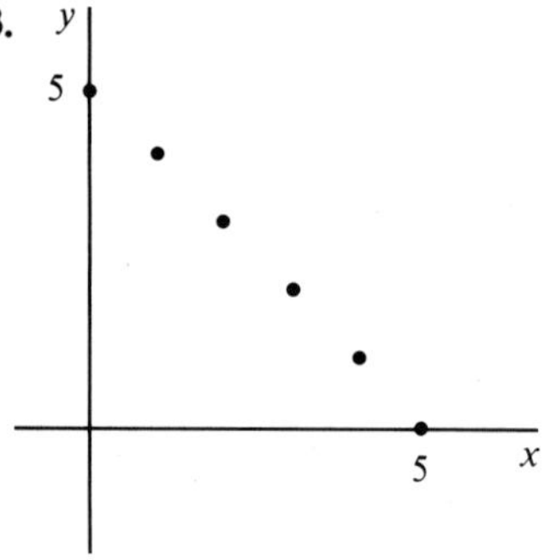

15.
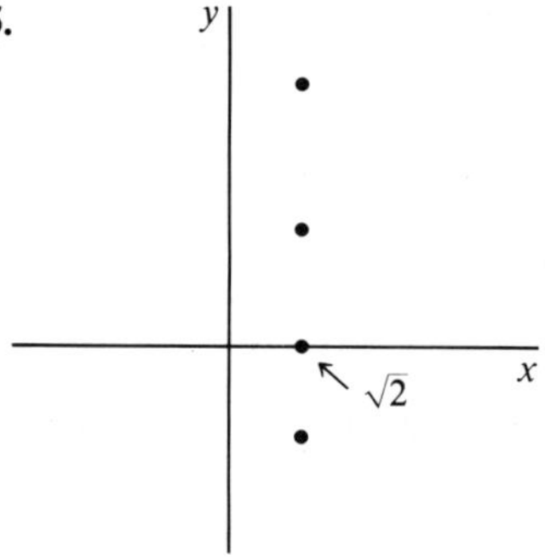

17.
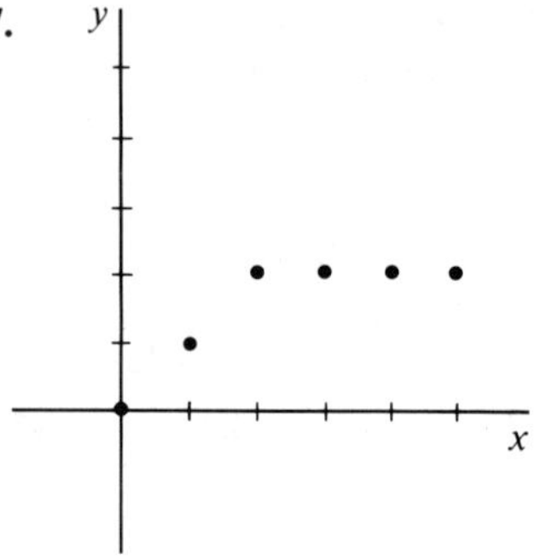

19.
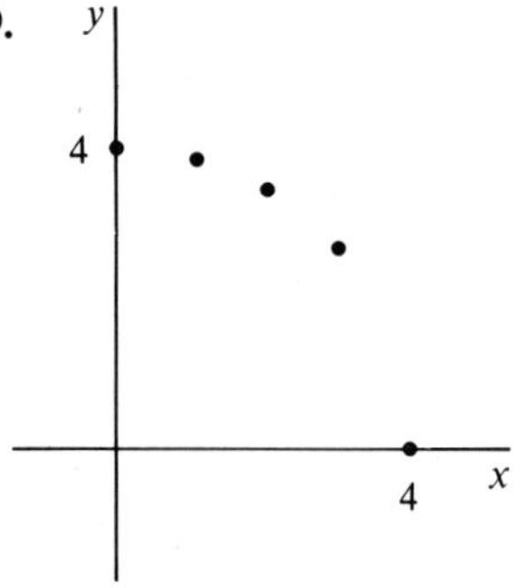

21.
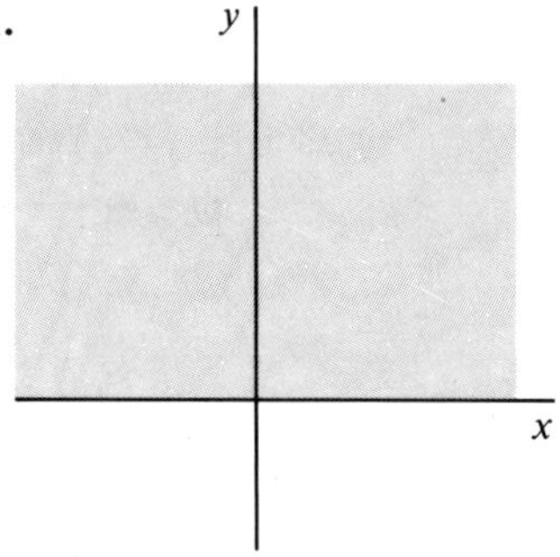

23.
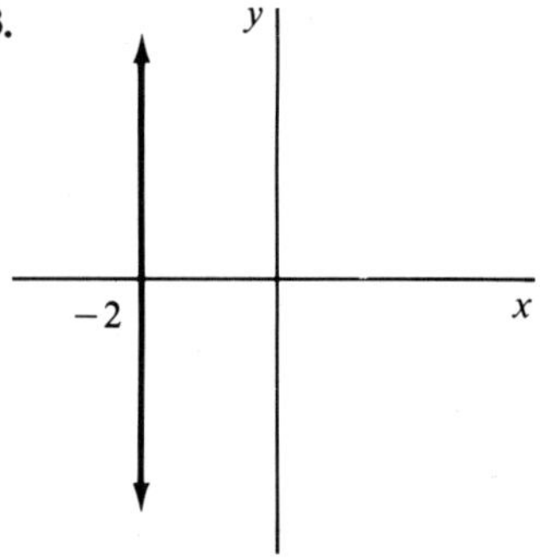

25.
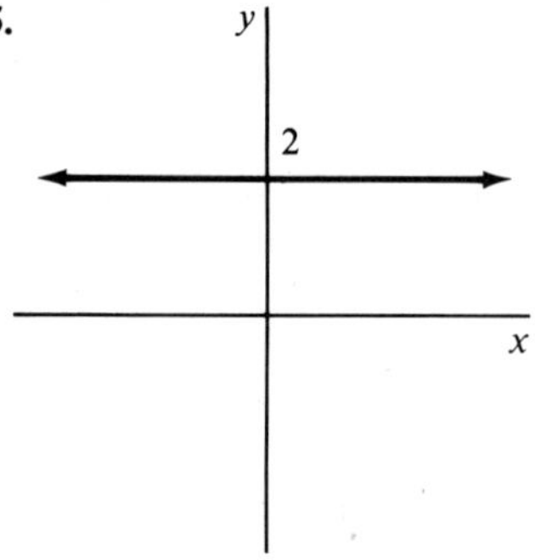

27.
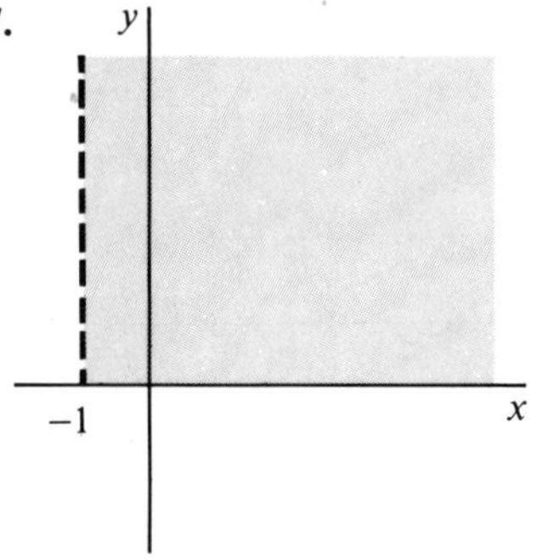

29.
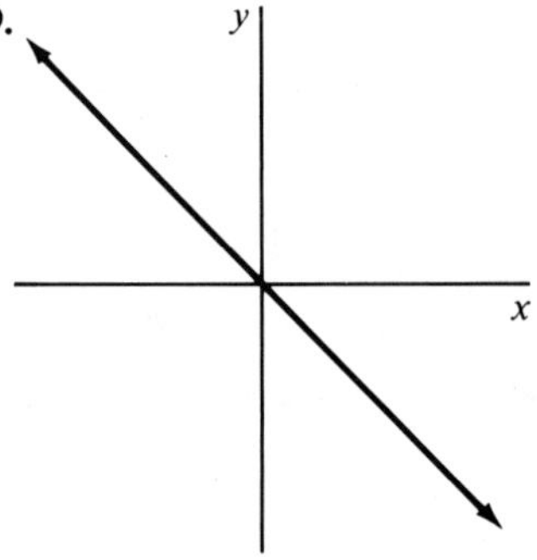

31. No common points **33.** $\sqrt{2}; (-\frac{1}{2}, \frac{7}{2})$ **35.** $\frac{5}{4}; (\frac{1}{2}, -\frac{1}{8})$ **37.** 8.2; (3.35, 4.55)
39. $2\sqrt{4+\sqrt{3}} \approx 4.8; \left(\frac{2-\sqrt{3}}{2}, -\frac{9}{2}\right)$ **41.** $2\sqrt{x+y}$ **43.** $2|y|$ **45.** $y = -2$

Section 3.2 (page 82)

1. $v = kt$ **3.** $r = k/\sqrt{p}$ **5.** $m = kx^2y^3$ **7.** $y = kh^4/g^2$ **9.** $n = k/(rt)$ **11.** 252 mi
13. 62.5 lb sodium, 37.5 lb chlorine **15.** 4.44 and 3.56 ft **17.** \$7005 **19.** 0.15 **21.** $y = 6$
23. $z = 1$ **25.** 64 ft/sec **27.** $C = 28.3¢$ **29.** $I = 1$ ft-cand. **31.** $P = 200$ w
33. 0.6 amps **35.** \$2300 **37. a.** Directly proportional to t^2 **b.** Constant
c. Directly proportional to t

Section 3.3 (page 90)

1. Function **3.** Function **5.** Function **7.** Not a function **9.** Function
11. Not a function **13.** (a) and (b) **15.** D: all reals; R: all reals **17.** $D: x \geq 0$; $R: y \geq 0$
19. D: all reals; R: all reals **21.** $D: x \leq 0$; $R: f(x) \geq 0$ **23.** $D: x \geq 1$; $R: f(x) \geq 0$
25. **a.** 10 **b.** $3\pi + 1$ **c.** $3z + 1$ **d.** $3(x - h) + 1$ **e.** 3 **f.** All reals **g.** 3
27. $2x + h$ **29.** $2x - 2 + h$ **31.** $3x^2 + 3xh + h^2$ **33.** Odd **35.** Odd **37.** Neither
39. Even **41.** $4x^2 - 48x + 135$ **43.** $9x^4 - 54x^3 + 81x^2$ **45.** $x = 1, -3$ **47.** $x = 0, \frac{2}{3}$
49. **a.** x_2/x_1 **b.** $f(1/x) = kx$; $1/f(x) = x/k$ **c.** $f(x^2) = k/x^2$; $[f(x)]^2 = k^2/x^2$
d. $-k/x(x + h)$ **e.** $f(x) + 1 = (x + k)/x$; $f(x + 1) = k/(x + 1)$
f. $f(x_1 + x_2) = k/(x_1 + x_2)$; $f(x_1) + f(x_2) = k(x_1 + x_2)/x_1x_2$ **g.** $af(x) = ak/x$; $f(ax) = k/ax$
51. -11.6918 **53.** 2.366 A **55.** $P = 0.705w - 150$

Section 3.4 (page 98)

1. **a.** Function **b.** Not a function **3.** **a.** Not a function **b.** Function
5. **a.** Increasing for all x **b.** Decreasing for all x **c.** Increasing for $x < -1$, decreasing for $x > -1$

7.

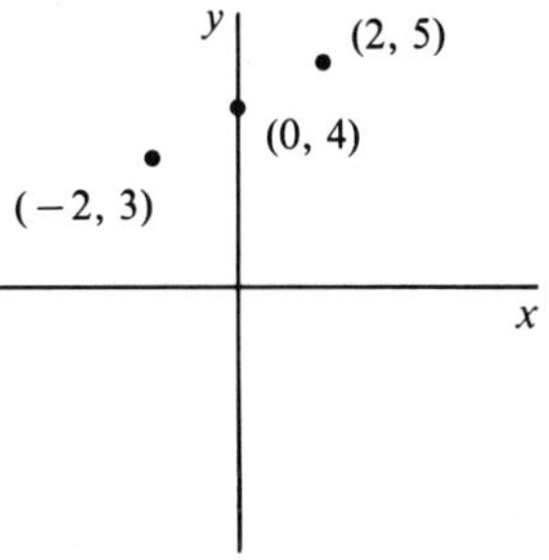

D: $-2, 0, 2$
R: 3, 4, 5

9.

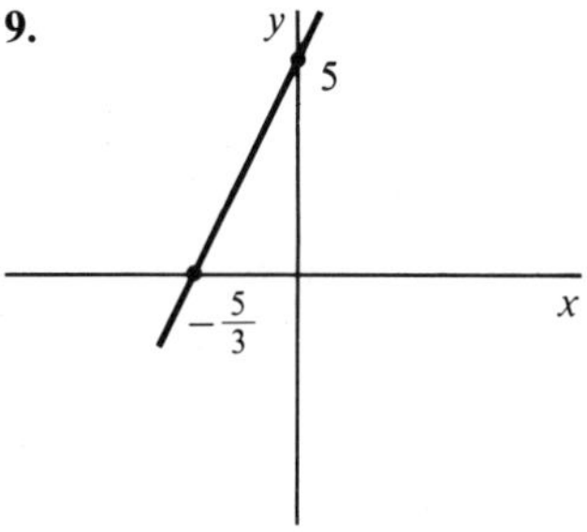

D: all reals
R: all reals

11.

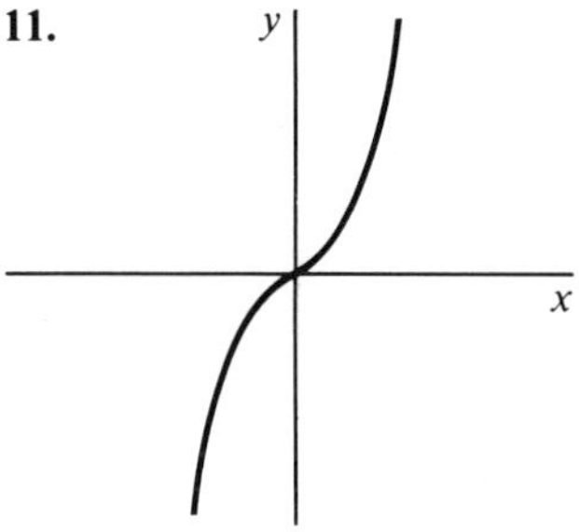

D: all reals
R: all reals

13.

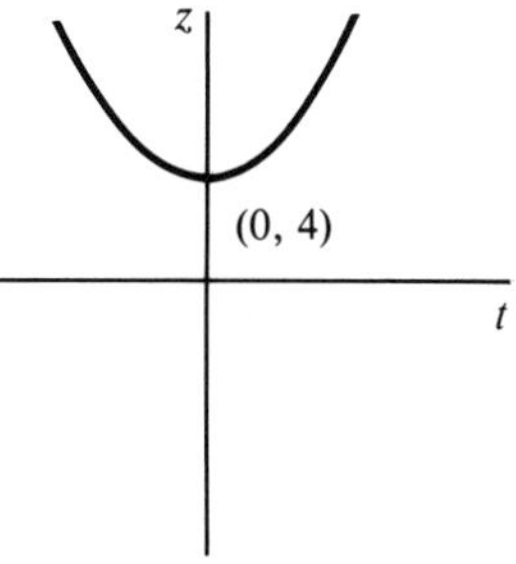

D: all reals
R: all reals ≥ 4

15.

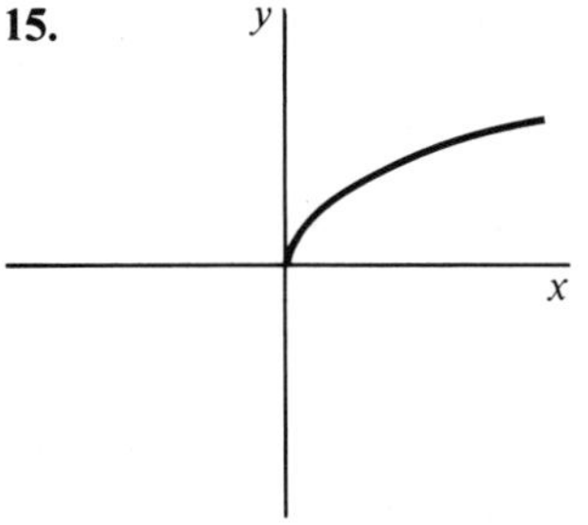

$D: x \geq 0$
$R: y \geq 0$

17.

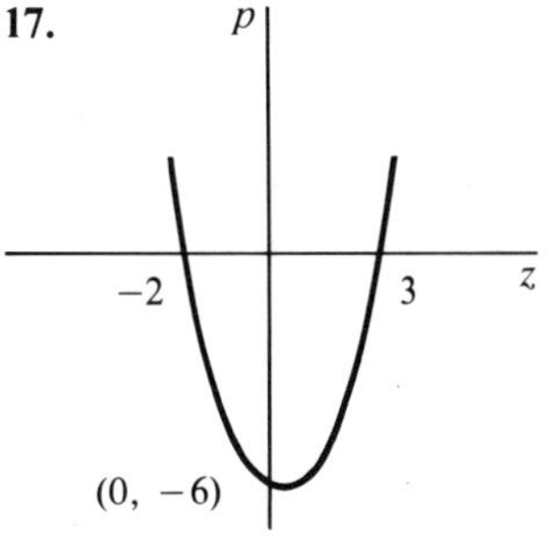

D: all z
$R: p \geq -6.25$

19.

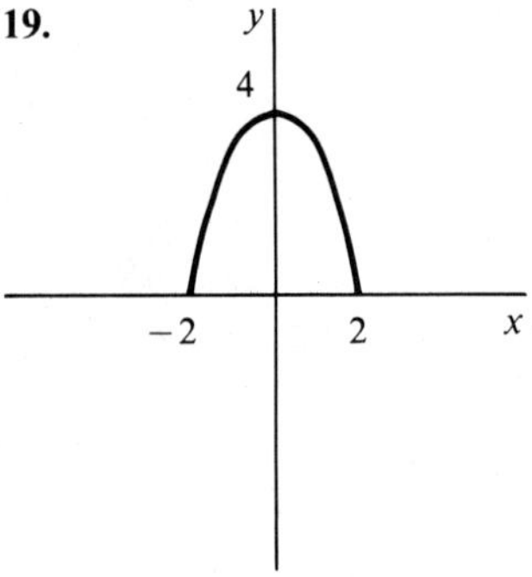

D: $-2 \le x \le 2$
R: $0 \le y \le 4$

21.

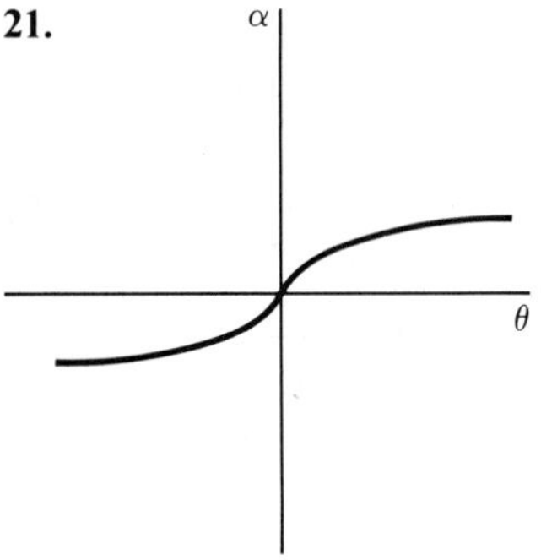

D: all θ
R: all α

23.

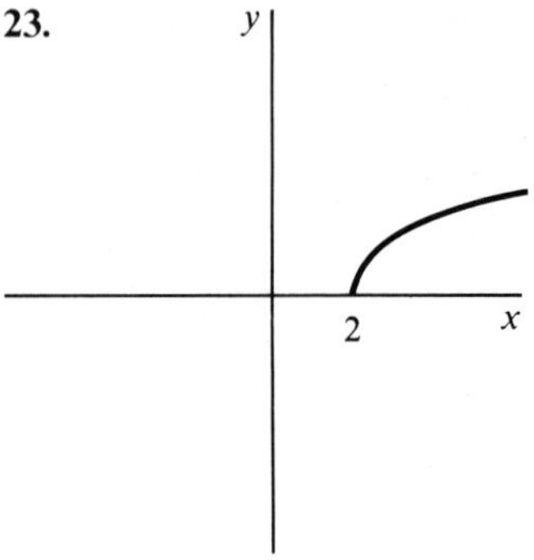

D: $x \ge 2$
R: $y \ge 0$

25.

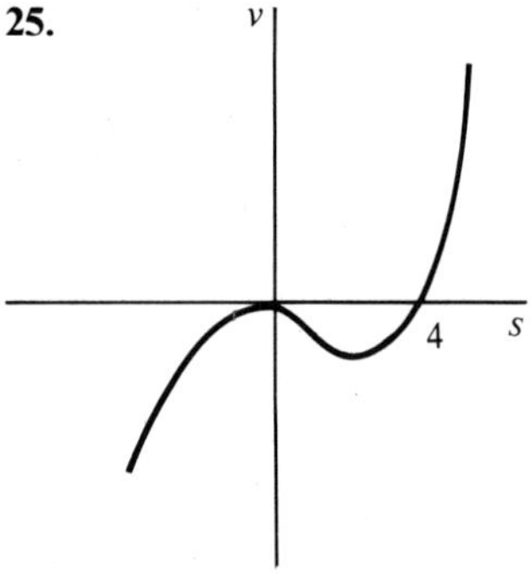

D: all s
R: all v

27.

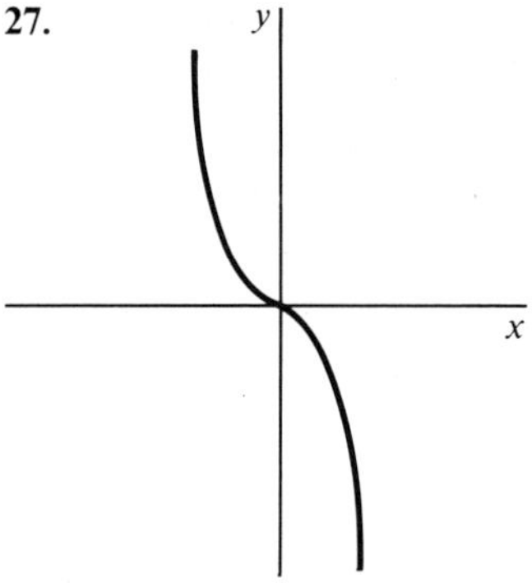

D: all x
R: all y

29.

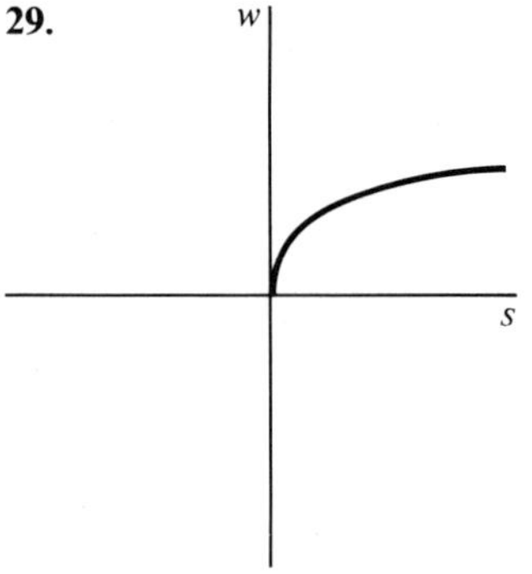

31.

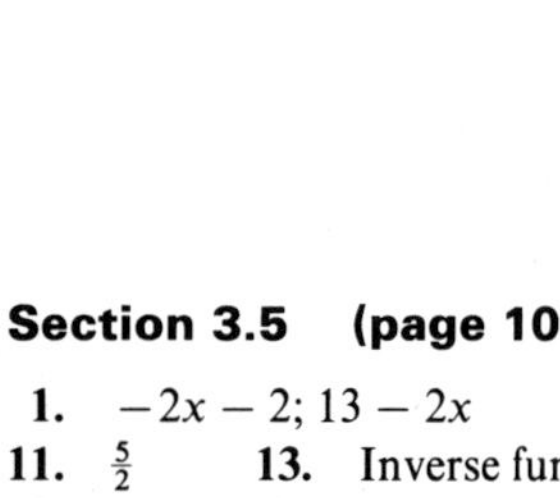

33.

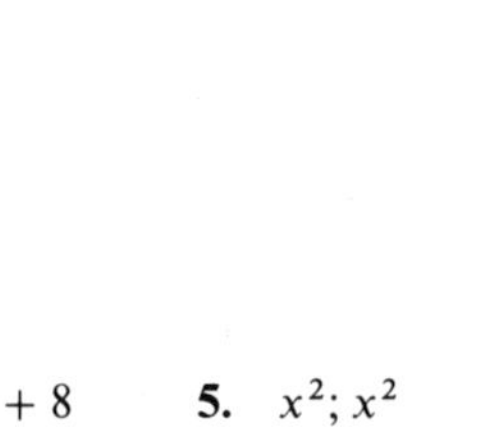

35.

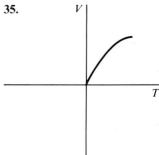

Section 3.5 (page 106)

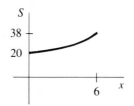

1. $-2x - 2$; $13 - 2x$ **3.** $6x + 4$; $6x + 8$ **5.** x^2; x^2 **7.** $x - 1$; $(x^3 - 1)^{1/3}$ **9.** $\frac{3}{2}$
11. $\frac{5}{2}$ **13.** Inverse functions **15.** Not inverse functions **17.** Inverse functions
19. Inverse functions **27.** $f^{-1}(x) = x + 3$ **29.** $f^{-1}(x) = (1 - x)/x$ **31.** $f^{-1}(x) = (1 + x)/(1 - x)$
33. 3; None **35.** $\{(7, 3), (9, 5), (3, 7), (5, 9)\}$ **37.** No inverse function
39. $\{(3, -2), (4, -1), (0, 0)\}$ **41.** No inverse function

Review Exercises for Chapter 3 (page 107)

1. 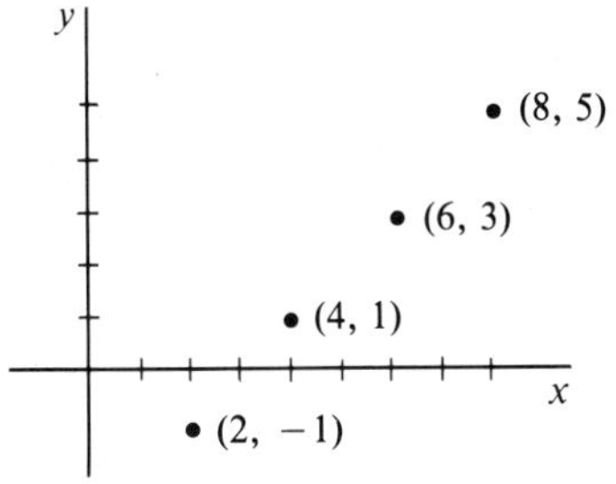

3. $\sqrt{89}$ 5. 6.67 lb/ft^2 7. \$0.40 9. 2000 lb

11. Function 13. Not a function 15. Function 17. Not a function 19. Function

21. D: all reals; R: all nonnegative reals 23. D: all reals ≥ 3; R: all nonnegative reals

25. 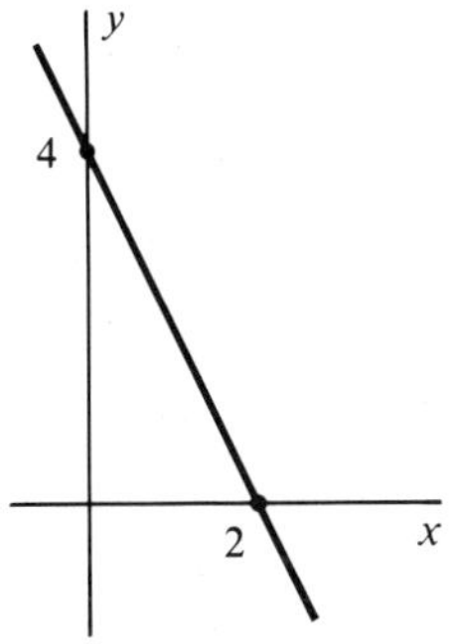

27. 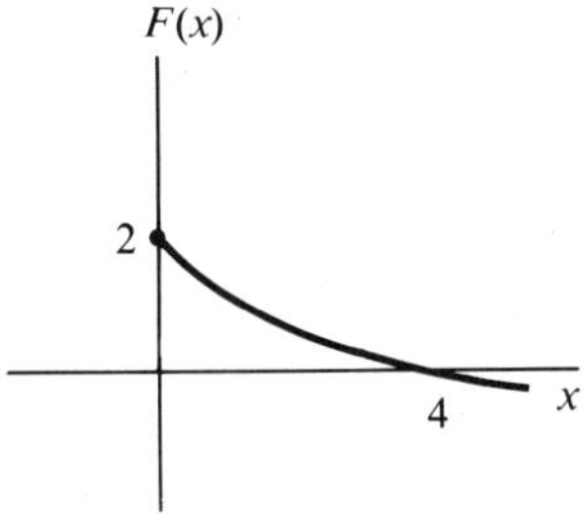

29. 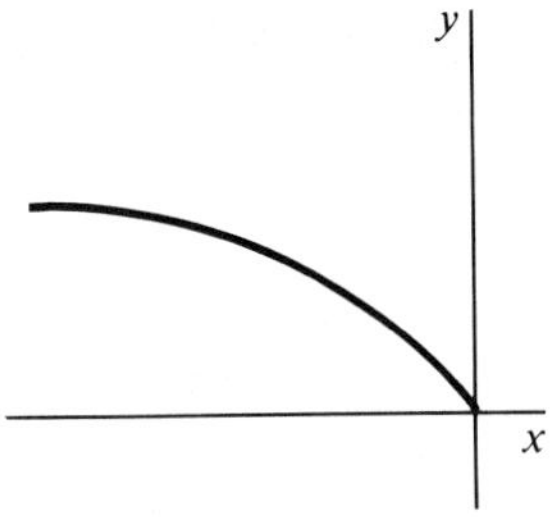

31. $\{(5, 2), (0, -1), (3, 7)\}$ 33. $f^{-1}(x) = (x - 5)/2$ 35. $g^{-1}(x) = (1 - 2x)/x$

37. $f(g(x)) = 11 - 3x$; $g(f(x)) = 5 - 3x$ 39. $f(g(x)) = x/(1 - x)$; $g(f(x)) = x - 1$

Section 4.1 (page 116)

1. 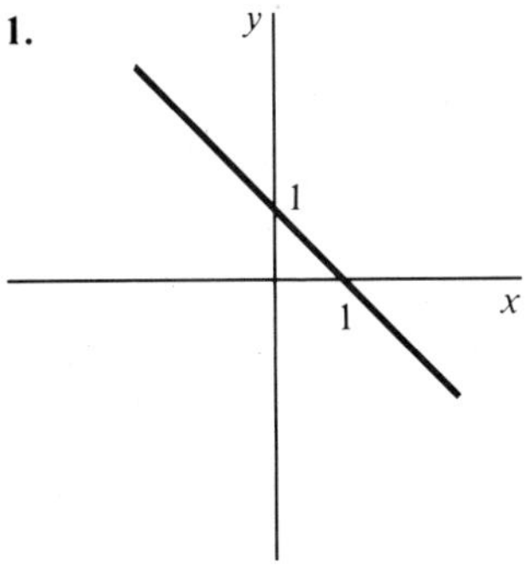

3. 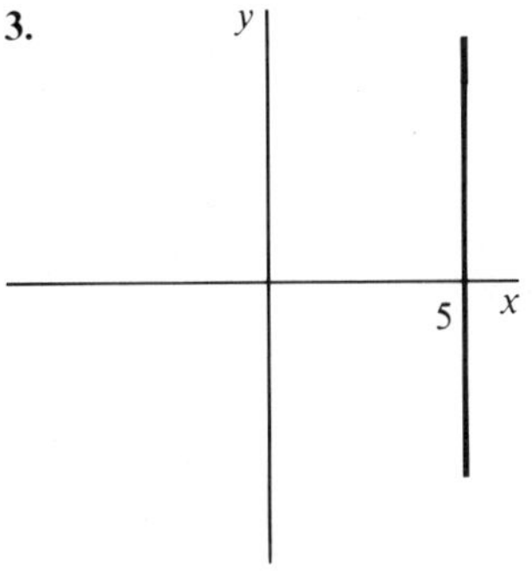

5. 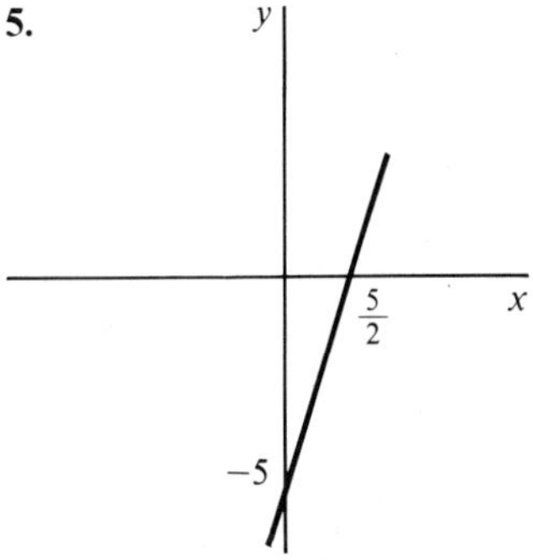

7.

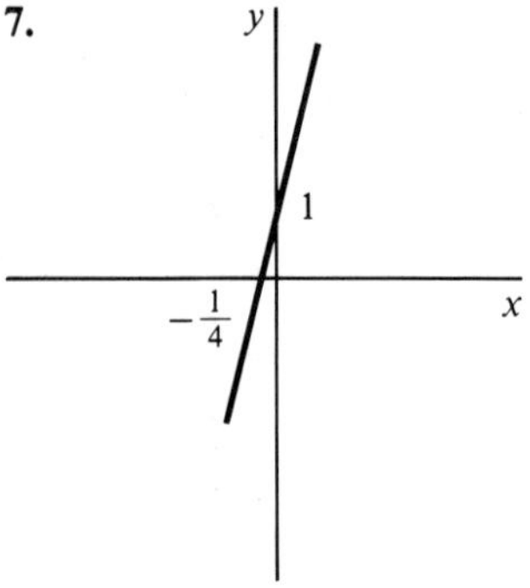

9.

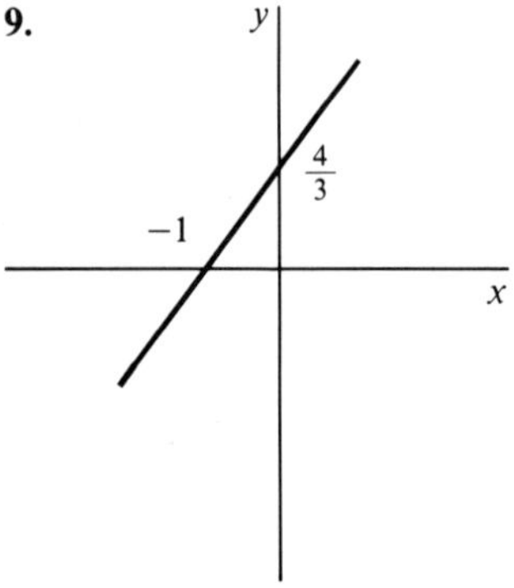

11.

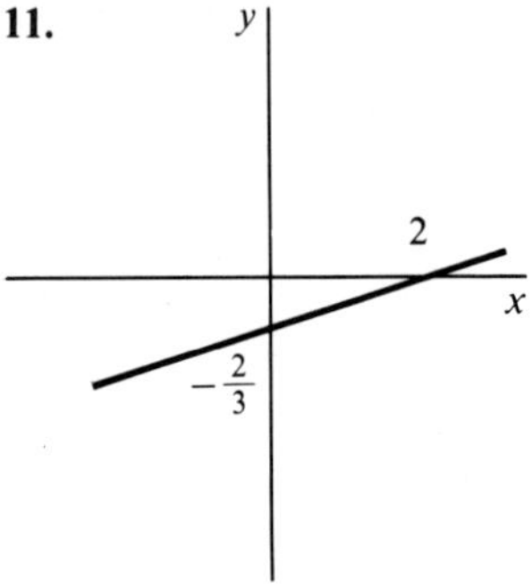

13. $m = \frac{1}{2}$ **15.** $m = -\frac{5}{4}$ **17.** $m = \frac{4}{3}$ **19.** $m = 0$ **21.** $x - 2y = -8$ **23.** $7x + y = 33$
25. $x + 5y = 16$ **27.** $2y - 3x = 1$ **29.** $5y - 2x = 10$ **31.** $m = \frac{2}{3}, b = -\frac{5}{3}$
33. $m = -1, b = 2$ **35.** $m = \frac{1}{2}, b = -2$ **37.** $m = \frac{1}{2}, b = \frac{5}{2}$ **39.** $m = 0, b = 5$
41. $m = \frac{1}{5}, b = \frac{7}{5}$ **43.** $2x - 3y = -4$ **45.** $x + y = 8$ **47.** $2x + 3y = 8$ **49.** $7x + 5y = 0$
51. $3x + y = -5$ **53.** No answer required **55.** $\frac{x}{2} + \frac{y}{2/3} = 1$

Section 4.2 (page 120)

1. **a.** \$1900 **b.** \$6.33 **c.** \$5.80 **d.** \$5.00 **e.** 320 **3.** **a.** \$2.00 **b.** \$200
c. No change **d.** 0, 100, 350 **5.** **a.** \$84,300 **b.** \$37,820 **c.** 1091
7. **a.** \$18,500 **b.** \$5,500 loss **c.** 72,000 **9.** $I = V/12$ **11.** \$225 **13.** \$151.11

15.

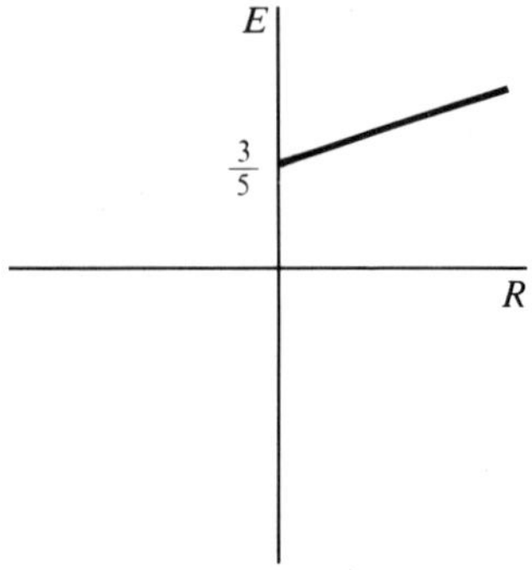

Section 4.3 (page 128)

1. *D*: all *x*
R: $f(x) \geq -4$
Zeros $x = -2, 2$
Intercept (0, −4)
Vertex (0, −4)

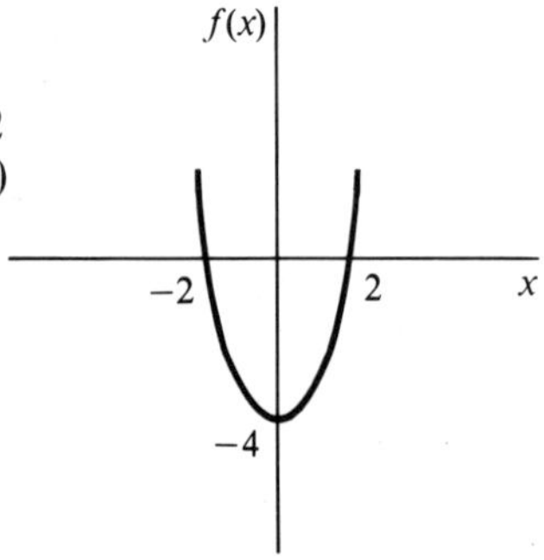

3. *D*: all *x*
R: $y \geq 1$
No zeros
Intercept (0, 1)
Vertex (0, 1)

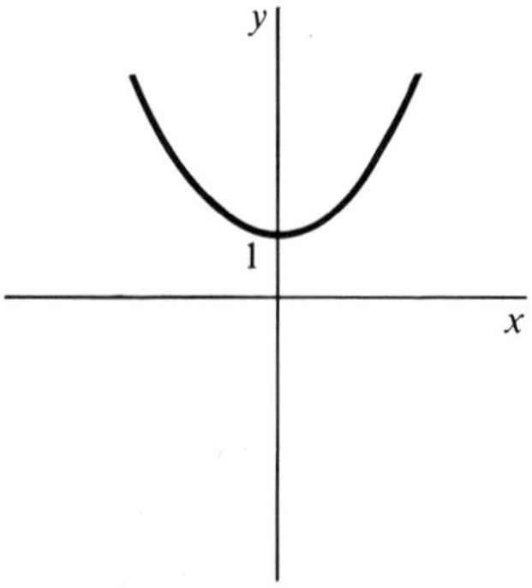

5. D: all x
R: $f(x) \leq 9$
Zeros $x = -3, 3$
Intercept (0, 9)
Vertex (0, 9)

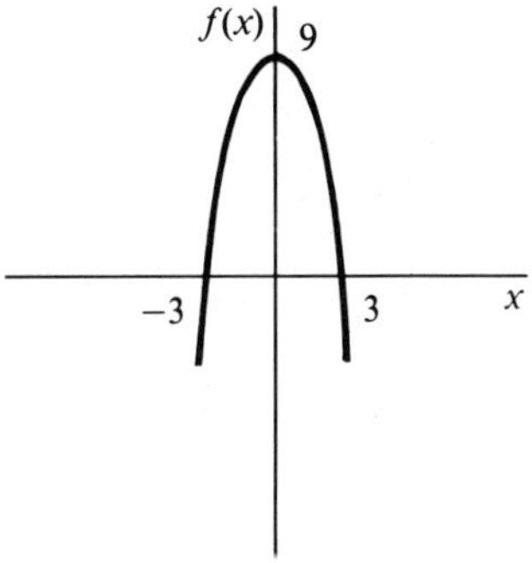

7. D: all t
R: $x(t) \geq -9/4$
Zeros $t = 0, 3$
Intercept (0, 0)
Vertex $(\frac{3}{2}, -\frac{9}{4})$

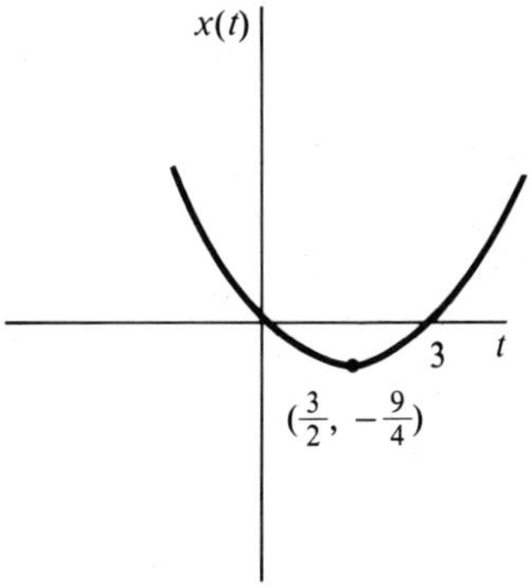

9. D: all x
R: $y \geq -\frac{1}{4}$
Zeros $x = 2, 3$
Intercept (0, 6)
Vertex $(\frac{5}{2}, -\frac{1}{4})$

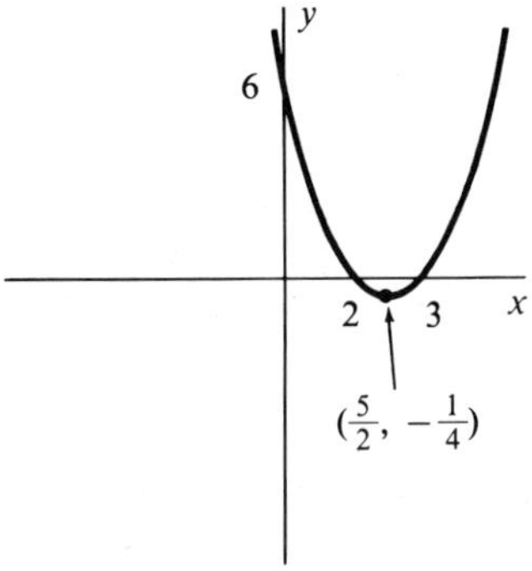

11. D: all x
R: $y \geq 2/3$
No zeros
Intercept (0, 1)
Vertex $(-\frac{1}{3}, \frac{2}{3})$

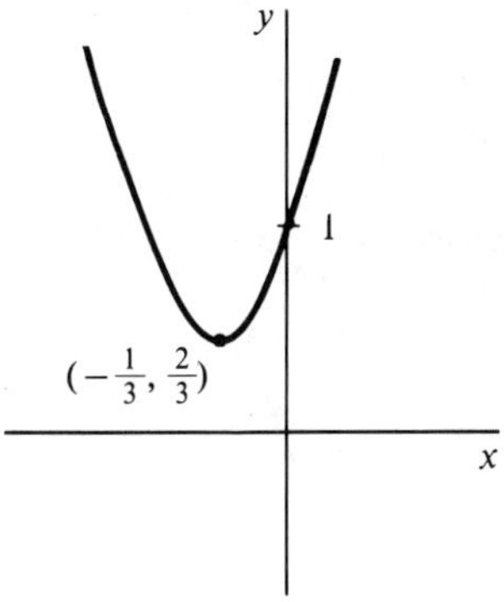

13. D: all x
R: $y \leq \frac{9}{4}$
Zeros $x = -1, 2$
Intercept (0, 2)
Vertex $(\frac{1}{2}, \frac{9}{4})$

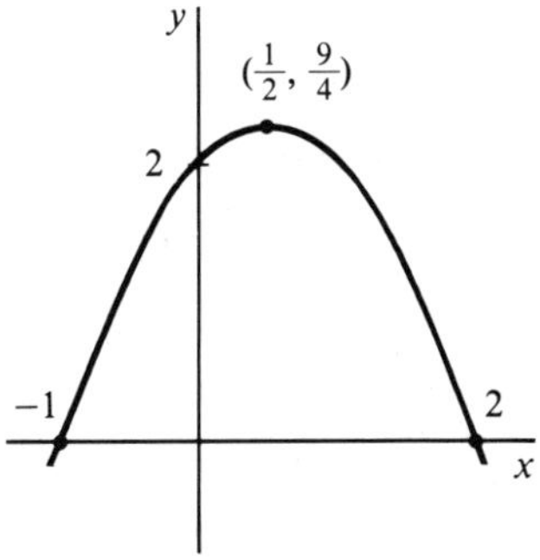

15. D: all x
R: $f(x) \geq -\frac{49}{8}$
Zeros $x = -1, 5/2$
Intercept $(0, -5)$
Vertex $(\frac{3}{4}, -\frac{49}{8})$

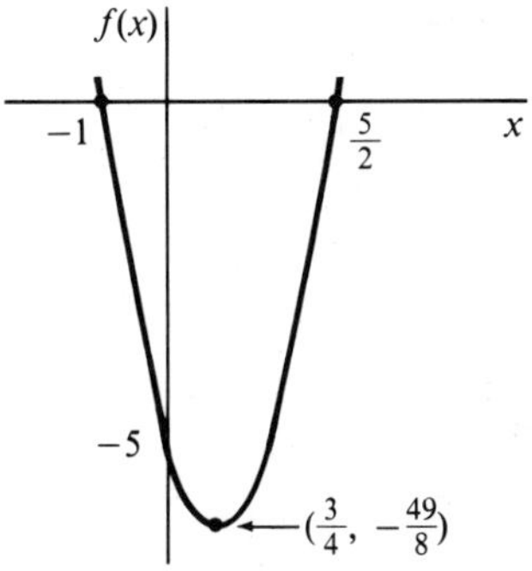

17. D: all x
R: $y \leq \frac{13}{4}$
Zeros $x = (1 \pm \sqrt{13})/2$
Intercept (0, 3)
Vertex $(\frac{1}{2}, \frac{13}{4})$

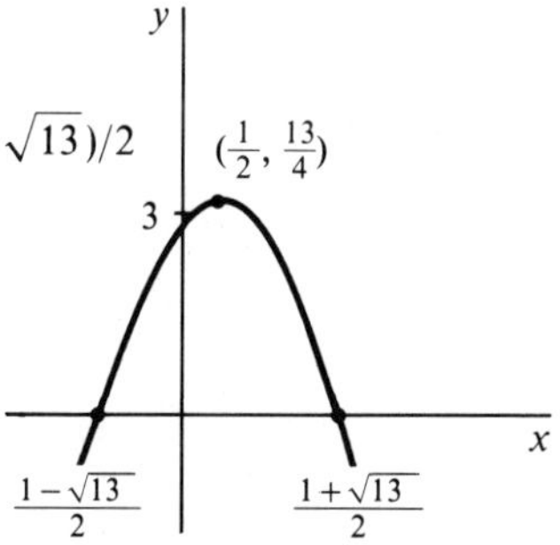

19. D: all x
R: $G(x) \geq \frac{3}{4}$
No zeros
Intercept (0, 1)
Vertex $(-\frac{1}{2}, \frac{3}{4})$

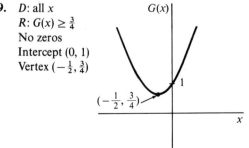

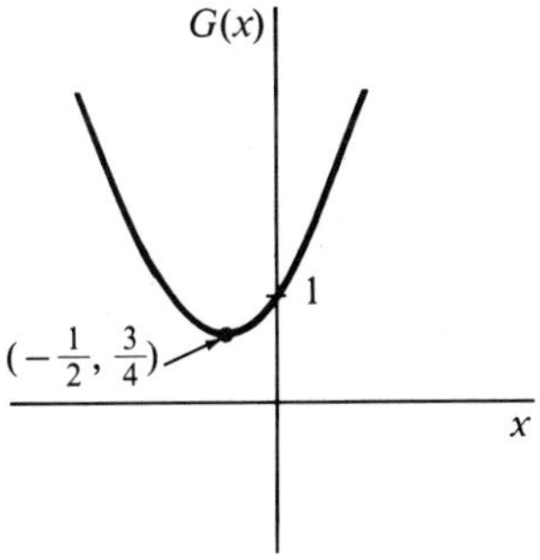

21. $y = x^2 - 2x$ **23.** $y = x^2 - 2x + 1$ **25.** $y = -x^2 - 4x - 3$ **27.** $y = \frac{2}{3}x^2 - \frac{4}{3}x - 2$
29. $y = -\frac{1}{10}x^2 - \frac{3}{10}x + 1$ **31.** Symmetric with respect to the x-axis

33.

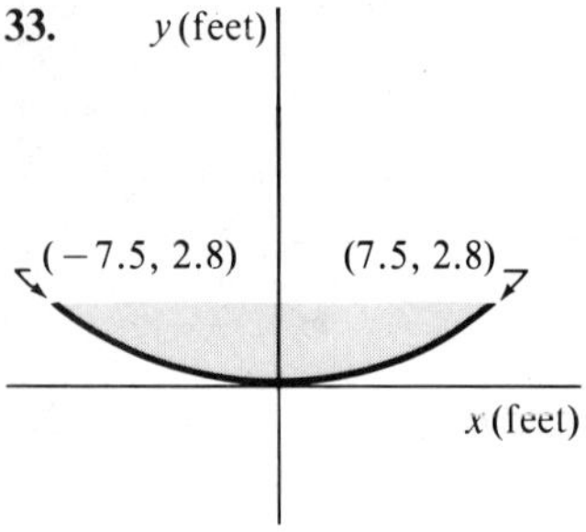

35. **a.**

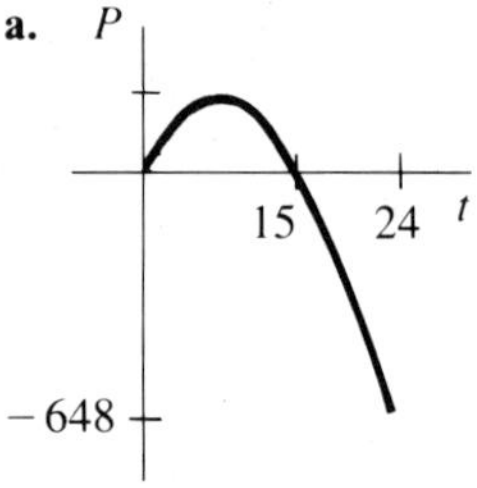

b. $0 < t < 15$
c. $15 < t < 24$
d. 15 hr

37. $v_{max} = 500$ fps at $t = 4$ sec
$v = 0$ at $t = 4 + 2\sqrt{5} \approx 8.47$ sec

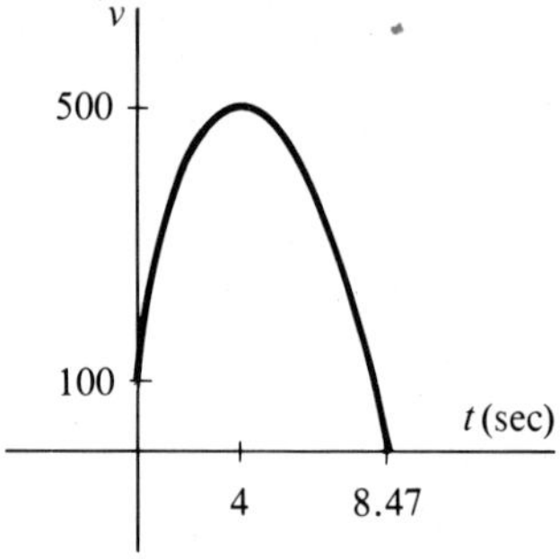

39. It is not.

Section 4.4 (page 136)

1.

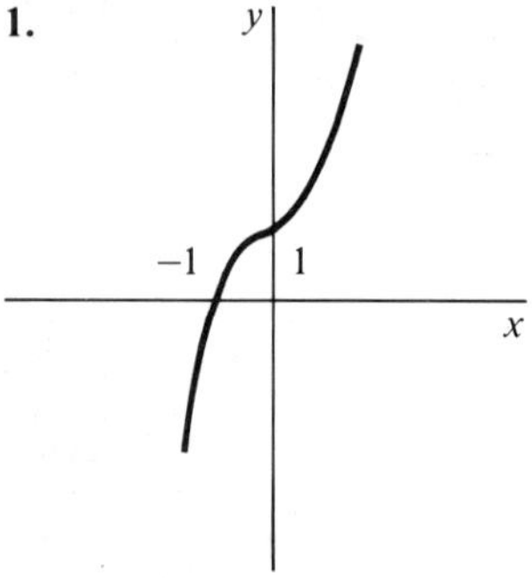

3.

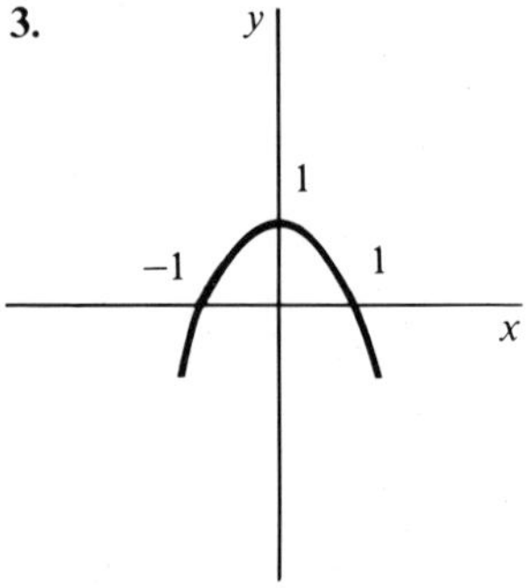

5.

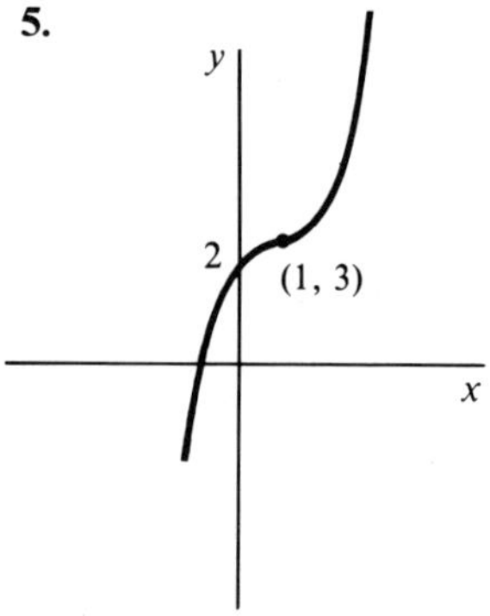

7.

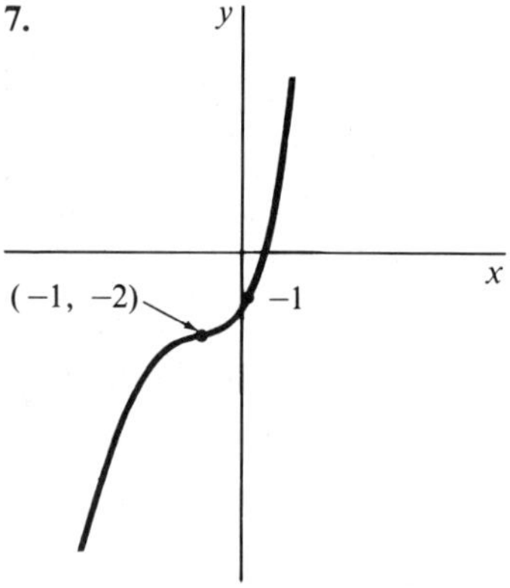

9.

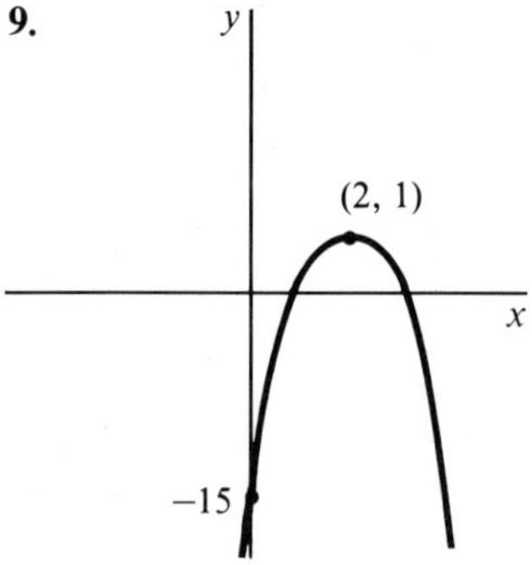

11.

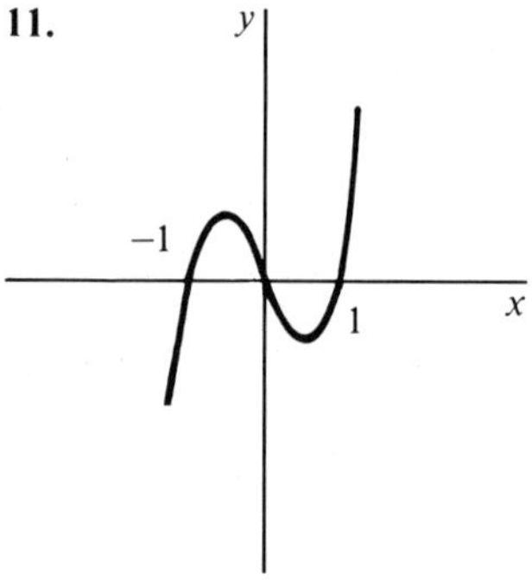

13.

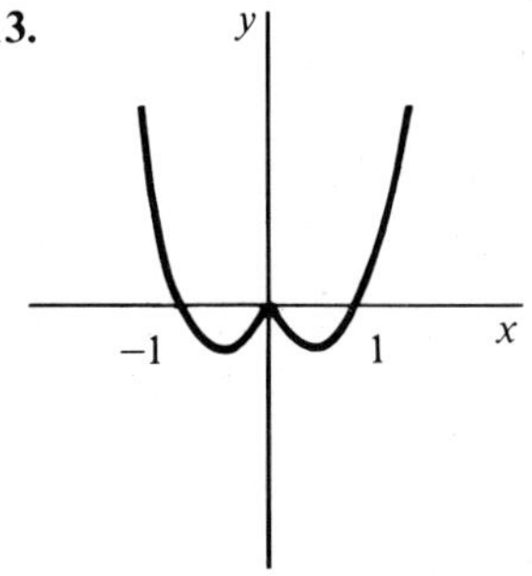

15.

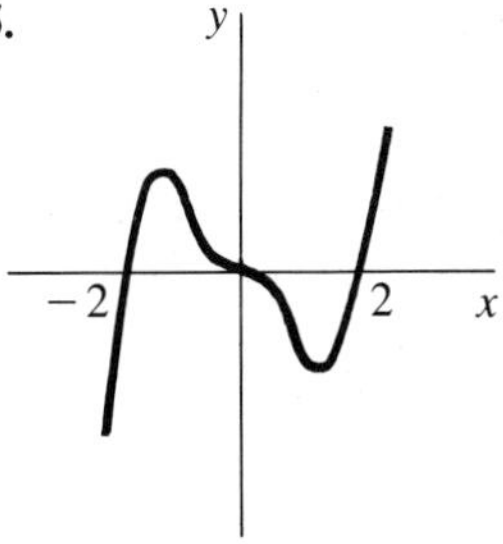

17.

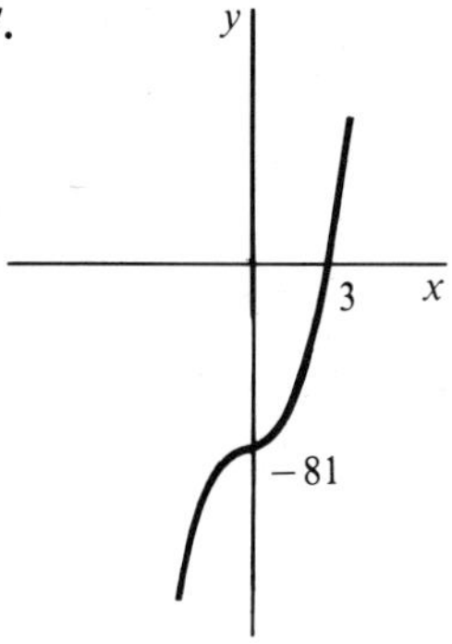

19.

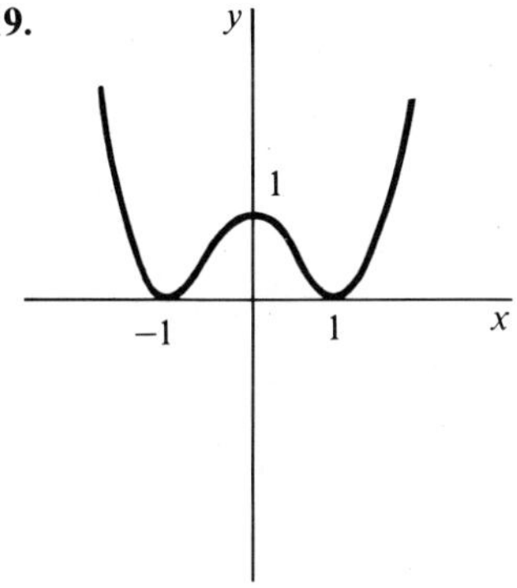

21.

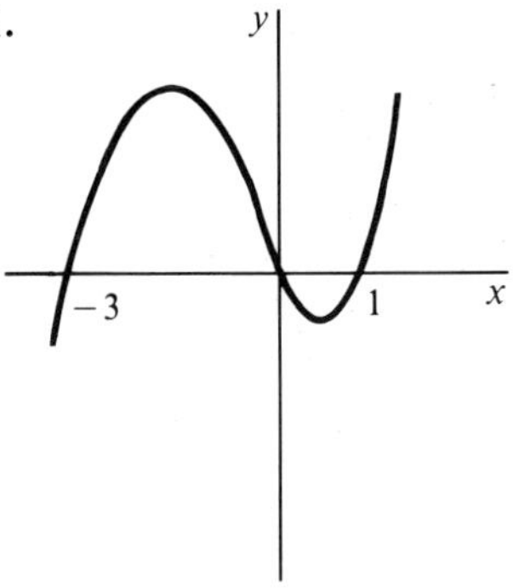

23.

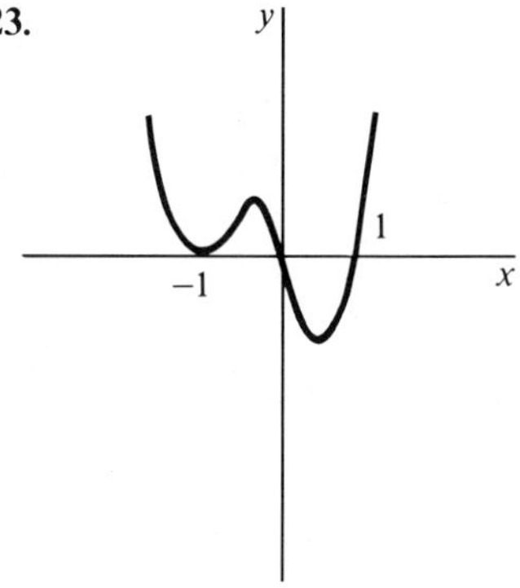

25.

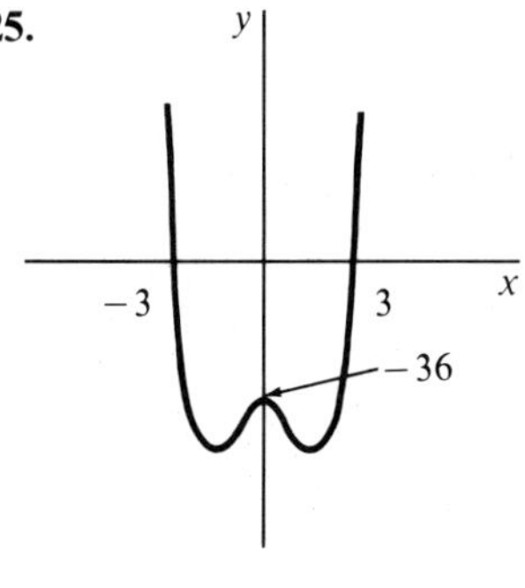

27.

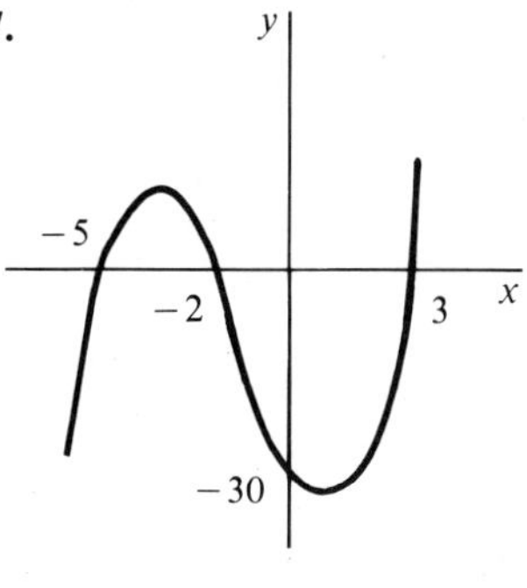

29.

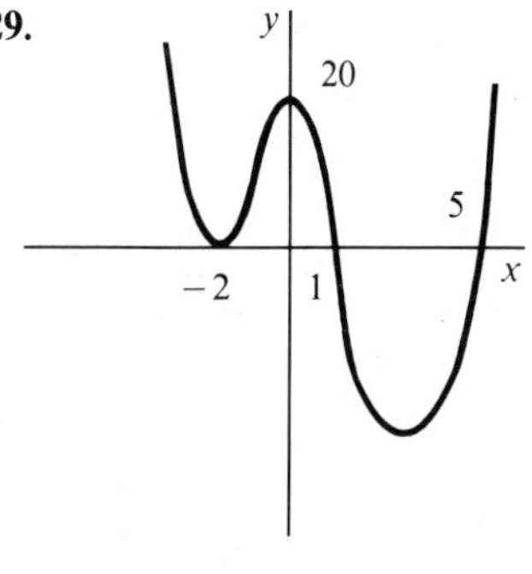

Section 4.5 (page 141)

1.

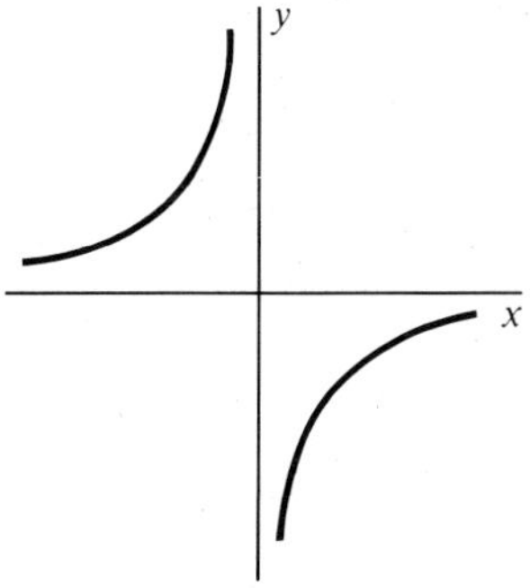

3.

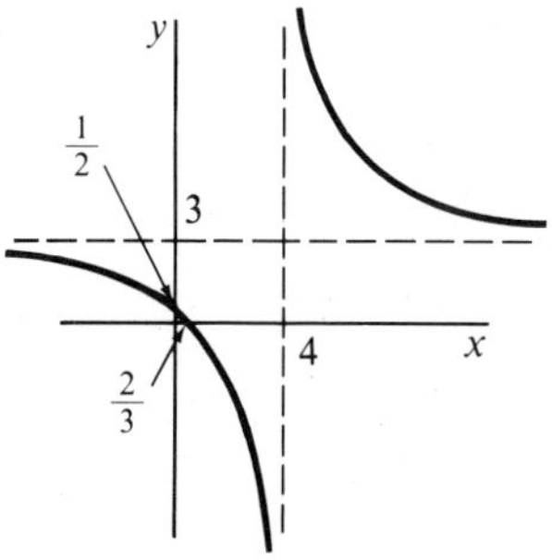

5.

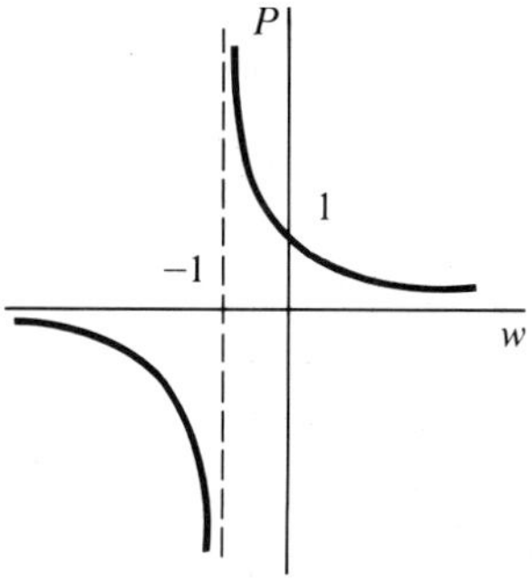

7.

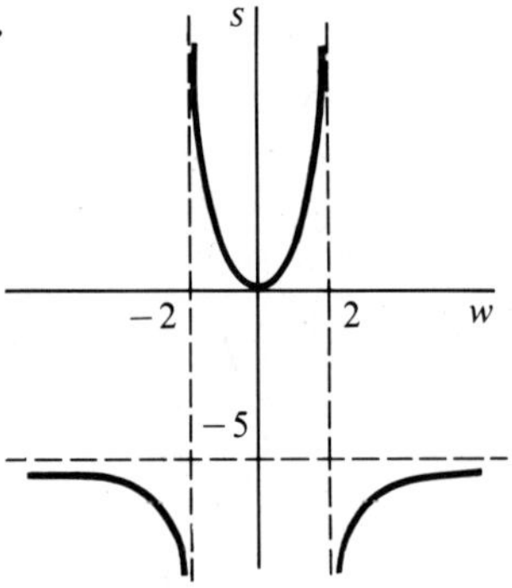

9.

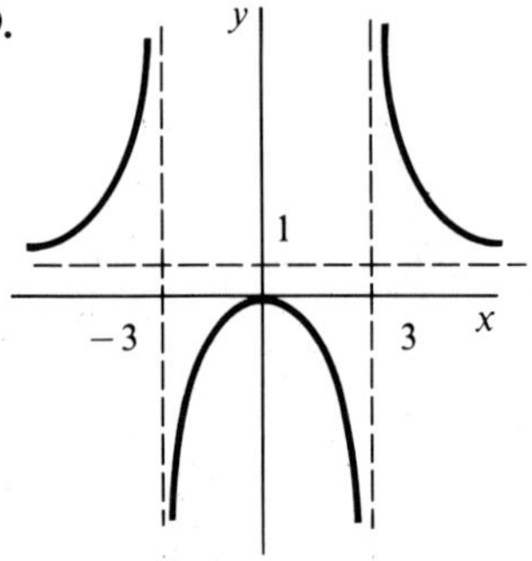

11.

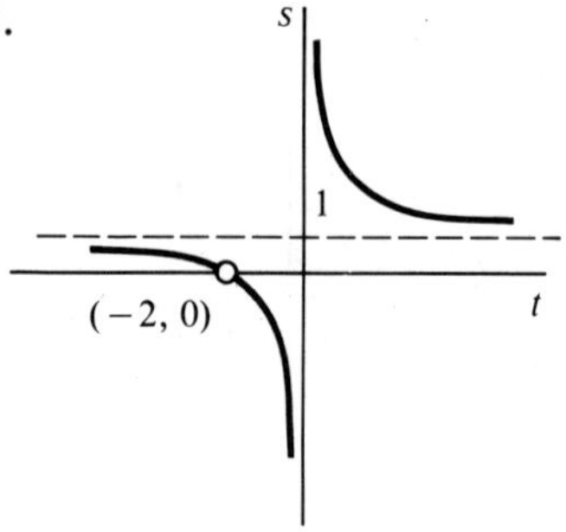

13.

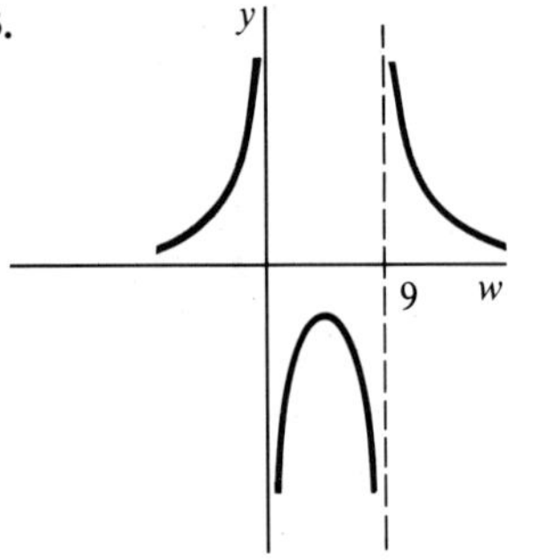

15.

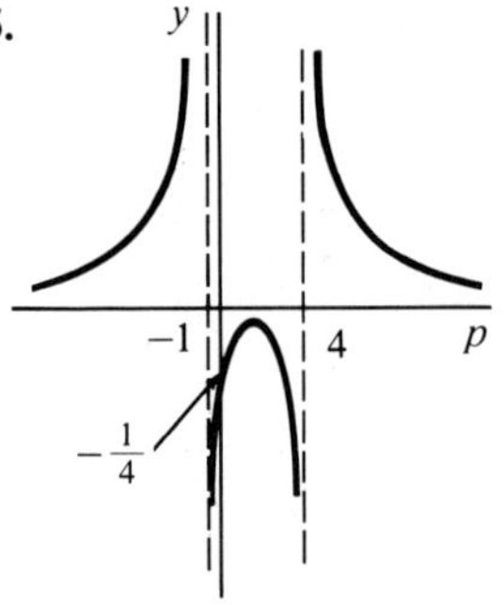

17.

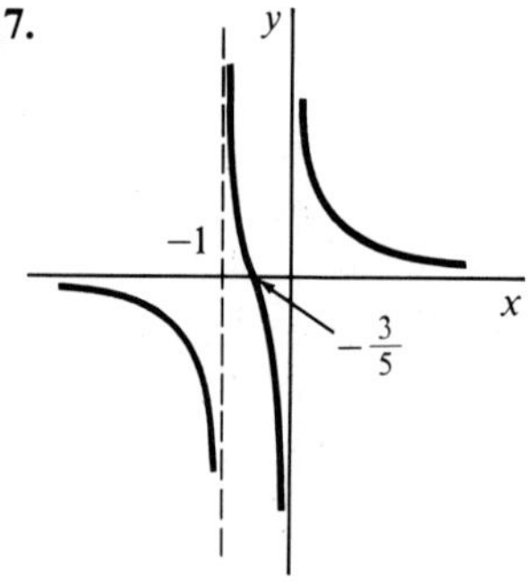

19.

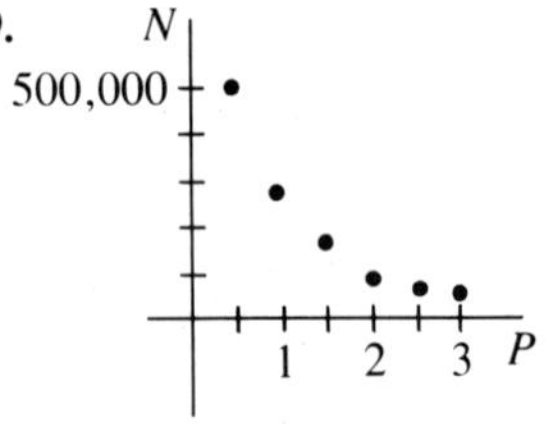

21.

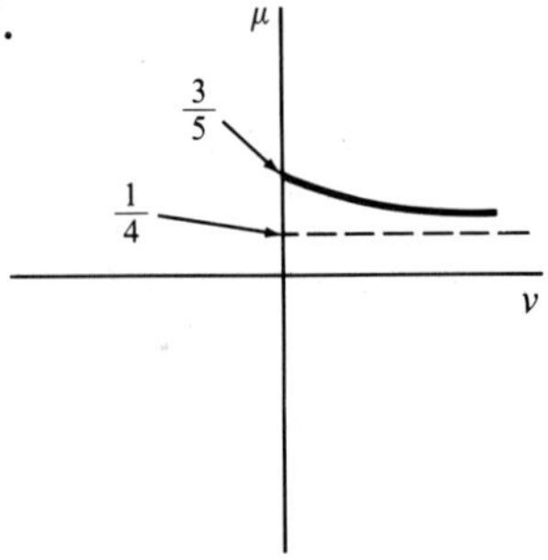

Section 4.6 (page 146)

1.

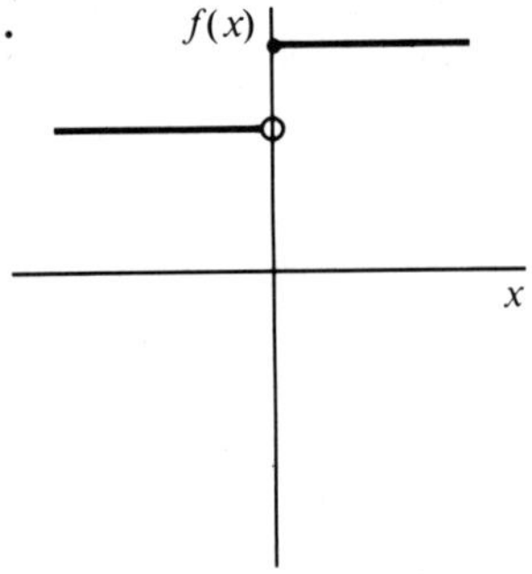

3.

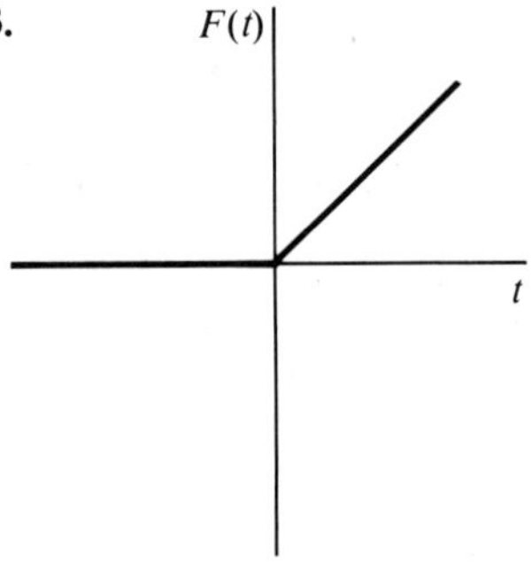

5.

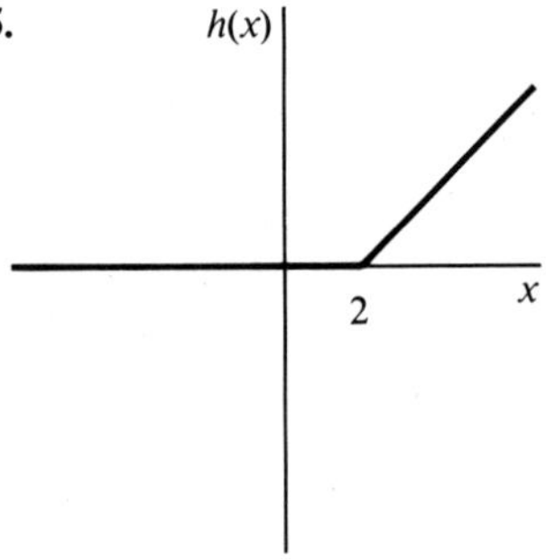

7.

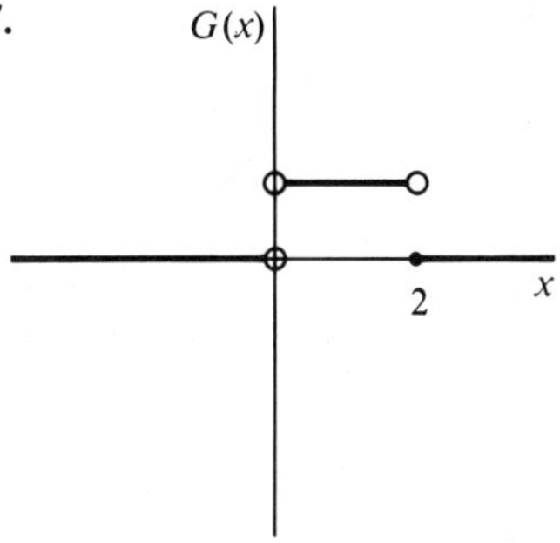

9.

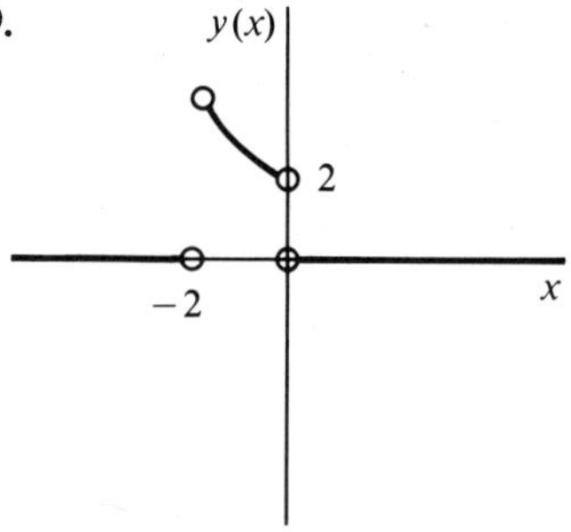

11.

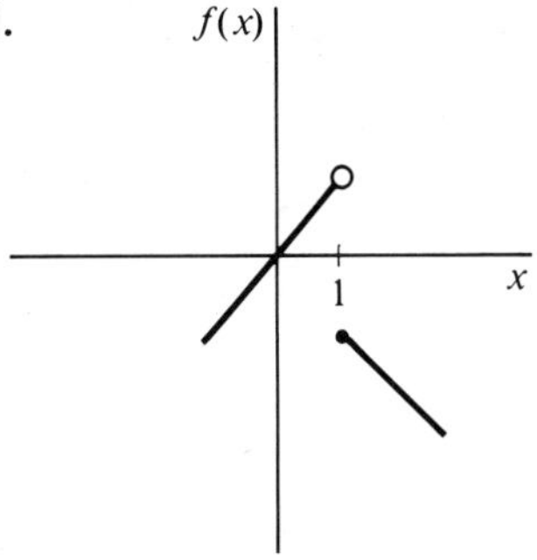

13.

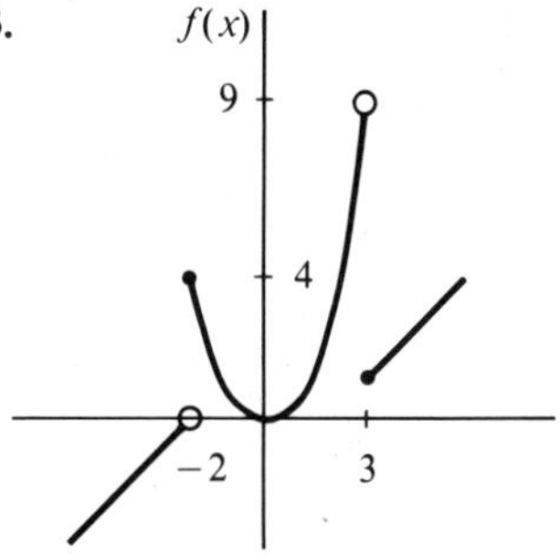

15.

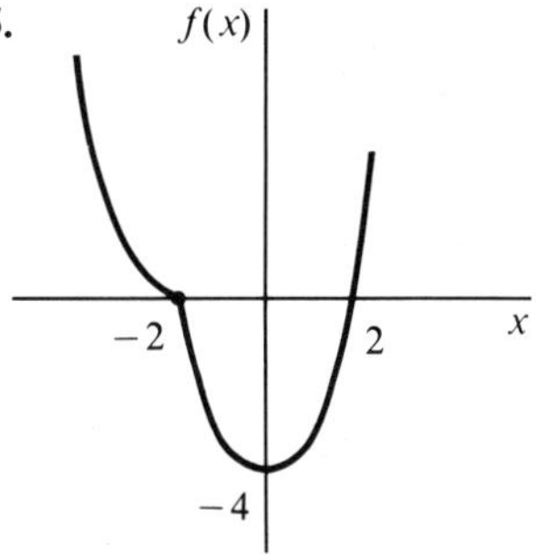

17.

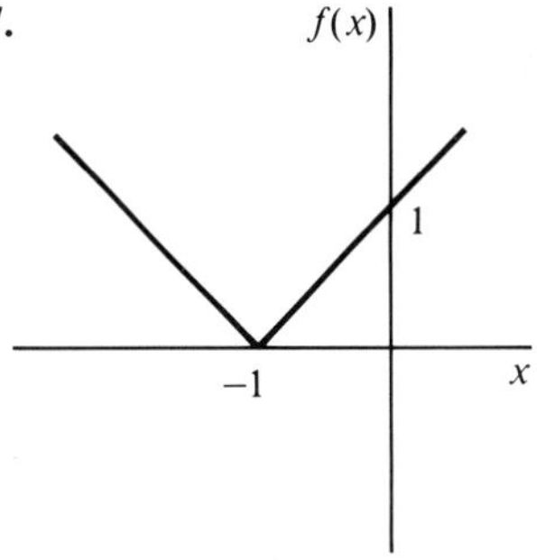

19.

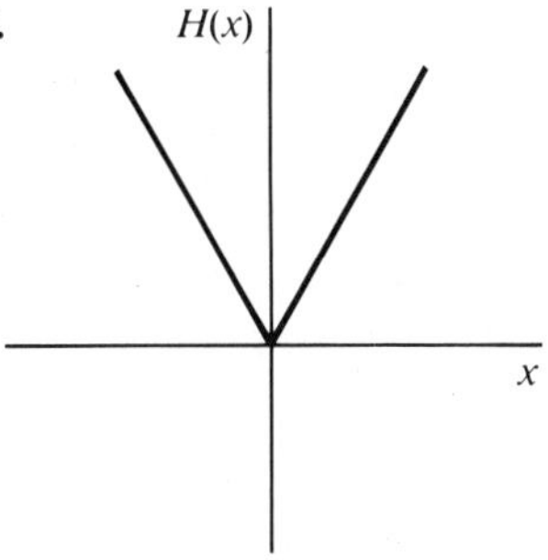

21.

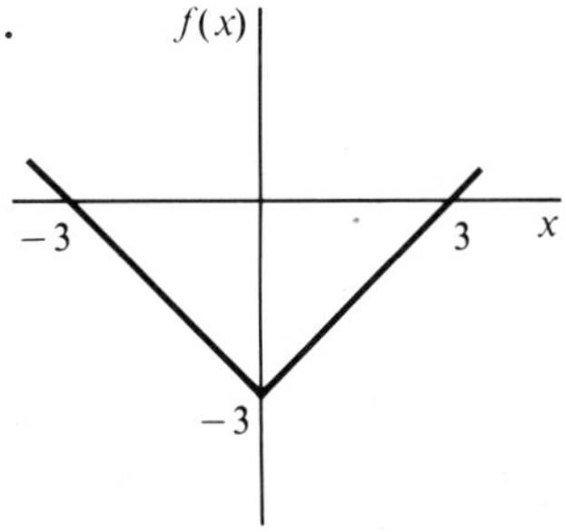

23.

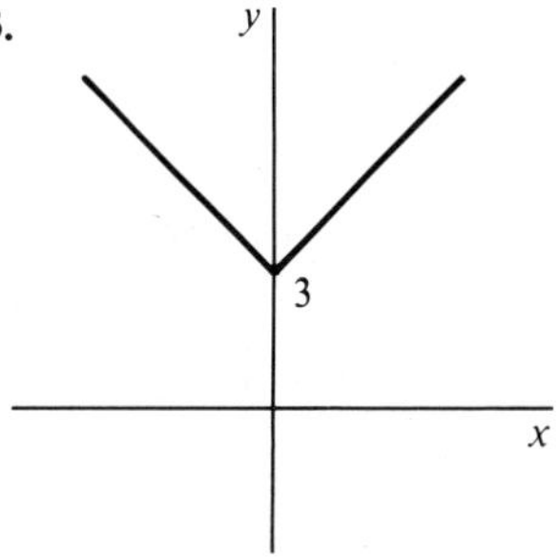

25.

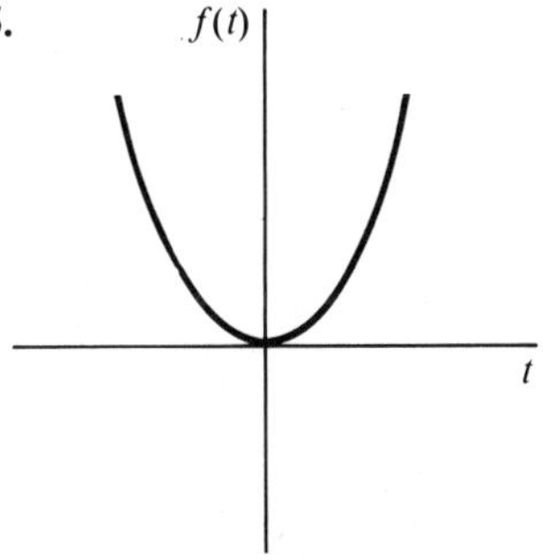

27.

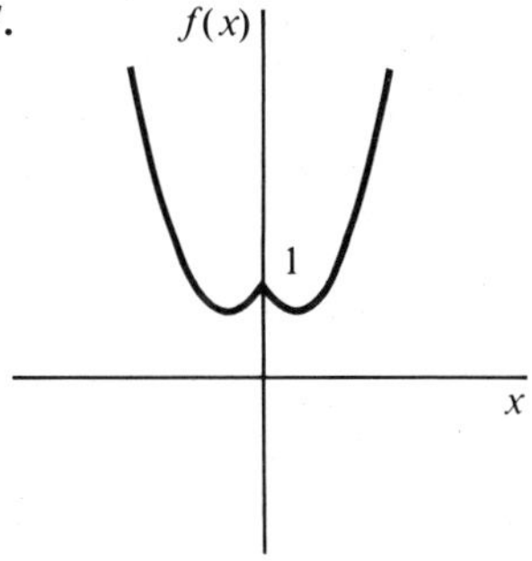

29.

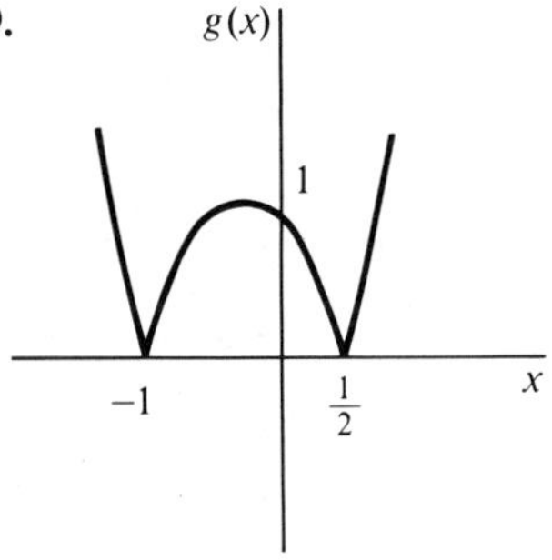

31.

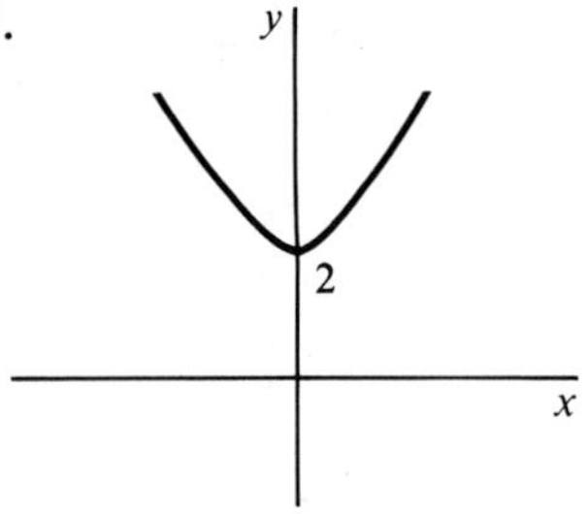

33.

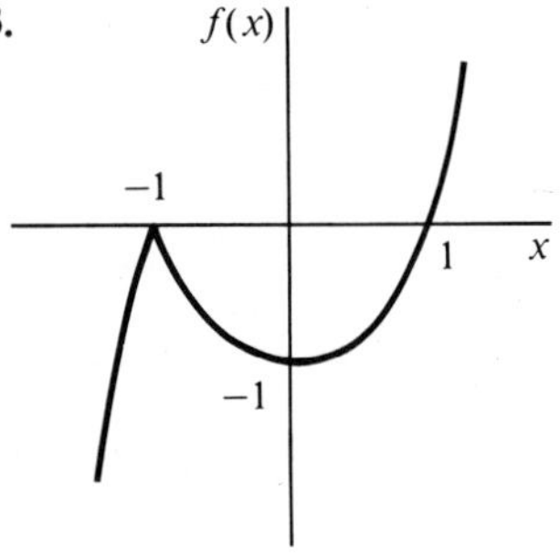

35.

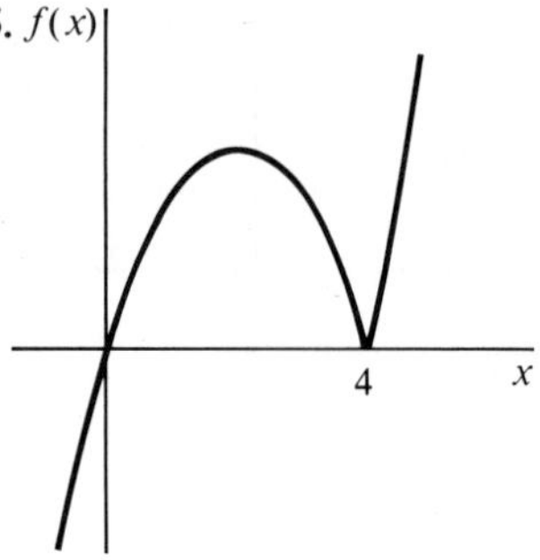

37. Let $x = 2$, $y = -3$.

39.

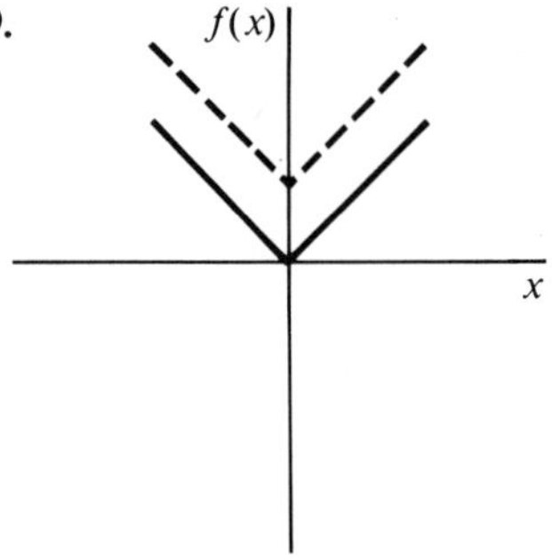

41.

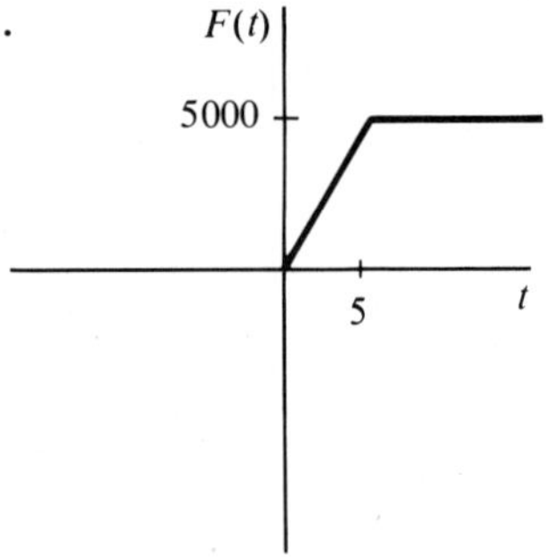

43.

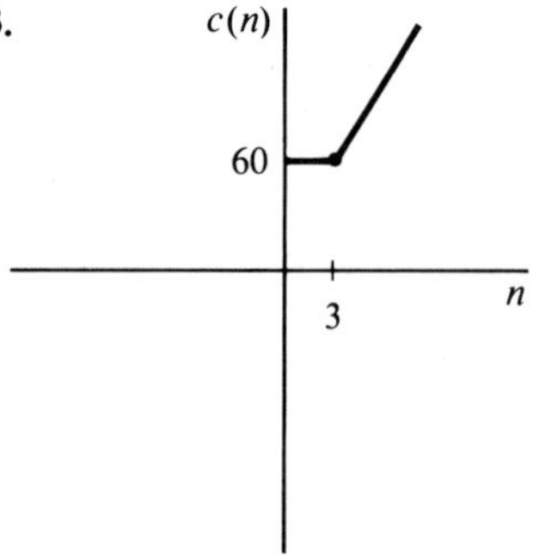

45.

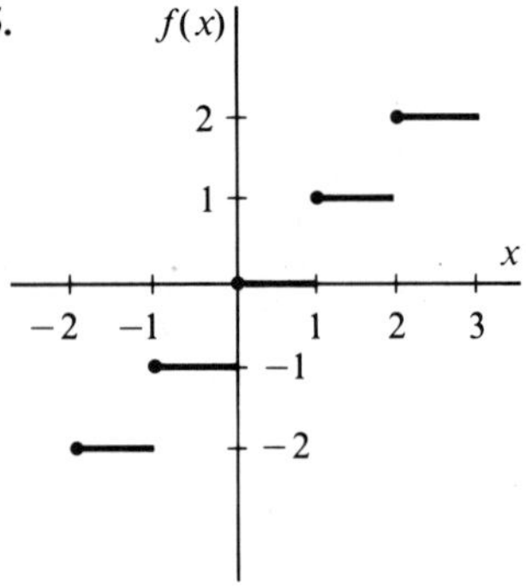

47.

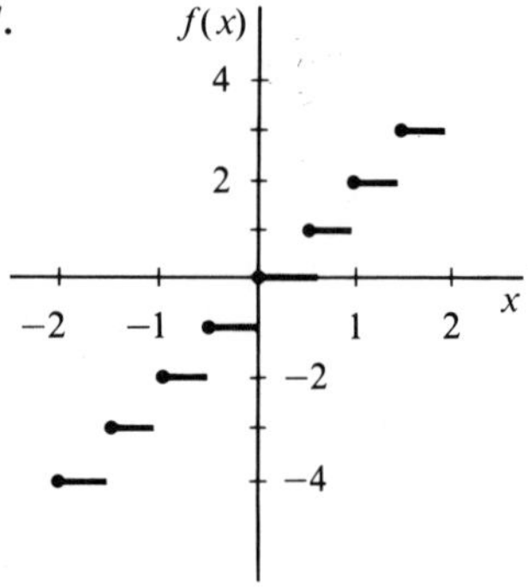

49.

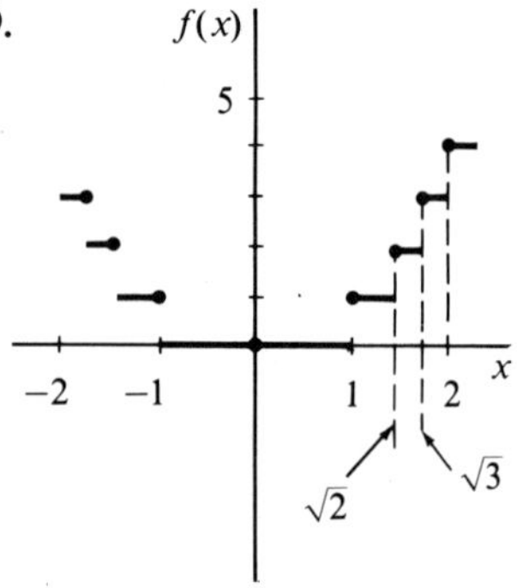

51.

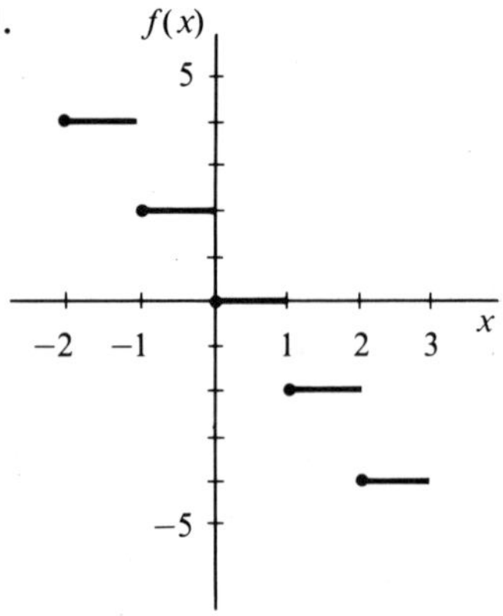

53.

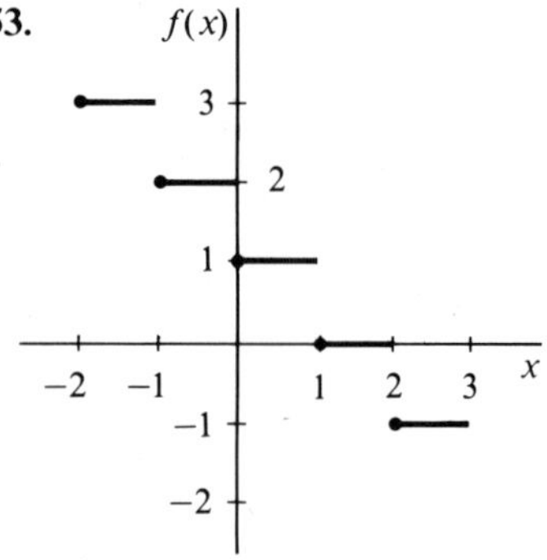

55.

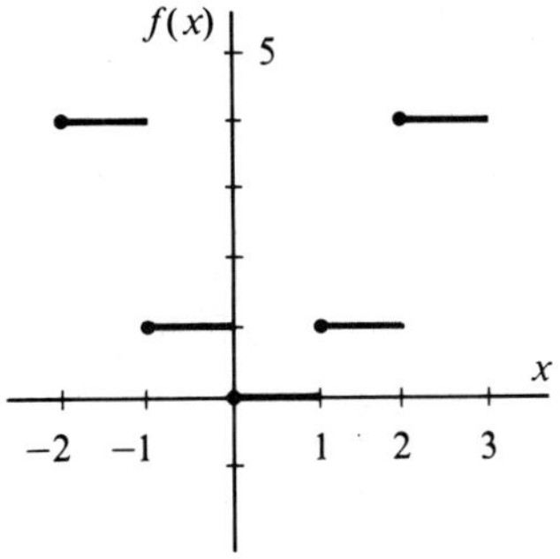

Review Exercises for Chapter 4 (page 148)

1.

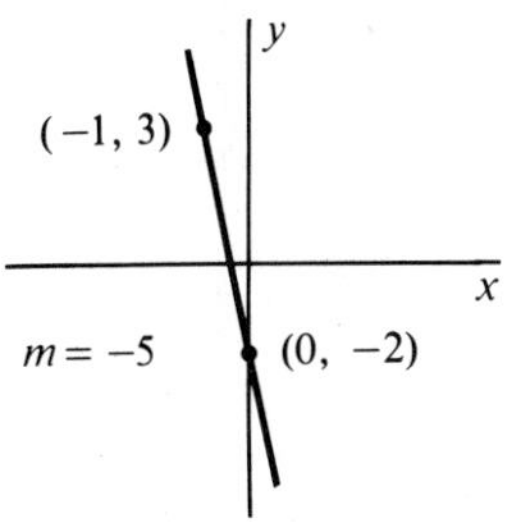

3.

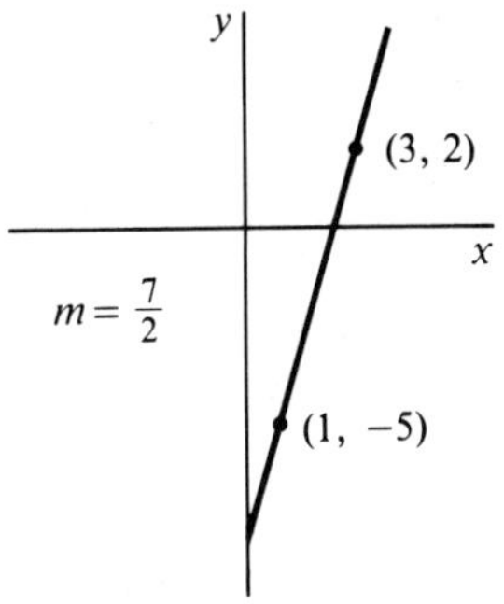

5.

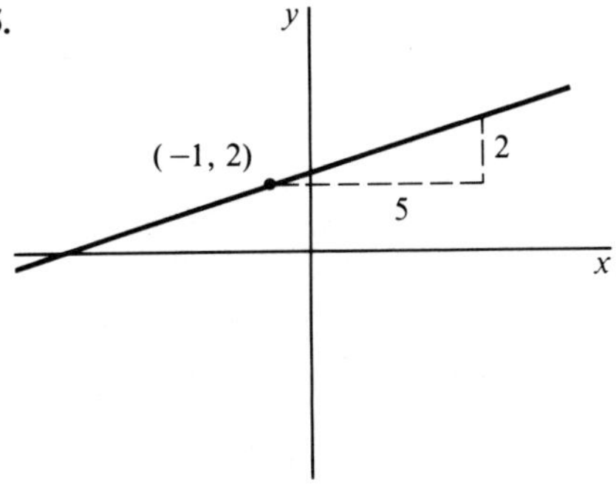

7. $-\frac{6}{5}$

9. $y + 2x - 5 = 0$

11. $4y + x - 15 = 0$

13. slope: $-\frac{2}{7}$
y-intercept: $-\frac{3}{7}$

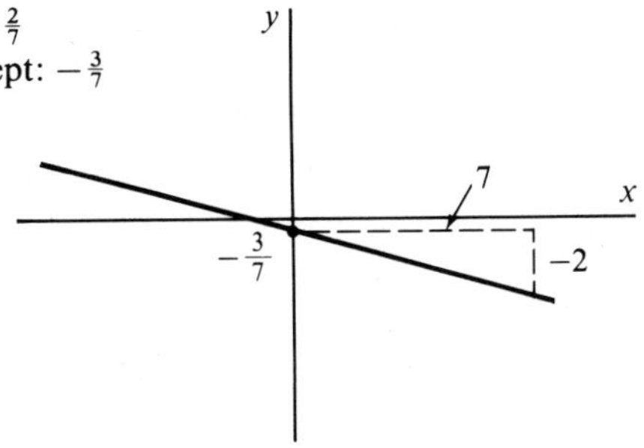

15. slope: $\frac{1}{2}$
y-intercept: $-\frac{1}{6}$

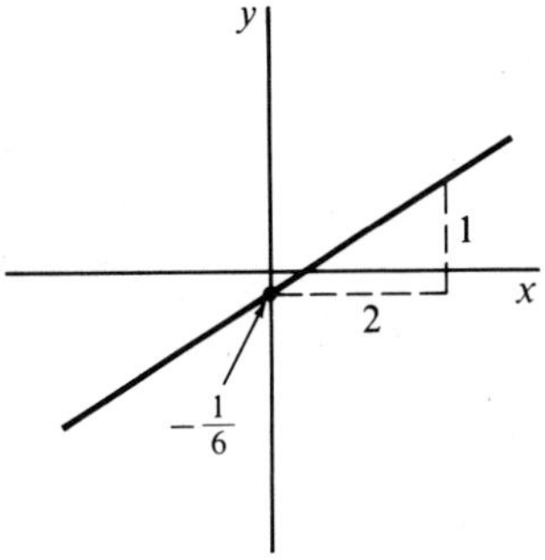

17. $4x + 2y = 5$ **19.** $3x + y = 1$

21.

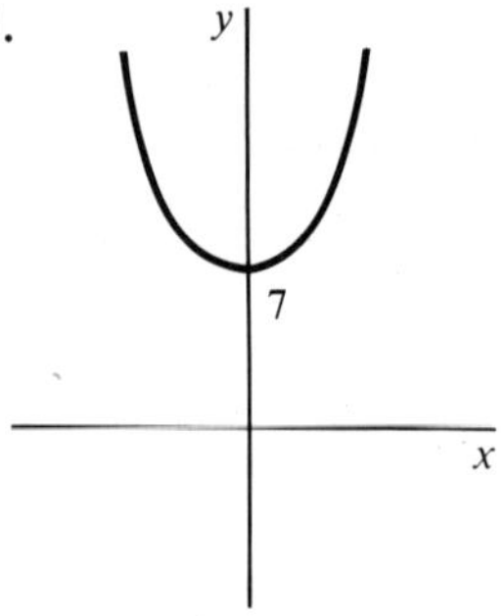

23.

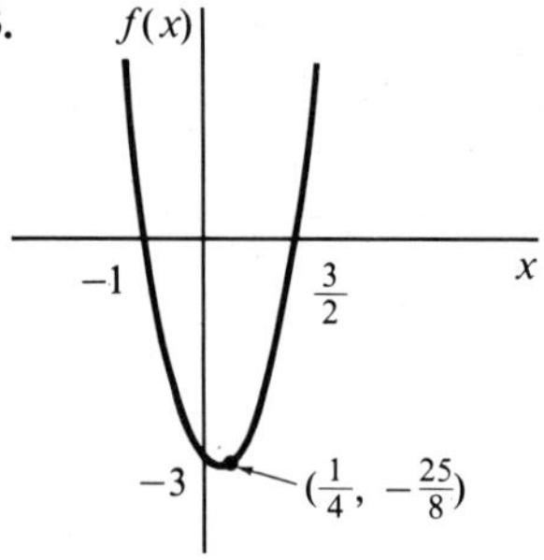

25.

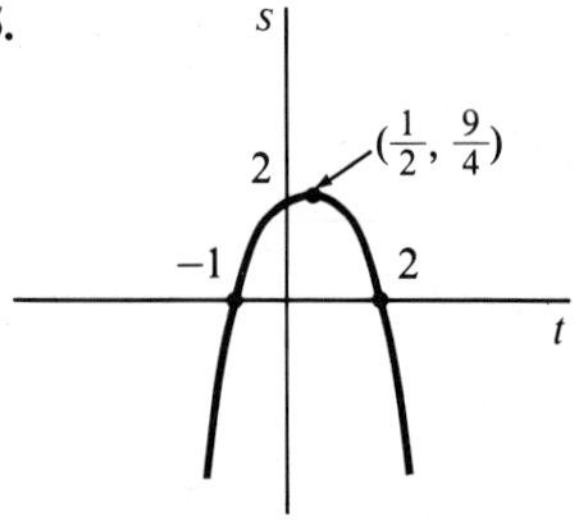

27. $y = -\frac{1}{12}(x + 2)(x - 6)$ **29.** $y = \frac{2}{3}(x + 1)(x + 3)$

31.

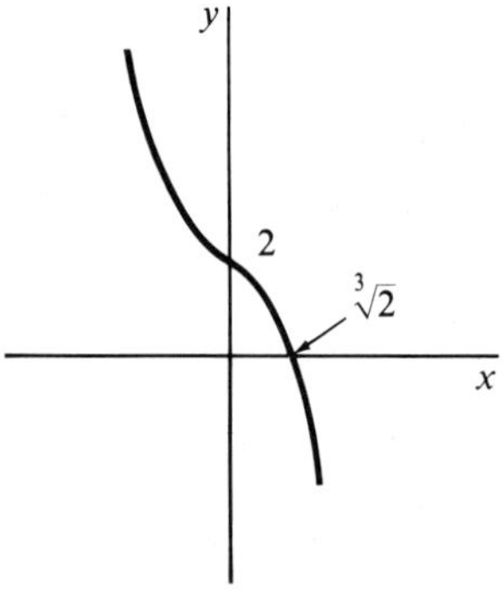

33.

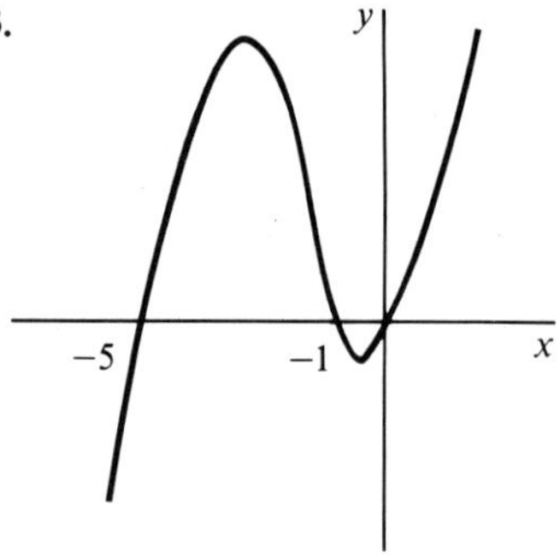

35.

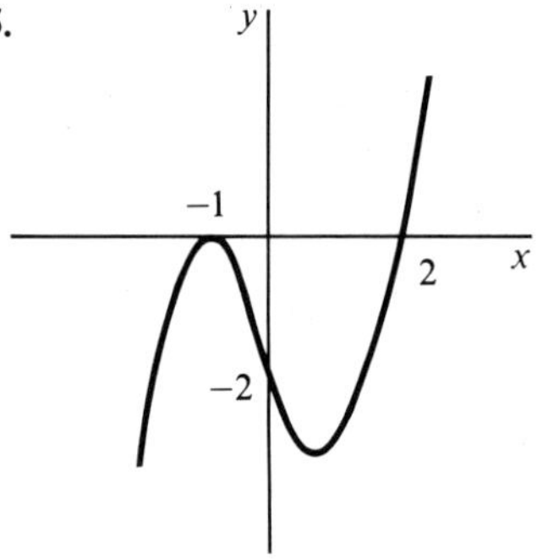

37.

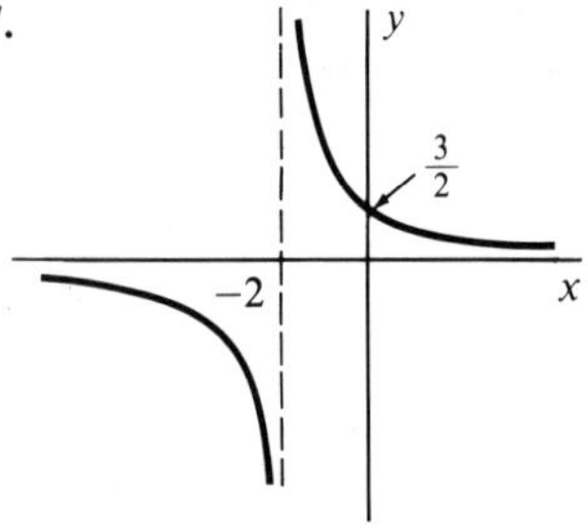

39.

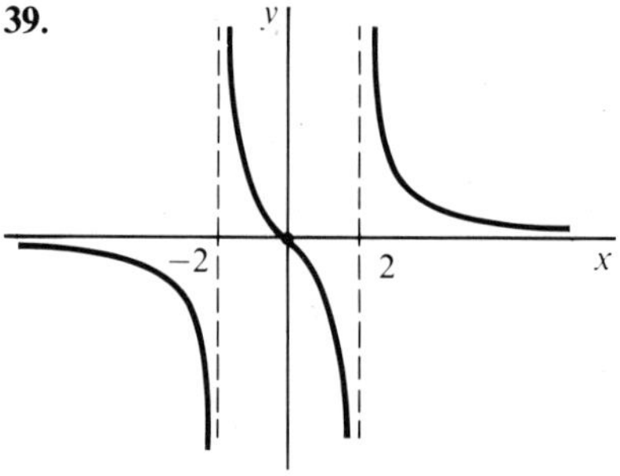

41.

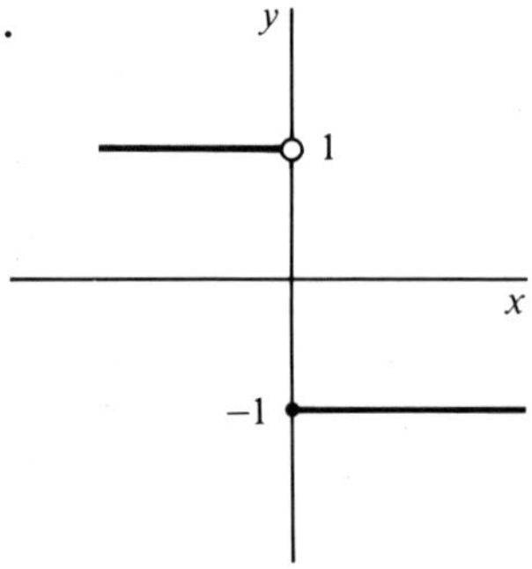

43.

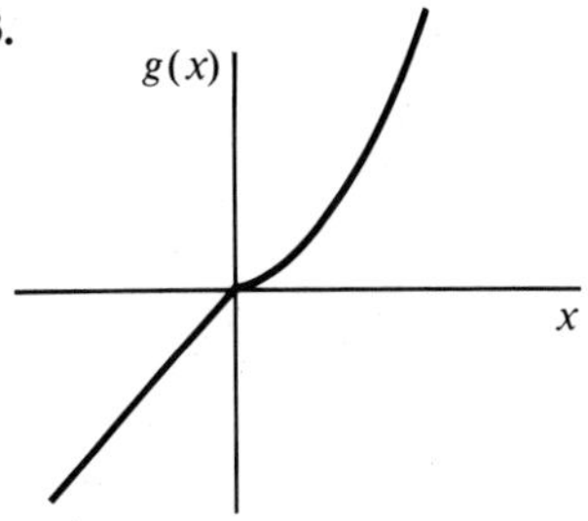

45.

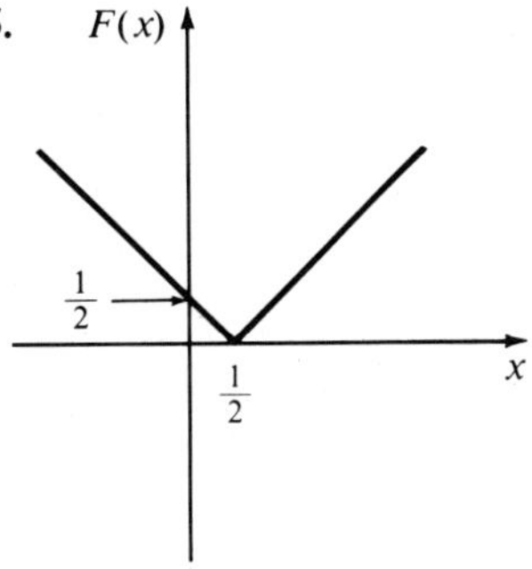

47.

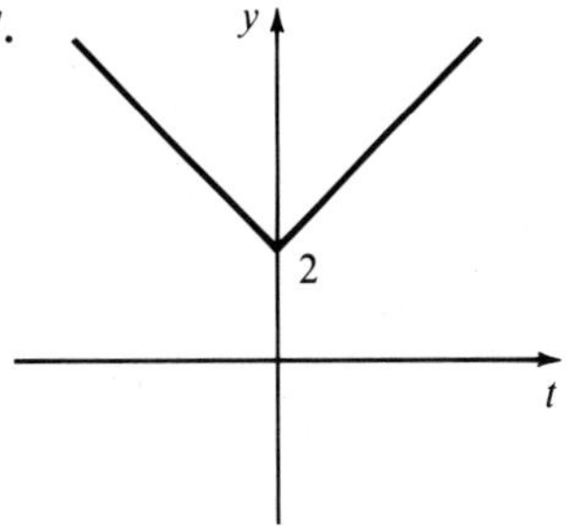

49.

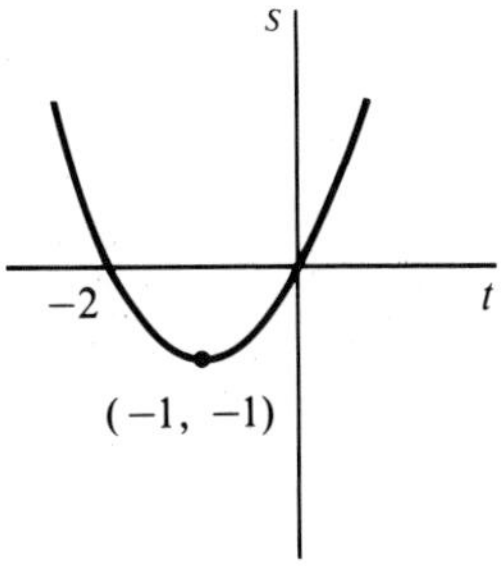

51.

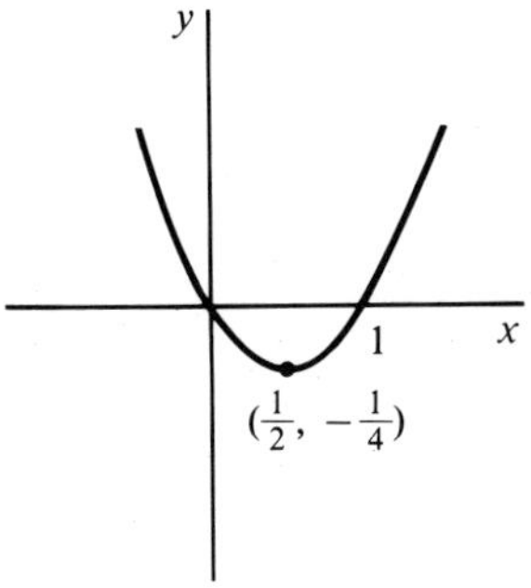

53.

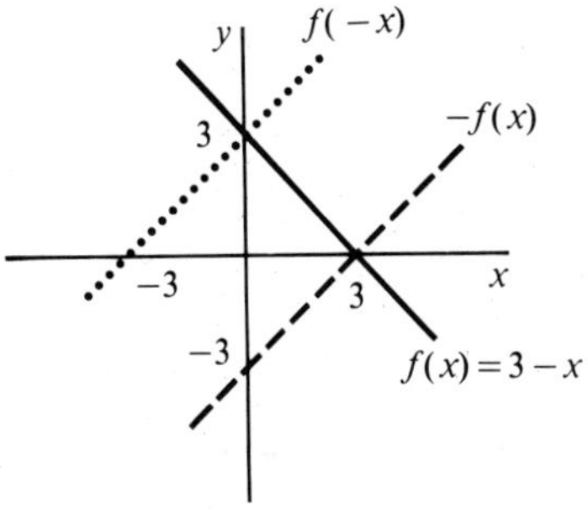

55.

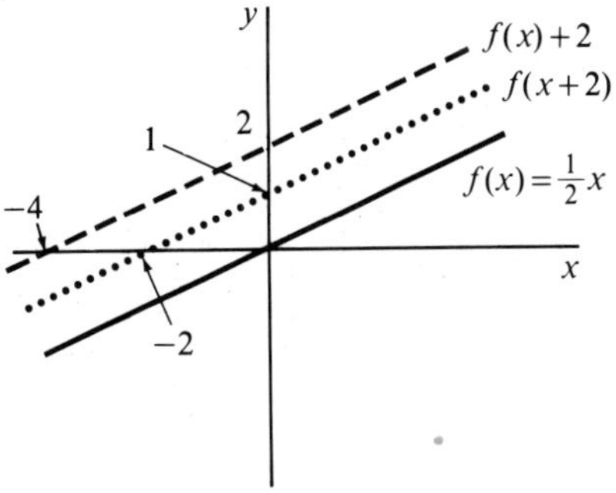

57. $v = \frac{13}{6}t + \frac{98}{6}$ **59.** $\frac{9}{50}$ **61. a.**

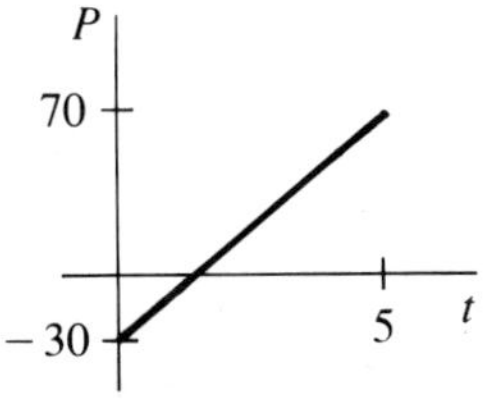

b. After $1\frac{1}{2}$ years

63. **a.** $P = 12n - 5500, 0 \le n \le 850$ **b.**

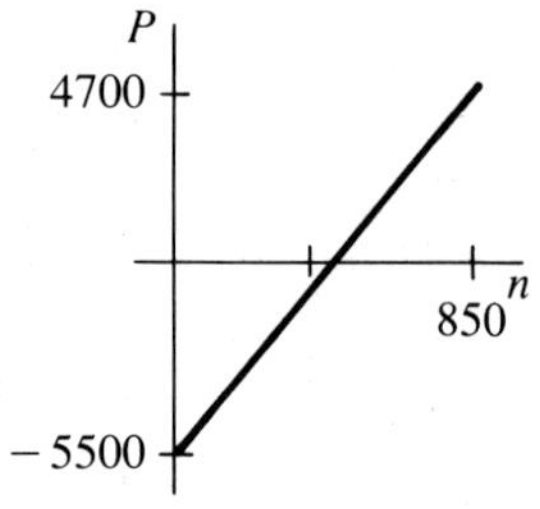

c. 459

65.

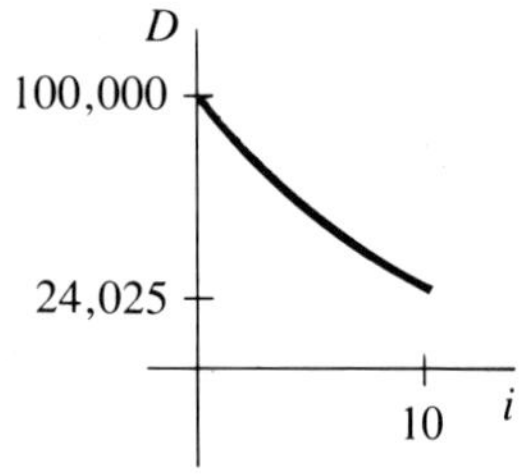

Section 5.1 (page 156)

1. $\frac{4}{9}$ **3.** $-\frac{2}{5}$ **5.** 1 **7.** 0 **9.** -2

11.

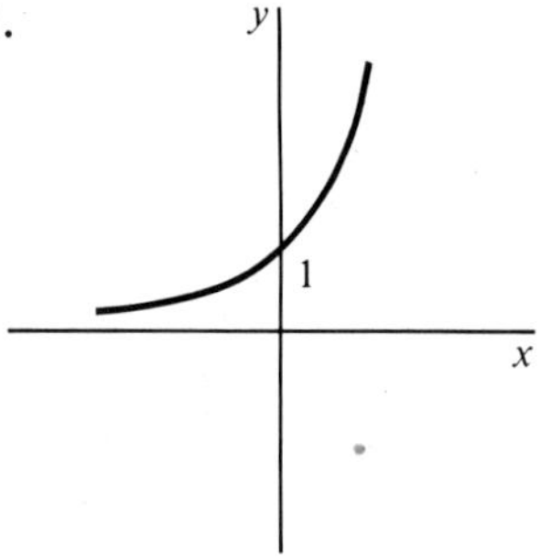

13.

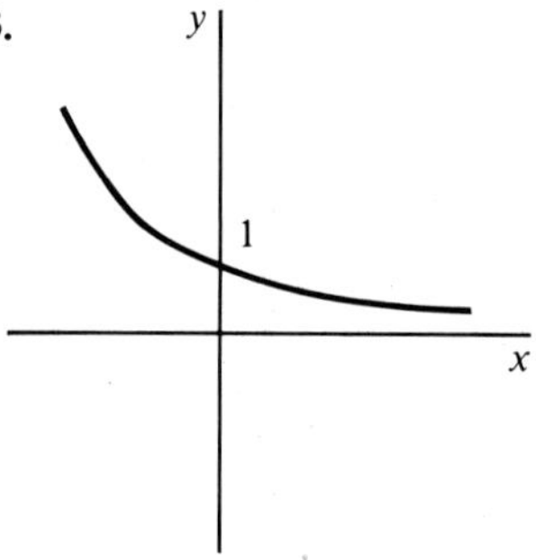

15.

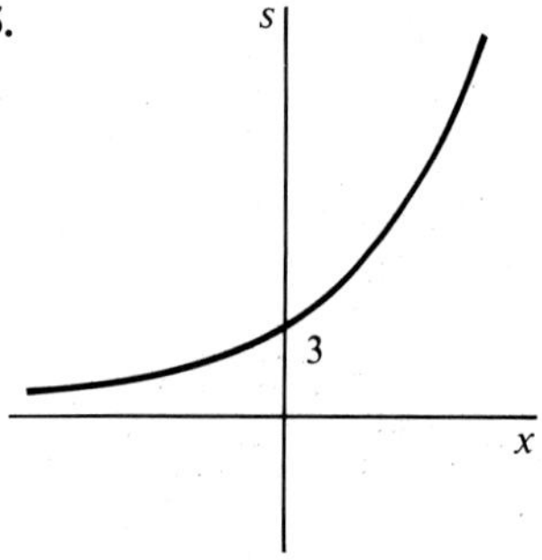

17.

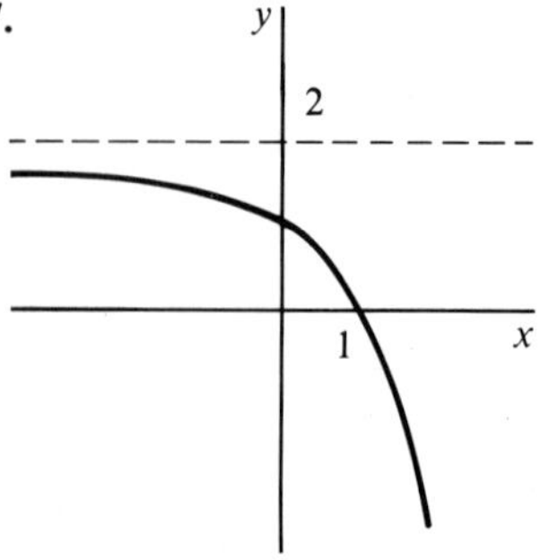

19.

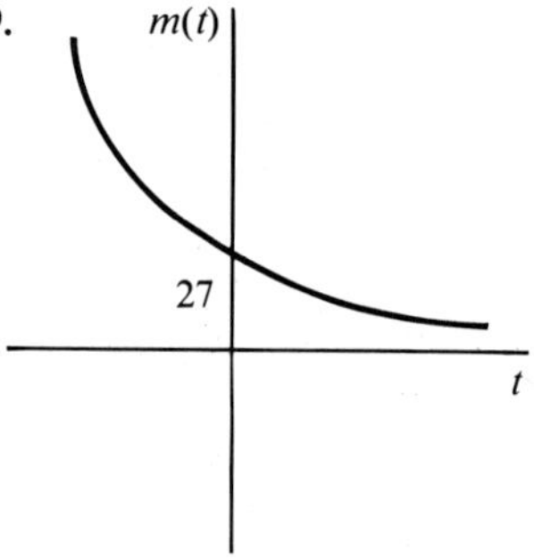

21.

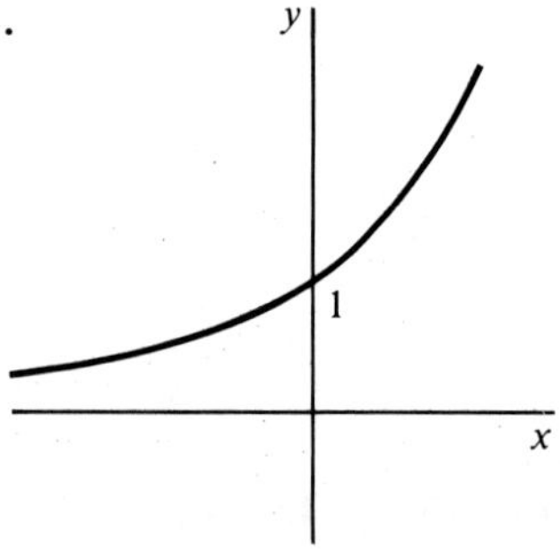

23.

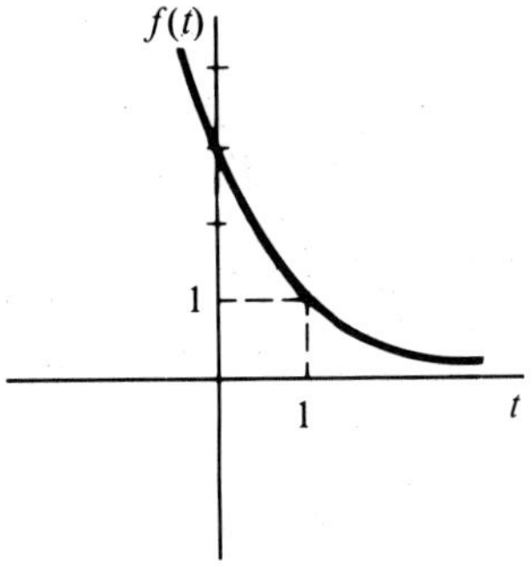

25.

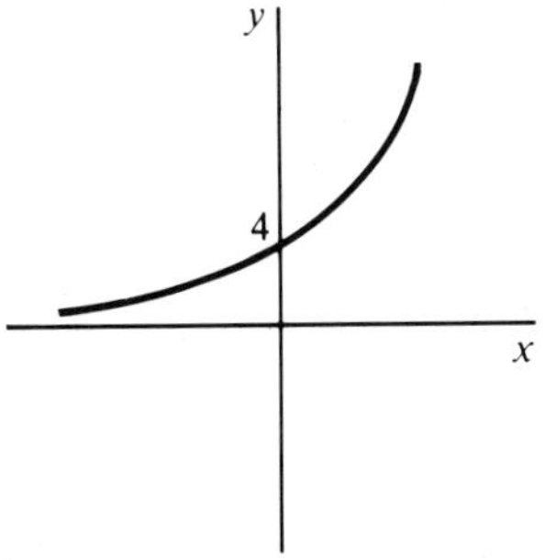

27. **a.** 2.7 **b.** 8.8 **c.** 2.8 **d.** 0.35 **e.** 1.3
29. $y = 1$ for all x
31. Reflection in the x-axis
33. The same curve
35. The same curve shifted 3 units in the negative x direction
37. $m = m_0(\frac{1}{2})^t$
39. $R = R_0(2)^{0.1T}$
41. $S = 500{,}000(0.98)^t$; $S(4) \approx 461{,}000$
43. \$123.09
45. \$1410.60
47. \$632.46

Section 5.2 (page 160)

1.

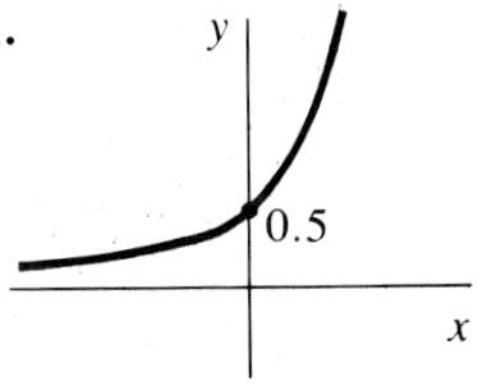

3.

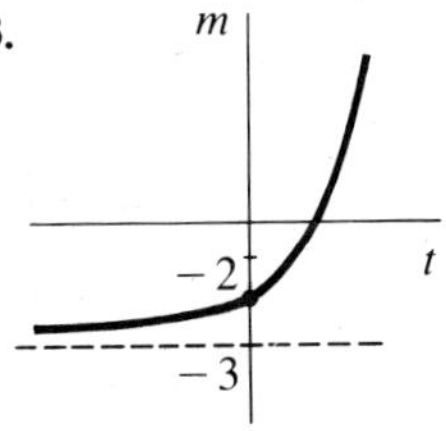

5.

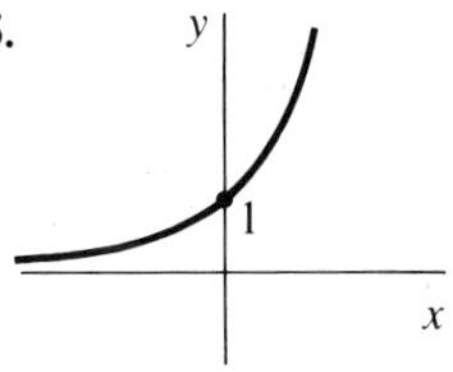

7.

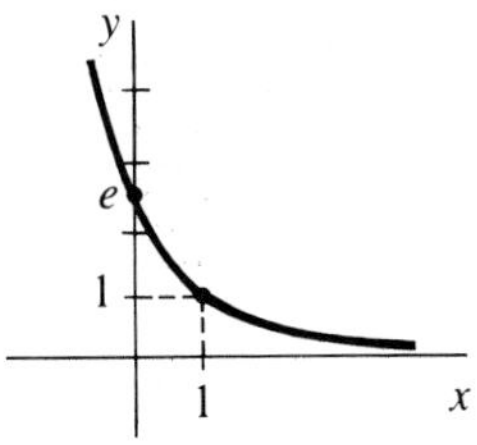

9.

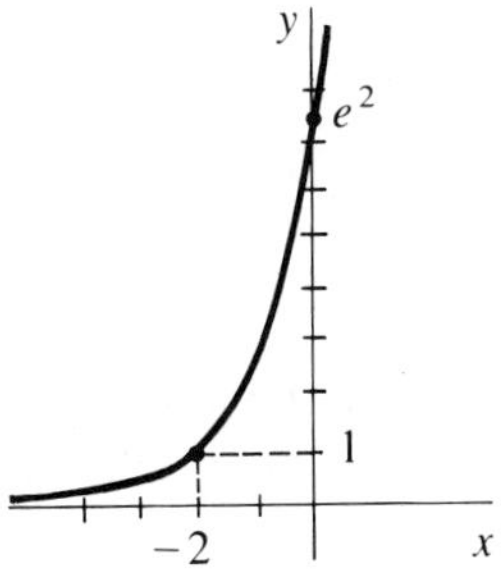

11. 2878.3 m/sec
13. 230.2°
15. 7 days
17. 10.026
19. 22.68

Section 5.3 (page 166)

1. $\log_2 x = 3$
3. $\log_5 M = -3$
5. $\log_7 L = 2$
7. $b = 2$
9. $b = 10$
11. 10,000
13. 10
15. 4
17. 9
19. 2
21. a
23. 8
25. 36
27. 6
29. $-\frac{5}{2}$
31. $-1 < x < 8$
33. $4 \le x \le 8$

35.

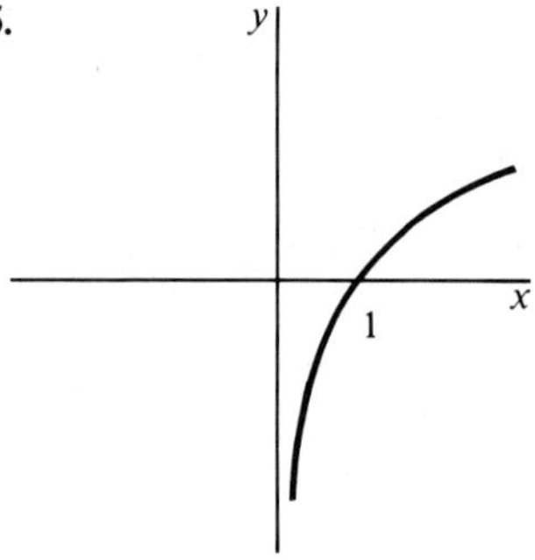

37.

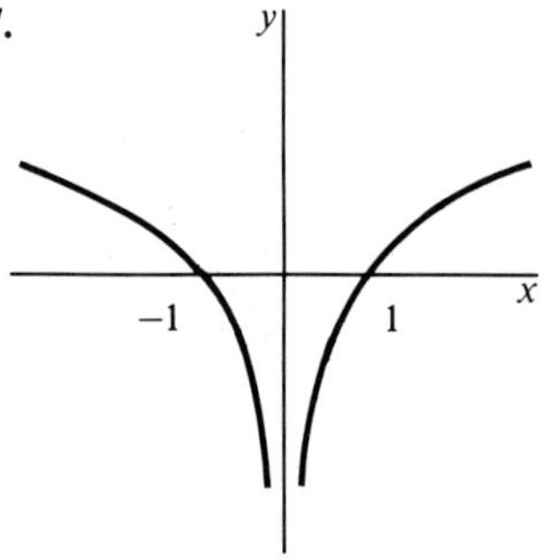

39.

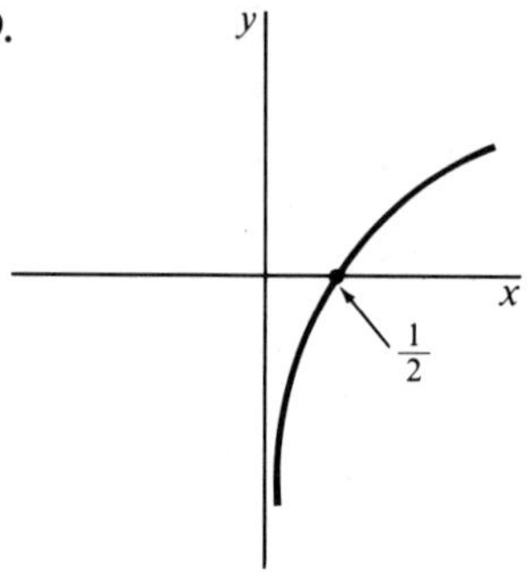

41.

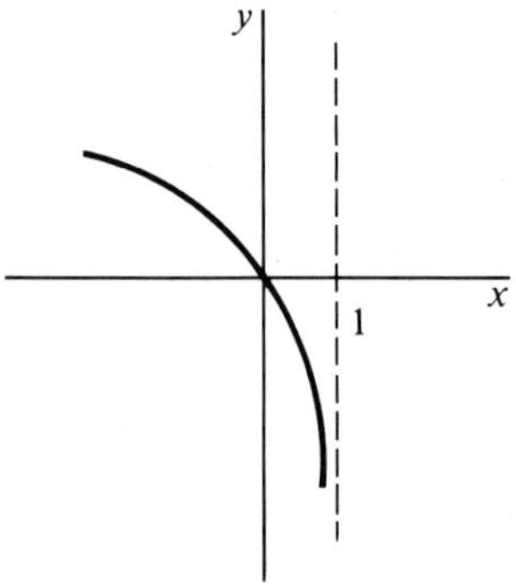

43.

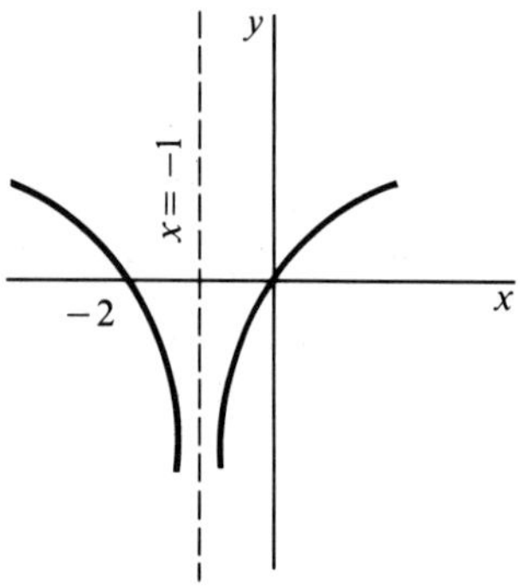

45. Reflection in the x-axis **47.** Two branches: the negative branch is the reflection of $y = \log x$ in the x-axis.
49. Curve moved 3 units in the negative x direction **51.** 2 **53.** 10 **55.** (1, 0)
57. No answer required **59.** Reflections of each other in $y = x$ **61.** -0.3010 **63.** 1
65. -1 **67.** -0.69315 **69.** 3.4657 time units

Section 5.4 (page 168)

1. 9 **3.** $\frac{1}{2}$ **5.** 6 **7.** 24 **9.** 0.1761 **11.** 1.0791 **13.** 1.9542 **15.** 0.3495
17. 3.3801 **19.** -2.8539 **21.** $\log_2 x$ **23.** 0 **25.** $\log \dfrac{5t(t^2-4)^2}{\sqrt{t+3}}$
27. $\log \dfrac{u^3}{(u+1)^2(u-1)^5}$ **31.** The same for $x > 0$. For $x < 0$, $\log x^2$ is defined, $2 \log x$ is not.
33. Both are -2. **35.** **a.** Multiply each ordinate value by p. **b.** Move curve up $\log p$ units.
c. Move curve p units to the left. **d.** Move curve down $\log p$ units.

Section 5.5 (page 171)

1. -1.553 **3.** $x = 0, x = \log 2 \approx 0.301$ **5.** 0.5850 **7.** 13.97 **9.** $x > \ln 2.5/\ln 2 \approx 1.32$
11. $x = 10$ **13.** $x = 1, 10^4$ **15.** $x = 1$, $x = 10^{\sqrt{3}} \approx 53.96$, $x = 10^{-\sqrt{3}} \approx 0.0185$ **17.** $x = 5$ **19.** $x = 2 + \sqrt{5} \approx 4.236$
21. $x = 6$ **23.** $x = \sqrt{6}$ **25.** $x > \frac{1}{9}$ **27.** $x = \ln(2 + \sqrt{3}) \approx 1.317$, $x = \ln(2 - \sqrt{3}) \approx -1.317$
29. The logarithm is a 1-to-1 function. **31.** $k = 0.02476$ **33.** 173.3 days **35.** 52.5 hr

Review Exercises for Chapter 5 (page 171)

1. -8.55 **3.** $4, -1$ **5.** -0.465 **7.** 1000 **9.** 4 **11.** 2 **13.** 1.188

15.

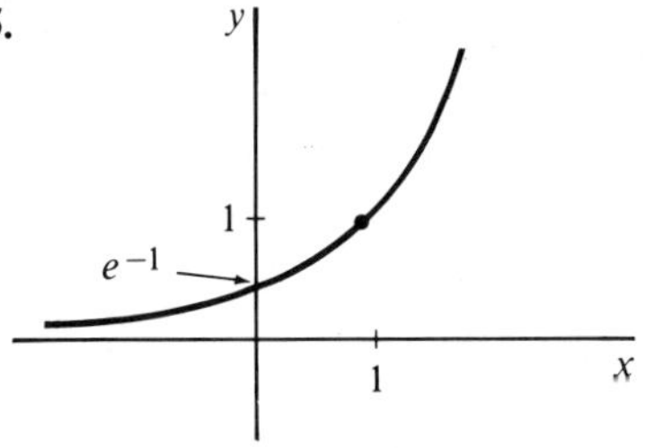

17.

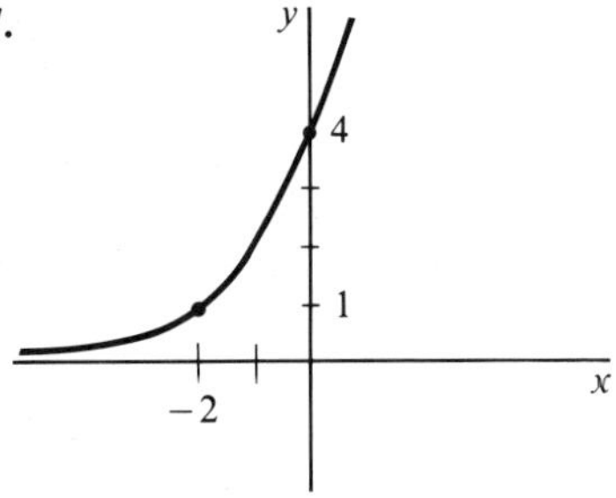

19.

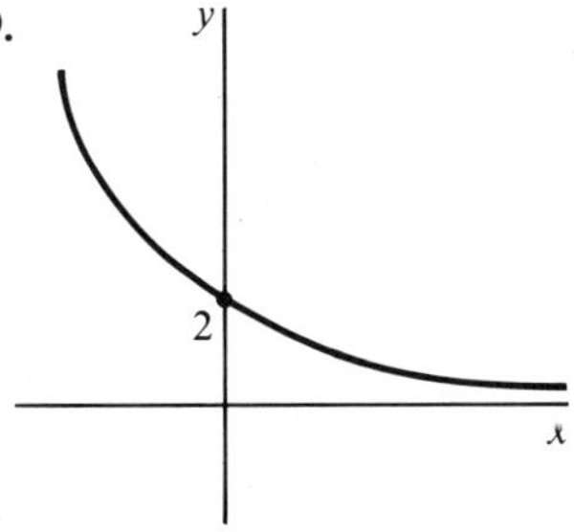

21.

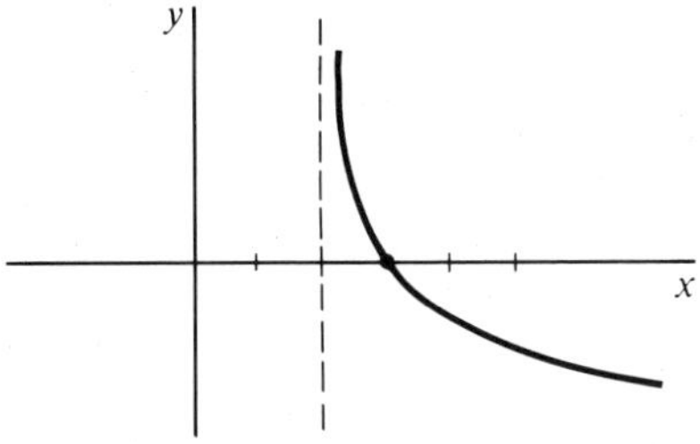

23.

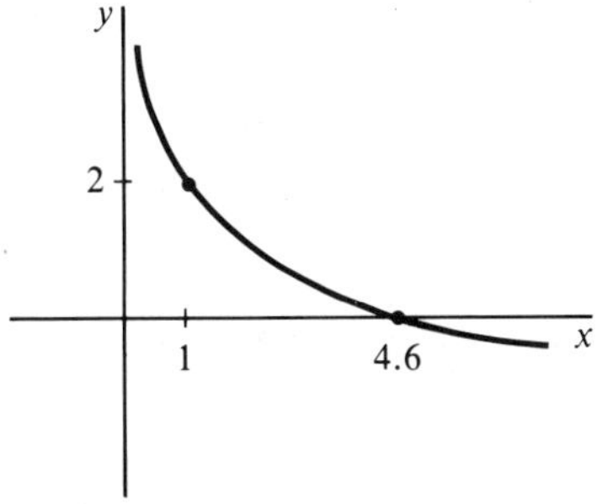

25. $3 \log x$ **27.** $\log_2 (2x^4)$ **29.** $\log_5 [x^3/(2x-3)]$ **31.** $x = 1.322$ **33.** $x = 3.819$
35. $x = 10^{10}$ **37.** $x = 2$ **39.** $x = 5$ **41.** 2.77 years

43.

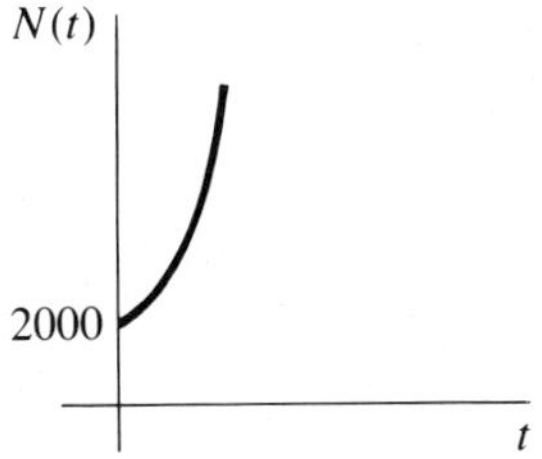

45. 1.77 mg

Section 6.1 (page 184)

1. $(-3, -2)$ **3.** $(5, 2)$ **5.** Dependent **7.** Inconsistent **9.** $(\frac{8}{5}, \frac{14}{5})$ **11.** $(\frac{1}{4}, -\frac{3}{4})$
13. $(\frac{10}{9}, \frac{53}{63})$ **15.** $r = 1, s = -2$ **17.** Inconsistent **19.** $(3, 1)$ **21.** $(-4, 2)$
23. Dependent **25.** $(-5, 4)$ **27.** $w = 3, z = 4$ **29.** $(-2, -2)$ **31.** $A = 14, B = 11$
33. $(8, 4)$ **35.** $a = 0, b = \frac{1}{2}$ **37.** 6.75 and 0.75 mph **39.** $\frac{10}{3}$ and $\frac{20}{3}$ lb
41. 20 nickels and 15 dimes **43.** 18 and 22.5 min **45.** 617.2 ft
47. Demand: $p = -3x + 700$; Supply: $p = \frac{2}{3}x + 250$; $x = 123$, $p = \$332$

Section 6.2 (page 187)

1. $(0, 0), (1, 1)$ **3.** $(1, 1)$ **5.** $(0, -1), (\frac{1}{2}, 0)$ **7.** No solution **9.** $(-1 \pm \sqrt{3}, 7 \mp 2\sqrt{3})$

11. $(\pm\sqrt{3}, -1)$ **13.** $(0, \pm 2)$ **15.** No solution **17.** $(\pm 1, 0)$ **19.** $(-\frac{11}{2}, -\frac{9}{2})$
21. $(0, \pm\sqrt{2})$ **23.** No solution **25.** $a = b = \pm 4$ **27.** No solution **29.** $(\pm 2\sqrt{3}, 2)$
31. $(1, 0)$ **33.** $(15, 15)$ **35.** $x = 10, p = \$16$

Section 6.3 (page 194)

1. $(2, 4)$ **3.** $(2, 1)$ **5.** $(-\frac{3}{4}, 2, 3)$ **7.** $(8, 5, 6)$ **9.** $(6, \frac{5}{3}, 2)$ **11.** Dependent
13. $(3, 2, -1)$ **15.** Inconsistent **17.** Dependent **19.** $(4, -3, 2)$ **21.** $(1, -1, 2, 3)$
23. $(0, 1, -1, 2)$ **25.** $n = 246, d = 226, q = 428$ **27.** $l_1 = 15, l_2 = 17, l_3 = 13$

Section 6.4 (page 201)

1. $\begin{bmatrix} 4 & 2 \\ 2 & 1 \end{bmatrix}; \begin{bmatrix} 6 & -2 \\ 0 & 1 \end{bmatrix}; \begin{bmatrix} 10 & 0 \\ 2 & 2 \end{bmatrix}$ **3.** $\begin{bmatrix} 2 & 2 & 5 \\ 4 & 5 & 7 \end{bmatrix}; \begin{bmatrix} 0 & 2 & 1 \\ 4 & -5 & -5 \end{bmatrix}; \begin{bmatrix} 2 & 4 & 6 \\ 8 & 0 & 2 \end{bmatrix}$

5. $\begin{bmatrix} 8 \\ -1 \\ 7 \end{bmatrix}; \begin{bmatrix} -6 \\ 1 \\ -3 \end{bmatrix}; \begin{bmatrix} 2 \\ 0 \\ 4 \end{bmatrix}$ **7.** $[-1 \quad 5 \quad 1]$; $[1 \quad 1 \quad 1]$; $[0 \quad 6 \quad 2]$

9. Cannot be done because A is 2×2 and B is 2×1 **11.** $AB = \begin{bmatrix} -5 & 10 \\ 0 & 2 \end{bmatrix}$; $BA = \begin{bmatrix} -3 & 2 \\ 5 & 0 \end{bmatrix}$

13. Cannot be done because number of columns of A does not equal number of rows of B

15. $AB = \begin{bmatrix} -2 & 0 \\ 10 & 0 \end{bmatrix}$; $BA = [-2]$ **17.** $AB = \begin{bmatrix} 4 \\ -1 \end{bmatrix}$; BA cannot be done

19. $AB = \begin{bmatrix} 12 & 15 \\ 13 & 13 \\ -1 & 4 \end{bmatrix}$; BA cannot be done **27.** The associative property of multiplication

31. $(A + B)^2 = A^2 + AB + BA + B^2$

Section 6.5 (page 208)

1. $\begin{bmatrix} 0 & 1 \\ 1 & 0 \end{bmatrix}$ **3.** $\begin{bmatrix} 0 & 1 \\ 1 & -2 \end{bmatrix}$ **5.** $\begin{bmatrix} \frac{1}{2} & 0 & 0 \\ 0 & \frac{1}{3} & 0 \\ 0 & 0 & \frac{1}{5} \end{bmatrix}$ **7.** $\begin{bmatrix} 0 & 0 & -1 \\ -2 & 1 & 0 \\ 1 & 0 & 1 \end{bmatrix}$

9. The inverse does not exist. **11.** $\begin{bmatrix} 1/a & -b/ad \\ 0 & 1/d \end{bmatrix}$ **13.** $\begin{bmatrix} -1 & 1 & 5 \\ 0 & \frac{1}{4} & \frac{1}{2} \\ 1 & -1 & -4 \end{bmatrix}$

15. $\begin{bmatrix} -\frac{5}{3} & \frac{8}{3} & -1 \\ 0 & 1 & -\frac{1}{2} \\ -\frac{1}{3} & \frac{1}{3} & 0 \end{bmatrix}$ **17.** $x = y = \frac{4}{3}$ **19.** $x = \frac{2}{5}, y = \frac{3}{5}, z = \frac{1}{5}$ **21.** $x = -1, y = 2, z = 1$

23. $x = 4, y = 2, z = 0$ **25.** There is no solution since system is inconsistent.

Section 6.6 (page 214)

1. -2 **3.** -2 **5.** 24 **7.** 0 **9.** 44 **11.** -123 **13.** 89 **15.** -96
17. 165 **19.** $x = \pm 1$ **21.** -70 **23.** $x = -3$ **25.** 5

Section 6.7 (page 219)

1. (2, 0) **3.** (5, 2) **5.** Dependent **7.** Inconsistent **9.** $(\frac{8}{5}, \frac{14}{5})$ **11.** $(-1, -4)$
13. $(7, 3, -2)$ **15.** $r = 3, s = -3, t = 4$ **17.** $(-135, -101, -7)$ **19.** (0, 0, 0)
21. $(\frac{496}{636}, -\frac{291}{636}, -\frac{270}{636})$ **23.** $l = 13$ cm, $w = 7$ cm **25.** 5 sec **27.** 8 dimes
29. $l_1 = \frac{65}{3}$ m, $l_2 = \frac{50}{3}$ m, $l_3 = \frac{35}{3}$ m **31.** $u' = FQ_2/(R_1Q_2 - R_2Q_1)$; $v' = -FR_2/(R_1Q_2 - R_2Q_1)$
33. $a = -\frac{11}{3}, b = \frac{5}{3}, c = 1$ **35.** $a = \frac{2}{3}, c = -\frac{2}{3}$

Section 6.8 (page 224)

1.
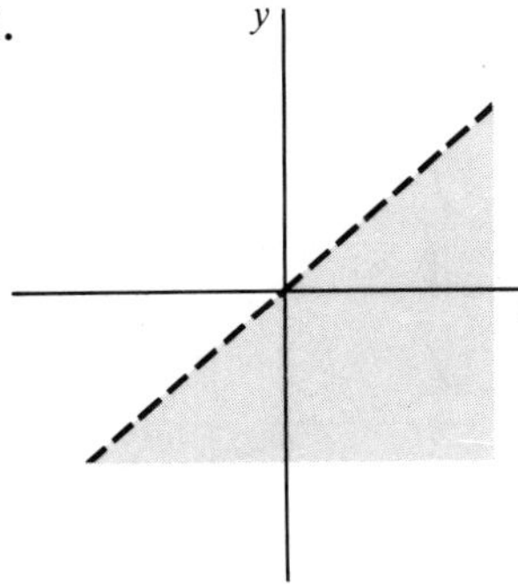

3.
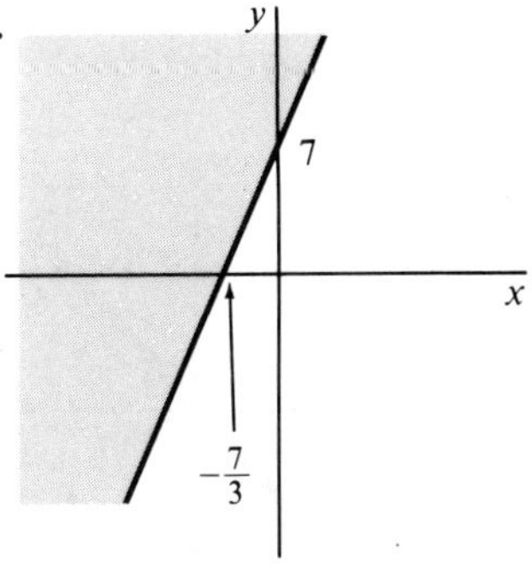

5.
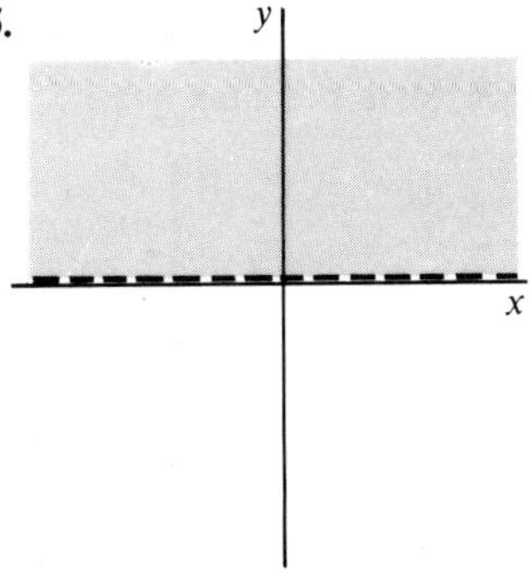

7.
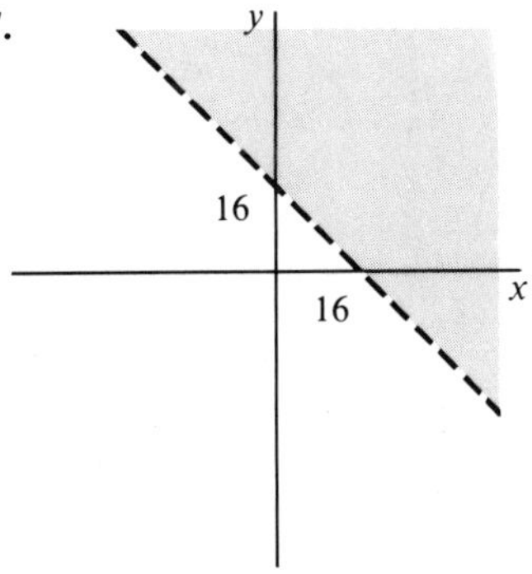

9.
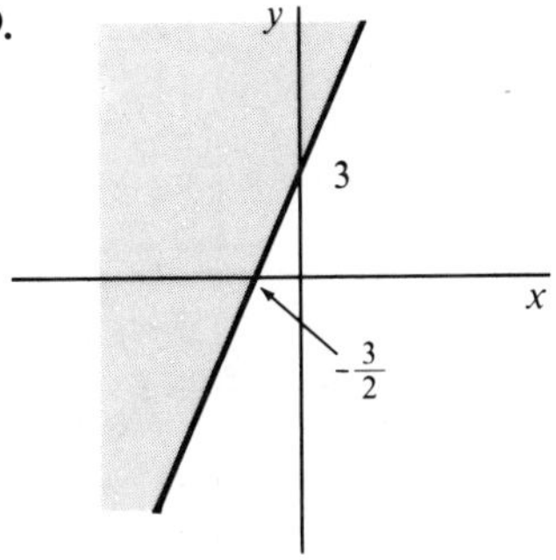

11.
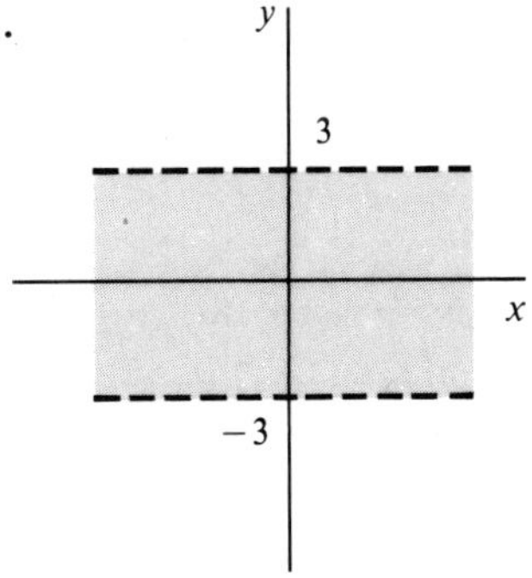

13.
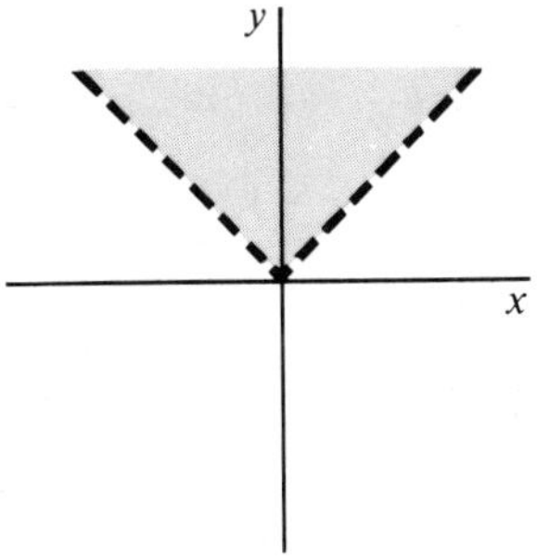

15.
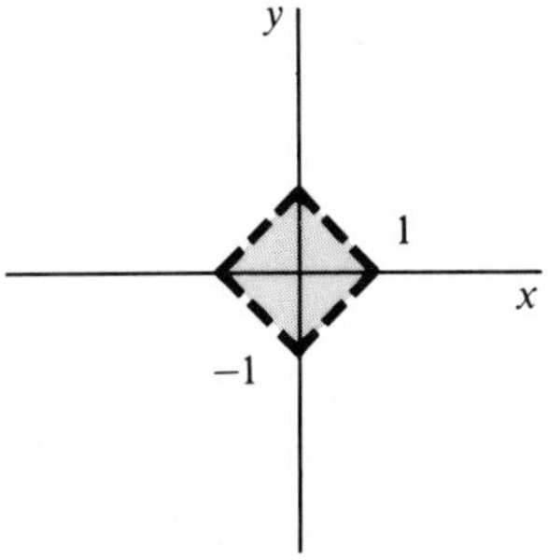

17. $C < -\frac{160}{9}$

19.

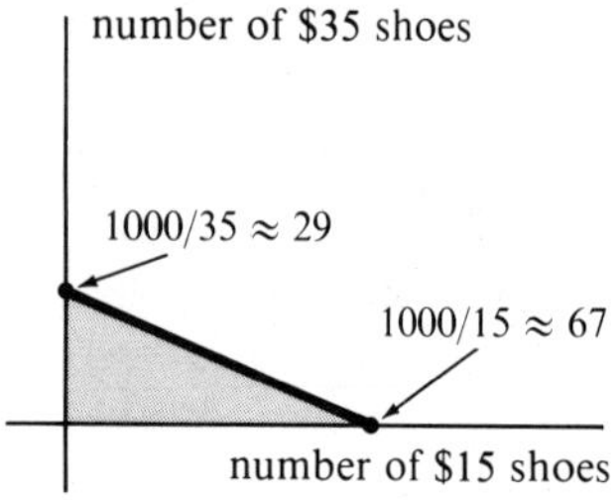

Sections 6.9 and 6.10 (page 229)

1.

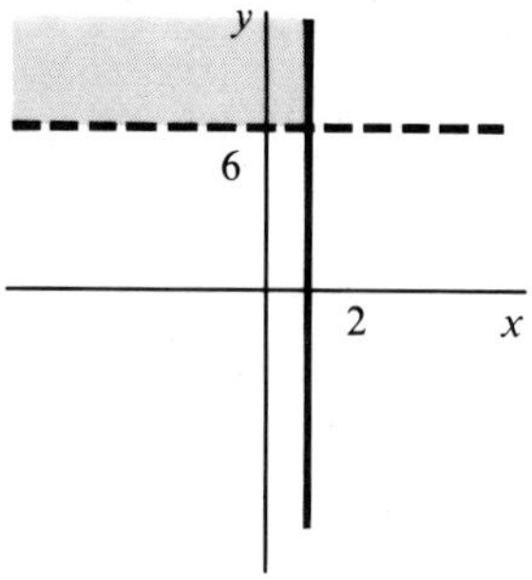

3.

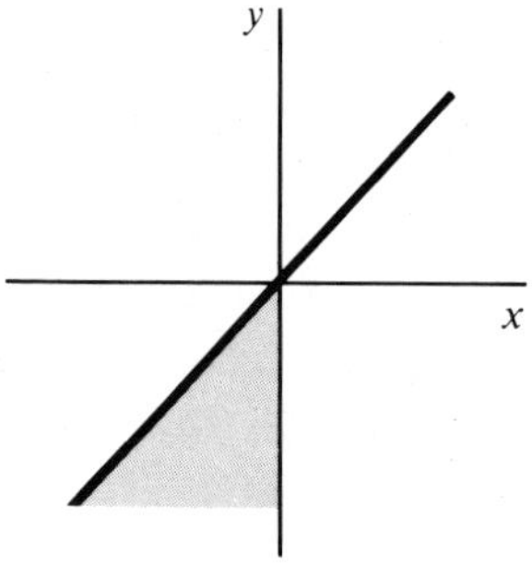

5.

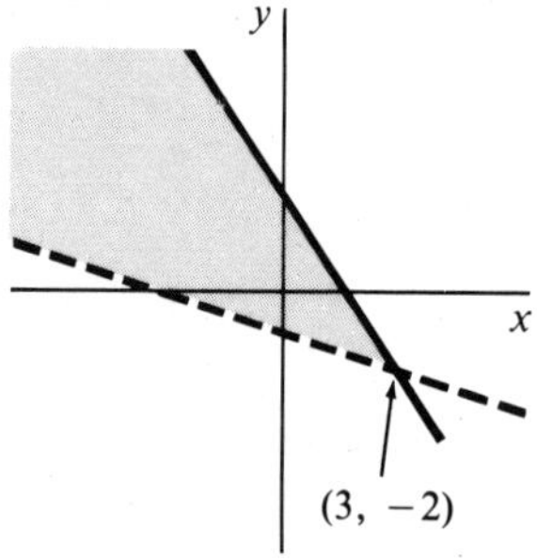

7.

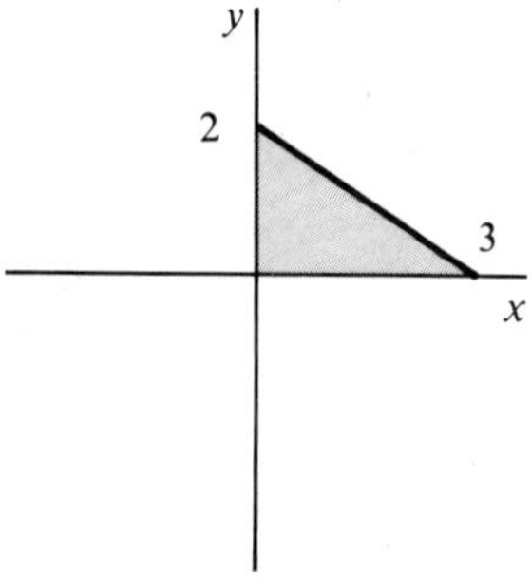

9.

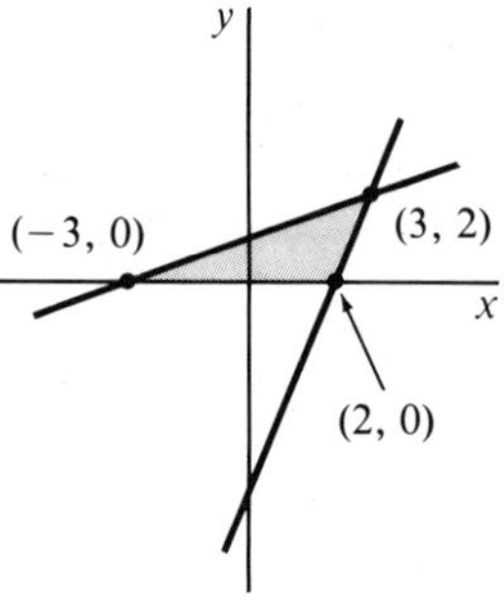

11.

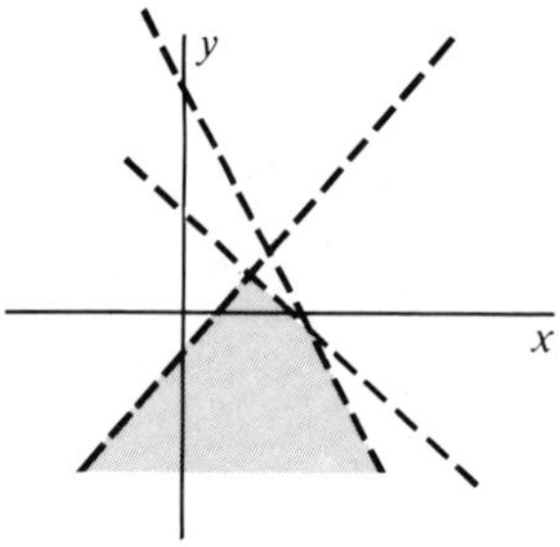

13.

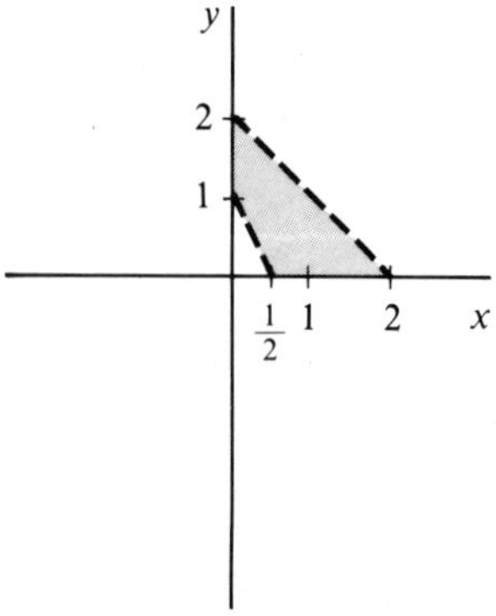

15.

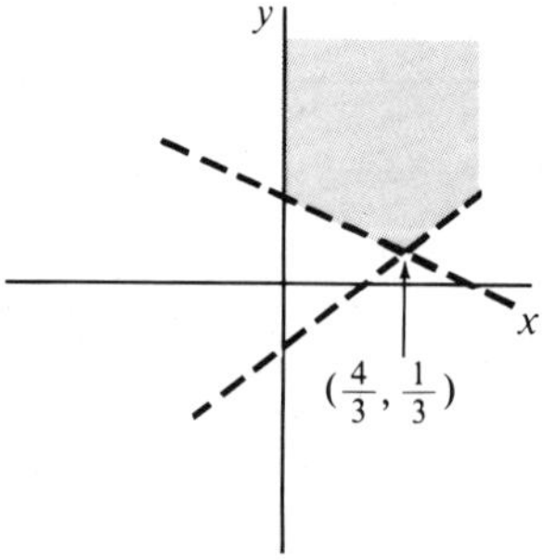

17. 10 at (4, 2) **19.** 25 at (5, 0) **21. a.** 10 at (2, 2) **b.** 9 at (3, 0) **23.** $\frac{9}{2}$ at $(0, \frac{3}{2})$

25. $\frac{15}{2}$ at $(\frac{5}{2}, 0)$ **27.** $x = 15$, $y = 30$

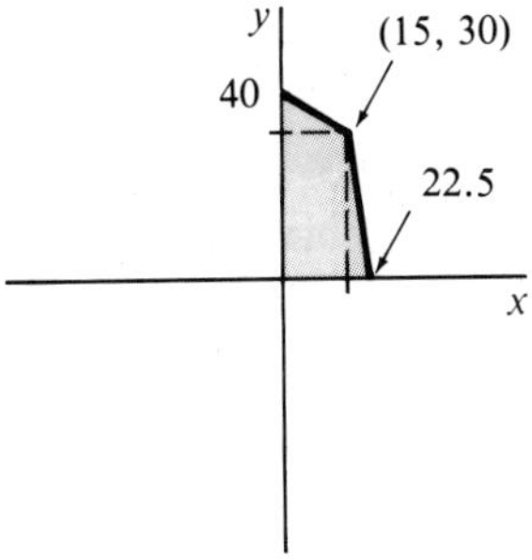

29. \$13,300 at 8.5%
\$6,700 at 7.0%

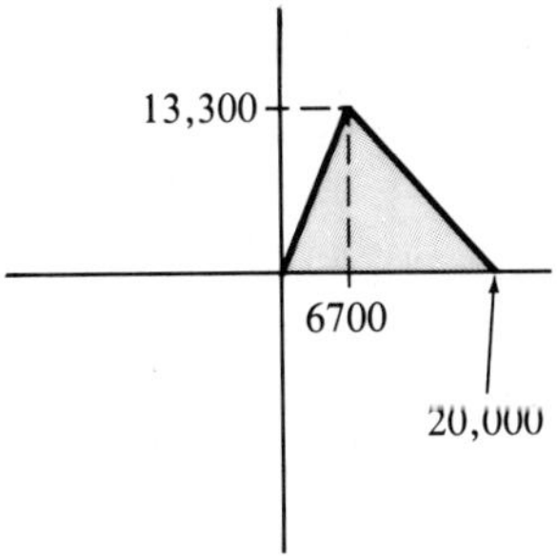

Review Exercises for Chapter 6 (page 230)

1. (2, 1) **3.** $s = \frac{41}{7}, t = -\frac{22}{7}$ **5.** $x = 3, z = -3$ **7.** $(\frac{5}{2}, -1, -\frac{1}{2})$ **9.** $(-13, -2, -6)$

11. (1, 2) **13.** $(2, \frac{1}{2})$ **15.** (4, 3, 2) **17.** $(-2, -4), (3, -9)$ **19.** $(\pm 2, \pm\sqrt{2})$

21. Cannot be done: A is 2×2, B is 2×3 **23.** $\begin{bmatrix} -2 & 8 & 8 \\ 2 & 1 & 5 \\ -2 & 11 & 0 \end{bmatrix}$

25. $AB = [\,0\,]; BA = \begin{bmatrix} -2 & -3 & 1 \\ 4 & 6 & -2 \\ 8 & 12 & -4 \end{bmatrix}$ **27.** $AB = \begin{bmatrix} 9 & -13 \\ 15 & -9 \end{bmatrix}; \; BA = \begin{bmatrix} 1 & -5 \\ 23 & -1 \end{bmatrix}$

29. $AB = \begin{bmatrix} 1 & -12 \\ 12 & -4 \end{bmatrix}; \; BA = \begin{bmatrix} -8 & 2 & -5 \\ 10 & 1 & 1 \\ 40 & 4 & 4 \end{bmatrix}$ **31.** $\begin{bmatrix} -\frac{1}{2} & \frac{1}{2} \\ \frac{3}{4} & -\frac{1}{4} \end{bmatrix}$ **33.** $\begin{bmatrix} -\frac{5}{17} & \frac{4}{17} \\ \frac{3}{17} & \frac{1}{17} \end{bmatrix}$

35. The inverse does not exist. **37.** (1, 2) **39.** $(2, \frac{1}{2})$ **41.** (4, 3, 2) **43.** 7 **45.** -14

47. 0 **49.** 38 **51.** 7 **53.** $x = \frac{2}{5}$ **55.** $(-2, -9)$ **57.** $(\frac{5}{3}, -3, -\frac{2}{3})$

59. Dependent **61.** 46.5°, 43.5° **63.** \$125,000 at 9%, \$625,000 at 11%

65. 25 gal (10%), 75 gal (30%), 150 gal (50%)

67.

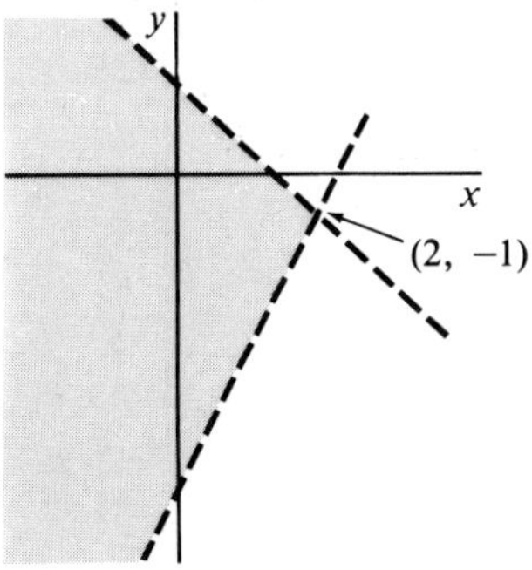

69.

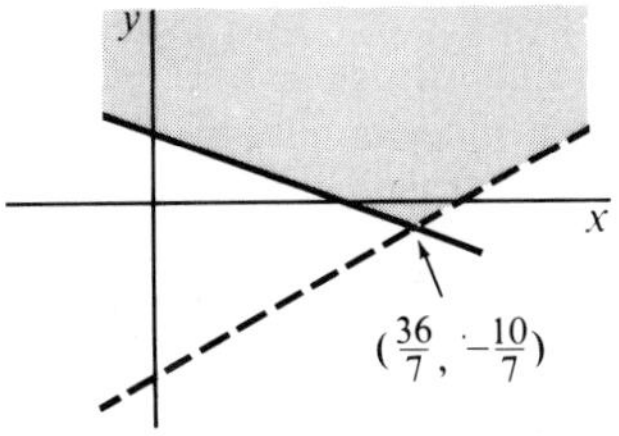

71. $x = 0$, $y = 12$
$P_{max} = 24$

73. $x = 2$, $y = 2$
$P_{min} = 16$

Section 7.1 (page 240)

1. 2.24, 63.4° **3.** 3.00, 61.9° **5.** 5.66, $-135°$ **7.** 5, $-36.9°$ **9.** 6.24, 106.1°
11. (6.43, 7.66) **13.** (11.34, 7.69) **15.** $(-90.63, 129.43)$ **17.** $(-33.32, -27.96)$
19. $(9.43, -4.40)$ **21.** 25, 36.87° **23.** 71.5, 75.83° **25.** 0.153, 31.6° **27.** 10.6, 318.8°
29. 7.3, 254.1° **31.** Horizontal 73.3 lb
Vertical 15.8 lb **33.** 948.7 mph **35.** 5.83 mph
59.04° with shore line

Section 7.2 (page 245)

1. 5**i** + **j** **3.** -6**i** $-$ 2**j** **5.** **i** $-$ 3**j** **7.** -4**j** **9.** 6**i** $-$ 7**j** **11.** 35.19, 51.2°
13. 13.36, 73.0° **15.** 65.58, 131.4° **17.** 395.1, $-64.0°$ **19.** 304 mph, 80.5° N of W
21. 163.8 lb **23.** 119.9 lb, 30.8° **25.** 1678.6 fps, 14.2° below the horizontal

Section 7.3 (page 250)

1. 1 **3.** 41 **5.** 1 **7.** 529.9 **9.** -3688 **11.** 337.4 **13.** 37.87°
15. 176.8° **17.** 529.8 ft-lb **19.** 433 ft-lb

Section 7.4 (page 253)

1. $6i$ **3.** $12i$ **5.** $i\sqrt{6}/2$ **7.** i **9.** -1 **11.** 2 **13.** $4 - i; \sqrt{17}$
15. $-1 - i; \sqrt{2}$ **17.** $x = \pm 3, y = -3$ **19.** $x = -\frac{3}{2}, y = \frac{5}{2}$ **21.** $7 + 5i$ **23.** $-2 + 3i$
25. 4 **27.** $3 + i$ **29.** $-7 + 22i$ **31.** 26 **33.** $13 + 8\sqrt{3}i$ **35.** $18 + 24i$
37. $(5 - i)/2$ **39.** $(6 + 9i)/13$ **41.** $-i/5$ **43.** $\dfrac{(-4 + 3\sqrt{2}) - (12 + \sqrt{2})i}{18}$ **47.** $b = 0$

Section 7.5 (page 258)

1. $7 + 6i$ **3.** $2 + 4i$ **5.** $-1 - 3i$ **7.** $-1 + 3i$ **9.** 10 **11.** $-1 + 8i$
13. $3 + (\sqrt{3} + 1)i$

15.
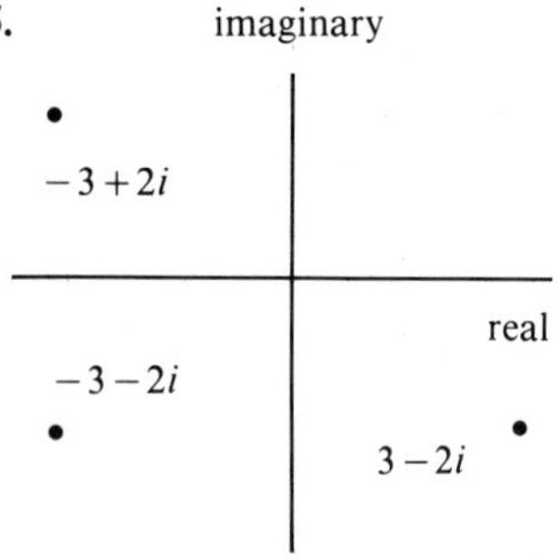

17.
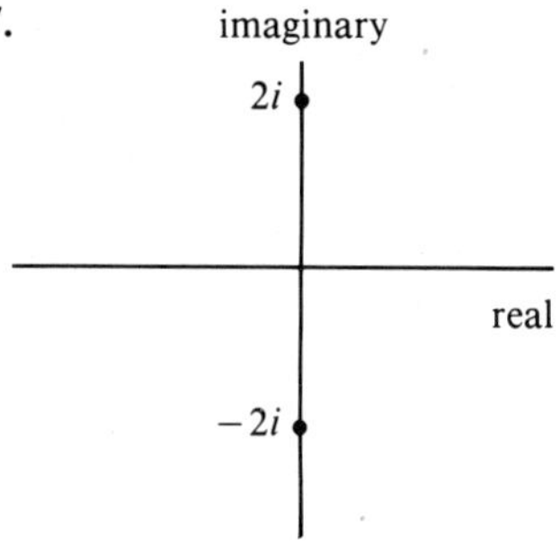

19.
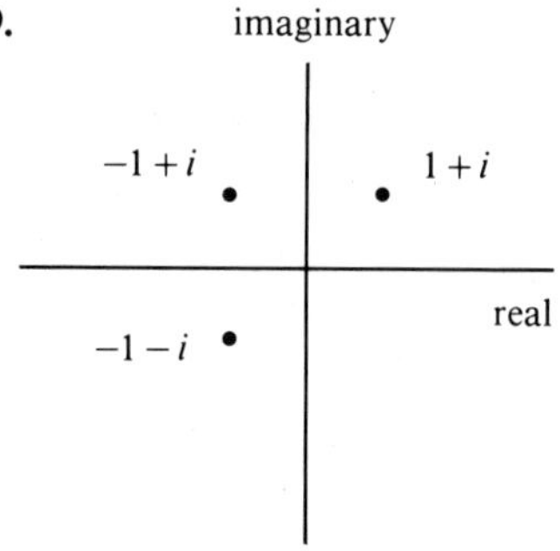

21. 2 cis $(-60°)$ **23.** 3 cis 41°49′ **25.** 9 cis 0° **27.** 5 cis $(-53°8')$ **29.** $\sqrt{61}$ cis $(-50°12')$
31. $\sqrt{3} + i$ **33.** $\dfrac{5\sqrt{2}}{2}(-1 + i)$ **35.** $\dfrac{-3 - \sqrt{3}i}{2}$ **37.** $\dfrac{3 - 3\sqrt{3}i}{2}$ **39.** $9.397 + 3.420i$
41. 12 cis 90° **43.** 2 cis 330° **45.** 20 cis 135° **47.** 10 cis 23°8′ **49.** 5 cis $(-60°)$
51. 2 cis 7°30′ **53.** $\dfrac{\sqrt{2}}{2}$ cis $(-75°)$ **55.** $\dfrac{4}{\sqrt{2}}$ cis $(-45°)$

Section 7.6 (page 262)

1. 8 cis 0° **3.** 9 cis 240° **5.** $128\sqrt{2}$ cis 315° **7.** 128 cis 330° **9.** 841 cis 272°48′

11. 1 cis 0° = 1
1 cis 72° = .3090 + .9511i
1 cis 144° = −.8090 + .5878i
1 cis 216° = −.8090 − .5878i
1 cis 288° = .3090 − .9511i

13. 1 cis 22°30′ = .9238 + .3827i
1 cis 112°30′ = −.3827 + .9239i
1 cis 202°30′ = −.9238 − .3827i
1 cis 292°30′ = .3827 − .9239i

15. $\sqrt[4]{2}$ cis 22°30′
$\sqrt[4]{2}$ cis 202°30′

17. $\sqrt[6]{2}$ cis $(25° + M \cdot 60°)$, $M = 0, 1, 2, 3, 4, 5$

19. $\sqrt[4]{2}(\sqrt{3}/2 + i/2)$
$\sqrt[4]{2}(-1/2 + i\sqrt{3}/2)$
$\sqrt[4]{2}(-\sqrt{3}/2 - i/2)$
$\sqrt[4]{2}(1/2 - i\sqrt{3}/2)$

21. *Hint:* $\cos 2\theta$ is the real part of $(\text{cis } \theta)^2$.

23. 4 cis 60° = $2 + 2\sqrt{3}i$
4 cis 180° = −4
4 cis 300° = $2 - 2\sqrt{3}i$

Review Exercises for Chapter 7 (page 262)

1. Magnitude: $\sqrt{34}$, $\theta = 120.96°$ **3.** Magnitude: 6.25, $\theta = -59.81°$
5. Magnitude: $\sqrt{\pi + 2} = 2.268$, $\theta = -51.4°$ **7.** −10.84, −11.22 **9.** −881.58, 472.03
11. 6**i** + 5**j** **13.** 3**i** **15.** −4**j** **17.** 148.9**i** + 105.1**j**, (182.3, 35.2°)
19. 0.433**i** + 1.133**j**, (1.21, 1.2 rad) **21.** −12, 126.9° **23.** −7, 127.9° **25.** 3, 53.1°
27. 8153, 11.5° **29.** −0.235, 111.2° **31.** $-2 + 6i = 2\sqrt{10}$ cis 108.4° **33.** $6i = 6$ cis 90°
35. $-3 + i = \sqrt{10}$ cis 161.6° **37.** $5 + 14i = \sqrt{221}$ cis 70.3° **39.** $2.06 - 1.192i = 2.38$ cis (−30.1°)
41. 4 cis 69.72° = $1.39 + 3.75i$ **43.** $\frac{11}{17} + \frac{10}{17}i = \frac{\sqrt{221}}{17}$ cis 42.3° **45.** $-14.7 - 5.35i = 7\sqrt{5}$ cis 200°
47. $200 + 0i = 200$ cis 0° **49.** $-0.16 + 0.99i = 1.00$ cis 99.2° **51.** 1 cis 60°, 1 cis 180°, 1 cis 300°
53. 1 cis 30°, 1 cis 150°, 1 cis 270° **55.** $2^{1/6}$ cis 45°, $2^{1/6}$ cis 165°, $2^{1/6}$ cis 285° **57.** $10^{5/2}$ cis 357.8°
59. Magnitude: 4.22, $\theta = -36.3°$ **61.** Vector form: 5**i** − 3**j**, −**i** + 3**j**; Angle: 139.4°
63. **a.** −3, 2 **b.** 1, 2 **c.** 2 **65.** $1.9 - 0.7i = 2.02$ cis (−20.2°)

Sections 8.1 and 8.2 (page 270)

1. $x - 5 - \frac{3}{x - 1}$ **3.** $x^2 + x - 4 + \frac{8}{x + 1}$ **5.** $2x^2 - 8x + 17 - \frac{35}{x + 2}$
7. $3x^3 - 6x^2 + 8x - 16 + \frac{17}{x + 1}$ **9.** $x^3 - 2x^2 + 2x - 1$ **11.** $2x^2 - 3x + 2$
13. $-x^2 + 4x - 2 - \frac{5}{x + 1}$ **15.** $x^2 + 7x + 10$ **17.** $3x^2 - 10 + \frac{11}{x^2 + 1}$ **19.** $2x - 1$
21. Factor **23.** Not a factor **25.** Factor **27.** Not a factor **29.** Factor **31.** Factor
33. Factor **35.** Factor **37.** $y = -(x + 1)(x - 1)(x - 2)$ **39.** $y = \frac{3}{4}(x - 1)^2(x - 2)^2$
41. $y = \frac{-\sqrt{2}}{5}(x - \sqrt{2})(x^2 - 4x + 5)$

Section 8.3 (page 275)

1. $x - 1$ **3.** $x^2 + 3 + \frac{5}{x - 2}$ **5.** $x^2 - \frac{1}{2}x - \frac{11}{4} + \frac{83}{8(x + \frac{1}{2})}$ **7.** $x^3 + 2x^2 + 8x + 24$

9. $-3x^4 - 6x^3 - 12x^2 - 24x - 41 - \dfrac{74}{x-2}$ **11.** $3x^2 - 21x + 30$ **13.** 28 **15.** $-\frac{1}{8}$

17. -1.9506 **19.** $-10 - 6i$ **21.** 0 **23.** $\frac{4}{3}$ **25.** $1 + \dfrac{5}{2\sqrt{2}}$ **27.** 36 **29.** -6665

31. 61.8832

Section 8.4 (page 279)

1. $1, -1, -2$ **3.** $-2, \pm i$ **5.** $-\frac{5}{2}, 1 \pm \sqrt{5}$ **7.** $-1, -2, 2, 3$ **9.** $\frac{1}{3}, (3 \pm i\sqrt{3})/2$
11. $-1, -1, -1, 3$ **13.** $-\frac{2}{3}, (1 \pm i\sqrt{2})/3$ **15.** $\frac{1}{2}, (1 \pm i\sqrt{7})/2$ **17.** $-1, 1, 2, -1 \pm i\sqrt{3}$
19. $(x+1)\left(x+\dfrac{5}{2}+\dfrac{\sqrt{37}}{2}\right)\left(x+\dfrac{5}{2}-\dfrac{\sqrt{37}}{2}\right)$ **21.** $4(x+\frac{1}{2})\left(x+\dfrac{3}{4}+i\dfrac{\sqrt{15}}{4}\right)\left(x+\dfrac{3}{4}-i\dfrac{\sqrt{15}}{4}\right)$
23. $2x(2x-3)\left(x+\dfrac{1}{4}+\dfrac{\sqrt{217}}{4}\right)\left(x+\dfrac{1}{4}-\dfrac{\sqrt{217}}{4}\right)$ **25.** $(0, 0), (1, 1), (-1 \pm i, -4)$
27. $(2, 1), (\frac{2}{3}, -\frac{1}{3}), \left(-1, \dfrac{-1 \pm i\sqrt{15}}{8}\right)$ **29.** 23

Section 8.5 (page 285)

1. 1 negative, 2 complex **3.** 1 positive, 1 negative, 2 complex
5. 1 positive, 2 complex or 1 positive, 2 negative
7. 3 positive, 2 complex or 3 positive, 2 negative or 1 positive, 4 complex or 1 positive, 2 negative, 2 complex
9. 2 positive, 2 negative, 2 complex or 2 positive, 4 complex or 2 negative, 4 complex or 6 complex
11. 0.27 **13.** 1.25 **15.** 3.07 **17.** -0.33 **19.** 2.14 **21.** -2.27

23.

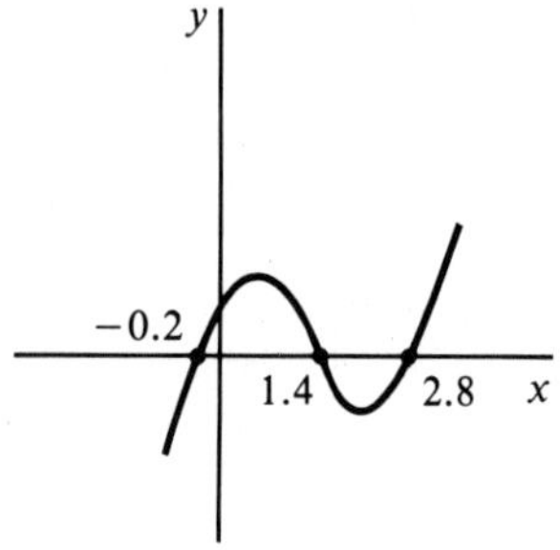

25.

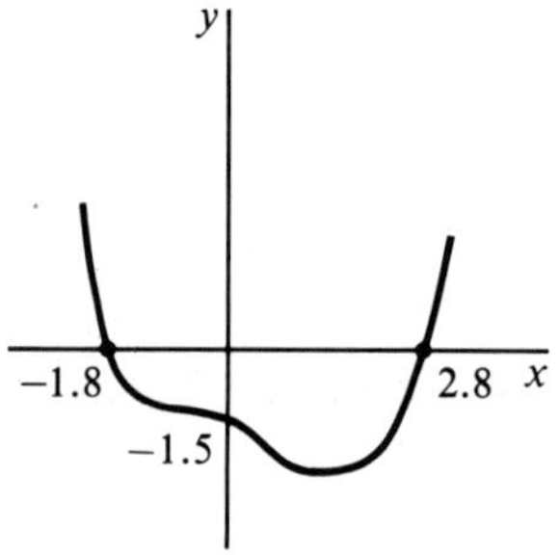

27.

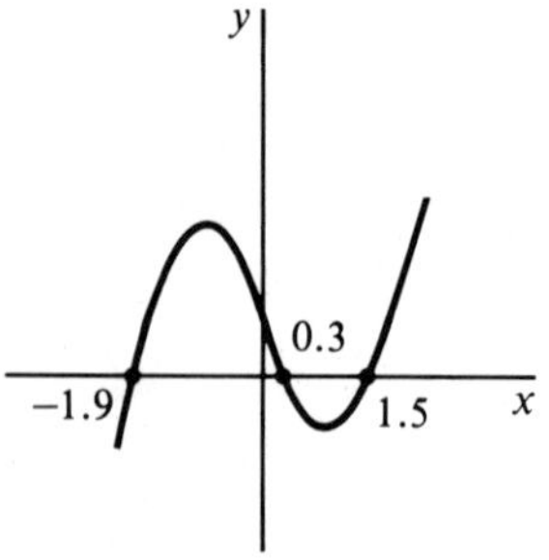

29.

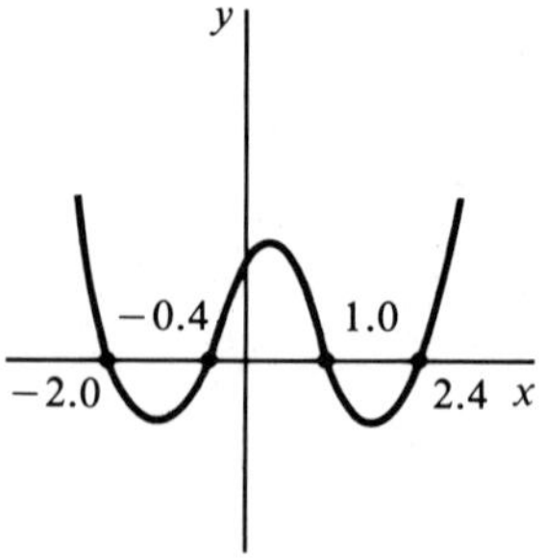

Section 8.6 (page 289)

1. $\dfrac{2/3}{x+5} + \dfrac{1/3}{x-1}$ **3.** $\dfrac{1}{x} - \dfrac{1}{x+1}$ **5.** $\dfrac{1/2}{x} + \dfrac{2}{x+5} - \dfrac{1/2}{x+2}$ **7.** $\dfrac{1/2}{x+5} + \dfrac{1/2}{x+1}$

9. $-\dfrac{6}{x} + \dfrac{7}{x-1} - \dfrac{2}{(x-1)^2}$ **11.** $\dfrac{1}{x} - \dfrac{1}{x+1} - \dfrac{1}{(x+1)^2}$ **13.** $\dfrac{-1}{x+1} + \dfrac{2}{x-1} + \dfrac{3}{3-2x}$

15. $\dfrac{2}{x-1} + \dfrac{1}{(x-1)^2}$ **17.** $\dfrac{1}{x} + \dfrac{1}{x^2+2}$ **19.** $\dfrac{1}{2x+3} - \dfrac{1}{x^2+2x+4}$ **21.** $\dfrac{2x-1}{x^2+2x+3} - \dfrac{x}{x^2+5}$

Review Exercises for Chapter 8 (page 289)

1. $x-2;\ R=2$ **3.** $3x+5;\ R=14$ **5.** $2x^2+x-\frac{1}{2};\ R=\frac{3}{4}$ **7.** $3x^4-2x^3+2x^2-x;\ R=-2$
9. $\frac{2}{3}x^3+\frac{2}{9}x^2+\frac{2}{27}x+\frac{29}{81};\ R=-\frac{52}{81}$ **11.** Not a factor **13.** Factor **15.** Not a factor
17. $-\frac{1}{10}(x-2)(x^2+1)(x^2-4x+5)$ **19.** $2(x^2+1)(x^2+4)$
21. $\frac{25}{24}(x+2)(x+1)(x-1)(x-3)(x-4)$ **23.** $-2, 1, \pm i$ **25.** $-2, -1, 1, 1$ **27.** $1, 3 \pm \sqrt{10}$
29. $-\frac{1}{2}, 1 \pm i$ **31.** 1 positive, 1 negative; -1.06, 1.21 **33.** 1 positive; 1.003
35. 2 positive, 1 negative; -1.71, 0.38, 1.32 **37.** $3/(x-1) + (-3x+5)/(x^2+4)$
39. $-1/(x-1) + (2x+5)/(x^2+4)$ **41.**

x	$P(x) - \sin x$
0.01	-0.0000002
0.1	-0.000167
0.2	-0.00133
0.5	-0.021092

43. 6.09 ohms **45.** $r = 0.553$

Section 9.1 (page 294)

1. 2, 3, 4, 5, 6 **3.** 2, 0, 2, 0, 2 **5.** $-1, 1, -1, 1, -1$ **7.** $\frac{3}{2}, \frac{4}{3}, \frac{5}{4}, \frac{6}{5}, \frac{7}{6}$ **9.** 1, 4, 9, 16, 25
11. 3, 5, 7, 9, 11 **13.** $1, \frac{1}{4}, \frac{1}{9}, \frac{1}{16}, \frac{1}{25}$ **15.** $\frac{5}{2}, \frac{5}{4}, \frac{5}{8}, \frac{5}{16}, \frac{5}{32}$ **17.** $3, 3^2, 3^4, 3^8, 3^{16}$
19. $10, -5, 10, -5, 10$ **21.** $2n$ **23.** $3n-2$ **25.** n^2 **27.** $(4000)(.75)^4 = \$1265.63$

Section 9.2 (page 297)

1. 1.093 **3.** 55 **5.** 45 **7.** 20 **9.** 10 **11.** $x_1+x_2+x_3+x_4+x_5$
13. $\sum_{k=1}^{4} k$ **15.** $\sum_{k=1}^{4} k^2$ **17.** $\sum_{k=1}^{5} 2^k x$ **19.** True **21.** True **23.** True
25. $a_1 = 2$, $a_n = 0, n \geq 2$ **27.** $a_1 = -1$, $a_n = 2(-1)^n$

Section 9.3 (page 300)

1. Yes, 1 **3.** Yes, 2 **5.** Yes, 3 **7.** No **9.** No **11.** $a_n = 3n-1$ **13.** 1
15. -90 **17.** 48 **19.** 50 **21.** -70 **23.** n^2 **27.** 3, 4, 5, 6, 7
29. $1, 0, -1, -2, -3$ **31.** 7, 9, 11, 13, 15 **33.** $f(x) = 3x$ **35.** $f(x) = 3x+1$
37. $f(x) = 3x+2$

Section 9.4 (page 303)

1. Yes, 3, $a_k = (4)3^{k-1}$ **3.** No **5.** Yes, -2, $a_k = (\frac{1}{3})(-2)^{k-1}$ **7.** Yes, $\frac{1}{2}$, $a_k = (\frac{1}{2})^k$

9. $a_4 = 375, S_4 = 468$ **11.** $r = \pm 2, S_5 = 155$ or 55 **13.** $\dfrac{-1024}{19{,}683}$ **15.** 726

17. $\frac{3^{11}-1}{2^{10}}-2$ **19.** $\frac{315}{64}$ **21.** $\frac{21}{64}$ **23.** 7 strokes **25.** $f(x) = 2^{x-1}$ **27.** 3, 9, 27, 81, 243
29. $\frac{1}{2}, \frac{1}{4}, \frac{1}{8}, \frac{1}{16}, \frac{1}{32}$ **31.** Speed $= 2^{(T-T_0)/10}$ **33.** 7 percent **35.** 1 day; 3.32 days

Section 9.5 (page 307)

1. $x^6 - 6x^5y + 15x^4y^2 - 20x^3y^3 + 15x^2y^4 - 6xy^5 + y^6$
3. $243x^5 - 405x^4y + 270x^3y^2 - 90x^2y^3 + 15xy^4 - y^5$ **5.** $x^5 + 5x^3 + 10x + \frac{10}{x} + \frac{5}{x^3} + \frac{1}{x^5}$
7. $y^6 + 9y^4x + 27y^2x^2 + 27x^3$ **9.** $x^3 + 6x^2\sqrt{xy} + 15x^2y + 20xy\sqrt{xy} + 15xy^2 + 6y^2\sqrt{xy} + y^3$
11. $x^{4/3} + 4x^{1/4} + 6x^{-5/6} + 4x^{-23/12} + x^{-3}$ **13.** 19.4481 **15.** $x^{-9/4} - 3x^{-3/4} + 3x^{3/4} - x^{9/4}$
17. $120\sqrt{xy}x^3y$ **19.** $-\frac{20!3^9 7^{11}}{11!9!}x^{27}y^{11/3}$ **21.** -10 **23.** $\frac{70}{81}$ **25.** 121.6 **27.** 63.52
29. 6 **31.** 4.899 **33.** 1.913194 **35.** 3.107 **37.** 2.9907 **39.** 9.8995
41. 3.076×10^{15} **43.** 2.6525×10^{32}

Section 9.6 (page 310)

1. 840, 35 **3.** 11 **7.** 56 **9.** 24 **11.** 181,440 **13.** 3744
15. 250 **17.** 182

Section 9.7 (page 313)

1. $\frac{1}{4}$ **3.** $\frac{3}{8}, \frac{5}{8}$ **5.** $\frac{1}{2}$ **7.** $\frac{3}{8}$ **9.** $\frac{10}{13}$ **11.** $\frac{5}{16}$ **13.** $\frac{21}{65}$ **15.** $\frac{6}{55}$
17. $\frac{1}{18}$ **19.** 2162/54145

Review Exercises for Chapter 9 (page 317)

1. $a_n = 2n - 1$ **3.** $a_n = 3(2n - 1)$ **5.** $a_n = 1$ **7.** $a_n = 2^n$ **9.** $a_n = (-5)^n$ **11.** 400
13. 1200 **15.** 20 **17.** 2,097,150 **19.** 7.9472×10^{13} **21.** 6 **23.** 50 **25.** $-\frac{9}{52}$
27. True **29.** False **31.** $\frac{-10!}{5!5!} = -252$ **33.** $x^4 - 20x^3y + 150x^2y^2 - 500xy^3 + 625y^4$
35. 2.495 **37.** $2^{20} = 1{,}048{,}576$ **39.** $\frac{5!}{3!} = 20, \frac{100!}{98!} = 9900$ **41.** $2n(2n - 1)(2n - 2)$
43. 1/52 **45.** 1/2 **47.** 35/128 **49.** 1/9

Section 10.1 (page 323)

1. Focus $(-2, 0)$
Directrix $x = 2$
Right chord $(-2, 4), (-2, -4)$

3. Focus $(0, \frac{3}{2})$
Directrix $y = -\frac{3}{2}$
Right chord $(-3, \frac{3}{2}), (3, \frac{3}{2})$

5. Focus $(-4, 0)$
Directrix $x = 4$
Right chord $(-4, 8), (4, 8)$

7. Focus $(\frac{3}{4}, 0)$
Directrix $x = -\frac{3}{4}$
Right chord $(\frac{3}{4}, \frac{3}{2}), (\frac{3}{4}, -\frac{3}{2})$

9. Focus $(-\frac{1}{2}, 0)$
Directrix $x = \frac{1}{2}$
Right chord $(-\frac{1}{2}, 1), (-\frac{1}{2}, -1)$

11. $x^2 = 8y$

13. $y^2 = 6x$ **15.** $x^2 = -4y$ **17.** $x^2 = y$ **19.** $(0, 0), (-2, 1)$ **21.** $(.09, -1.05)$
23. $x^2 = 1000y$

Section 10.2 (page 328)

1. Ellipse
   $a = 5$
   $b = \sqrt{5}$
   Foci $(0, \pm 2\sqrt{5})$
3. Ellipse
   $a = 2$
   $b = 1$
   Foci $(0, \pm\sqrt{3})$
5. Circle
   $r = 3$
7. Ellipse
   $a = \sqrt{12}$
   $b = \sqrt{8}$
   Foci $(\pm 2, 0)$
9. Ellipse
   $a = 1$
   $b = \frac{2}{3}$
   Foci $(0, \pm\frac{1}{3}\sqrt{5})$
11. $9x^2 + 16y^2 = 144$
13. $100x^2 + 9y^2 = 225$
15. $9x^2 + 25y^2 = 225$
17. $15x^2 + 16y^2 = 240$
19. $4x^2 + 21y^2 = 25$
21. $(1.3, -1.9), (-1.3, 1.9)$
23. $(.94, .88), (-.94, .88)$
25. $9x^2 + 100y^2 = 225$

27.

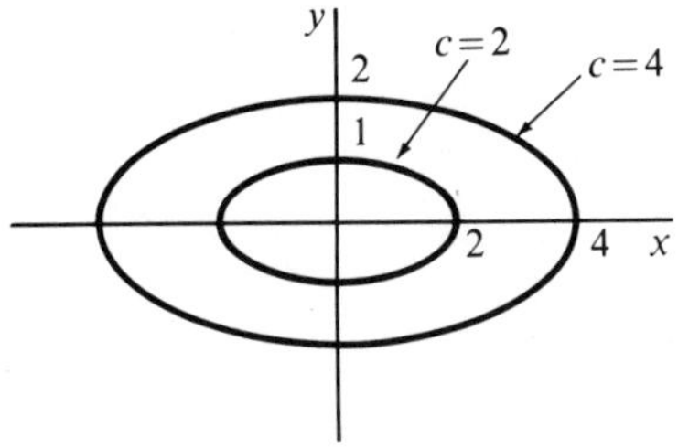

29.

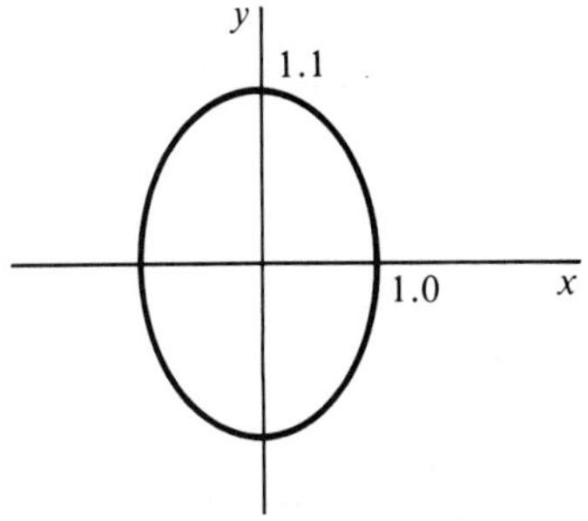

Section 10.3 (page 333)

1. $a = 4$
   $b = 4$
   foci $(\pm\sqrt{32}, 0)$
3. $a = 3$
   $b = 2$
   foci $(\pm\sqrt{13}, 0)$
5. $a = 5$
   $b = 2$
   foci $(0, \pm\sqrt{29})$
7. $a = \frac{5}{2}$
   $b = \frac{5}{4}$
   foci $(\pm\frac{5}{4}\sqrt{5}, 0)$
9. $a = 1$
   $b = 1$
   foci $(\pm\sqrt{2}, 0)$
11. $9x^2 - 16y^2 = 144$
13. $4y^2 - x^2 = 4$
15. $13x^2 - 36y^2 = 117$
17. $4y^2 - x^2 = 64$
19. $y^2 - 10x^2 = 9$
23.

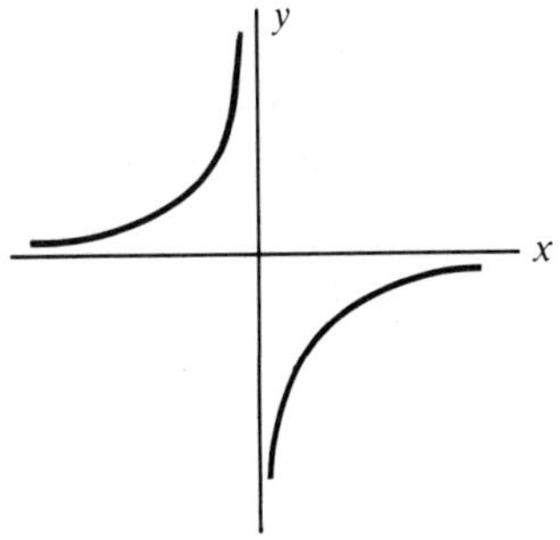

Section 10.4 (page 336)

1. $8x = y^2 - 2y + 25$
3. $12y = -13 + 2x - x^2$
5. $4x = y^2 - 4y + 8$
7. $7x^2 + 16y^2 - 28x - 32y - 68 = 0$
9. $16x^2 + y^2 - 16x + 8y + 4 = 0$
11. $3x^2 + 4y^2 + 24x - 24y + 72 = 0$
13. $64y^2 - 49x^2 - 98x - 256y = 577$
15. $7x^2 - 9y^2 - 28x + 18y = 44$
17. $x^2 - 4y^2 + 4x - 16y - 16 = 0$
19. $(x - h)^2 + y^2 = r^2$

21. $y^2 = 4a(x - h)$ **23.** $(x - r)^2 + y^2 = r^2$ **25.**

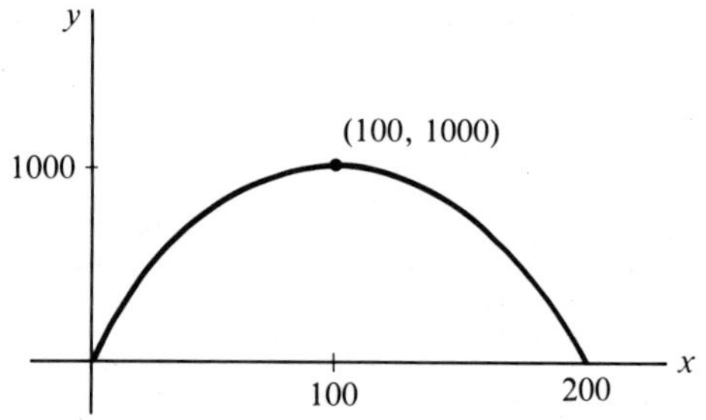

Section 10.5 (page 340)

1. $[(3\sqrt{3} + 1)/2, (-3 + \sqrt{3})/2]$ **3.** $[(-\sqrt{3} - 1)/2, (1 - \sqrt{3})/2]$ **5.** $[(2\sqrt{3} - 1)/2, (-2 - \sqrt{3})/2]$
7. $y' = \frac{1}{3}x'$ **9.** $(2 + 7\sqrt{3})x' + (7 - 2\sqrt{3})y' = 6$ **11.** $4x'^2 + y'^2 = 4$
13. $x'^2 + y'^2 + \sqrt{3}x' - y' = 0$ **15.** $53°8'$ **17.** $x'^2 + 2y'^2 = 1$
19. $\dfrac{x'^2}{.828} - \dfrac{y'^2}{4.828} = 1$ **21.** $\dfrac{x'^2}{2} + \dfrac{y'^2}{\frac{2}{3}} = 1$

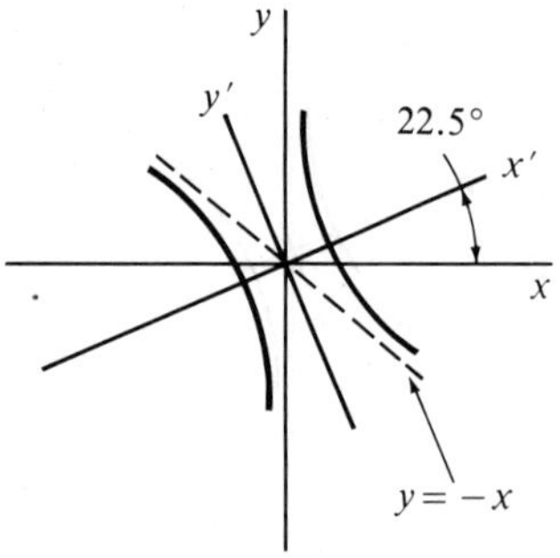

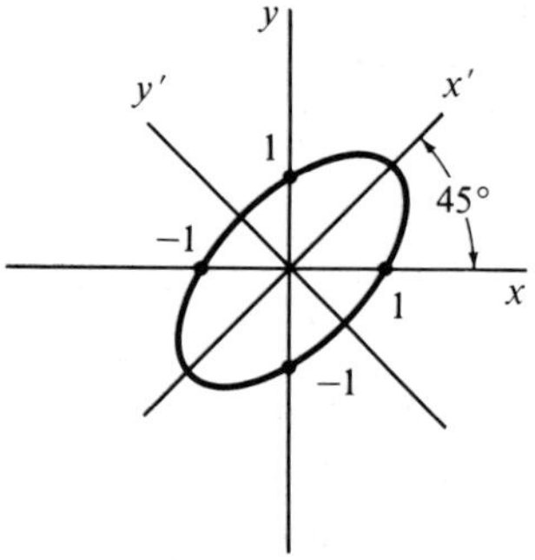

Section 10.6 (page 344)

1. $(x + 2)^2 + (y + 3)^2 = 3^2$ **3.** $\dfrac{(x + 1)^2}{4} + \dfrac{(y + 1)^2}{9} = 1$ **5.** $\dfrac{(x - 2)^2}{25} - \dfrac{y^2}{25} = 1$

7. $(x - 3)^2 = 3(y + 3)$ **9.** $(y - \frac{1}{2})^2 = -\frac{1}{2}(x - \frac{3}{2})$ **11.** $\dfrac{(x + 1)^2}{1} - \dfrac{(y - 1)^2}{4} = 1$

13. $\dfrac{(x - 1)^2}{4} + \dfrac{(y + 2)^2}{9} = 1$ **15.** $\dfrac{(y - \frac{1}{2})^2}{\frac{1}{4}} - \dfrac{x^2}{\frac{1}{2}} = 1$ **17.** $\dfrac{(x + 2)^2}{7} - \dfrac{y^2}{7} = 1$

19. $(x + \frac{5}{2})^2 = y - \frac{3}{4}$ **21.** $\dfrac{x'^2}{1} - \dfrac{y'^2}{\frac{9}{4}} = 1$ **23.** $\dfrac{x'^2}{\frac{22}{7}} - \dfrac{y'^2}{4} = 1$

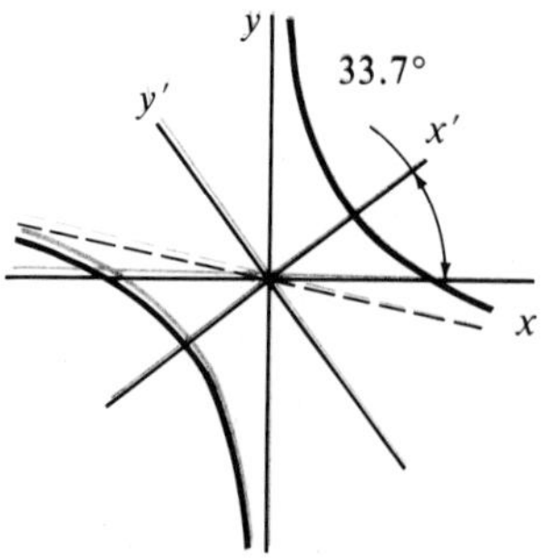

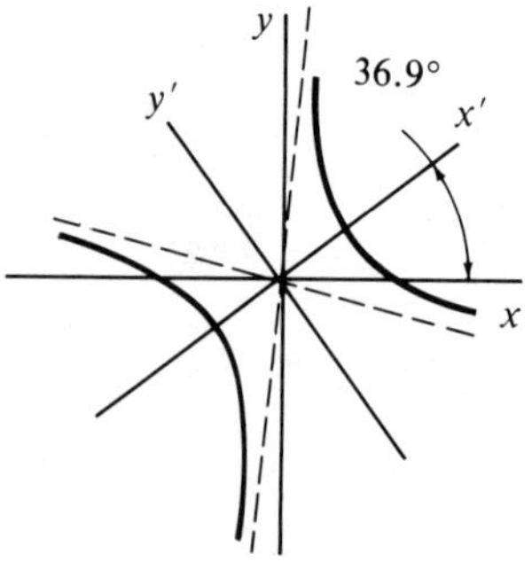

25. Ellipse

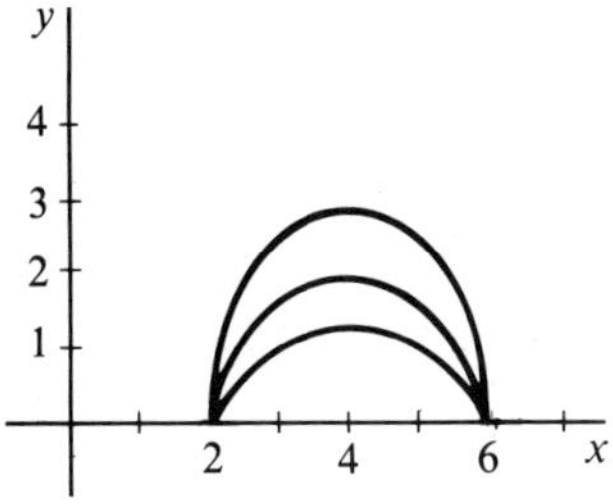

27. Parabola: $y^2 = 10x + 25$

Section 10.7 (page 349)

1.

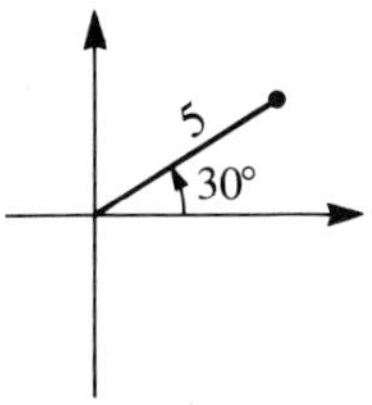

3.

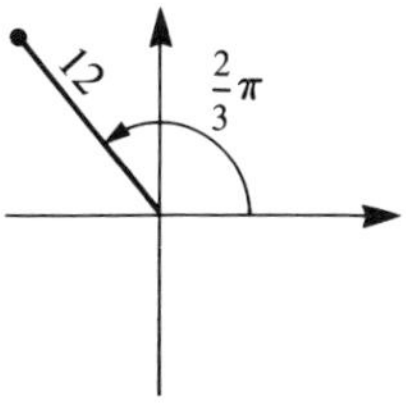

5.

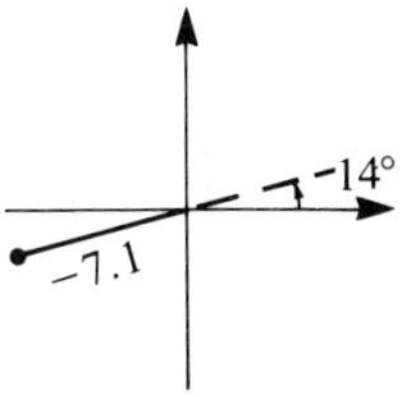

7.

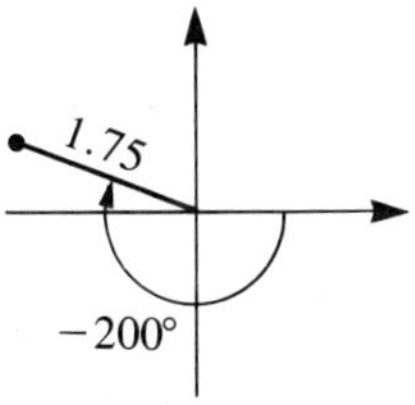

9.

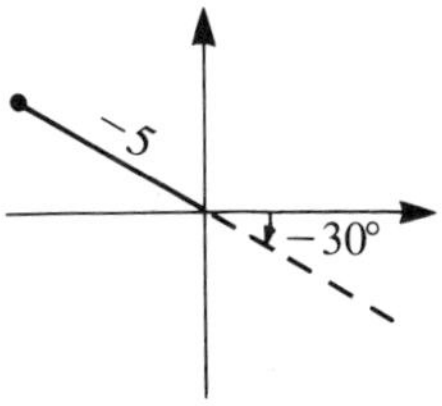

11. $r(2\cos\theta + 3\sin\theta) = 6$ **13.** $r = 4\cos\theta$ **15.** $r^2(\cos^2\theta + 4\sin^2\theta) = 4$ **17.** $r\cos^2\theta = 4\sin\theta$
19. $x^2 + y^2 = 25$ **21.** $x^2 + y^2 = 10y$ **23.** $x^2 + y^2 = (x^2 + y^2)^{1/2} + 2y$ **25.** $y^2 = 25 - 10x$

27.

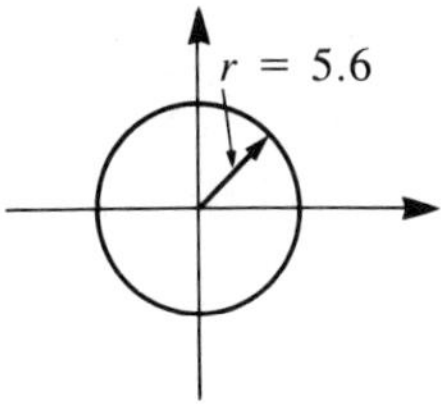

29.

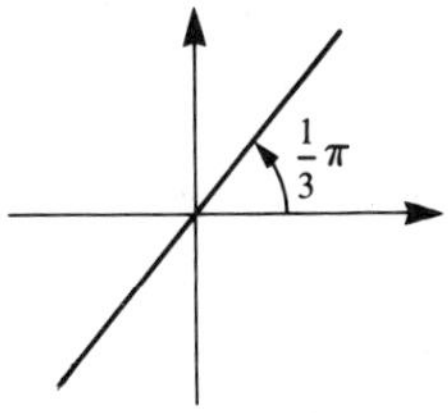

31.

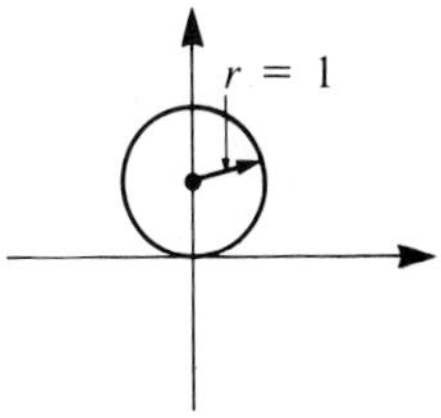

33.

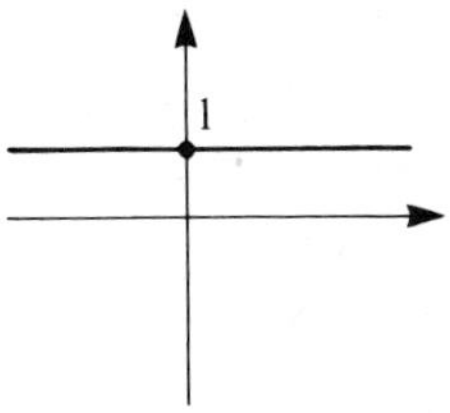

35.

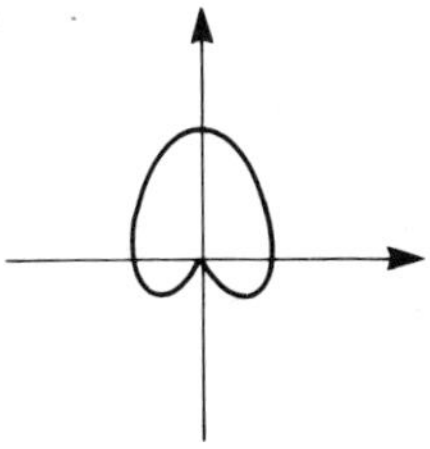

37.

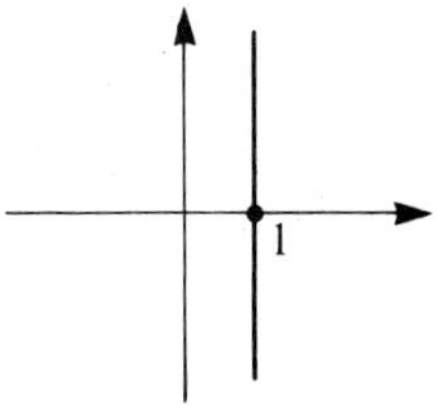

39.

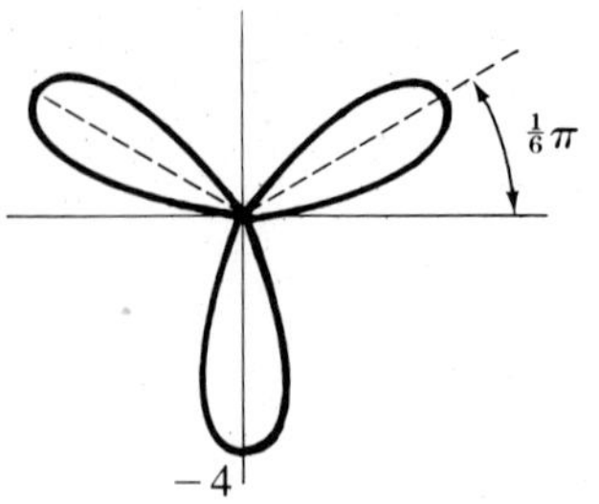

41.

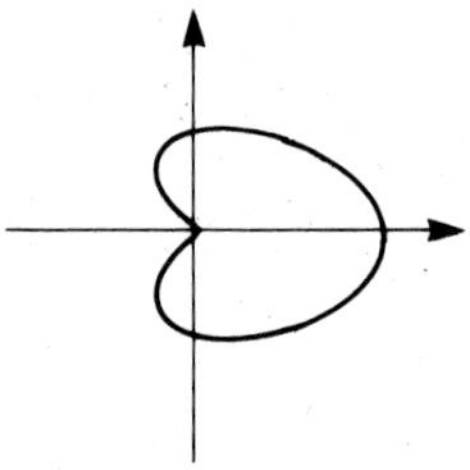

43. $3x^2 + 4y^2 - 2x - 1 = 0$

Review Exercises for Chapter 10 (page 350)

1. Parabola
Vertex (0, 0)
Focus $(0, -\frac{3}{4})$

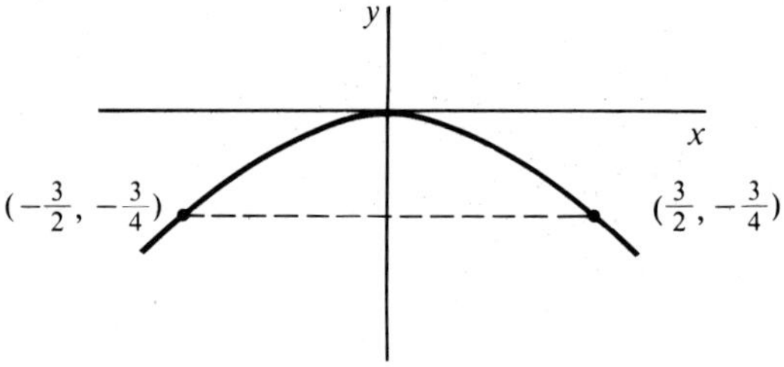

3. Circle
Center (0, −2)
Radius = 3

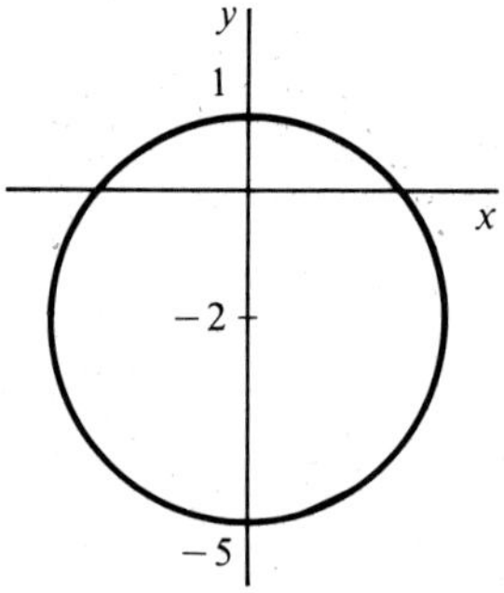

5. Hyperbola
Center (−1, −1)
$a = 1$
$b = 1$
$c = \sqrt{2}$

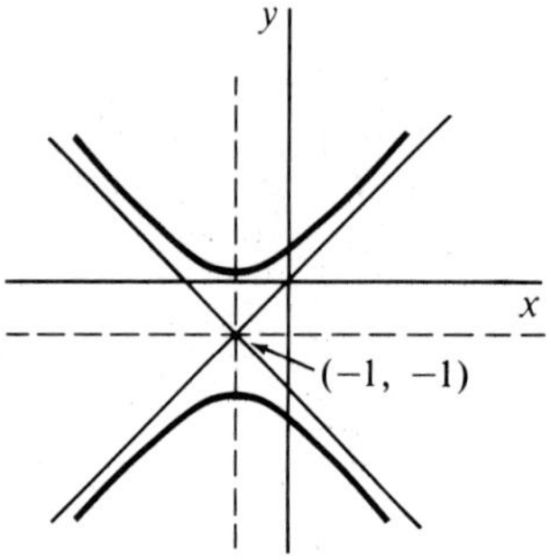

7. Hyperbola
Center (0, 0)
$a = 10$
$b = 10$
$c = 10\sqrt{2}$

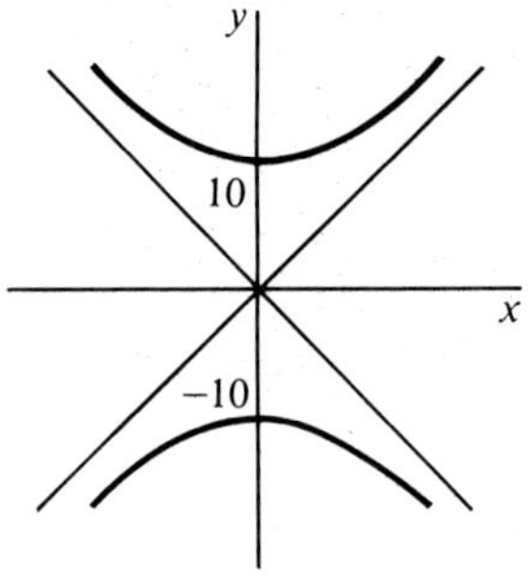

9. Ellipse
Center $(-\frac{3}{2}, 0)$
$a = \sqrt{\frac{23}{2}} \approx 3.4$
$b = \sqrt{\frac{23}{4}} \approx 2.4$
$c = \sqrt{\frac{23}{4}} \approx 2.4$

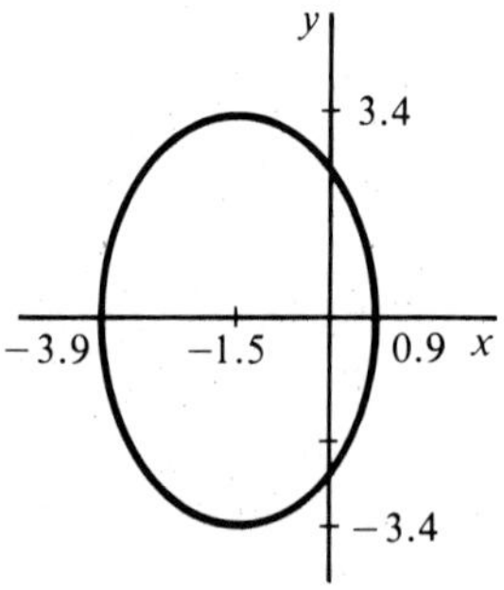

11. $y^2 = -8(x - 2)$

13. $(x + 1)^2 + (y - 2)^2 = 64$ **15.** $x^2/16 + y^2/12 = 1$ **17.** $(x - 3)^2/16 - (y - 4)^2/64 = 1$
19. 9 ft from center **21.** $(0.67, -0.33)$ and $(0.5, 0)$
25. $r \sin \theta = 3$ **27.** $\tan \theta = 2$ **29.** $r^2 = \dfrac{1}{4 \cos^2 \theta + \sin^2 \theta}$

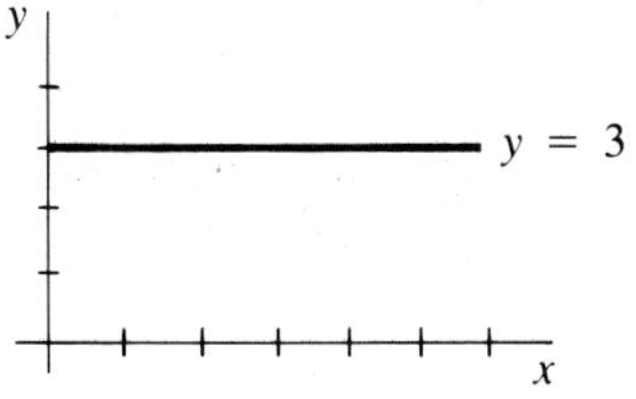

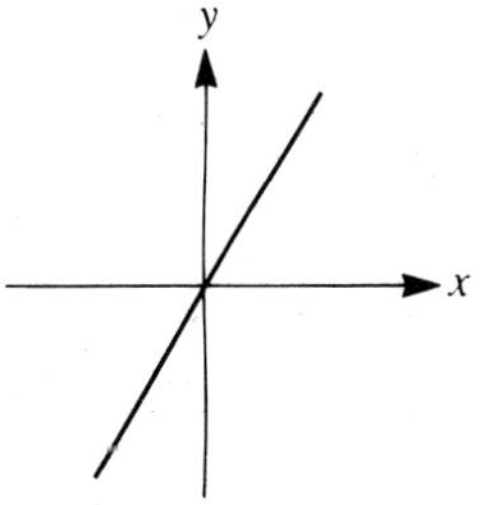

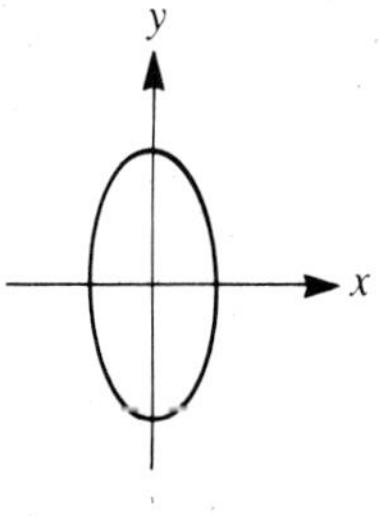

31. $x^2 + y^2 = 4$ **33.** $x^2 + 4y = 4$ **35.** $x^2 + y^2 - 3x = 0$

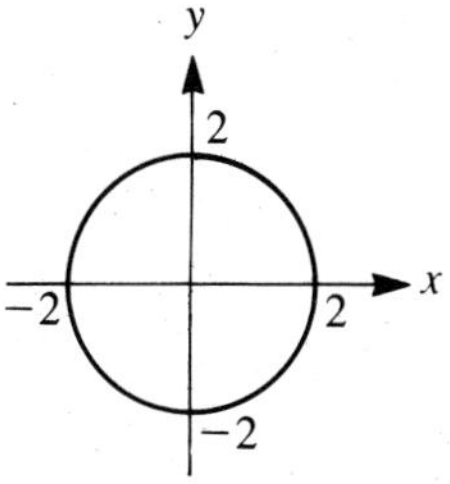

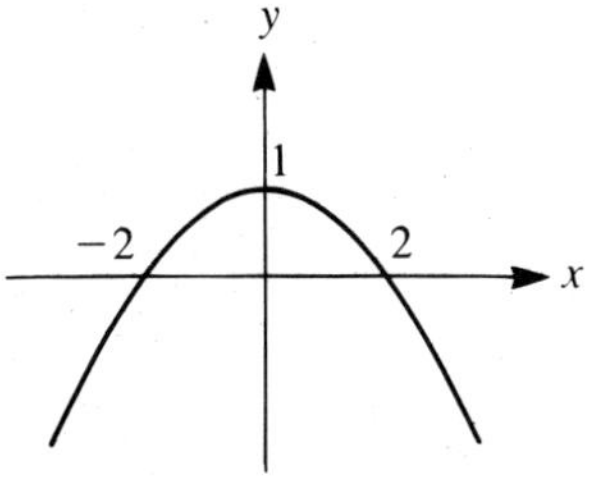

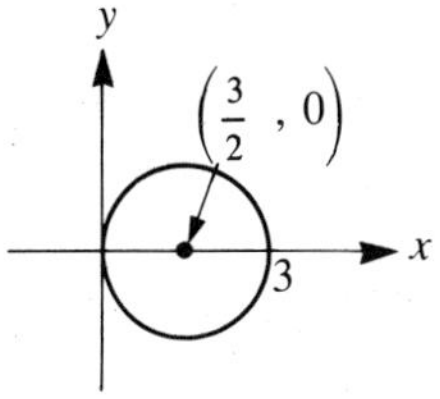

37. $(x^2 + y^2)^{3/2} = 2xy$ **39.** $x^2 + y^2 = 1$

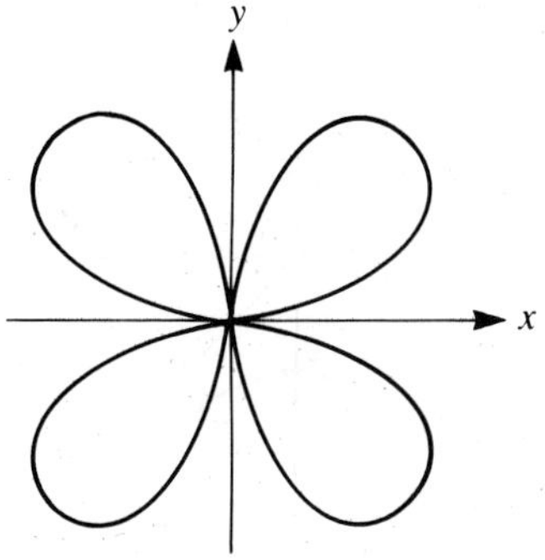

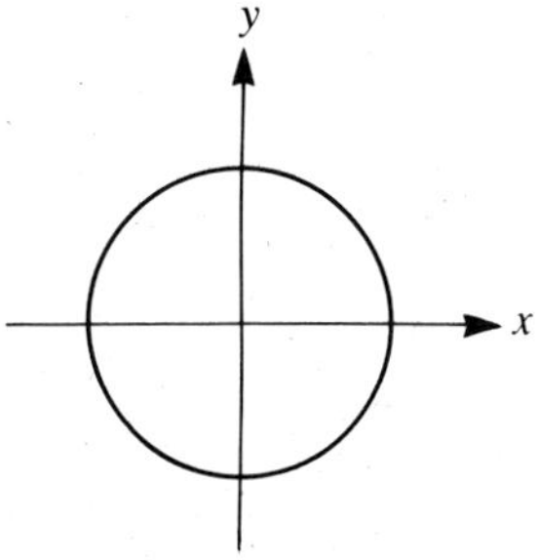

Appendix A (page 353)

1. Three **3.** Four **5.** One **7.** Two **9.** Four **11.** 9820 **13.** 54.7
15. 0.0658 **17.** 39.8 **19.** 1.00 **21.** 21.50 **23.** 1.92 **25.** 65 **27.** 2.6
29. 2280 **31.** 139.7

Index